D1596671

WILLOW RUN COMMUNITY SCHOOLS
DEPARTMENT OF SPECIAL EDUCATION
2171 E. MICHIGAN AVE.
YPSILANTI, MI 48198

Psychotherapy With Adolescents

Psychotherapy
With Adolescents

RICHARD A. GARDNER, M.D.

Clinical Professor of Child Psychiatry
Columbia University
College of Physicians and Surgeons

Creative Therapeutics
155 County Road, Cresskill, New Jersey   07626-0317

Library of Congress Cataloging-in-Publication Data

Gardner, Richard A.
    Psychotherapy with adolescents / Richard A. Gardner.
      p.   cm.
    Includes bibliographies and index.
    ISBN 0-933812-18-3
    1. Adolescent psychotherapy.   I. Title.
RJ503.G38   1988
616.89'14--dc19
DNLM/DLC
for Library of Congress   88-20280
                                     CIP

I dedicate this book to

My teachers at The Bronx High School of Science and Columbia College.

Their formidable influence on me during my own adolescence — as teachers, models, and mentors — has served me well throughout the course of my life.

This book represents only one small derivative of their influence.

Other Books by Richard A. Gardner

The Boys and Girls Book About Divorce
Therapeutic Communication with Children: The Mutual Storytelling
    Technique
Dr. Gardner's Stories About the Real World, Volume I
Dr. Gardner's Stories About the Real World, Volume II
Dr. Gardner's Fairy Tales for Today's Children
Understanding Children: A Parents Guide to Child Rearing
MBD: The Family Book About Minimal Brain Dysfunction
Psychotherapeutic Approaches to the Resistant Child
Psychotherapy with Children of Divorce
Dr. Gardner's Modern Fairy Tales
The Parents Book About Divorce
The Boys and Girls Book About One-Parent Families
The Objective Diagnosis of Minimal Brain Dysfunction
Dorothy and the Lizard of Oz
Dr. Gardner's Fables for Our Times
The Boys and Girls Book About Stepfamilies
Family Evaluation in Child Custody Litigation
Separation Anxiety Disorder: Psychodynamics and Psychotherapy
Child Custody Litigation: A Guide for Parents and Mental Health
    Professionals
The Psychotherapeutic Techniques of Richard A. Gardner
Hyperactivity, The So-Called Attention-Deficit Disorder, and The
    Group of MBD Syndromes
The Parental Alienation Syndrome and the Differentiation Between
    Fabricated and Genuine Child Sex Abuse
Psychotherapy of Psychogenic Learning Disabilities

Contents

Acknowledgments

I wish to express my gratitude to my secretaries, Linda Gould, Carol Gibbon, and Donna La Tourette for their dedication to the typing of the manuscript of this book in its various renditions. I am indeed fortunate to have such committed assistants. I am grateful, as well, to Robert Mulholland for his astute editing of the manuscript. He did more than edit; he gave good reasons for his changes and taught me some useful grammatical principles in the course of our work together. I appreciate the contributions of Jo-Nell Long and Elizabeth Quackenbush for their careful reading of the page proofs. I am also grateful to Robert Tebbenhoff of Lind Graphics for his valuable contributions to the production of this book, from manuscript to final volume.

My greatest debt, however, is to my adolescent patients who have taught me much over the years about the kinds of problems they can have. From their parents, as well, I have learned much that is included here. Although their names and other identifying data have been disguised, their experiences have been recorded herein. My hope is that what I have learned from them will be put to good use through this book and will contribute to the prevention and alleviation of grief and stress in others.

INTRODUCTION

This book represents the cumulative experience of over 30 years of working intensively with adolescent patients. It includes references to the works of others who have influenced my thinking as well as my own ideas regarding how to conduct psychotherapy with adolescents. But even those theories and techniques that I consider my own were probably thought of by others in the past. New and unique ideas are very rare; it is only that others have not published the innovative theories and approaches described herein or I have not come across them in my researches. But this should be of little concern to the reader. What is important is that this is the amalgam of the ideas and techniques I have found most useful in work with adolescents. The reader does well to select from that which is presented here those elements that seem reasonable and those that show promise for effective utilization.

My next point was said better previously by D.J. Holmes (1964) in the preface to his book *The Adolescent in Psychotherapy*:

> In our teaching we frequently go the way of the arrogant house mouse who advised the shivering grasshopper that he

would survive the winter better if he were to change into a mouse. Heartened by the suggestion, the grasshopper inquired how he might proceed with this, and the mouse replied: "I can only give you the general idea—you will have to work out the details for yourself.

During the course of my training, all too often my supervisors only gave me general principles. Most of the details I had to work out myself. Holmes' book provides many useful details. And this book, published almost 25 years later, provides additional details. Like Holmes' it is not intended to be a comprehensive statement of all forms of treatment for all adolescent disorders. No one book could encompass such an ambitious plan. Rather, it focuses on the areas with which I have had the most experience and presents those therapeutic techniques that I have found most reliable in the course of my work.

Of the three age groups—childhood, adolescence, and adulthood—adolescence is generally viewed as the most difficult to work with psychotherapeutically. The youngsters' arrogance, rebellion, and general unreceptivity to adult authority results in their often being viewed as extremely poor candidates for psychotherapy. There are even therapists who will work with children and adults but who steer clear of adolescents. Working with each of these three groups has its advantages and disadvantages. Each group has its areas of receptivity and areas of unreceptivity. All things considered, however, I believe the adolescents are the easiest group in which to bring about psychotherapeutic change—and this is especially the case for youngsters from the mid- to late-adolescent period.

The rambunctiousness and distractibility of younger children make them difficult candidates for treatment and one must utilize a wide variety of seductive techniques in order to engage them. In contrast, the adult patient generally exhibits none of these childlike characteristics, but comes to treatment with deeply-entrenched problems that may have been years in the making. Also, an adult's opportunity for flexibility in such areas as job and marriage may be seriously compromised, thereby reducing the chance that one may alter environmental factors operative in the development and perpetuation of the psychopathology. The adolescent is halfway between these two groups. Adolescents (especially the older ones) will often sit and talk—the rebellious and sneering facade notwithstanding. Their narcissism is so enormous that they can spend hours talking about the minutiae of themselves, their appearance, their clothing, etc. And this is just the kind of thing we want people to do in treatment. Also, their life situation is one which still allows for significant flexibility because they are not locked, like most adults, into fixed vocational and personal arrangements. And, because of their youth, their problems are not generally as deeply entrenched as those of the adult (but certainly more so than those of the young child).

In addition, of the three age groups, adolescents are the best candidates for group psychotherapy. Group therapy for younger children is most often a disaster because of their rambunctiousness, distractibility, and disinclination to sit around in a circle and talk about their problems. Adults are generally receptive to this sort of thing, but they are not as dependent on the opinions of their peers as the adolescent. Adolescents are very much group animals. Their antennae are continually out searching for the signals emanating from their peers. They may distrust their therapists because they equate them with parents and others of that ilk, but they trust their peers who know what's "in" and what's "the latest." They join in with their peers in believing that adolescents are the incarnation of all the wisdom that has ever existed in the history of the human race. Accordingly, they are receptive to availing themselves of the sage advice that their fellow teenagers can provide them.

Of the three age groups, adolescents may very well be the most introspective. They may preoccupy themselves with fundamental questions of the world, the universe, God, and the meaning of life. These same deliberations make them good candidates for introspection into the causes of their underlying psychological processes. Although they may be rebellious, they are still at a stage in life where they are quite dependent on adults, especially their parents and teachers. Although they need to rebel against their parents, in order to achieve a reasonable degree of independence and autonomy, they may not have to rebel against their teachers and teacher surrogates (and a therapist is a teacher surrogate). Their receptivity to the therapist, then, may be greater than that enjoyed with adults and younger children (especially the latter).

Another factor that may contribute to adolescents' being good candidates for treatment relates to educational and career choices. Previously, adult life was viewed as being an infinite number of years away. Most children do not feel any compulsion to concern themselves with such remote future eventualities. In adolescence (particularly late adolescence) the future is almost here. The youngster stands at the doorstep of adult life and may suffer many anxieties about education and career. These fears will enhance his or her motivation to enlist the aid of a therapist to help sort out the options and work through the problems interfering with one's choice. In short, the immediacy of the situation can enhance the adolescent's motivation for therapy. Accordingly, when one considers all these factors, I find myself significantly attracted to many of my adolescent patients and have more optimism regarding their therapeutic prognosis than I have for patients in the other two age groups.

The book begins in Chapter One with the description of certain developmental conflicts of adolescence, the understanding of which I consider important if one is to deal effectively with adolescent psychopathology. Some of these developmental theories are derived from the work of others and some of the ideas are considered to be my own (at least I have never read them elsewhere). Because so much of adolescent psychopathology is an outgrowth of these conflicts, it is important that the reader review these from the start. I consider particularly important the theory proposed of the five stages in the development of what I refer to as the *internal guilt-evoking mechanisms*. I consider this theory of particular value in understanding and treating antisocial youngsters. However, extensions of it are applicable to our understanding of the increasing psychopathy of Western society (a phenomenon that I mention on a number of occasions throughout the course of this book). In that chapter I also introduce the term *delusions of invulnerability*. Although just about everyone who works with adolescents is aware of this phenomenon, and although others may very well have utilized the term, I have not seen it nor heard it used. I consider it a useful concept for understanding many of the psychological phenomena that we are dealing with when we treat adolescent patients.

In Chapter Two I discuss certain environmental situations (especially family) that are conducive to the development of psychopathological reactions in adolescence. I place particular focus on factors that result in the deprivation of parental affection—a common central element in bringing about psychopathology. It may be of interest to the reader to appreciate that prior to the 1940s, therapists did not generally see a link between childhood psychopathology and deprivation of parental affection. This is a relationship that we routinely investigate in our evaluations of youngsters who come for treatment. Nowhere in Freud's description of Little Hans is there any mention of this potential relationship. It is reasonable to conclude that Freud may not have even considered this linkage. In fact, he tells us that he considered Hans' parents to be healthy people who had not in any way exposed their child to psychopathological processes within themselves nor were they utilizing what he considered to be improper child-rearing tactics. Freud presents as support of this conclusion the statement that the mother had been in psychoanalytic treatment with him and the father was a friend. Clearly, we can only assume then that Freud considered himself to have "cured" the mother and that any person who would be a friend of his could not possibly suffer with psychopathology.

Chapter Three is devoted to a detailed description of the two-hour initial evaluation that I conduct with the youngster and both parents. I do not follow the traditional approach of seeing the parents alone first and then seeing the child. I prefer to see at the outset the flesh and blood human being who is likely to become my patient. In that two-hour meeting I can interview the youngster and parents in any possible combination. This gives me the opportunity to learn about intrapsychic as well as interpersonal processes. Chapter Four is devoted to a detailed description of the intensive evaluation I conduct for patients who are going into treatment. This is an exhaustive data-collection process, which includes individual interviews with the patient and each of the parents. It also includes joint interviews with the parents together as well as a family interview. The information so obtained not only serves as a foundation for treatment but the relationships that I form with the patient and parents during this comprehensive evaluation serve as a foundation for that which will ensue.

In Chapter Five I provide a statement of what I consider to be the central factors operative in the development of psychogenic symptoms and the therapeutic process that is designed to alleviate them. It is a statement of what I consider these factors to be at this point, after doing psychotherapy for over 30 years. It is not the same statement that I would have made 10 and 20 years ago, nor might it be the statement that I might make ten years from now. It is crucial that therapists read this chapter if they are to understand optimally my psychotherapeutic approaches.

Chapter Six is devoted to a discussion of the factors that contribute to the development of a good therapist-patient relationship, without which there can be no meaningful psychotherapy. Although there can be productive electroconvulsive therapy, drug therapy, and even behavior modification without a good relationship between the therapist and patient, psychotherapy is not likely to be successful unless the relationship is a good one. When the therapist-patient relationship is impaired, there is no receptivity to what the therapist has to say, no emulation of him or her, and thereby no identification with the therapist's personality traits and values. And all of these processes are necessary if there is to be any therapeutic change.

Chapter Seven is devoted to the topic of confidentiality. This is important to discuss because my therapeutic approach is one in which I work significantly with parents and other members of the youngster's family, both individually and in joint interviews. On the one hand, the adolescent needs work alone with the therapist as a step toward separation from the family and the development of autonomy. On the other hand, one still wants to have close relationships with family members because of the important therapeutic benefits to be derived from such involvement. There is a trade-off here and at times a dilemma. In this chapter I describe the position I take with regard to this issue.

Chapter Eight is devoted to the technical details of conducting individual, face-to-face psychotherapy with adolescents. Although theoretical material is provided, the emphasis is on technical considerations. Numerous clinical vignettes complement the text and provide the examiner with clinical examples that demonstrate my theoretical principles. In Chapter Nine I discuss in detail the utilization of *The Talking, Feeling, and Doing Game* in the treatment of adolescents, especially younger adolescents. Younger adolescents present a problem for the therapist. They are generally too old to involve themselves in projective play, especially doll play. Accordingly, these rich sources of information about the patient's underlying psychodynamics are not available to the therapist. Yet, the younger ones are not comfortable sitting in a room with a therapist, for 45 or 50 minutes, with his or her beady eyes staring and asking what they want to talk about. Older adolescents are much more receptive to such direct inquiries. *The Talking, Feeling, and Doing Game* provides younger adolescents with a vehicle that facilitates self-expression and revelation. My experience has been that many patients in this age bracket will ask to play the game and openly state that they play it because it "gives me ideas about things to talk about."

As mentioned, adolescents, because of their narcissism and introspective tendencies, may be excellent candidates for introspective psychotherapy. And some of them (especially those who are very bright) may be excellent candidates for psychoanalytic inquiry. Chapter Ten focuses on this technique, with special emphasis on dream psychoanalysis. I present here what I consider to be an excellent statement of the different kinds of dreams and the functions they serve. Freud's contribution, in which he emphasized the wish-fulfillment function of dreams, cannot be underestimated. However, I believe that his view was a somewhat narrow one and he did not give enough attention to other functions that dreams serve—especially their function of alerting the dreamer to danger.

Chapter Eleven is devoted to group therapy, the supreme form of therapy for the adolescent. These youngsters travel in groups and thrive in groups. Their dependency on their peers is a step up from their dependency on their parents and a step toward their ultimate autonomy and independence. Group therapy derives therapeutic mileage from this phenomenon. Therapists who do not utilize group therapy with adolescents are depriving themselves of a valuable therapeutic modality for youngsters in this age bracket. Of the three ages (childhood, adolescence, and adulthood), I consider group therapy to be most efficacious for the adolescent group. Chapter Twelve is devoted to a description of the kinds of work I do with parents and the kinds of advice I provide them when working with their adolescents. The therapist who excludes close work with parents is making a serious mistake. One can still provide the adolescent with separate individual sessions, confidentiality, and other experiences necessary to develop autonomy, yet still have ongoing contact with the parents.

Chapter Thirteen focuses on the treatment of antisocial youngsters. Although comments about the treatment of such patients are made throughout the book, a special chapter is devoted to their therapy because of the ubiquity of this problem. Chapter Fourteen is devoted to a discussion of depression, suicide, medication, and hospitalization. Last, in Chapter Fifteen, I present my views on the future of the field of psychiatry—with particular emphasis on adolescent psychiatry. Although present trends have produced pessimism in me regarding the future of psychodynamic psychotherapy, I still believe that there is enough value in the modality to enable it to survive and ultimately flourish.

ONE

SELECTED DEVELOPMENTAL CONSIDERATIONS RELEVANT TO ADOLESCENT TREATMENT

Of the three age brackets: childhood, adolescence, and adulthood, the adolescent period is the one in which the differentiation between normality and pathology is most difficult. The main reason for this is that the adolescent period is normally so tumultuous that it is common for youngsters to exhibit behavior so bizarre that it could be considered psychotic—especially if exhibited at other age levels. Accordingly, it may be extremely difficult to ascertain the line at which the normal "craziness" of adolescence ends and pathological manifestations begin.

The problem is further compounded because many therapists may be easily misled into believing that the adolescent is more mature than he or she really is. The examiner may equate physical maturity with psychological maturity and thereby believe that the adolescent is capable of acting much more judiciously than is actually possible for youngsters in that phase of life. A good guideline for the therapist when assessing and treating adolescents is to view them as having the bodies of adults, but the minds of children. Although physiologically capable of procreation they are

1

generally psychologically incapable of taking care of themselves, let alone progeny. Furthermore, the therapist should not be deceived by the adolescent who scores at the 99th percentile on the SATs. Although that youngster's brain may very well be hypertrophied in certain cognitive areas, the rest of the brain substance may be functioning at infantile levels. I often say that the therapist does well to consider the adolescent as one whose pneumoencephalogram would reveal the head to be largely filled with air, with the cortical substance reduced to pea-sized material lying at the base of the skull just above the brain stem.

These principles apply especially to the traditional poor judgment of the adolescent. Considering the short stay that the adolescent has had thus far on earth, and considering the paucity of experiences that he or she has had, it could not but be otherwise. Good judgment derives from and must be based on experience, and the adolescent has not been around long enough to have enough experiences to enable him or her to have reliable judgment in many areas of living. The cigarette companies know this well. They can rely on the adolescent's being gullible enough to believe that smoking a cigarette makes one more mature and/or attractive to the opposite sex. They can rely upon adolescents' delusions of invulnerability (about which I will have much to say throughout the course of this book) enabling them to deny that cigarette smoking will increase the risk that someday they will get cancer of the lung and/or one or more of the other diseases caused by cigarette smoking. A few years later, when the young adult finally realizes how he or she has been duped, it is too late—so deep-seated may be the tobacco addiction.

Politicians and military leaders also know well how poor is the judgment of adolescents. Visiting any military cemetery, especially those wherein are buried battle casualties of wars fought prior to the 20th century, one cannot but note how young were the boys who fell in battle. Traditionally, wars have been fought by teenagers, or even youngsters no more than 10 to 12 years of age. It is only in the 20th century that we have required our soldiers to be 17 or 18 years of age. Leaders know well that adolescents are physically strong enough to fight wars, but mentally weak and gullible enough to believe propaganda, stirring war cries, and exhortations that evoke murderous rage. They know also that adolescents, because of their delusions of invulnerability, can charge into battle believing that all those around them may fall, but that they somehow will survive. Recently I learned that the motto of the 82nd Airborne Division of the U.S. Army is *Death Before Dishonor*. I personally would much prefer *dishonor before death*. If my choice is only (and it is unlikely that it will be) between death and humiliation, I'll choose *humiliation* anytime. Call me any name you want: "coward," "yellow," "chicken-shit," etc. I'll still choose disgrace. Somehow adolescents do not seem to appreciate this obvious wisdom.

It is also important for the therapist to appreciate that many of the adolescent behavioral manifestations we refer to as symptoms are outgrowths of normal adolescent developmental conflicts and stages. Accordingly, in this first chapter I focus on what I consider to be some of the most important of these. I am not claiming to present an all-encompassing theory of development. In fact, I do not believe that anyone has thus far been able to do so. All of the proposed developmental theories I know of, whether they be those of Freud, Erikson, or Piaget (to mention three of the most well known) are still selective. They focus only on relatively narrow aspects of the developmental process. I present here developmental considerations that I have found to be most important in understanding adolescent psychopathology, which is often best viewed as an outgrowth of these normal developmental stages. Without the understanding of what is normal, therapists are compromised in their ability to understand and treat what is abnormal in their adolescent patients.

One last introductory comment. The reader may be familiar with Francois Villon's "But where are the snows of yesteryear?" One can similarly ask the question "But where are the adolescents of yesteryear?" Where are the crazy kids, juvenile delinquents, and other adolescent maniacs who have caused their parents so much grief? The answer is that most of them have blended into the mainstream of adult life. They are no longer walking the streets in their weird costumes, an eyesore to behold. They are no longer keeping the neighbors up all hours of the night with their earsplitting music and raucous drinking. Most of the delinquents are no longer committing their crimes. Most end up as solid citizens. It is important for the therapist to appreciate this because it provides some optimism when one is considering the prognosis of the adolescent patient. It also provides therapists with the reassurance that time is on their side and that even if the therapy is unsuccessful there is a high degree of probability that the adolescent will end up a sober and solid citizen anyway.

A THEORY OF THE DEVELOPMENT
OF THE CAPACITY TO
EXPERIENCE GUILT

I use the word *guilt* to refer to the feeling of low self-worth individuals experience when they have entertained thoughts, experienced feelings, or performed deeds that they have been taught are wrong or bad by significant figures in childhood (especially parents). Each society, culture, and family has its own collection of such phenomena that are considered unacceptable. Not only has the individual been *taught* that these thoughts, feelings, and acts are wrong but he or she has come to *believe* that they are so. Furthermore, although the earliest significant figures are generally the parents and/or their surrogates, others such as teachers and clergymen also play a role in teaching children what is good, bad, right, and wrong.

The word *guilt* that I am referring to here is very different from the word *guilt* that is used by the judge who asks the accused whether he or she pleads guilty or innocent: "Do you admit that you committed the crime or do you deny it?" The judge uses the word guilt to refer to a purely *external* phenomenon, i.e., whether or not a particular act was indeed performed. In contrast, I am referring to an *internal* psychological phenomenon that may result from the performance of such an act. A criminal may admit guilt (perpetration) but not feel guilt (reactive self-loathing). These two utilizations of the word guilt are so different that they should probably be represented by two entirely different words. Nor am I referring here to a *third* use of the word guilt: the delusion a person has that an event was his or her fault. There are children, for example, who believe that their parents' divorce was their fault—that the divorce was the result of their transgressions. Such children may then develop the delusion that their parents will reconcile if they were never again to so transgress. The feelings of self-blame here are basically related to the need to gain control over an uncontrollable situation (R.A. Gardner, 1969, 1970). Unless specifically mentioned otherwise, I will be using the term guilt to refer only to the first category: the feeling of low self-worth that is associated with thoughts, feelings, and deeds that one has been taught are bad or wrong.

I have specifically avoided using the word *superego* in this discussion because its use sometimes introduces confusion. In S. Freud's original concept the superego was considered to be a composite of the conscience (the agency via which guilt is evoked) and the ego-ideal (the collection of images of the standards by which one wishes to live, especially those derived from early childhood models). The word superego, however, is often used as if it were just synonymous with conscience, or the guilt-evoking mechanisms. In order to avoid such confusion, I will rarely use the term superego, but rather use the term guilt—to refer only to the first of the three aforementioned types.

The ability of people to experience guilt is crucial for the survival of civilized societies. Without it individuals prey upon one another in a predatory world in which no one can feel safe. Under such circumstances leaders must be constantly policing their followers to insure compliance with standards and rules. Guilt internalizes the standards of the society so that leaders can relax somewhat their vigil. The members of the society can then be relied upon to some extent to police themselves and deter themselves from engaging in unacceptable behavior. Many forms of psychopathology involve either weakness or exaggerated utilization of the guilt-evoking mechanisms. Various forms of antisocial behavior are often the result of weakness of the guilt-evoking mechanisms; and some forms of neurotic disturbance are caused by an exaggerated utilization of these processes.

I present here a theory of the development of the guilt-evoking mechanisms. My theory is derived from information gathered over the years, both from my patients and the works of others. It is basically a synthesis of ideas, many of which have been described previously. Though I have not seen this particular synthesis elsewhere, I suspect others have viewed the development of the guilt-evoking mechanisms in a similar way. It is a multi-step process and I will proceed developmentally from the earliest to the latest steps.

The Genetic-Neurological Substrate

It is obvious that guilt, like all other mental processes, must have a neurological substrate. To have a thought one must have nerve cells. It is reasonable also to state that lower animals do not have the capacity to develop guilt. They do not have an internalized inhibitory mechanism that results in a lowering of their self-esteem when they perform an act which is considered reprehensible by others in their environment. Although some may claim that lower animals do have such capacity (especially beloved domesticated pets), most would agree that the capacity for such guilt is far less than that which the human being is capable of developing. Many who work intensively with higher apes also claim for them the capacity for what appears to be guilt. I do not believe, however, that higher apes have the capacity to develop the *degree* of sophisticated guilt-evoking mechanisms of which humans are capable. It is reasonable, therefore, to speculate that the intermediary forms between the higher apes and homo sapiens developed progressively more complex neurological structures that serve as a substrate for environmentally-induced, guilt-evoking mechanisms.

At any given point along this evolutionary continuum it is reasonable to consider there to have been a range with regard to the guilt-evoking capacity, a range that might very well have represented itself on a bell-shaped curve. Also, over time, the mean of this curve shifted progressively to the right as the average individual exhibited ever more sophisticated capacity to develop guilt. It is also reasonable to speculate that one factor operative in this shift was an environmental selective process in which there was preferential survival of those who had the capacity to deter themselves from antisocial behavior by these internal inhibitory mechanisms. In contrast, those who were poorly endowed with such a neurological substrate were less likely to develop the internalized guilt-evoking mechanisms, more likely therefore to exhibit antisocial behavior, and more likely therefore to get punished, incarcerated, and even killed for their transgressions—thereby selectively removing from the genetic pool those individuals with weak consciences. Unfortunately, we still appear to have a long way to go in this regard. (I am not suggesting any particular method for such removal; I am only stating that their representation is still very much with us.)

If this theory is correct, then it is reasonable to view children today as also falling somewhere along the continuum of the bell-shaped curve, from a low genetically determined neurologically based guilt-potential substrate to a very powerful capacity for the development of such mechanisms. It is important to appreciate that this theory does not preclude the environmental input into any individual's final functioning in this area. An individual with a very sophisticated, complex, and highly developed capacity for guilt evocation needs very little environmental input to manifest what might be considered a normal or even a high degree of guilt. In contrast, individuals who are poorly endowed with these neurological structures may require formidable environmental guilt-engendering exposures to develop guilty feelings. And many may not be able to do so, even with optimum exposure to such influences.

I recognize that this concept is somewhat reminiscent of the 19th-century theory of the "constitutional psychopath." At that time there was a prevailing view that some individuals were born to be psychopaths because of a constitutional weakness in the capacity to develop guilt mechanisms. One 20th century derivative of this notion was the so-called "bad seed" child who was destined from birth to be "bad." Primarily as an outgrowth of the psychoanalytic movement in the 20th century, the concept of the constitutional psychopath is generally considered to be somewhat outdated. My theory here may be viewed as an attempt to disinter this now presumably defunct concept. I have no problem doing this as long as the reader appreciates that I still view psychopathy to be multidetermined and that only a small segment of those who are psychopathic are so because of a genetically determined weak neurological substrate for the implantation of environmental guilt-evoking mechanisms. Whereas the 19th century concept was all inclusive and served as an explanation for all psychopathy, my view is that a *small* percentage of psychopaths are best viewed as manifesting psychopathy because of a constitutional or genetically based neurological weakness.

One confirmation I have for this theory is my observation on numerous occasions of families in which one child showed evidences of an extremely weak capacity to develop guilt, whereas other siblings and the parents manifested normal guilt capacity. After detailed evaluation and prolonged therapy, I was unable to delineate the family factors that caused the child's impairment and reluctantly came to agree with the parents that the patient might have been "born that way." Of course, one could always argue that the environment of each child in a family is different from every other sibling, and that each child enters into and grows up in a different family constellation. Although this is certainly the case, it does not explain satisfactorily the isolated child (one of three, or four, or five, regardless of sequence of birth) who exhibits impairment in this area. I am not claiming that these anecdotal and incidental observations are "proof" of my theory; only that they lend some confirmation to it.

The genetic-neurological factor is the substrate upon which all subsequent factors (to be described) are supported. When it is weak all subsequent factors rest on an unstable foundation and the internalized guilt-evoking mechanisms are likely to be compromised. Each factor presented below must occur in the proper sequence if the whole structure is to be stable. I do not believe that one can "skip" any particular step and still end up with an adult who has the capacity for a strong sense of guilt.

Imprinting

Imprinting in Lower Animals   In recent years ethologists have described the phenomenon of *imprinting*. This term refers to a response pattern that develops in the earliest hours of life, arises under very specific circumstances, and cannot be extinguished by subsequent experiences. This response pattern occurs during what is referred to as the *critical period* because it will not develop if the same circumstances are operative significantly before or significantly after this particular segment of time.

Some of the seminal work in this area was done by K. Lorenz (1937, 1950) who introduced the term *imprinting* to refer to this phenomenon. Lorenz worked primarily with Greylag geese, but the principles of the imprinting process have been verified in many other species by a variety of workers. The basic principle is well demonstrated by studies on ducklings, for example, those conducted by E.H. Hess (1966). The fertilized egg of a duck is removed from the nest of the biological mother and placed in the nest of a surrogate duck. Once hatched, the duckling is allowed to remain with the surrogate mother during the first two to three days of life, during which time the duckling will demonstrate various manifestations of an attachment bond with the surrogate. One of these is the tendency to follow her wherever she goes. If, after the first few days, the duckling is returned to the nest of its biological mother, it will show few if any manifestations of attachment, especially the "following" response. And no amount of effort on the biological mother's part to involve the duckling will be successful.

If one studies this phenomenon further, one finds that there is a critical period during which this attachment response develops, and that involvement with the surrogate before and after this critical period is less likely to result in the formation of an attachment bond. For Mallard ducklings the critical period is from 13 to 16 hours. The imprinting response cannot be viewed as an example of a learned reflex in that it cannot be "taught" before or after the critical period, and it cannot be extinguished by traditional negative reinforcement. Furthermore, it is somewhat indiscriminate in that if the surrogate is a mechanical toy the bond will develop in association with it and the duckling will follow the mechanical toy throughout its life—no matter how many attempts are made to get it to follow the biological mother. Attempts to suppress the response by such techniques as shocking the duckling each time it touches the mechanical toy will often serve instead to strengthen the response. This further demonstrates the point that this phenomenon is not to be considered an example of a learned or conditioned response. Last, if the egg is hatched in a situation in which the newborn duckling is deprived of all contact with any kind of moving figure, animate or inanimate, for a length of time that extends beyond the critical period, then no following response at all will be evoked. Under these circumstances the duckling will not be capable of attaching itself to any caretaking figure, whether it be the biological mother, a surrogate mother, or a human being. The implications of this last phenomenon will be discussed in detail subsequently. It is reasonable to assume that the capacity to form the imprinted response is genetically programmed in that each species has its own critical period for the elicitation of it. Accordingly, I consider it reasonable to refer to it as *instinctual*.

The Question of Imprinting in Human Beings   I believe that human infants exhibit a similar phenomenon during the earliest months of life. I do not believe, however, that it is so specific that one can measure accurately an exact critical period—as one can in lower animals. One of the ways in which human beings differ from lower animals is the flexibility of the instinctual response and its capacity to be modified to varying degrees by the individuals themselves and the social environment. Certain birds, for example, are compelled to perform specific ritualistic mating dances during the mating season. They have no choice but to do so. The capacity for the particular response is programmed into their genes and is elicited by certain environmental stimuli that occur at specific times of the year. Although we human beings have procreative urges that produce the desire to mate, we are not compelled to act out on these instinctual responses in a reflex manner. We have a certain amount of conscious control over them and our social environment can play a significant role in modifying these instinctive responses.

Like the duckling, the human infant forms an attachment bond with its mother or her surrogate. If the human infant is not provided tender loving care during infancy, the child may literally waste away and die. In less extreme situations—in which the caretaker simply does not provide significant affection, tenderness, cuddling, protection, etc.—the infant is not likely to form this bond and, I believe, may never form it. Like the duckling who does not develop a following response if it has been deprived of contact with moving figures for a time that extends beyond the critical period, humans who have been significantly deprived during their critical periods for imprinting will similarly be unable to form an attachment bond—regardless of how benevolent, devoted, dedicated, and loving the caretaking individual. Although I cannot specify a particular segment of time—such as one can with a duckling and other lower species—I believe that this critical period exists in humans within the first few months of life. I cannot be more specific. To do so would be not only presumptuous, but would imply a specificity that probably does not exist in humans. And, as is true of lower species, if a human infant does not form this bond during the critical period *it can never be formed*. I believe that one of the results of the failure to develop this bond is that the individual will never develop significantly strong internalized guilt-evoking mechanisms. Just as the aforementioned genetic-neurological factor serves as a substrate for the imprinted factor, the imprinted factor serves as a substrate for the subsequent contributions (to be described below) to the development of the internalized guilt-evoking mechanisms. Without such imprinting there will be no guilt, because without it the next steps will not be successfully accomplished.

The Pleasure-Pain Stage

At the earliest levels of life, young infants deter themselves from behavior that may be detrimental to themselves and/or society by following the pleasure-pain principle. In the healthy family situation the pleasure the child experiences from being "good" or doing the "right" things results from the love and affection the child receives when it manifests such behavior. And the healthiest form of discipline is the threatened loss of such affection. The mother of a three-year-old may say, "Mary, I'm very proud of you. You've been a wonderful girl *all* day. You've been very good to your little brother and helped Mommy feed him. You're very useful to have around the house. I'm so happy with you that I want to give you a big hug and a kiss (mother hugs child affectionately and kisses her on both cheeks). I'm so happy with you today that I want to tell Daddy all about how good you were as soon as he comes home." Such a child is not only likely to respond with enhanced feelings of self-worth and a glow of loving tenderness toward mother, but is also likely to remember well what those behavioral patterns were that evoked such wonderful responses from mother. These patterns then are likely to be repeated in future situations in order to elicit similar positive reinforcement from mother.

On another day, however, the same mother may say, "Mary, I've had it with you today. I'm so upset with you, I'm ready to climb the walls. I don't know what's got into you today. You've been a mess from the minute you got up. You spilled your milk, threw your muffin on the floor and stepped on it and, worst of all, you poked your little baby brother in the eye. Thank God nothing happened to him. Just go to your room and stay away from me. I'm ready to explode. I can't wait until your father comes home so he can take care of you." I do not believe that these comments reflect any deficiency on this mother's part. Her statements are natural and humane, and they get across the message to the child that the unacceptable behavior is going to result in temporary loss of affection from her mother. I consider such comments to reflect healthy and humane forms of punishment in the upbringing of children. It is an extremely effective way of "helping the child remember" to be good.

But more direct examples of punishment are also important in healthy and humane upbringing. A two-year-old who runs into the street will not be deterred from doing so by being lectured on the dangers of automobiles. The child has little capacity to project him- or herself into the future and appreciate the ultimate consequences of such irresponsible behavior. A slap on the backside or strong castigation is much more likely to be effective. The child learns restraint with the internal message: "If I run into the street, my mother or father will hit me—I'd better not." Living for the moment, the child at that age cannot be expected to say, "I'd better not run into the street because some day I might get hit by a car." As long as the slap on the backside does not produce physical trauma—but is more psychologically than physically painful—I would consider it to be a healthy form of punishment in the learning process.

Crucial to the child's successfully passing through this stage in a healthy fashion is the presence of a loving parent or parental surrogate. In the earlier stage of imprinting, the primary goal was to establish an attachment bond with an affectionate parenting figure. There was little in the way of formal cognitive processes operating. In this phase, the affectionate parenting figure must be present to provide linguistic input in the service of teaching the child what is good, bad, right, and wrong. Linguistic and cognitive factors are operative here, but the learning is based on simple pleasure-pain principles. If such significant figures are absent then the child is not going to accomplish this phase successfully. And the learning occurs because of the affection the child will predictably receive when "good" and the threat of its withdrawal when "bad."

Once again, the hierarchal nature of the sequence in the development of the internalized guilt-evoking mechanisms requires that the previous stages be present if the next stage is to be accomplished. Accordingly, a child with a genetic-neurological factor with high guilt-evoking potential, who may have had good imprinting and the development of a strong attachment bond, will not successfully accomplish this third phase if the parenting figure is removed, not sufficiently present, or significantly unpredictable in providing positive reinforcement. Also, it is difficult to ascertain the exact time span when this phase is operative. Roughly, I believe it begins at the time when the child starts to appreciate formal language, during the end of the first year of life. There is no particular time of life when this phase comes to an end; however, the earlier in life the conditioning is provided by loving figures, the stronger will be its effects and the more important it will be in the child's development.

The Shame Stage

In the fourth stage, the shame stage, the child's primary deterrent to performing a prohibited act is the fear that he or she will be discovered by significant environmental figures who will then reject him or her. Of importance here is the child's fear of being *seen* performing the transgression by parents or surrogates, and thereby rejected. It is as if the child is standing in the middle of a circle of parenting figures all of whom are pointing at him or her and simultaneously shouting "shame on you!" This stage coincides with E.H. Erikson's (1950) second stage in which the primary conflict to be resolved is that of "Autonomy vs. Shame." Erikson makes reference to the ashamed person's words to the observers: "God damn your eyes." At this stage, the deterrent forces are still externalized; one blushes in front of someone, not alone. In Eastern cultures, such as the Japanese, shame as a deterrent to undesirable behavior is ubiquitous. When a man commits a crime his whole family suffers disgrace and it is not simply the individual who need be ashamed. (This is probably one of the reasons for the low crime rate in countries like Japan.) In this phase, as well, there must be caring figures who still provide praise and affection when the child is "good" and who care enough to threaten loss of affection (at this stage "publicly") when the child exhibits undesirable behavior. There is a definite similarity between the pleasure-pain and the shame stage in that in both an external factor operates to discourage unacceptable behavior. They differ, however, in that in the pleasure-pain stage the deterrent can be any of a variety of external noxious stimuli—both physical and psychological. In the shame stage a very specific external threat is employed, namely, the overt disapproval of one or more significant figures in a public (as opposed to private) setting.

The Guilt Stage

In the fifth and final stage, the self-blame or guilt stage, the child has internalized the parental values. Here, the inner rather than the outer voice deters (G. Piers and M.B. Singer, 1953). This corresponds to Erikson's (1950) third stage, "Guilt versus Initiative." Alone and unobserved, the child suffers the admonition of the voices of the internalized authorities. Once this phase has been reached, the parents can relax their vigil. The child can be trusted to behave because this mechanism is powerful—so powerful that it not only functions with exaggerated severity, but lends itself well to the formation of many psychopathological mechanisms.

S. Freud considered the ages of three to five to be important ones in superego development. He related this to the resolution of the Oedipus complex. According to Freud, boys develop incestuous designs on their mothers during this phase and anticipate that their fathers will castrate them in punishment for these illicit cravings, which violate the incest taboo. In order to protect themselves from this consequence, they incorporate their fathers' superego dictates against incest. In this process, they also carry down from their fathers' superegos other dictates that are designed to inhibit a wide variety of unacceptable behaviors via the formation of guilt. I am in agreement with Freud that there is indeed rapid development of the child's capacity to experience guilt during this phase. However, I am not in agreement with him that it has anything to do with the resolution of the Oedipus complex. (I have discussed in detail elsewhere 1973a, 1986a my views on the Oedipus complex.) Rather, I believe that this is the period in children's lives when they are beginning to spend significant amounts of time outside the parental home. They start attending nursery school and begin visiting the homes of other children, unaccompanied by their parents. In these new situations they have to learn the "rules" of the new authorities who take command over their lives. In order to adjust properly in these new environments they must learn quickly the new rules or else suffer rejection. I believe that children's rapid superego development during this phase is much more reasonably explained by these developments in the child's life than by anything related to sexual attraction toward the parent of the opposite sex.

In this phase, as well, there must be present in the child's environment loving and affectionate individuals with whom the child will identify and whom the child will emulate. Without such identification and emulation there will be no incorporation and internalization of the parental standards. Such incorporation is central to the development of the guilt-evoking mechanisms. The child then has his or her own guidelines for behavior and will secretly feel a sense of low self-worth if these rules are broken. Guilt, therefore, differs from shame. One is ashamed only when others learn of the reprehensible behavior; when there is guilt, only the perpetrator need know. Shame is public; guilt is private.

I have defined guilt as the feeling of low self-worth that an individual experiences after having thoughts, experiencing feelings, or performing deeds which one has learned in early childhood are unacceptable to significant figures. I believe that this mechanism is central to what we refer to as guilt, but there are other operative factors. One of these is the capacity to put oneself in another person's position. This is another cognitive capacity which, although separate from guilt, is also an element within it. Let us take, for example: "It is bad and wrong to hurt other people." One could simply say that an individual might feel guilty if he or she were to break this rule, because such transgression had been associated with criticism and/or loss of parental affection in early childhood. However, it is reasonable also to say that this rule will be strengthened if the individual appreciates that the person whom one has harmed will suffer. Such appreciation is likely to strengthen the internalized guilt-evoking mechanisms. Another cognitive factor that is operative in the guilt mechanism is the ability to project oneself into the future, especially the appreciation of the future consequences of one's unacceptable behavior. The anticipation of pain or pleasure, as mentioned, is operative in the development of guilt. In order to utilize this contributing factor, however, the individual must have the cognitive capacity to project him- or herself into the future.

Accordingly, there are two kinds of projective mechanisms operative in guilt: 1) The capacity to project oneself into the position of those who might suffer from one's transgressions and 2) the ability to project oneself into the future in order to appreciate the possible consequences (both positive and negative) of one's behavior. These mechanisms also have their own evolutionary development and it is reasonable to speculate that the aforementioned bell-shaped curves are applicable to these mechanisms as well. Consequently, it is probable that individuals vary with regard to the genetic endowment that determines the strength of these functions. Accordingly, children with weak superegos may very well have these genetic impairments contributing to their difficulties.

I believe that there are gender differences in the strength of the internal guilt-evoking mechanisms. Specifically, I believe that women are more likely to feel guilt on a genetic basis than men and are more likely, as well, to be able to put themselves in the position of other people, i.e., exhibit sympathy and empathy. I believe that this difference not only exists but also that it cannot be explained simply as due to environmental influences. Up until the 20th century men were primarily the hunters and fighters (protectors and warriors) and women were primarily the child rearers. I am not placing any particular value judgments on these role differences; I am only stating that this is what the situation was. Men who were genetically strong in hunting/fighting capacities were more likely to survive than those who were weak in these areas. The weaker ones were more likely to fall in battle and less likely to protect their families from enemies. They were also less likely to compete successfully for food for themselves and their families. Accordingly, they were less likely to pass their genes down to subsequent generations. Women who were stronger in the child-rearing realm were more likely viewed as desirable mates and their genes, therefore, were more likely to be passed down to their progeny.

Now to go more specifically to the guilt-evoking mechanisms. Men with high development of the capacity for guilt were generally less effective warriors than those who were more psychopathically inclined. To be a good soldier one must not think too long about the fact that one is murdering another individual—depriving that person thereby of the one life he or she has on this earth. Guilt-ridden neurotics make the poorest soldiers; criminal psychopaths probably make the best soldiers. Wars give them the opportunity to murder and plunder with social sanction. In contrast, there was no particular survival advantage for women with low genetic programming for the guilt-evoking mechanisms. In fact, having strong guilt mechanisms may have been of preferential value to them in that it lessened the likelihood that they would abandon their children or treat them badly. This difference in the sexes, justifies, I believe, my view that men today are less likely to feel guilt than women. I believe that this is *one* of the reasons why there are many more male than female criminals.

Women also are generally more sympathetic and empathetic than men. I believe that this difference relates also to the aforementioned evolutionary selective processes. Putting oneself in the position of one's enemy lessens the likelihood of killing that individual. Weakness in this capacity is an asset on the battlefield. Strength in such capacity is an asset in child rearing. Babies cannot verbalize their needs. The mother's sympathy and empathy, the ability to project herself into the child's position and understand its needs, was crucial for the survival of the human species. This speculation, therefore, explains this gender difference.

The ability to project oneself into the future may also have genetically determined gender differences. The opposite of this capacity is generally referred to as impulsivity. Although the warrior must utilize such thinking to some degree, there must be a certain weakness in this area when one goes into battle. There must be the capacity to deny that one may get killed. Such denial requires some blindness to future consequences and more attention to immediate action. As men are recruited to march off to war, they have to deny that they might not march back. The effective soldier must often shoot first and ask questions later. Impulsivity, then, over the course of history, may have contributed to the survival of men. Women, in contrast, had to be thinking more about the future if their babies were to survive. Quietly thinking about the future was probably conducive to the survival of women. I am not claiming that conducting warfare does not involve any consideration of the future; I am only claiming that conducting successful warfare, at the foot-soldier level, involves more impulsivity than quiet deliberation. The generals, behind the lines, can indulge themselves in future planning and strategies. Consistent with this theory is my belief that there would probably be less war in this world if women were the leaders of nations. Unfortunately, at this time, it is more often the case that women who are able to reach such levels of power and influence are generally those who have taken on male qualities of combativeness, competition, and ruthlessness. Perhaps that was the only way they could have reached their high positions in today's world. Later in this chapter, in my discussion of differences in mating patterns, I will make reference to these speculations again.

Clinical Implications of the Theory

I believe this theory has important implications for therapy. If I am correct, then many patients who present with deficiencies in their capacity to feel guilt have a poor therapeutic prognosis. One cannot change the genes and so those whose impairments in this area relate to weak genetic-neurological programming are not likely to be helped by a psychotherapeutic approach. Furthermore, those who (in addition or separately) have suffered deprivations of affection during the critical imprinting period of infancy are also not likely to be helped by treatment because of their deep-seated impairment in forming meaningful relationships. Although these are certainly pessimistic implications regarding the treatability of patients who have these defects, this should not be a reason for denying their reality. If this is the way the world is then we have to recognize and accept these realities and not delude ourselves into believing that we can help people whose disorders are not reversible by our psychotherapeutic techniques. One way of enhancing the efficiency of psychotherapy is to be more selective with regard to our patients and not attempt to treat those who are untreatable. Such differentiations also open up new avenues of research for *appropriate* therapeutic measures for those who are not candidates for our psychotherapeutic programs. A behavior modification approach, for example, probably offers more hope than psychotherapy for changing a psychopathic person who has not had a healthy imprinting experience with an affectionate parenting figure during early infancy. (I will discuss this further below.)

At this point I would like to present a clinical vignette that will serve as a basis for my subsequent discussion of the implications of this theory. A number of years ago I saw a 15-year-old boy named

Bob, who presented with moderately severe psychopathic behavior. He had become involved with a group of delinquent youngsters and had been picked up by the police on a number of occasions for recklessly driving stolen cars, stealing from department stores, and burglarizing homes. He had practically no motivation to learn in school, and had no hesitation cheating on tests. He would usually lie about his grades and often "lose" his report cards. He was disruptive in the classroom in a kind of playful and mocking way. He frequently propositioned his female cousins and on two occasions was found fondling the genitalia of little girls who were relatives.

The patient's mother was unmarried when she became pregnant at the age of 18. She was a seriously disturbed woman, who did not inform her family that she was pregnant. Rather, she found some excuse to remove herself entirely from her family and moved to a distant part of the city in which they lived. Over the course of the pregnancy there was good reason to believe that she deteriorated significantly, to the point that she was psychotic at the time of Bob's birth. She took the newborn infant home to an apartment, where she lived alone, and would often leave the child alone for hours and even days. During these periods the child would not be fed and would lie crying in his own wastes. After numerous interventions by neighbors, the child's neglect was brought to the attention of the police and subsequently of the mother's family. By that time the child was about five months of age. It took another six months, however, before the mother was finally declared unfit and the child was turned over to the mother's sister, who was married and five years the mother's senior. It was the maternal aunt who raised the patient and brought him to me.

In the initial session she said: "Doctor, since the day he came into my home, when he was about one year old, I've been turning myself inside out trying to be a mother to this child. But nothing's worked. In spite of all my efforts, he still treats me like a piece of furniture. I think that if I died today, he wouldn't even cry. He has absolutely no feelings for people. He never feels guilty about anything he's done and punishments don't seem to work. I've tried them all. He couldn't care less whether I send him to his room, ground him, take away television, take away his allowance, or anything else. Nothing works! He's never ashamed of anything he's done. He often says he's sorry and then he apologizes, but he just does that to get people off his back. I know him well enough to know that he really doesn't mean it. Sometimes he can convince people that he's really sorry about what he's done, but he just goes on and does what he wants anyway—no matter how terrible. He lives for the moment and doesn't seem to concern himself with the future consequences of what he does.... He has no concern for other people's feelings. I've never seen him cry about anything terrible that has happened to another person, even death. He's been to a couple of funerals now. One was the funeral of my mother two years ago and he showed absolutely no emotion at all.... My other two children are just fine. In fact, I've done less for them, even though they're my own biological offsprings, than I've done for him. Sometimes they resent how much I go out of my way for him because I feel I have to keep trying.... He has never known his mother. She's been in the hospital all these years. A few years ago I took Bob to visit her and he couldn't care less one way or the other. So we never went again. I just didn't see the point.... He's also a con man. He can put on a sweet smile and con people into doing things for him. I started taking him to psychiatrists when he was about seven. You're the fifth one. The others all said the same thing. They said they couldn't help him and that maybe when he's older he might be helped. You've come very highly recommended and I hope you can help him."

In my interview with Bob he was calm and "smooth." At no point did he exhibit any manifestations of guilt over his various forms of antisocial behavior. When I pointed out to him that his reckless driving was dangerous and might result in people being killed, he shrugged his shoulders and said, "No one lives forever." When I reminded him that he himself might be killed, he replied, "I don't drive that fast." When I asked him about his fondling the genitalia of little girls he replied, "It was fun. I told them I was only tickling them. I don't know why everybody's getting so upset." Bob showed absolutely no interest in coming for treatment, but stated that he would come if his mother insisted because it made her happy. He didn't think that he had any problems and so thought treatment would be a waste of time and money.

I informed Bob's mother (I will call her *mother* because psychologically she was, even though biologically she was his aunt) that I regretted that I could not be of help to him. I explained to her my belief that he had not formed a psychological tie with an affectionate adult during a critical period for such bonding during the first year of his life and that there was no possibility that he would be able to do this subsequently. I discussed with her the phenomenon of imprinting and compared Bob to the duckling who had been deprived completely of meaningful caretaking input during the critical period of his infancy. I explained to her, as well, that for psychotherapy to be meaningful, the patient must have a good relationship with the therapist. Because Bob was not capable of forming a meaningful affectionate relationship, he did not satisfy a primary and fundamental criterion for successful treatment. I explained to her that if he had shown any evidence, no matter how small, of having formed a meaningful relationship with another human being throughout the course of his life, I would consider revising my conclusion. However, I pointed out to her that there was no evidence that he had done so, and that even his relationship with her was one that could not satisfy the criterion of being a genuinely human one. She had described Bob as treating her "like a piece of furniture," and I agreed that this was basically the way he viewed all other human beings.

The mother pleadingly asked me if I would still try to treat him. I told her that without conviction for the possibility of a positive therapeutic outcome, I would be exploiting her. Again, she repeated that I had come highly recommended and that I was her last hope. Again, I tried to impress upon her the futility of a psychotherapeutic program, but finally agreed to try for a few sessions with the full understanding that the likelihood of my helping Bob was practically zero. And the prediction came true. We discontinued after a few months of treatment, when I felt that I was getting absolutely nowhere. One could argue that my initial pessimism resulted in my fulfilling my prophecy that therapy would be doomed. In response, I believe that the failure of therapy had nothing to do with my initial prophecy, but was related to the child's being untreatable because of the aforementioned reasons. And I believe, further, that even the most optimistic therapist (whose optimism would have to be based on delusion) would still have come forth with the same result. During the four or five years following the cessation of Bob's treatment I intermittently received letters from other therapists and clinics asking for reports. Obviously, the mother did not give up and I doubt seriously whether the subsequent therapists were successful.

Bob's case demonstrates in an extreme way the principles outlined in the theory presented above. But he is not the typical patient who presents with antisocial behavior. The more typical youngster has generally suffered less serious compromises at the levels of imprinting and the subsequent pleasure/pain, shame, and guilt levels. These children are more readily treatable because they have had at least some experience with a meaningful relationship during the imprinting phase and so have the potential for forming a relationship with the therapist.

The therapist does well to view antisocial behavior on a continuum. At one end is the extreme psychopath who may have a high genetic loading for psychopathy (because of a weak genetically based substrate to serve as the foundation for guilt-evoking mechanisms), and/or who has suffered formidable deprivations of affection during the imprinting period, and/or who has experienced antisocial inducing influences during the three phases in which parental disciplinary measures influence the development of the conscience. At the other end of the continuum is the normal, healthy child who has not suffered any significant deficiencies in the five levels of development of the internalized guilt-evoking mechanisms. The closer the child is to the healthy end of the continuum the greater the likelihood a therapeutic relationship will be possible and potentially useful.

A scenario sometimes seen in television sitcoms is that of a severely antisocial boy of seven or eight who has spent practically all his life being shuttled from one foster home to another. He is then adopted by Mr. and Mrs. *Goody Two Shoes* who take him under their benevolent wings and provide him with love, understanding, and sympathy. Whereas at the beginning of the program, the school principal is tearing his hair out with frustration over the boy's delinquent antics, by the end of the program he is a class leader, star student, and the loveliest little fellow you could imagine. All this is Hollywood pap and is just another one of the fairy tales that sell a product. Unfortunately, gullible listeners believe this stuff and will use it as a guideline when adopting children who have had formidable deprivations in the early years of their lives. Promulgating this myth is a disservice to all concerned. Elsewhere in this book, I will be making reference to this theory when it provides a useful explanation for the clinical phenomena being discussed.

REBELLION

Adolescent rebellion can be divided into three types: 1) healthy and constructive rebellion, 2) neutral and/or innocuous rebellion, and 3) destructive rebellion. It is extremely important for the examiner to make these differentiations, especially because of their therapeutic importance. Healthy or constructive rebellion should be encouraged; neutral or innocuous rebellion might very well be left alone; destructive rebellion must be discouraged.

Accordingly, rebellion may not be all that bad. Constructive rebellion may very well be considered the stuff of which progress is made. In fact, if not for constructive rebellion we might still be living in caves. There are societies in which centuries pass and there is absolutely no difference in lifestyle from one generation to the next. The family may remain living in the same home for hundreds of years. There is no rebellion; and there is no progress. One could argue that my criticism of this lifestyle is a reflection of a prejudiced value judgment, and that my preference for societies that progress over those in which one generation is no different from the next reflects an inappropriate bias. I cannot deny that people in the nonprogressive category might very well lead fulfilling and enriched lives. In such societies, however, we do not observe the impetus to make new discoveries, expand human knowledge, and solve ever-present problems. If one has appendicitis, it's nice to know there are surgeons around who can perform the life-saving appendectomy. When giving birth and the baby is "stuck," it's nice to know there are obstetricians around who can perform a caesarean delivery that may very well save the life of both the mother and child. These are just two of countless examples of the benefits of progress—benefits which, I believe, far outweigh what appear to me to be the disadvantages (I would say stagnation) of a nonprogressive society.

Rebellion is an important element in human progress. The rebellious person is basically saying: "I do not agree with that which those before me have accepted as fact. I will reject it, or I will expand upon it, or improve it." The people whom we refer to as geniuses are often individuals who are able to look upon a generally accepted fact—something believed by the vast majority of their predecessors—question it, and not only consider the possibility that it is wrong, but prove it to be so. Albert Einstein is just one such example. Prior to his time, the consensus among scientists was that light is weightless. Einstein believed that light has weight—not very heavy, but weight nevertheless. In his famous eclipse experiment he demonstrated that light waves bend as they pass celestial bodies and that only an entity with some weight would exhibit such changes in its path. Einstein also questioned the general notion that time passes at a fixed rate. He demonstrated that the rate at which time passes is related to the speed of the platform on which one measures time's rate of passage. Although these differences are significant only when one approaches the speed of light, he still proved that the rates of time passage do indeed change at these extremely high speeds. Although this may not appear to be of much practical interest to the everyday person, it has profound implications for our understanding of the nature of the universe. It was healthy rebellion on Einstein's part that was a central factor in these important discoveries.

Another more practical and mundane example: Up until the last 10 to 15 years, Rh + babies who were born to Rh- mothers might develop erythroblastosis fetalis, a disease that might be fatal or crippling. The people who developed RhoGAM, a drug that can prevent the development of this disorder in such babies, had to reject some basic immunological principles before they could proceed with their work. They had to disbelieve what was being said by most professors and most textbooks, namely, that the baby's Rh + cells cross the placenta during the intrauterine period and stimulate the mother to produce antibodies to Rh + cells during the course of the pregnancy. Once this notion was tested and rejected, and it was found that the baby's Rh + cells only entered the mother's circulation at the time of delivery, the investigators were able to go on with their important work. Again, healthy rebellion was a central element in this important discovery from which mankind has benefited immensely.

As mentioned, the various developmental issues focused on in this chapter are not completely separate from one another; there is much overlap. Rebellion is no exception to this principle. I discuss rebellion first because it infuses many of the other conflicts and problems with which adolescents must deal, especially their dependency problems, their attempts at forming a separate identity, and the maneuvers that they utilize to enhance their self-esteem. Rebellion can serve to compensate for feelings of inadequacy. Rebellion, especially when it is associated with great anger, may provide the youngster with a feeling of strength and power that he or she does not actually possess. And this is especially the case when the rebellion takes place in the context of a group, which generally provides the youngster with a sense of power far greater than he or she possesses. It is truly an example of the principle of the whole being greater than the sum of its parts. Rebellion can very well be viewed as the energizer of the adolescent's solutions to these basic developmental problems. It adds a vitality to the problem-solving processes and to the solutions themselves and thereby enhances the likelihood that they will be effective.

The examiner should try to ascertain in which of the three aforementioned categories the rebellion lies—healthy, neutral, or destructive—and should attempt to determine the point at which normal and expected adolescent rebellion ends and the pathological begins. These differentiations may sometimes be very difficult. For example, in recent years some adolescents have become deeply identified with the "punk rock" movement. These youngsters pride themselves on bizarre and outlandish dress that is not only gaudy but designed to frighten. Infused in all of this is a strong sadistic element; their songs often center on themes of violence and murder. Is this necessarily pathological? Although I do not claim vast experience with this group, from what I know of them I would consider their preoccupation with these sadistic themes to be pathological— especially if the youngster engages in antisocial behavior as an outgrowth of participation in such a group. Accordingly, I would say that such membership is at best a prepathological manifestation and certainly a warning sign that the youngster may very well move into the pathological realm.

Another example: A number of years ago a mother brought a 13-year-old girl to me for treatment. While cleaning her daughter's room one morning she found a note on her desk that she had written to a friend. It had not yet been folded or put into an envelope for mailing. The segment that was particularly upsetting to the mother read: "Dear Mary, I had a great time at your house this weekend. Thanks for inviting me. That was a real great time we had with the boys you invited over. I really liked that big guy, the 18-year-old. I really liked sucking his big cock." Not surprisingly, the mother was shocked by the "discovery" of this letter, considered it a definite sign of severe psychopathology, and requested the earliest possible appointment with me. On the basis of my evaluation I concluded that there had been no such encounter and that the note was left as a prank. Examiners do well to work on the assumption that unsealed letters left in "public" places are placed there so that they will be read by those who are likely to notice them. People who genuinely do not wish their letters read do not make such "mistakes."

Was this a pathological act? The question cannot be answered without considering the broader context in which the letter was written. In this girl's case, it was an isolated example of a "prank" and she was basically functioning well in all areas: school, the neighborhood, and at home. Had she not been functioning well in these areas, and had this been one of a series of such pranks, then I would have considered her to have had problems warranting treatment. In this case, I advised the mother that I saw no reason for treatment at that point and that I was taking the girl's statement at face value. It was an age-appropriate prank (although probably a little more creative than that devised by most 13-year-old girls). I also advised the mother to call me if there was a repetition of such antics and asked her to call in a few months, even if there were no such recurrences, in order to inform me of the outcome. The mother did indeed call me a few months later and told me that there had been no repetition of pranks of this kind. My final conclusion, then, was that this prank was an example of normal adolescent rebellion in the somewhat creative and provocative category.

Another example: An 18-year-old girl, while sitting at the dinner table with her family, nonchalantly says, "You know, I've missed my period this month. I wonder if I'm pregnant?" Is dropping such a *bomb* necessarily pathological? Again, one cannot come to a conclusion unless one considers the total context of the setting in which the comment was made. If the girl, for example, engages in indiscriminate sex in order to compensate for feelings of low self-worth, then that is her primary problem. If she is feigning nonchalance as a way of covering up underlying fears of pregnancy, then one must still look into other aspects of the situation before deciding whether psychopathology is present. If she is frequently dropping provocations of this kind, totally unrelated to real events, then the problem is not one of pregnancy, but provocation. And persistent provocation is pathological. My hope here is that the reader will be impressed with the fact that placement of adolescent rebellion into one of the three aforementioned categories may not be easy. In many situations, therefore, one must explore a variety of factors in the attempt to make such a determination.

It is important also for the therapist to appreciate that adolescent rebellion does not exist separate from the reactions of the individuals against whom the youngster is rebelling. An important determinant as to whether or not the rebellion will have served its purposes is whether parents and other adult authorities are shocked, disgusted, nauseated, or react in other ways that reveal their revulsion from the rebellious act. If the parents do not provide these reactions, the youngster is deprived of one of the important gratifications of the rebellious act. Failure of parents to respond in these ways may result in the youngster's feeling the need to utilize more dramatic methods of rebellion. In such cases this may result in a shift from innocuous to pathological modes of rebellion.

A good example of this phenomenon is the long-hair style that became common in the early to mid-1960s, primarily as a result of the popularity of The Beatles. Of all the forms of adolescent rebellion one could imagine, I believe long hair is one of the most innocuous, and therein lies the ingenuity of the person who first devised this mode of adolescent rebellion. I do not know who he or she was, but I believe that the individual may have contributed more to the lessening of violence on earth than many who have won Nobel Peace Prizes. After all, what more innocuous way could there be to rebel than to grow one's hair long? However, the success of this maneuver relies upon parental revulsion. Otherwise, the rug is pulled out from under it and the youngster may have to resort to more dramatic methods of rebellion.

During the time when the long-hair mode of rebellion was in vogue, I would generally recommend that parents provide the youngster with reasonable degrees of revulsion in order to insure the perpetuation of this innocuous rebellious maneuver. This interchange typifies the kind of conversation I recommended at that time. It takes place between 16-year-old Tom, whose hair is down below his shoulders, and his father.

Father: Tom, I would like to have a chat with you, son.

Tom (as if granting a favor): Yeah, Pop. What is it you want?

Father (apologetically): Well, Tom, it's just that I would like to have a father-son talk with you, boy.

Tom (impatiently): Yeah what is it, Dad?

Father: Well, Tom, the first thing I want you to know is that your mother and I *love you deeply*.

Tom: Yeah, Dad, I know that. What do you have in mind?

Father (hesitantly): Well, son, I'm going to make a criticism of you, but I want you to know that it doesn't mean that I don't love you very much.

Tom (now even more impatient): I know, Dad. Will you please get to the point. What's the bottom line?

Father: Well, Tom, to tell you the truth, it's that hair of yours. To tell you the truth, it really upsets your mother and me to see you that way, especially because from the back we can't tell whether you're a boy or a girl.

Tom (angrily): This is a *free* country and I'll wear my hair any way I want!

Father: Listen, Tom, I recognize that. I know you're free to wear your hair any way you want. However, I have the freedom to tell you how upset I am over it.

Tom: Well, is that all?

Father: No. There's more. You see this Saturday night your mother and I are having some dinner guests, some people from the office. Some of them are senior people in my firm and it's important that we make a good impression.

Tom: So what's that got to do with me?

Father: Well, son, you see it's that hair. It's not that we don't love you, but it'll be a little embarrassing for us if the guests see you. Therefore, your mother and I would both appreciate if you would leave the house about 7:00 or 7:30 on

Saturday night. They'll be coming at about 8:00 and, to be honest with you, it'll be a little embarrassing for us if they see you this way. Also, your mother and I have decided that you can extend your curfew Saturday and can come home around 1:00 a.m. We expect the guests to leave around midnight.

Tom (even more angrily): No one's going to tell me when I leave this house and when I come back. This is a free country and this is *my* house also. What is this a jail or a penitentiary or something? If you're ashamed of me that's your problem, not mine. There's nothing wrong with the way I wear my hair. That's the way *I* like it. And if those asshole friends of yours don't like my hair, that's their problem.

Father (somewhat timidly): Please don't get angry, Tom. It's just that we want you to know how we feel about it. We just hoped you'd take our feelings into consideration and not embarrass us Saturday night. We don't want you to feel that this house isn't yours; it's just that we want you to take our feelings into consideration here.

Tom (getting up): Well you're not taking my feelings into consideration and I'll come and go when I please. (Exit Tom.)

That Saturday evening Tom will stay in his room until approximately 8:30, to insure that even the latest guest will have by then arrived. Then, wearing his heaviest boots, he will stomp down the stairs (to insure that everyone can hear him approaching) and make a grand entrance into the dining room, hair waving in the breeze. He'll make the rounds of all the guests, politely inquiring about their welfare and that of their children. A more sensitive and well-mannered boy would be hard to imagine. Each greeting of each guest will be accompanied by enough head-nodding to insure once again that his mane is fully displayed. And one can be sure, as well, that he will prance into the house at 11:30 p.m., before any of the guests have left, in order to once again insure that his grand entrance will be noticed by the guests—who will politely hide their revulsion. Of course, Tom will be acutely sensitive to the suppressed disgust of the guests and the embarrassment he has caused his parents. This is the scenario I recommended during the 60s and 70s. Those parents who were wise enough to follow this advice and who carried out their role helped prevent their children's having to resort to more dramatic and serious forms of rebellion.

One of the purposes of adolescent rebellion is to help mobilize the youngster to leave the home and assuage the anxieties attendant to such separation. The facts are that the vast majority of parents will be far more loving and affectionate of the adolescent than any other human being on earth. Except for the most rejecting and abusive parents, most are willing to make more sacrifices and to provide more guidance, support, affection, and money than any other person on earth. Furthermore, they will take more "shit" from the adolescent than any other human being. I suspect that on some level (probably *very* deep in the unconscious) the adolescent is appreciative of this and thereby fears the separation. By viewing the parents as village idiots, as anachronisms from the Middle Ages, as people who are not up with the latest trends, the adolescent can justify rebellion and refusal to comply with parental standards. Rebellion, then, may serve to lessen separation anxieties. Such rebellion also has the fringe benefit of helping the parents deal with their own "empty nest syndrome." On the one hand, the parents anticipate that the home will be somewhat lonely when the adolescent is gone. On the other hand, the *Sturm und Drang* of adolescent rebellion is often such a nuisance and a source of ongoing provocation for the parents that there is also a sense of relief when the youngster is finally out of the house.

DEPENDENCY CONFLICTS

Twentieth-century teenagers are growing up in a somewhat unique environment in that their childhoods are being artificially prolonged by the demands of our modern technological society. Prior to this century, children generally were considered adults as early as the age of six or seven, but no later than puberty, and were expected to go out into the adult world and assume adult responsibilities. Such expectations are no longer realistic in modern technological societies. The many years of training required to achieve competence in most occupations is so great that one cannot reasonably expect youngsters to complete their education and training until the late teens and beyond.

Accordingly, the realities are that most teenagers *are* dependent upon their parents for food, clothing, shelter, and the other necessities of life. With physical dependency comes psychological dependency—the adolescent's attempts to deny it notwithstanding. The adolescent would like to believe that he or she is truly independent of the parents and tries to deny frequently the humiliating realization that just the opposite is most often the case. The adolescent is perpetually proclaiming independence in a situation where there is significant dependence. Accordingly, the sense of independence is specious. In earlier centuries the transition from childhood to adulthood was short. Youngsters had little time to gratify dependency needs because they were so swept up in the fight for survival. They were too preoccupied with the acquisition of the bare necessities of life to indulge themselves in the kind of frivolous dependency conflicts that are so widespread today. In short, many of the adolescent phenomena we are discussing in this book are manifestations of 20th-century indulgences, especially in affluent families and societies.

Dependence on Parents vs. Rejection of Parents

A common way in which adolescents deal with the transition from dependence to independence is to scorn and denigrate their parents. I recall my daughter Nancy, when she was three-years-old, sitting between her mother and me saying, "Mommy, you're the best mommy in the whole wide world and I'm the luckiest little girl in the whole world to have a mommy as wonderful as you. And Daddy, you're the best daddy in the whole world, and I'm the luckiest little girl in the whole world to have a daddy like you. I don't ever want to leave this house in my whole life. I want to stay living here with the two of you forever and ever." Her mother and I welled up with joy and pride after such a wonderful and loving comment. However, if a child is making the same statement at the age of 18, the parents have problems! Somewhere along the line the child has to give up the notion of living with the parents for the rest of his or her life, or else the youngster will be crippled with regard to entering into adult society as a self-sufficient individual.

One way in which the separation becomes easier and the dependency longings are squelched is to transform the parents from

loving, kind, and giving individuals into morons, loathsome oddballs, and people who have not been keeping up with the latest
developments in mankind's progress and who know nothing about
"where it's all at." Once the parents are transformed into such
despicable imbeciles, it is much easier for the adolescent to have the
courage to go forth into the cold cruel world. The reality is that no
one will ever treat the adolescent as well as the parents do. Even the
most ardent lover is not as likely to make the sacrifices and tolerate
the privations that a parent will. By denigrating the parents the
adolescent can deny this obvious reality and provide him- or herself
with an excuse to "get out of that shit-house once and for all." It
would be nice if this could solve the dependency problem. Such
deprecation of the parents is rarely successful in resolving the
dependency problem, however, because the reality is that the
youngster is still very much dependent on the parents – denigration
and rejection of them notwithstanding. Scorning them is easy; it
does not provide, however, the wherewithal for genuinely independent living. Now that the parents have been transformed into stupid
ogres, however, it is more difficult to believe that they can be
reliable sources of gratification of the youngster's still ever-pressing
dependency needs.

Many adolescents take the position that parents should provide their services from hidden places. This concept of the ideal
parent derives from the belief that only children and babies do
things with their parents, but mature individuals no longer have
such infantile needs. Accordingly, it may be a source of mortification for an adolescent to be seen in public with a parent. This
phenomenon was demonstrated well a number of years ago when I
was shopping one Saturday afternoon with my youngest daughter,
Julie, then 14 years old. We were strolling through a mall, nonchalantly window shopping. Suddenly, the following interchange took
place:

> *Julie* (speaking very firmly and slowly): Dad, don't turn
> around. Don't look sideways. Don't look back. Just look
> straight ahead and follow me.

I suspected that Julie had seen some friends and the prospect of
their seeing her with her father (ugh!) was mortifying to her.

Accordingly, she wanted to get out of that mall as fast as possible, without being seen. I did not consider it useful to confront Julie with my speculation. Rather, I decided that it would be judicious to go along with the plan.

> *Gardner* (feigning curiosity): Why do you want me to do that, Julie?
> *Julie* (firmly): Don't ask questions. Just do what I say. Let's get out of here as soon as we can.
> *Gardner*: Okay.

I then began following Julie. Her steps were deliberate, stiff, and mechanical and so were mine. Neither of us even turned sideways (and certainly not backwards) as we hastily left the store. I suspected, however, that if a store detective were to have seen us at that point, he probably would have stopped us as two "suspicious characters" in that we certainly appeared as if we had something to hide and might very well have been sneaking out with stolen goods. I complied here with Julie's request because of my appreciation that she needed to be seen as a separate entity from her father, and that her humiliation at the prospect of being seen with me in public was a normal adolescent manifestation of her need to break away from me and be seen by herself and others as a separate person.

On another occasion, while sitting in the living room, Julie initiated the following conversation:

> *Julie*: You know, Dad, you turn me off!
> *Gardner*: Why do you say that, Julie?
> *Julie*: I don't know, just everything about you turns me off.
> *Gardner*: Well, Julie, you know that I'm always receptive to try to rectify any deficiencies I may have, especially deficiencies that may be interfering with the relationship I have with my children. So if you'll be just a little more specific, perhaps we can do something about this problem of my "turning you off."
> *Julie*: I don't know, it's just your whole lifestyle!
> *Gardner*: Well, Julie, it's very difficult for me to respond to that. If you could pinpoint some particular aspects of my lifestyle that are particularly alienating to you, then I would be in a better position to address myself to them. Perhaps I would

be in agreement with you that these qualities are indeed deficiencies, that their removal would improve our relationship, and would make you less critical of my lifestyle. However, it may be that I might not be in agreement with you, and then I would do nothing about them. However, I'm in no position to make such a decision until you can be more specific about what these possible deficiencies are.

Julie: I can't think of them right now.

Gardner: Well, why don't you give it some thought and when you can be more specific about what these characteristics are, then I'll be happy to address myself to them. Then I can promise you great receptivity to trying to change them, if I'm in agreement with you that they are indeed defects.

Julie never brought up the subject again. A classical Freudian analyst might say that her statement that I "turned her off" was a manifestation of the suppression of sexual feelings toward me. Although I cannot deny this possibility, I am dubious. I believe that the comment stemmed more from her need to totally reject my "lifestyle" in order to provide a sense of independence for herself. Some adolescent youngsters will manifest such rejection of their parents' lifestyle by embracing a religious creed that is totally antithetical to theirs. Others embrace political philosophies that are exactly the opposite of their parents' deep-seated convictions. Children of highly academically oriented parents may decide that they want to think seriously about a menial career that does not require formal education. A healthy youngster entertains these alternatives in constructive ways; the unhealthy youngster may do so in a self-destructive manner.

Transfer of Dependency from Parents to Peers

Adolescents cannot allow themselves the humiliation of overt expression of their still-present dependency desires and must gratify these symbolically, surreptitiously, or by structuring a situation in such a way that they are seemingly coerced into such gratification. One of the ways in which the adolescent satisfies the now suppressed and repressed dependency needs is to transfer dependency gratification from parents to peers. Via this maneuver adolescents convince themselves that they are no longer dependent because the parents have been rejected. However, one does not have to look too deeply into the nature of their relationships with peers to see how dependent they basically are. Under the guise of considering themselves independent thinkers, adolescents are extremely dependent on peer pressure and peer opinion. They feel compelled to embrace the ideology in vogue with their peers, regardless of how absurd. They are slavishly dependent on the adolescent clothing styles that are "in" at that moment and fear diverting from them, even in the smallest way. This reflex dependency on their peers may get them into trouble, e.g., when they fear being the only one in a group who does not engage in a particular form of antisocial behavior. Many become addicted to smoking because they cannot tolerate the prospect of being the only one in their group who doesn't smoke.

In mid-1987, there was a movie in which an adolescent boy did a handstand on the front of an automobile driven by a friend. This act of bravado was copied many times over by youngsters all across the United States—with the result that at least a few were killed while involved in this stunt. Such dependency on peers contributes to the seemingly inexplicable waves of bizarre behavior that periodically break out. For example, it is well known that the widespread reporting of two or more adolescent suicides in the same community is likely to result in an "epidemic" of further adolescent suicides. Some newspapers make it a policy not to report such events because of their awareness of this phenomenon. Such is the power of adolescents' dependency on peers and the forces within them that drive them to mimic behavior that is in vogue among teenagers.

This dependence is demonstrated well by an experience I once had with my son Andrew, then 14 years old. He was preparing to go to summer camp, in this instance a tennis camp. As his mother and I were helping him with his final packing, he became increasingly agitated. This is the conversation that ensued:

> *Gardner*: What's the trouble, Andy?
> *Andrew*: I don't know whether to put my stuff in a duffel bag or a suitcase. I'm afraid if I use a duffel bag, that most of the kids will have suitcases and I'll be embarrassed. Also, I'm

scared that if I choose the suitcase, most of the kids will have duffel bags and then I'll look different and funny.

Gardner: Andy, I've got an idea. First, let me ask you a question. Which do you think is more likely, duffel bags or suitcases?

Andrew: I would say duffel bags in favor of suitcases by a ratio of 51 to 49. (Andy was always mathematically inclined.)

Gardner: Well, I have a suggestion. Why don't we put your stuff in a duffel bag, and we'll take an empty suitcase and put it in the trunk of the car. Then we'll drive past the bus stop, as if we're strangers, and we'll look the situation over to see whether there are more duffel bags or more suitcases. If there are more duffel bags, then out you'll go and everything will be all right. However, if there are more suitcases, then we'll just drive on, as if we don't even belong there, and find an empty lot or alley a few blocks away. Then, when no one is looking, we'll switch things and then we'll drive you back to the bus stop.

Andrew: Gee Dad, every once in a while you say things that make me realize you aren't so stupid after all!

The vignette demonstrates, of course, the need of the adolescent to denigrate his father. The main point here, however, is the obvious one that this bright boy was still slavishly dependent on his peers, so much so that he would experience terrible mortification if he packed his clothing in the less common carrier. It is important for the reader to appreciate, however, that this dependency on the group should not be just viewed merely as a kind of pathological substitute of peers for parents. Rather, it is a step outside the home and is best viewed as a necessary part of the adolescent's transition to independence.

I recall a personal experience when in junior high school that demonstrates quite well the strength of the adolescent's dependency on peers. There were two classmates of mine who were well known for their antisocial antics. One day, as we were leaving an English class, to move on to mathematics, the two boys decided to make what was then called a "stink bomb." This was prepared by mixing photographic negatives with paper and then igniting the "bomb." The smoke was particularly noxious and calculated to produce revulsion in even the most phlegmatic. Because of the obvious fire danger, stink bombs were generally utilized outdoors.

In this case, however, the boys thought it would be a great idea to throw a stink bomb into a desk as we left the English class to go on to mathematics. They chose English because the teacher was one who had great difficulty controlling the class and was easy prey for tormentors. She had just left the room at the time the boys ignited the bomb. As I filed out of the room with my classmates I saw the smoke pouring out of the desk. My immediate impulse was to go over to the desk, pull out its contents, and stomp out the flames. What stopped me was the anticipation that my classmates would call me "chickenshit" and accuse me of a variety of other forms of cowardice. About five minutes later, soon after we were seated in mathematics, we heard the inevitable sound of a fire alarm. Approximately 2,000 students quickly left the building as the fire department engines surrounded it. Fortunately, no one was injured and the amount of damage done to the classroom was minimal.

In those days there were repercussions for such behavior in the New York City Public Schools. (Unfortunately, such incidents are probably commonplace today with few consequences, except for the most egregious offenders.) The boys were expelled. The class they were expelled from was an honor's class, then referred to as a "rapid advance" class. Most of us in that track went on to highly competitive academic high school programs. These boys did not. I know nothing of what ultimately happened to them. Perhaps their expulsion and failure to go on to a specialized academic high school did not affect their lives one iota. Perhaps their failure to have gone on to a more demanding high school played a role in their not having achieved as much in life as they might otherwise have. I can only wonder whether if I had had the courage at that time to stomp out the flames the boys might have led very different lives. Although I do not know whether my having acted more assertively would have protected them from the dire consequences of what ultimately occurred, I do know that my failure to do so was a reflection of typical adolescent passivity and fear of doing that which might engender the rejection and/or disapproval of peers.

Another way in which the adolescent can satisfy dependency cravings in a socially acceptable manner is to "fall in love." I will discuss in detail my views on romantic love in a later section of this chapter. Here I focus on its value for socially acceptable dependency gratifications. As part of the obsessive involvement with the loved partner the individual is ever craving to be in the presence of the loved one and feels lost when that party is not available. The dependency may often be parasitic, and one of the ways in which the relationship may become compromised is the feeling on the part of at least one of the parties that he or she is being drained and constrained by the other. Their physical caressing of one another is certainly reminiscent of the pattern of the parent and the infant. If the reader concludes from this that I am suggesting that all lovemaking is pathological, that would be a serious error. We all need some dependency gratifications. In a mature loving relationship between a man and a woman these play a definite but relatively small role. In adolescent romantic love (regardless of the age of the person) the dependency gratifications reach pathological levels, as manifested by the obsessiveness with which the individuals crave them. The common term "puppy love" is applicable here—implying as it does that the relationship is much more like two little puppies snuggling up against one another than more mature loving partners whose relationship is a far richer one with less time spent in infantile gratifications.

The adolescent's dependence on peers can be utilized in a healthy way in group therapy. I will discuss group therapy in detail in Chapter Eleven. Here, I mention it only in the context of its value in utilizing the adolescent's dependency on peers for therapeutic purposes. The therapist is viewed as close enough to the parents to be distrusted. As mentioned, he or she is not considered to be up with the latest trends, whereas one's peers are. Because the adolescent views peers as omniscient, he or she considers them far more judicious choices when seeking those to depend on for guidance. Therapists who do not make use of these all-knowing individuals in their therapeutic groups are depriving themselves of valuable assistants in the treatment process.

Dependency on Heroes and Mentors

Another way in which adolescents gratify their dependency needs and, at the same time, transfer dependency gratifications away from parents is to involve themselves with heroes. Movie stars and athletes probably are the most well-known examples of this phenomenon. Adolescents not only emulate and identify with film stars, but try to conform to their lifestyles. Another and more blatant manifestation of such hero worship is the phenomenon of the religious cult in which the followers become slavishly dependent on their leader—who may be viewed as God appointed, God derived, or even God incarnate. Healthier adolescents may become involved with a revered teacher or mentor. This person may become a respected confidant and there may be many healthy elements in this relationship, especially if the teacher exhibits qualities that would serve the youngster well to emulate. Also, if the dependency gratifications are kept within healthy boundaries then the relationship may be even more salutary. Many accomplished people consider themselves to have lifelong debts to their mentors, because of the formidable positive influences they have had on their lives.

The "Winter Camp" College

College is an institution that provides many adolescents with gratification of pathological dependency needs. I believe that most colleges in the United States are not serving primarily as educational institutions; rather, they are serving as what I call "winter camps" for immature youngsters. Most youngsters attending colleges are not really looking for an education, but for another four years of prolongation of their dependent state. We have a unique disease in the United States which I call *the college disease*. Millions of parents believe that it is crucial that their children attend college and really believe that the schools to which they are sending their children are actually serving educational purposes. When there is a demand for something there will always be individuals who will be pleased to provide a supply of the item, especially when there is good money to be made in the business. Most college institutions in the United States are basically businesses. Yes, they have their academic hierarchy, their assistant professors, associate professors, and full professors. They have their college-style buildings (especially red brick and ivy), their alumni associations, their football teams, and their fund-raising campaigns. But the vast majority of students are not there to learn; rather they are there primarily to have a "good time"—which often includes significant indulgence in alcohol, drugs, and sex. When the "students" are not engaged in these activities, they go through the motion of attending classes, but little is learned. Grade-inflation insures that even those with borderline intelligence will get high grades. It is rare for someone to flunk out. And why should they fail? Does one kick a good customer out of the store? If a customer's parents are willing to continue to pay for the services provided, it would be self-destructive of the college in this highly competitive market to cut off a predictable supply of money because of the student's failure to consume the product being offered.

It is important for the reader to appreciate my use of the word *most*. I did not say that the aforementioned criticisms apply to *all* collegiate institutions and *all* students. If I had to give a percentage of those academic institutions in the U.S. that fit the above description, I would say that it is in the 75 to 80 percent range. My main purpose in mentioning this here relates to the use of these colleges for the gratification of pathological dependency needs. Such colleges also serve as a mechanism for transferring dependency from parents to those who administer these institutions. And thwarting college authorities (especially by antisocial behavior and refusal to study) is often a mere transfer of rebellion from parents to school authorities—a rebellion in which the dependency denial element is often operative.

The Role of Coercion in Providing Adolescents with Dependency Gratification

Adolescents may often structure situations in such a way that they get themselves coerced into satisfying their dependency needs. Therapists do well to appreciate this phenomenon. Psychotherapy is basically a dependent situation. In fact, it may be one of the most dependent. Many adolescents, however, cannot openly state that they need treatment, but may inwardly recognize their need for it. Such youngsters may require coercion to provide them with the excuse to attend the sessions. An adolescent will often state that the only reason he or she comes to treatment is because "my mother makes me." I have had adolescent boys, over six feet tall, weighing over 200 pounds, telling me that their 95-pound scrawny mothers, "make them come to treatment." The therapist who responds to this with incredulity and tries to help such a youngster appreciate that his mother cannot possibly force him into therapy is making an error. And, if the therapist goes further and tries to impress upon such a youngster that therapy is only for people who can consciously appreciate that they have problems, and who are motivated to change them, then that therapist is making an even worse technical error. Such confrontations will only deprive the adolescent of the excuse needed for attending the sessions and may result in the youngster leaving treatment. My usual response to such a comment is to say something along these lines: "Yeah, I understand, parents have a way of forcing kids into doing a lot of things they don't want to. But as long as you're here, and your parents are paying for it anyway, why don't we use the time? So what's on your mind? What would you like to talk about?" One boy, in this situation, stood up following the aforementioned comment, reached deeply into his pocket, pulled out a crumbled slip of paper, and said, "Well, I have this dream here...." When entering group adolescent therapy, most newcomers are asked by other members why they have come to the group. A common response includes parental coercion and denial of any psychological difficulties at all. I find it interesting that most often other group members do not pin the youngster down on this point. Rather, "they understand" and then go on directly to discuss "problems."

Hospitals and prisons may also provide an adolescent with dependency gratifications, without the youngster's having to appreciate that this is one of the functions they are serving. In both of these situations the adolescent can profess that he or she was forced into the institution and the purpose of residence therein has nothing to do with dependency gratification, but treatment and rehabilitation. One need not look hard, however, to see how these institutions provide a formidable amount of dependency gratification. The youngster's life is structured 24 hours a day by powerful authorities upon whom the youngster is dependent. However, the youngster need not openly admit that these institutions provide dependency gratifications. In prison, especially, these are well hidden because everybody knows that prisoners are tough characters who resent authority, never cry, and have nothing but hatred for those who have incarcerated them. They have nothing but scorn for those who predictably provide them with three meals a day, a bed, clothing, and other basic necessities of life.

IDENTITY CONFUSION

Adolescents are often confused about their identities. This is not surprising considering that they are part child and part adult. For most youngsters, however, the transition is quite rapid—some seeming to have been transformed in a matter of months. One girl goes to summer camp flat-chested and comes back buxom at the end of the summer. Another youngster "shoots up like a string bean" in a matter of a few months. I recall when I was about 16 years old, standing in front of my apartment house in the Bronx, in New York City where I grew up. I must have grown about five or six inches in the previous year. I looked like one could "slide me under the door." As I was standing there, a little boy of about five years of age was walking past me. He stopped, looked up at me and said, "Are you a boy or a man?" I hesitated, thought a minute about his question, and then responded, "You know, I really don't know." And I really didn't know. Like most adolescents I felt I was some of both and neither of both—at the same time.

Adolescents need to have a separate identity from their parents if they are to break away in a healthy fashion. They often don't know what identity to take, only that it must be one that is different from that of their parents. Accordingly, it is common during this period for adolescents to suddenly decide to change their religion from that of their parents. Children from religious families abruptly become agnostics or atheists, much to the chagrin of their parents. Sometimes such religious conversions follow fads as in 1960s and 1970s when Zen Buddhism was very much in vogue. Similarly, a youngster who previously couldn't care less about politics suddenly becomes obsessed with a particular political philosophy. Politically conservative parents find themselves (much to their embarrassment) with a super-liberal adolescent in their midst. Less common are the liberal parents who suddenly find themselves with an ultra-conservative. Adolescent clothing styles, as well, are often adopted in the service of establishing a separate identity. However, one will generally find the adolescent slavishly dependent on peers for information about the particular styles that are in vogue at the time, the style that is designed to be just the opposite of what is preferred by the adult generation.

In the mid-1970s a 14-year-old girl once came to a session quite upset. When I asked her what was wrong she replied, "I'm having a lot of trouble with my father lately. Up until a couple of months ago he was just like any other father. He wore standard suits and went to the office each day with his attaché case. However, in the last few months, he's become totally different. He suddenly started wearing these bell-bottom jeans that all the kids are wearing now. He wears these open collars in order to show the hair on his chest. He's also wearing these beads around his neck. They sure look stupid. He walks around the house with this little radio with an ear plug in his ear listening to rock music. Up until now all he wanted to hear was classical stuff. Now he's starting to grow this Afro haircut. I don't know what he's doing with an Afro haircut. We're Jewish and it looks stupid on him. When my friends come to the house he wants to sit around, Yoga-style, and have rap sessions with us. It's all very embarrassing and I'm ashamed to bring my friends to the house anymore. I know what's wrong with him. He's having an *identity crisis*. He's 49 years old and can't stand the fact that he's soon going to be 50. I think he's trying to recapture his youth."

One could argue that such a father might be perfect for an adolescent in that "being one of the guys" would be just what a youngster would want, i.e., a parent, who is "on the same wavelength" and can relate to the youngster at his or her own level. Such a position does not take into consideration the importance of the adolescent's having a separate identity. A youngster with a father like that may be driven back into conservative clothing in order to establish a separate identity. I am in full agreement with the girl's analysis of her father's behavior, namely, that he was truly having an "identity crisis" and was trying to recapture his youth because of his inability to accept gracefully the aging process.

Typically, adolescents are quite receptive to detailed information about how they appear to others. Girls, especially, will spend long hours discussing with one another the details of their appearance: their eyes, ears, noses, breasts, figures, etc. Generally, they are painfully dissatisfied with the most minute deviation from what they consider to be some idealized norm. And such differences may cause them significant grief. It is common for an adolescent to stand in front of the mirror for many hours in order to master the exact pose, complexion, coiffure, etc. that they consider necessary to acquire. This cannot be considered simple narcissism; rather, it relates more to the desire to get information about one's identity and to provide oneself with an identity that would be acceptable to one's peers. The same behavior in adult life would justifiably be labeled narcissism, the ubiquity of such behavior notwithstanding. During lovemaking, as well, the two youngsters may spend long hours describing in detail their opinions on the loved one's various body parts. They seem never to tire of what to the adult might appear to be an endless discussion on picayune topics.

The parents of a 14-year-old girl once described a problem they had with their daughter during a vacation trip to the Caribbean. The family was preparing to go out to the beach, but the girl adamantly refused to join them. She claimed there was a disfiguring pimple on her face, which she was quite certain would be apparent to all on the beach. No one in the family had noticed any particular disfiguration and when she was asked where it was, she pointed to a small, almost microscopic, pimple on her chin. Reassurances that this "pimple" could hardly be seen, even from six inches, were to no avail. She insisted that her appearance on the beach would subject her to terrible mortification. Finally, she was prevailed upon to join the family, but only did so after she had covered her head almost completely with a towel. As she walked on the beach, she parted the towel in front—just enough to see her way to the beach chair. She walked quickly through the crowd to lessen the likelihood that her "defect" would be noticed and thereby become the subject of conversation of all the vacationers. Then, when she finally reached her beach chair, she was sure to place the towel in such a position that it covered her "scar." This youngster was exhibiting typical adolescent fear of appearing atypical; yet, at the same time, she professed to be an independent thinker, unconcerned with the opinions of others—especially her parents and other adults.

Therapists do well to utilize this propensity of adolescents to dwell on the minutiae of their appearance. Often the adolescent who was unreceptive to therapeutic involvement may be willing to involve him or herself in long discussions on this subject. Providing this service can entrench the relationship between the youngster and the therapist and may pave the way to other discussions that might not have been possible previously.

In the process of forming a separate identity adolescents are likely to model themselves after others, especially older teenagers and certain adults (but not consciously the parents). Sometimes these models are very specific, such as a movie star or teacher. At other times these identifications are nonspecific, such as the "macho man" or the "sexy woman." The cigarette companies are well aware of this phenomenon and capitalize on it to a significant degree. They have been successful in getting adolescents to believe that smoking a cigarette makes one appear adult and to consider the cigarette to be the ticket of admission into adult society. They can rely, as well, on the adolescent's aforementioned delusion of invulnerability to deny the health consequences of cigarette addiction. Companies that peddle alcohol are also appreciative of this phenomenon. They too have convinced adolescents to equate drinking with adulthood and they also know that the adolescent is simple-minded enough to deny the possibility of addiction in him- or herself.

During this period, as well, there may be experimentation with a number of different identities. It is almost like the changing hobbies of the latency-aged child: one month the child is into one hobby and the next month into another. These transitional identifications are best viewed as steps toward finding one's own identity, after trying out that of others.

For many (if not most) adolescents group identity plays an important role in this transitional process. For many the group almost becomes a substitute family. It is as if the adolescent is saying: "I am no longer a member of my family; I am now a member of this group." Senior members of the group may be reacted to as if they were substitute parents, even though the adolescent may be the last one to admit this. Many adolescents are likely to gravitate toward healthy groups that have salutary goals. These include sports, social contribution, recreation, etc. Some adolescents gain identity as good students; others are good in sports; and others may select music, theater, or art to gain a sense of a special identity. Some may pride themselves on being the kind of a person who is quite social and has many friends. And many can claim competence in two or more of these areas, which produces a more enhanced sense of personal identity.

If a youngster reaches puberty and has not developed a strong sense of identity in one or more of these areas, then the individual is likely to utilize pathological mechanisms for gaining a sense of identity. One such method is to gravitate toward pathological groups, especially those involved with substance abuse and/or antisocial behavior. Often they are attracted to these fringe groups because they have not developed the skills and personality patterns that would enable them to join meaningfully with youngsters who are members of the healthier groups. However, for such adolescents the choice may be between a fringe group and no group at all. In such a situation, most choose the fringe group. The adolescent generally works on the theory that it is better to be a member of an antisocial gang than not to be recognized as a human being in any way at all. Better to be a drug addict than someone who isn't even noticed. Rather have the reputation of a "slut" than be someone whom no one ever talks about at all. Often, there is little or no conscious realization that they are making such a choice. Rather, they rationalize with other group members that they are superior to their traditional peers in that they know "where it's all at" while the others do not. Their scorn of normal youngsters merely serves to compensate for and deny the feelings of rejection and isolation that they harbor within.

E. Erikson (1968) considers the adolescent's identity confusion to be a central element in psychological development at that age level. He refers to this stage as "Identity vs. Role Confusion." He states that during this phase adolescents "... are now primarily concerned with what they appear to be in the eyes of others as compared to what they feel they are and with the question of how to connect the roles and skills cultivated earlier for the occupational prototypes of the day... and they are ever ready to install lasting idols and ideals as guardians of a final identity." Erickson also addresses himself to the traditional intolerance that adolescents have toward others who do not live up entirely to the specific codes of the group. He states that "... such intolerance is a defense against a sense of identity confusion. For adolescents not only help one another temporarily through much discomfort by forming cliques and by stereotyping themselves, their ideals, their enemies, they also perversely test each other's capacity to pledge fidelity. The readiness for such testing also explains the appeal which simple and cruel totalitarian doctrines have on the minds of the youth of such countries and classes as have lost or are losing their group identities...."

One of the important purposes of all this, obviously, is the ultimate acquisition of an adult identity. The process involves proceeding along a course that leads to a career or role in the adult society of their parents. In association with these identity and career role considerations adolescents may spend significant time wondering about the world, the universe, and where they fit in. They have grave concerns about the future course of their lives and wonder about exactly what roles they will play. As children, the future seemed like a million years away; now it is at their very doorsteps. Definite choices have to be made soon, *by them*; they can no longer be made *for them*. They have to try to envision themselves in various careers and social positions and take appropriate steps toward the attainment of these goals. All this can be very anxiety provoking; the decisions are awesome; they affect the youngster's whole life, and he or she may regret forever the decisions now being made. At its best and healthiest, this identity search can be a rewarding and creative period of self-discovery—these anxieties notwithstanding. Even when the confusion becomes so great that the term "identity crisis" seems appropriate, it might not be a deleterious experience.

There are those who can handle this crisis only by taking "time out" to "find themselves." They have to remove themselves from their main activities, to take stock, to think, to try new things, and to try to see things from another vantage point. Most accomplish this on evenings and weekends while remaining in school (at least until graduation from high school). Others, however, may have to leave school (whether it be high school or beyond) in order to do this. When this occurs it may be very difficult to ascertain whether the step is a healthy one. One way of determining this is to observe what the youngsters are doing while they are trying to "find themselves." If they are actively out in the world—involved, committed, trying to make it on their own—then it may very well be a salutary experience. However, if they withdraw into themselves and find solutions through philosophizing about them—without having reality experiences against which to test their ideas—they may be labeling the withdrawal an "identity crisis" in order to cover up its pathological significance to both themselves and those around them. If the pursuit of the "true self" requires parasitic dependence on parents and involves no meaningful efforts toward self-sufficiency, then it is probably sick. If "doing their own thing" means a life of hedonistic self-indulgence at the parents' expense (or at the expense of anyone else who is misguided enough to support this way of life), then there is more of a "crisis" going on than just that of "identity." In addition, the longer it takes for the youngster to accomplish this task, the greater the likelihood it is pathological.

Never before in the history of the world have so many youngsters been so indulged. Never before has Western society been more affluent. Never before has there been such a long gap between the time one is born and the time one is capable of self-sufficiency. Never before has there been so much psychologizing to parents about what their children are doing, how to "understand" them, and how to bring them up to be psychologically healthier. There is probably no better example of a sick fusion of all these phenomena than a disturbed adolescent's being supported (financially and psychologically) in a neurotic (and even psychotic) flight from reality with the rationalization (borrowed from psychology) that the youngster is only having an "identity crisis."

COMPENSATING FOR FEELINGS
OF INADEQUACY

Alfred Adler took issue with Freud regarding his emphasis on sexuality as the central element in the development of psychopathological processes. He considered feelings of inadequacy and the various methods people utilize to compensate for them to be more important factors. I am in agreement with Adler on this point. Although I believe that Adler took his theory too far—thereby repeating Freud's mistake of exaggerated emphasis on one point—he has nevertheless provided us with valuable insights into the factors that contribute to the development of psychopathology. In fact, there may not be a single psychopathological symptom that does not relate, at least in part, to the problem of feelings of inadequacy and the attempts to deal with it. H.L. Mencken said that "self-confidence is the delusion that others don't know how inadequate you feel about yourself." There is great wisdom in this statement. When a therapist says that a patient is suffering with low self-esteem, I believe that what is really being said is that the therapist believes that the patient's feelings of self-worth are lower than his or her own. (And this may or may not be the case.) More specifically, I believe that most symptoms contain, in part, an element that serves to enhance self-worth or to avoid situations that may lower it.

Examples are not difficult to find. In fact, one could randomly select any symptom and not have too much difficulty finding confirmation for this principle. Consider the common student symptom of cheating on tests. Youngsters who cheat on tests do not believe they have the capacity to get a good grade honestly (they may or may not have such ability) and fear the feelings of low self-worth that they will suffer if they do poorly. Children who bribe others for friendships do not believe they have the personality qualities that will predictably attract companions and have to delude themselves into believing that those who are "bought off" are genuinely friends. In this way they protect themselves from ego-debasing feelings of loneliness. Those who brag are generally individuals who feel inadequate; those who have the "real stuff" generally do not need to brag. Delusional grandiosity is the extreme example of this mechanism. Paranoid projections often include an element of attributing to others the self-denigratory feelings that one harbors within oneself. Considering others to be falsely criticizing is less ego-debasing than recognizing that the criticisms are self-derived and genuinely valid. Of course, there are many symptoms in which the self-esteem element plays only a small role; however, I do not know of a symptom in which it plays no role at all.

Adolescents have much to feel inadequate about. In our modern technological society they generally cannot acquire the skills necessary for them to function independently, yet they would like to believe that they can. The disparity between their actual situation and that which they fantasize can contribute to feelings of inadequacy. A common way with which adolescents deal with the feelings of inadequacy that derive from this obvious disparity is by scorning their elders and viewing them as "idiots." This mechanism of compensation is especially seen among the intellectual types who will use their newfound knowledge to lord their superiority over their elders. They may try to flaunt their knowledge to their parents and thereby show them up as imbeciles. They commonly do this with teachers and relish the opportunity to point out the inevitable errors that any teacher will occasionally make. They generally fail to appreciate how limited is their knowledge and that by virtue of their youth they cannot possibly have accumulated the depth and breadth of information that serves as a solid foundation for the expertise of their elders. I am not claiming that their elders are *necessarily* more knowledgeable and wiser, only that there is a greater likelihood that this will be the case.

Mention has already been made of the adolescents' delusions of invulnerability. I consider this an important adolescent manifestation which, in part, serves to compensate for feelings of low self-worth. Military leaders are well aware of the phenomenon. Adolescents make wonderful soldiers. They are old enough to have the physical stamina and strength to fight, yet simple-minded enough to believe that they are not likely to be killed. They can thereby be encouraged to walk into the cannon's mouth and believe that those around them may fall, but they, somehow, will be spared. Visit any military graveyard; look at the ages of those who are buried there; the average in 20th-century cemeteries is the late teens. In earlier centuries it was the early to mid-teens. In short, wars have been fought primarily by children. Adults are smart enough to stay far behind the lines and spare themselves.

Mechanisms to compensate for feelings of inadequacy pervade the adolescent's life. Adolescent girls will spend many hours a day attempting to improve their appearance. The multi-billion dollar cosmetic industry is not simply for adult women, but for adolescents as well. The industry knows that the best time to get women "hooked" on these products is during the adolescent years, when people are most vulnerable to believing the advertising and most likely to be obsessed with their appearance. These preoccupations are not simply for the purpose of attracting the opposite sex; they also serve to enhance feelings of self-worth. (The two go together.) Concern with the details of one's appearance also serves to insure admission to the peer group—admission often being dependent on scrupulous imitation of the prevailing style. Acceptance into the group also serves to compensate for feelings of low self-worth, because such acceptance essentially communicates the message that the youngster is indeed a worthwhile individual if he or she can gain admission into a particular "exclusive" club.

The half-naked muscle men that we so frequently see in public may be spending hours each day subjecting themselves to the most grueling exercises in order to enjoy the fantasy that others are impressed with their power, strength, enormous muscles, etc. Competition over who can consume the most alcohol can also serve to compensate for feelings of low self-worth. The youngster may actually hate beer, but will guzzle down as many cans as possible in order to impress his peers and thereby enhance his feelings of self-worth. Or, he may brag about how fast he has driven his car, or how flashy or expensive it is. Advertising companies, of course, are very happy to capitalize on this inanity of thinking, which, of course, extends into adult years for many (if not most) people. Of significance here is that the attribute selected for self-aggrandizement is *easily* acquired. What many adolescents fail to appreciate is that easily acquired attributes do not enhance self-worth as well as those that require long hours of dedicated labor. It is no particular feat to drink formidable amounts of beer; it is a feat to play the violin well, to be a champion chess player, to be an extremely competent basketball player, or to get very high grades on one's college entrance examinations. Youngsters who do not believe they can achieve healthy self-confidence in the latter areas are likely to resort to the former.

There is an anecdote that demonstrates this point quite well. Actually, it is best told by first asking the listener if he or she can figure out the moral or the lesson of this story:

> One day a mouse was walking through the jungle and suddenly heard the deep voice of another animal crying out, "Help, help, help! I'm sinking in the quicksand. Please help me. Help, help, help!!" The mouse quickly ran to the source of the pleas and there saw a huge elephant sinking rapidly into the quicksand.
>
> The mouse ran over to the edge of the quicksand and yelled to the elephant, "Don't worry. I'll save you. I have a Cadillac and I'll use it to pull you out of the quicksand." At this

point, the mouse went over to his Cadillac and backed it up so that the rear bumper was at the edge of the pool of quicksand. He then yelled to the elephant, "Put your trunk around my rear bumper and I'll pull you out. Hurry, Hurry!" And so the elephant wrapped his trunk around the rear bumper of the Cadillac and the mouse after great effort, with grinding of his Cadillac's motors, was finally successful in pulling the elephant out of the quicksand.

After wiping himself off the elephant said to the mouse, "I want you to know that I will never forget what you've done for me here today. As you know, we elephants have wonderful memories and never forget anything. I want you to know, then, that if you're ever in trouble, just send word through the jungle and I'll do everything in my power to help you, even at the risk of my own life."

About a year later, the same elephant was walking through the jungle and he suddenly heard a little squeaky voice yelling, "Help, help, help! I'm sinking in the quicksand. Please come and help me. Please! Please!"

The elephant ran toward the source of the noise and there he saw this little mouse sinking in the quicksand. He then said, "Why you're the very same mouse who saved my life last year. As I told you then, I'll never forget the good deed you did for me. And so now I'm going to return the favor and I'm going to save your life." The elephant then went over to the edge of the quicksand and, while lowering his huge penis into it, said to the mouse, "Hurry, grab on to the end of my penis and I'll pull you out of the quicksand." And so the mouse reached up, grabbed on to the end of the elephant's penis, and the elephant pulling his penis in, hand over hand, finally pulled the mouse out of the quicksand! The end.

The listener is then asked for the moral or lesson of this story. (For those who haven't figured it out): "If you've got a big penis, you don't need a Cadillac!"

Sexual activities, as well, may serve to compensate for feelings of inadequacy. Adolescents are typically concerned with whether or not they are sexually attractive to members of the opposite sex. The best way to prove such attractiveness, of course, is to actually have sexual experiences. Normally, an adolescent boy will not feel that he is "a man" until he has had sexual relations. I do not consider this belief necessarily to be pathological, as long as it is put in proper perspective and the boy does not become obsessed with losing his virginity or walk around feeling worthless if he has not yet achieved the exalted status of nonvirgin. It is even within the normal range to relate the details of his sexual experiences to his peers, even with some exaggeration. Although there is some insensitivity here to the "reputation" of the girl involved, I consider such sharing and even boasting to be so common that I cannot necessarily label it patho-logical. It is really asking too much of a teenage boy to tell absolutely no one about his first sexual experience.

In recent years, however, there has been less stigma for the girls who have been used more for the purposes of the boys' self-aggrandizement than for sexual gratification. The boy who is obsessively preoccupied with the number of his "conquests" and who is frequently bragging about them is likely to have psychiatric difficulties, especially in the realm of low self-esteem. The more secure boy does not generally need to brag so extensively. And girls who feel inadequate may use sexual receptivity to attract boys and thereby prove to themselves that they are worthwhile. An element in girls' sexual promiscuity is the need to compensate for feelings of low self-worth. They are even willing to suffer the reputation of being a "slut" or a "whore" for the benefits they believe they are deriving in the realm of enhancing their self-worth.

E. Becker (1973, 1975) has proposed that a central element in the development of psychopathological symptoms is the denial of the painful feelings associated with our realization that someday we will die. One of the ways in which human beings differ significantly from lower animals is our ability to appreciate that we are mortal. It may be the greatest price we pay for our superior intelligence. Many psychological phenomena, both normal and abnormal, include the element of denial of our fallibility and mortality. We involve ourselves in activities in which we flirt with death in order to prove to ourselves that we, in contrast to other humans, need not be grasped by death's claws. We place ourselves in extremely precar-ious positions and then pride ourselves on our ability to come out unscathed. Sky-divers, tightrope walkers, mountain climbers, speed racers, and bullfighters are just a few examples of people with a strong need to prove to themselves that they, unlike others, are invulnerable to death. The general populace admires those who demonstrate such fearlessness and will make them heroes. However, the admirers need to maintain the delusion that their heroes are invulnerable. If events destroy the delusion, then the hero no longer serves his or her purpose and is dispensed with. Once Achilles is wounded in his heel, he is no longer revered. But it is a two-way arrangement. Achilles needs to feel invulnerable to compensate for the feelings of vulnerability he feels over his appreciation of his mortality. And his worshipers need to maintain the image that Achilles is invulnerable in order to give them hope that they are so as well.

This phenomenon is related to the aforementioned adolescent's delusion of invulnerability. The adolescent smokes and believes that he is immune to lung cancer and the other diseases caused by smoking. He drives at high speeds, while inebriated, and believes that he will neither be injured nor killed. He even plays "chicken" on the open road. For those not familiar with this "game," two cars—driving head on in the same lane—approach each other at high speeds. The first one who veers off the collision path is viewed as "chicken" and the "loser" of the game. It is not just simple-mindedness that is required for willingness to involve oneself in this idiocy. Also involved is the need to compensate for feelings of inadequacy by attempting to prove that one is indeed courageous. Another element, however, is its value in dealing with death fears. Once the youngsters have survived, they can flaunt their invulnerability to death.

I introduce my next point anecdotally. A number of years ago I visited my son Andrew's junior high school in association with a parent-teacher's meeting. The parents made the rounds of the various classrooms that their children were attending and met with their teachers. I was quite pleased with Andy's teachers, but the one that impressed me most was the shop teacher. This was basically the message he gave to the group of parents:

> I want to tell you, first, that I don't know very much about theories of teaching. In fact, to be absolutely honest, when I go to teachers' conferences I really don't understand what they're talking about when they speak about educational psychology

and philosophy. But I can tell you this: when a kid makes something here in the shop—something that he can be proud of—it really makes him feel good. (These were the days when there were no *hers* in shop class.) For example, if a kid makes a tree sign with the family name on it, and nails it up on a tree outside his house, he really feels good every time he walks into that house and sees *his* sign there. It really makes him proud. If a kid makes a little lamp—I have one here—it looks like a water pump and everytime you pull down the handle, a chain that is attached to it turns on the light, he really feels good about himself when he sees that lamp sitting there in the house and when he sees people using it, it really makes him feel good about himself....

And let's say I have a kid who is shy and timid. What I do is make that kid a *monitor* for the whole row. It's his job to be sure that no boy leaves his row without cleaning up completely. His job is to inspect that row before anyone can leave, and he inspects every kid's work bench to be sure that it's completely spic and span before that boy has permission to leave the room. And the monitor works under my authority. When I give a shy kid this kind of a job it really makes him stand taller. It makes him feel better about himself....

I want you to know that I run a tight ship here. In order to pass my course you've got to produce. Also, I've got to run a tight ship here because we have a lot of equipment that could be dangerous. We have electrical saws and drills here that could literally kill someone. So safety is *number one* here; I can't be lax in this room. The safety monitors, too, know that I mean business and there will be absolutely *no* horsing around in this shop. There is absolutely no running here. If a kid runs I boot him out for the day. And there's no wise-guy back talk. These kids have got to know that I'm boss around here and that I won't put up with any wise-ass characters....

Although some of this shop teacher's colleagues had Ph.D.s, I believe that he knew more about educational philosophy than most of them. This man was one of the most admired teachers in the school. He was the one, more than others, whom graduates would return to visit. This man knew about self-esteem and healthy ways to help youngters deal with the inevitable feelings of low self-worth with which adolescents (like all people) suffer. He knew that competence and hard work are very valuable antidotes to feelings of low self-worth and provide healthy self-esteem. He knew that vigorous self-discipline—when humane and reasonable—is also ego-enhancing. This man was "building character"—something we don't hear much about these days. I am convinced that this man probably did more good for his junior-high-school students than most of the other teachers in that school. Years later, most of the graduates, I am convinced, remembered little of what they had learned in their academic subjects; but I believe that the living experiences that this man provided his students probably contributed to lifelong personality changes of far greater educational value.

In recent years competition has been viewed by many educators and psychologists as a detrimental influence in personality development. Particular emphasis is given to the fact that those who lose in a competitive activity will suffer with low feelings of self-worth. I believe that this is a misguided view. I believe that proper discrimination has to be made between healthy and unhealthy competition. Success in competition can enhance self-esteem. We should not deprive the more successful ones from the ego-enhancement that comes from that success, even though those who lose may experience lowered feelings of self-worth. Furthermore, healthy individuals do not suffer psychologically traumatic feelings of low self-worth when they lose; nor do healthy individuals turn into egomaniacs when they win. In healthy competition there is respect for one's competitor and the appreciation that it's "not the end of the world" if one loses.

In healthy competition one puts the competition into proper perspective and recognizes that it is of secondary importance to the primary *activity* (sports, art, writing, debate, etc.) into which the competitive element has been introduced. In unhealthy competition the primary aim is to degrade, humiliate, and even slaughter one's opponent. Denigrating and even destroying the opponent is "the name of the game." Certainly, we could very well dispense with unhealthy competition; but we should preserve healthy competition and make every attempt to derive what benefits we can from it. If not for healthy competition we might still be living in caves; if not for unhealthy competition many people would not have suffered severe physical and psychological trauma, and even premature death.

Many schools in recent years have tried to remove competition entirely. There are "noncompetitive camps." I believe such attempts are naive and predictably will fail. When students in these situations still demonstrate competitive strivings, in spite of the allegedly noncompetitive atmosphere, the administrators claim that these children have been so imbued by society to be competitive that their own attempts to provide a healthier atmosphere have proven futile. I disagree. I believe that competitive strivings are locked into the genetic structure of the human animal. All other forms of life are in active competition for survival. Darwin said it well: "Survival of the fittest" is the basic law of evolution. Although we humans need not utilize our competitive strivings in the service of murdering one another, we certainly have residua of them which can be put into healthy channels.

One patient of mine attended a Quaker school which prided itself on being noncompetitive. Even the coaches were warned that the youngsters should be encouraged to play games for the fun of it and not to concern themselves with winning or losing. Unfortunately, this created problems when the Quaker school was playing against other schools in various sports. In these schools just the opposite was occurring, namely, the youngsters were being imbued with a "fighting spirit" and were being encouraged by their coaches to "get in there and win." An adolescent patient of mine was on the school's basketball team and described this pep talk given by the coach:

> Now listen you guys. What I'm telling you now is just between us. I don't want you to breath a word of this to the people upstairs in the classrooms. When you get out there in the field, I want you to wipe up the floor with those guys. I want you to burn their asses off. I want you to beat them into the ground.

Although one might take issue with this coach's use of language, and although one might say that he is going a little too far, I believe that his is basically the healthier approach to competitive sports. It is not that only fiercely competitive sports can be healthy. I certainly believe that one can engage in sports "just for the fun of it," without concerning oneself with who wins or loses. I also believe, however, that fiercely competitive sports too can be psychologically healthy — if put in proper perspective. Encouraging these boys to play their best in their basketball games is not encouraging them to be fiercely competitive in any other aspect of their lives, nor does it necessarily teach them to be insensitive to all human beings whom they may encounter.

An excellent example of many of the principles presented in this section on self-esteem is to be found in D. Holmes' book on adolescent psychotherapy (1964). Dr. Holmes has graciously given me permission to quote the following material from his book.

> At the outset I had very few doubts about how the recreational therapy program should work. Miss B, who was then in charge of girls' "RT," proposed that they all be required to attend a weekly swimming class, and I confidently advised her that this would be unwise. "All people," I explained, "have an inherent phylogenetic dread of water," and we could logically expect this to be pathologically exaggerated in mentally ill persons. (The reader will understand that the recollection of this incident worked upon me a distinctly emetic effect.) Swimming was declared an optional activity and failed after several weeks of trial because none of the girls attended.
>
> A similar plan for instructing the boys in the fundamentals of various physical skills was proposed by Mr. K, director of "RT" for the boys. I pointed out to him the need for emphasizing the recreational aspects of this activity, and further urged that competition and score-keeping be omitted in order not to intensify the low estimation in which our patients already held themselves.
>
> The "RT" staff strove conscientiously to carry out the program as it had been precisely and asininely defined, but in spite of their best efforts the patients refused to cooperate. They were scornful, rebellious, and utterly perverse in their refusal to have fun while discharging their pent up aggressive energy. It was all very disappointing, and once again I reminded myself that one could hardly expect more from sick, delinquent youngsters. They were told they needed the exer-

cise, and we tried to convince them of the therapeutic value of having a good time. Although they were rather casually required to attend the regularly scheduled daytime "RT" sessions, individual patients who were unusually "threatened" by fear of physical injury or competition were frequently excused.

A few months after the opening of the service, I began to hear disturbing reports from several of the boys about how things were being changed in "RT." Jerry, a 15-year-old delinquent boy, explained in persuasive detail his reasons for refusing to attend the activity any longer. He explained that it wasn't fun any more. For the past three weeks, five days per week, they had done nothing but figure eight basketball drill, shooting practice, and running laps. Mr. K, Jerry observed, was a "mean bastard" who gave them neither praise nor respite. He was routinely requiring each boy to run an additional lap for each deliberate "mistake" made during drill and was holding them overtime, making them late for dinner whenever the entire group lagged in completing the day's exercises.

Calisthenics, deep knee bends, and push-ups were required for warming up at the beginning of each hour. And to make matters even worse, Mr. K had started coming up on the ward before each period for the purpose of applying firm, personal, though unobtrusive pressure on each of the boys to attend.

It was a grim picture indeed, and in light of Jerry's proved capacity for revising reality to suit his convenience, there was little reason to believe that it could possibly be true. I spoke with Mr. K about it, and he modestly confirmed every detail of Jerry's account. It seemed to me that no great harm had been done, so I advised him to "ease up on the patterning approach and get back to recreation."

But, as it developed, there are some things too great for the human soul to endure—cruelty to children being one of them. Mr. K stood firm and courageously defended his approach without benefit of theoretical rationale. He simply insisted that "it's better for them."

We called in the head nurse, and she confirmed my suspicions that for the past several weeks the number of complaints from the boys about the "RT" sessions had increased markedly. However, she also noted that attempts to refuse the activity had fallen almost to zero. I decided to see for myself, and it was immediately apparent that Jerry had understated his complaints. After they had finished their grueling workout, I finally saw what I had long since despaired of ever seeing. The boys left the gymnasium perspiring, panting, and bone-weary. They complained lavishly and in chorus. They were bright-eyed, square-shouldered, and flushed with pride in the aftermath of battle. The evidence was incontestable.

From this moment on, "cruel regimentation" became the official guiding policy, and "recreation," in this area at least, gave way to physical education.

Explaining the psychological rationale for this paradoxical reaction was a simple matter, after the fact. Mr. K was advised to proceed according to his own judgment, with the added assurance we would be happy to provide the theoretical explanations for his successes after he had accomplished them.

Since then problems centering around the "RT" program have been isolated and infrequent occurrences. The physical education program, like the school, functions without a respectable rationale which can dignify it as therapy. The boys follow a year-round schedule of coaching in tackle football with full equipment, basketball, boxing, baseball, and track. Each of these endeavors requires *many consecutive weeks of monotonous drill, all without a prospect of immediate reward*. When they have acquired sufficient skill and strength to qualify for competition the boys are forthwith subjected to the "threat" of winning or losing. The approach has provided them with an *earned and well-deserved* sense of masculine accomplishment.

The physical education program for the girls also emphasized the teaching of physical skills, although it is not nearly as demanding as for the boys. Basketball, swimming, volleyball, modern dance, and choral music are stressed. Periodic courses in some of the fundamental do's and don't's of hairstyling, cosmetics, clothing, bearing, and posture are also included.

Despite their symphonic complaints the patients are as a group more dedicated to these activities than are the staff. They understand and readily accept the idea that intercurrent psychological symptoms are insufficient cause for their failing to fulfill this obligation to themselves.

SEXUAL DEVELOPMENT

Gender Differences in Mating Patterns

Adolescents' reactions to their sexual development are extremely important to understand if one is is to place in proper perspective the psychopathological reactions that may emerge from this developmental phenomenon and its attendant conflicts. The fact that I have placed it last in this section in no way means that it is the least important. The central conflict for many adolescents is that of gratifying or not gratifying their sexual urges. For the girl, the conflict is generally one between how much she should allow boys to gratify themselves with her and how much restraint she must show. If she avoids or rejects opportunities for sexual gratification she will suffer frustration; indulging herself such gratifications often results in fears that she will be viewed as promiscuous and thereby compromise her reputation. Furthermore, she may feel strongly that she wants the sexual experience to be associated with tenderness and emotional involvement and may find that boys are much less concerned with these aspects of the sexual experience—their professions of commitment to these values notwithstanding. For boys, especially after the mid-teens, the conflict is less internal than external. They generally want as much sex as they can get, and most often feel little guilt over their sexual experiences. The confict, more often, is between them and the girls who resist them, rather than between one intrapsychic compartment and another.

I do not believe that the aforementioned differences between boys and girls are entirely socially induced. Rather, I believe that genetic programming plays a role in these differences. I recognize that this is an unpopular thing to say at a time when male/female egalitarianism is very much in vogue. However, I believe that I have good arguments to support my position here. No one can deny that up until the 20th century men were primarily the hunters and fighters (protectors and warriors). Women, in contrast, were primarily the child rearers. I am making no statement regarding whether this was good or bad or right or wrong, only that it was the reality of the world up until the 20th century for the vast majority of societies on earth. Of course, there were and still are occasional societies in which this principle did not hold, but these exceptions do not in any way detract from the validity of my generalization. (There is always an island in the South Pacific that will demonstrate any point—in support or in refutation.)

It is reasonable to state that those men who were genetically strong in the hunting/fighting functions were more likely to survive than those who were not. Accordingly, those who were weaker in these functions were less likely to have food for survival or to protect themselves from their enemies. Consequently, their genes were not as likely to be passed down to subsequent generations. Also, those who were weak in these areas were less likely to attract women, in that women would tend to consider as desirable mates men who exhibited high capacity for food gathering for themselves and their children and high capability for protecting the potential family from enemies. This was another reason why genes of men who were weaker in these areas were less likely to survive in the genetic pool. Similarly, women who were stronger in the child-rearing realm were more likely to be viewed by men as desirable mates and their genes, as well, were more likely to be passed down to their progeny. And the greater aggressiveness of the male was not, I believe, simply confined to hunting and warring; it was also utilized in the service of mating. Specifically, more aggressive men were more likely to be successful in acquiring mates. And so we have another factor favoring the selective survival of more aggressive men.

Youngsters today of both sexes carry within them these genetic programs. Although we human beings are less beholden to our instinctual drives than are lower animals, we are still affected by them. A bird, for example, during the mating season, may have no choice other than to go through the mating ritual of its species. We humans have procreative urges, but we are not compelled to mate in any particular season nor are we compelled to follow rigid mating patterns of behavior. However, this does not preclude our being programmed for such mating patterns with the resultant pressure for their expression. In short, then, I believe that adolescent boys are more likely to be assertive and aggressive during this phase and adolescent girls more likely to be passive — present-day social pressures for egalitarianism notwithstanding.

There is another factor operative in what I believe to be gender differences in mating patterns during adolescence. This relates more directly to reproductive capacity. It is a principle of Darwin's theory of natural selection and survival of the fittest that each species generally produces far more offspring than can possibly survive. Those particular forms that are most adaptable to the environment in which they have been born are more likely to survive and perpetuate the species. Those that are less adaptable to the particular environment will generally die off. This is the central element in the Darwinian theory. If one examines this further, one finds that there are two factors operative here: *quantity* and *quality*. With regard to *quantity*, the number of offspring produced is far greater than can possibly survive in a particular environment.

With regard to *quality*, the quality or type of offspring that is most adaptable to the specific environment is more likely to survive. Accordingly, one must consider both quantity control and quality control. Furthermore, with regard to quantity, the general thrust is for an organism to produce as many offspring as possible, i.e., the greatest quantity possible — most often far more than will survive. With regard to quality, the general thrust is to select, narrow down, and restrict survival to those forms that will best adapt to and survive in a particular environment. The two processes of control, then, are antagonistic. The quantity control factors work toward the survival of the greatest number of offspring. The quality control factors operate to reduce and/or limit the number of offspring that will survive. Those forms that ultimately survive represent a balance of these two antagonistic forces.

In many forms of life one of the sexes is specifically designated to provide quantity and the other quality. Often, it is not difficult to determine which sex is primarily involved in which function. This is certainly the case for the human being. Men are clearly the ones involved in producing the greatest quantity of offspring and women are the quality controllers. If one were to simply view human beings as baby factories, whose main purpose is to perpetuate the species (a not absurd view), and if one were to ask the question which sex is more likely to produce a high quantity of offspring, it is clearly the male. If a man were to devote his whole life to the procreative process, it is reasonable that he could father one to two babies a day providing, of course, he was provided with women who were in the fertile stages of their menstrual cycles. Accordingly, the male is reasonably capable of fathering 500 babies a year. We know that we could start using males for this purpose at about the age of 13 or 14, but we do not know the upper age at which such utilization would no longer be possible. There are men in their 90s who have viable sperm. But let us, more practically, end the male's fecund period at 75, because most men do not live beyond that age and older men are less likely to father 500 babies a year. Accordingly, it is reasonable to say that the average male has a fecund period of 60 years. Fathering 500 babies a year for 60 years would enable a man to father 30,000 babies. (I am not addressing myself here to practicality; only to the issue of maximum possible reproductive capacity if one were to make use of men and women for this purpose.) In contrast, if a woman were to devote her fecund life to being a baby factory, she could reasonably reproduce one a year from age 13 to about 54 (the oldest "proven" age at which a woman has been demonstrated to give birth). This will give her approximately 40 babies. Accordingly, it is reasonable to conclude that the male is very much the one capable of producing the greatest quantity of offspring.

What I have said thus far relates purely to biological capacity. The next question relates to the actual behavior of each of the sexes regarding the procreative process. The *potential* for being a reproductive factory is there, but in practice individuals generally have other things to do with their lives besides fornicating and propagating. And probably the most important of these other functions is child rearing. If no concern is given to the protection of the young then the young will not survive and there would be no point to devoting one's life solely to manufacturing babies. This brings us to quality control, the second step necessary for species survival. It is here that women have played the more formidable role. In order to carry out this function, it behooved women to be more circumspect with regard to mate selection. Those who were so were more likely to be chosen as mates and more likely to pass their stronger child-rearing genes down to their offspring. Men, I believe, have been programmed to be promiscuous, i.e., to impregnate as many women as possible. From the roving bands of men in perpetual heat, a woman must select the man who is most likely to remain around after impregnation and serve the role of food gatherer and protector. In order to serve ideally in this capacity women do best to be less impulsive with regard to gratifying indiscriminately their sexual urges—in order that they assess more objectively a potential father of their children. Women who were slower in sexual arousal were more likely to be judicious in mate selection and, therefore, more likely to survive. They were more likely to select men who would provide food, clothing, shelter, and protection. Accordingly, I believe that the *average* (I did not say all) present-day woman is slower in sexual arousal than the average man. Once aroused, however, a woman is more likely to attempt to maintain an ongoing relationship with her mate.

The old saying is applicable here: "Men are looking for girls, and girls are looking for husbands." Men are on the prowl. They are not only out hunting for prey to kill and eat, but hunting for female prey to serve as sexual companions. From the roving bands of men in heat the woman must reject the large majority or else she will find herself impregnated by a man who has already gone on to the next cave or condo. She is much more concerned with relationships. I believe that this is one of the factors involved in women having greater orgastic capacity than men. Although the woman is more likely to need caressing and tender overtures to be aroused, once aroused she is more likely to remain aroused longer. The male reaches his orgasm and immediately goes into a refractory period ("zonks out," falls asleep). The vast majority of women have the potential for multiple orgasms. This serves, I believe, the purpose of enhancing procreative capacity. Her multiple orgastic capacity enables her to "hang in there longer" and insure that the male who is slow to ejaculation is likely to be sustained in his interest and involvement.

Last, I believe that what I have said here is one explanation for the fact that men are generally more likely to be sexually excited by visual stimuli, whereas women are more likely to respond to tactile stimuli. The roving bands of men spot their prey at a distance and can get excited merely at the sight of a woman. Women, however, need caressing, tenderness, and reassurance that the man will remain around for supplying food and protection for herself and her children. This is one of the reasons why men are more likely to be sexually aroused by visual pornographic material than women.

In today's world, boys' greater self-assertion in the "dating game" is generally not as blunt and crass as described above. More subtle techniques are utilized, techniques to impress the girl. One of the factors that enables "jocks" to endure the grueling periods of practice in their sports is the fantasy that they will win the affection of some pretty young girl in the stands. Academically/intellectually oriented youngsters are similarly trying to impress, but they are often interested in winning girls who are more "turned on" by their intellectual feats. And those boys who devote themselves to the arts have, somewhere not so far in the back of their minds, the fantasy that some girl will be turned on by *their* particular talents or skills.

Boys in our society are programmed to be the entertainers. They are encouraged to "show the girl a good time." And the girls are programmed to be entertained. The boys tell the jokes and the girls laugh at them. This is one of the reasons, I believe, why men have much greater memories for jokes than women. When men get together they are much more likely than women to spend their time swapping jokes, especially the ones that are making the rounds at that particular time. These joke-telling encounters serve many purposes. They provide men with the opportunity to compete with their peers for the reputation of having the greatest collection and/or telling them best. This is a male competitive endeavor. In addition, in the course of such competition, they enhance their repertoires of jokes for use in attracting women. The fact that women generally have less facility to recall jokes has nothing to do with any brain inferiority on their part. Men need to remember them if they are to be effective entertainers of women; women, as the traditional "entertainees," are less motivated to remember them. However, women do well to be receptive to laughing at them. If they are unreceptive to serving in this function, they may find themselves at a disadvantage when competing with other women for the attraction of men. This phenomenon, I believe, explains why there are so many more professional comedians who are male than female. The reader should know that I am not placing any value judgments in my comments regarding these different gender roles; I am only describing what I consider to be the reality of the world today.

This theory also serves as an explanation for the fact that most studies of marital infidelity conclude that married men are more likely to be sexually unfaithful than their wives. Although the gap has narrowed somewhat in recent years, with women's new liberation, men are still more likely to involve themselves with extramarital lovers than are their wives. Therapists who work with men toward the goal of reducing significantly their urges for sexual variety have a formidable task ahead of them because they are working against their patients' genetic programming. The more reasonable goal for most men, I believe, is to bring them to the point where their relationships with their wives are so good that the urge for infidelity will be reduced to the point of toleration. Such suppression can also be enhanced by guilt (both anticipatory and "after the fact"), by the desire to avoid the hassles and ego-debasement of surreptitiousness, and the belief that there is more to lose than gain if the affair becomes known to the wife, i.e., irreparable compromise, if not destruction, of the marital relationship.

In conclusion, then, I believe that females are likely to be more passive and desirous of exclusivity in their sexual/romantic involvement with men and that these differences are not simply culturally induced. As mentioned, I recognize that this is an unpopular thing to say in this age of sexual egalitarianism, but I believe that the aforementioned arguments provide compelling support for my position. Again, this is not to say that these patterns cannot be modified somewhat by environmental influences. I am only saying that therapists who counsel youngsters must be aware of these genetic factors and not deny their reality or make attempts to impose an unnatural egalitarianism on their patients, whether adolescent or adult.

Dealing with Sexual Urges

The Therapist's Values　　It is impossible to discuss adolescents' sexual urges without taking into consideration the therapist's values. For example, if the therapist believes that all sexual activity of any kind, heterosexual, auto-erotic, or homosexual is bad and sinful then that therapist is going to react very differently from the one who views such behavior as part of normal adolescent development. As I will discuss in detail in Chapter Five, I believe that all therapeutic interchange involves some attempt on the therapist's part to impose his or her own values on the patient. It is hoped that the values so imposed will be in the patient's best interests. Accordingly, I have no hesitation stating that the views on adolescent sexuality I presented here are reflective of my own values. I do not claim any right or wrong answers on this subject, only that these opinions on sexual behavior reflect my own values.

Take, for example, the issue of pre-marital sex. Perhaps it is the case that all pre-marital sex is indeed a sin and that those who engage in it will be punished by God, in this life and/or after death. Perhaps it is not a sin and there are no repercussions from higher powers for engaging in this activity. Therapists like myself, then, who sanction such behavior (in accordance with the limits described below) may very well be punished for having contributed to the corruption of youth. Accordingly, the therapist's work is "risky business" and therapists should appreciate this before entering the field.

Parents are certainly entitled to the therapist's views on these subjects. Of course, when presenting such opinions, the therapist does well to explore with the parents other aspects of the issue, especially their thoughts and feelings that might reflect psychopathology. The parents may not be receptive to such exploration, but they are still entitled to the therapist's position. If they are uncomfortable with the answers they receive, then the therapist does well to discuss the possibility of their seeing another therapist—someone who might have different values on these particular sexual issues. Under these circumstances I would generally not refer a specific person, but leave it to the parents to find someone whose values are the same as theirs. To make a specific referral only complicates matters. The new person may also not have values consistent with what the parents want and they may become critical and further irritated with both the original therapist as well as the one to whom they were referred. In addition, it is generally a bad policy to refer to a colleague whose therapeutic orientation is one for which the referrer does not have conviction.

For example, as will be discussed later in this book, I believe that behavior modification programs are contraindicated for many (but not all) children with antisocial, acting-out behavior. If I see a youngster in consultation for whom I consider a behavior modification program to be contraindicated, and the parents request a behavior modification program rather than the psychotherapeutically oriented program that I am recommending, I will not accede to their request that I refer them to someone who would provide behavior modification. The therapist who makes such a referral is similar to the surgeon who recommends appendectomy and, when the patient asks to have it treated with an ice bag and penicillin, refers them to a person who would be willing to provide such treatment. Although one could argue that different values on the subject of sex are not the same as different therapeutic persuasions, I am not in agreement. I would not refer to a therapist who believes that pre-marital sex is a sin, because I believe that such a therapist is going to induce inordinate guilt in the youngster—guilt that is psychopathological. Accordingly, I advise parents who have different values from mine to find for themselves another therapist, a therapist who will tell them what they want to hear.

Masturbation Adolescents do well to masturbate. It is one of the best ways to deal with sexual urges in a situation in which heterosexual activities cannot be readily satisfied. They should be helped to appreciate that there is absolutely no excuse why anyone in the world should walk around "horny." I am not recommending masturbation as being preferable to heterosexual experiences throughout life, only that in the early adolescent period it may be a superior form of sexual activity. In years past parents tended to induce great guilt in their children over masturbatory behavior; this is far less true today, but we are still not free from it. I believe that such guilt, in part, is directly related to parents' reacting negatively and even punitively to the occasional masturbatory activity of small children. I use the term *masturbatory activity* here to refer to the occasional touching of the genitalia that all children engage in. I am not referring to masturbation to orgasm, which generally is less frequently seen in pre-pubertal children (but can be present when there has been artificial stimulation, physical or psychological).

Some parents induce masturbatory guilt by carrying down to yet another generation what they have been taught about the practice. Others may be threatened by the child's masturbation because it may imply to them that the child is turning to him- or herself for gratification because the parent is inadequate in the capacity to provide it. Some parents are threatened by the activity because it presages (to them) heavier sex, with all its implications of promiscuity, pregnancy, and sexually transmitted diseases. They believe that squelching sexual expression early is likely to forestall and even prevent these dangers. Whatever its psychodynamics, the therapist does well to make every attempt to reduce such guilt if present. However, the alleviation of such guilt may not be necessary for the vast majority of adolescents today. I recall recently seeing in consultation a girl of 14 who sought my opinion because she was not yet masturbating and feared that she might be different from her friends who were doing so. She wondered whether she had a psychological problem. I certainly would not have been consulted for this purpose 15 to 20 years ago.

When discussing masturbation with adolescents I generally do not try to convey the notion that this practice is simply confined to people during this period. Rather, I inform them that it is a widespread practice at all ages and that it would generally be considered normal even when there is heterosexual opportunity. I inform them that the general opinion among mental health practitioners today is that it becomes pathological when a person routinely engages in it in preference to heterosexual activities or involves oneself in it to an obsessive degree. I tell them, as well, that when other opportunities for sexual gratification are not available, then it is perfectly healthy for masturbation to be the only outlet at that time. If the person routinely prefers the masturbatory outlet over seeking heterosexual experiences then there may be a problem. In the context of such a discussion I may tell the youngster the maxim: "If God didn't want people to masturbate, he wouldn't have made people's arms long enough to reach down there." Or I might quote the limerick:

> There once was a woman named Croft
> Who played with herself in a loft.
> Having reasoned that candles
> Rarely cause scandals,
> Besides which they never go soft.

For a girl who may have difficulty reaching orgasm I may recommend a vibrator or suggest that the youngster try other methods that may prove successful, such as a high-speed shower head. I try to assuage any guilt a youngster might have about being turned on by sexually explicit magazines. In fact, I have often said that an excellent confirmation present for a 13-year-old boy would be a five-year subscription to one of these magazines. For the 13-year-old girl, an analogous present would be a five-year subscription to a romantic love magazine and a vibrator.

In the last few years there have been additional reasons for my encouraging masturbation, specifically the risk of herpes and more recently AIDS. Any therapist who does not warn adolescent patients about the risk of these diseases is negligent. Because of the adolescent's capacity for delusions of invulnerability (the reader hasn't heard the last of this one), they are likely to consider themselves immune to these disorders. Therapists do well to instill a reasonable (not paralytic) amount of fear in adolescents when discussing these and other sexually transmitted diseases in order to counterbalance some of this delusion. Last, I wish to impress upon the reader that I do not routinely encourage the initiation of masturbation when working with adolescents. Rather, I encourage it among youngsters who have strong sexual urges, but do not have a reasonable outlet for them, and may find themselves getting into various kinds of difficulties because they do not give the masturbation option proper respect. Such difficulties would include promiscuity, frequenting prostitutes, seeking inappropriate partners, and suffering unnecessary sexual frustration.

Sexual Relationships　I believe it is normal and healthy for youngsters to begin having mild heterosexual experiences ("petting" and caressing) in the early to mid-adolescent period and to begin having sexual relations in mid- to late adolescence. Whether or not I think this is healthy is almost irrelevant, in that the vast majority of youngsters have had sexual relations by the late adolescent period anyway—regardless of what I or anyone else thinks about it. The therapist does well, however, to help the youngster differentiate sharply between sexual activity in which the sole purpose is some release and sexual activity in the context of a relationship. The youngster should be helped to appreciate that the latter is generally the more gratifying and rewarding experience. Some experience with the former, however, may still be useful in that one still learns better about this contrast from actual experience than from some statement made by the therapist.

As mentioned, it is crucial that the therapist impress upon youngsters the risks of sexually transmitted diseases, especially herpes and AIDS. The therapist should attempt to differentiate between sexual behavior that is normal and that which is abnormal. Abnormal sexual behavior generally involves compulsivity. In boys it can often serve to compensate for feelings of inadequacy. For such youngsters the therapist has to attempt to differentiate the normal boy's need to flaunt sexual "conquests" from the pathological degree of such boasting. This may be quite difficult because the normal boy is likely to brag significantly anyway. For girls, one of the most common reasons for promiscuity is feelings of low self-worth and the belief that the only way she can get a boy's attention is to provide sex. One must deal here with the underlying factors that have contributed to the feelings of low self-worth.

When discussing the sexual activities of adolescents, the subject of confidentiality often comes up. In Chapter Seven I will discuss in detail my views on confidentiality in treatment. As will be elaborated there, I do not consider sexual intercourse to be a "reportable" event to the parents of the adolescent in therapy. I will, however, *consider* reporting an adolescent's sexual behavior to parents if there are definite risks associated with it. Let us take, for example, the situation in which a girl is clearly trying to get pregnant. If, after discussion of the problem in individual and group therapy, she is still trying to do so, I believe that some communication with the parents is warranted. Or if promiscuity is exposing the youngster to sexually transmitted diseases, I would consider this also to be a reportable issue. It is not that the parents can do much about such a girl's sexual activities, but they may be able to take some precautions that may lessen the likelihood of the youngster's being exposed to these dangers. For example, they may be more circumspect with regard to leaving the girl at home alone when they go off at night and on weekends. And they might check more on where their daughter "actually" is when visiting the homes of friends.

A number of years ago I had an experience during one of my presentations that elucidates an important point with regard to confidentiality and a youngster's sexual activities. I was speaking to a group of pastoral counselors in Tennessee. They were mainly ministers, deeply committed to their religious beliefs. Following a presentation of mine on the treatment of adolescents I invited questions from the floor. One minister raised his hand and the following interchange took place:

> *Minister*: I'm having a problem in the treatment of a 16-year-old girl and I want your opinion on it.
> *Gardner*: Yes, what's the problem?
> *Minister- (somewhat dramatically)*: She's having sexual intercourse!
> *Gardner*: Yes. (This was said with intonation implying that I was waiting for more information.)
> *Minister*: That's it. She's *having sexual intercourse-!*
> *Gardner* (in a somewhat incredulous tone): I heard that. But what I want to know is *what* is the problem?
> *Minister* (somewhat angrily): That's the problem! She's having sex!
> *Gardner*: Why is that a problem?
> *Minister*: It's a problem because it's a *sin*, and I have an obligation to do everything possible to stop her from sinning.
> *Gardner*: How do you plan to do that?
> *Minister*: Well, the first thing I'm going to do is to tell her parents.
> *Gardner*: Let me say this to you. I suspect that what I am going to say now may never have been considered before by many of you. I suspect that many of you have never considered the possibility that sex before marriage may *not* be a sin. Now I do not claim to know *with certainty* whether or not it is. I know that some of you here believe deeply, with 100 percent certainty, that pre-marital sex is a sin. And you may be right. I just don't know. My guess is that it is not.
> All therapy involves the imposition of one's own values on one's patients. Clearly, the values of most of the people here in this room are different from many of mine. You (now turning to the questioner) may be correct that you must do everything to protect her from what you consider to be the consequences of her sins, both in this life and in the hereafter. I do not know whether you are or are not correct on this issue. However,

there is one thing I can say to you with 100 percent certainty. And that is this: If you do tell her parents against her will, you will no longer have a patient. The disclosure may very well protect her from eternal damnation, but it will have destroyed the therapy. This is a choice you must make.

Needless to say, I was never invited to return to speak again at that facility. In fact, I would suspect that they probably tried to find out who the person was who had so many screws loose in his head that he invited me to speak there in the first place. The vignette is presented because it demonstrates well my point regarding the importance of therapists' appreciating that they cannot avoid imposing their values on their patients; the sexual situation is only one example of this phenomenon. To try to follow the dictum that one should never impose one's values on one's patients is impossible. Therapists must appreciate that they are continually doing so; one has to accept the consequences of so doing, whether these consequences be here on earth or potentially in the hereafter.

Homosexuality   Here I discuss what I consider to be normal homosexual desires in adolescence. In Chapter Two I will discuss what I consider to be pathological manifestations of homosexuality. At the outset, I wish to state quite directly that I am not in agreement with those colleagues of mine who hold that obligatory homosexuality is a normal variant. By obligatory I refer to the person who is compelled to have homosexual experiences only, and has never had any desire for heterosexual experiences at any time in his or her life. I would also include in the pathological group those whose homosexual orientation is so strong that they have rarely, if ever, engaged in or had the desire for heterosexual activities, especially when opportunities for such behavior were readily available. Rather, they have sought and engaged in homosexual behavior only. I believe that for some people there may very well be a genetic predisposition to the development of homosexual behavior, but this does not negate the argument that such an orientation can be pathological. Most diseases, both organic and psychogenic, probably have genetic contributing determinants. Their presence does not warrant our concluding that they are therefore not disorders. I believe, however, that genetic predisposition notwithstanding, environmental factors play an important role in determining whether such predisposed individuals will develop into obligatory homosexuals. In Chapter Two I will elaborate in detail on my views on homosexuality. Here, I will focus on adolescent homosexual manifestations that are so common that I consider them to be within the normal range of behavior.

Even though we have experienced in recent years what has been referred to as the "sexual revolution," youngsters in early adolescence still do not generally have as much heterosexual opportunity as they would like. Under these circumstances, a certain amount of homosexual activity may be seen. The principle is similar to the one found among adults who are placed in situations in which heterosexual opportunity is either severely restricted or not possible at all. People in prison would be an excellent example of this. In past centuries sailors on long ocean voyages would serve as another example. Under these circumstances homosexuality is quite common and might very well be considered "normal."

I believe that in recent years there has been a shift among adolescent boys with regard to homosexual behavior. Prior to the last 10 to 15 years, many adolescent boys found outlets through mutual masturbation. This practice generally discontinued by the mid-teens when the boys began dating and having heterosexual experiences. Since the late 1960s and early 1970s boys have had more heterosexual opportunities and so this practice appears to be less widespread. When I have seen it, in the last 10 to 15 years, it generally occurs among those boys who are more homosexually oriented and are likely to take the homosexual route. Accordingly, it has different diagnostic significance in the 1980s than it had in the 1950s and early 1960s. What was then "normal" may now very well be a sign that the youngster is heading in a pathological direction.

A less overt form of homosexual gratification engaged in by early adolescent boys involves comparing penis size, especially in locker rooms and when lining up at urinals. There may be "horseplay" in which they grab one another's genitalia. Whereas in early childhood this was an inevitable part of wrestling matches in which one "grabbed for the soft spots," it takes on a new function in the early adolescent period. Specifically, it enables the youngster to get an idea of how "well hung" his peers are (in comparison to himself) and also provides for some mild and transient homosexual gratification.

With regard to girls, I have not seen any changes in recent years in their early adolescent "homosexual" patterns. Rather, their "homosexuality" in the early teen period does not generally manifest itself in overt sexual activity, such as mutual masturbation. Rather, they often develop "crushes" on other girls and become intimate confidǎntes of their friends. Mutual sexual involvement was and still is far less common. If anything, if there is some "normal" homosexuality occurring in girls in the 1980s it is to be found at the college level. There, girls who have not previously been introduced into homosexuality may become so, especially at all-girls institutions. These girls have, I believe, been swept up in what I consider to be a pathological environment, an environment in which homosexuality is viewed as a normal alternative and healthy lifestyle with no implications of psychopathology. (This will be discussed in greater detail in Chapter Two.) Some of these girls will, I believe, switch back onto the heterosexual track, the one they were destined to proceed on anyway. Others, however, especially those with a homosexual predisposition, may very well become more entrenched in the homosexual track—perhaps irretrievably.

I fully appreciate that many readers will take exception to what I have said here with regard to homosexuality. However, I believe that all readers will agree (those who agree with me about the etiology of homosexuality and those who do not) that it is important that I state clearly my position on this subject, both with regard to what I consider normal and what I consider to be pathological. I do not claim to have any final answers here. I do believe, however, that those who claim complete certainty on the issue of the etiology of homosexuality are somewhat premature considering our present state of knowledge (or, more accurately, ignorance) in this area.

Romantic Love

Romantic love is very much an adolescent phenomenon. It generally is not seen before the adolescent period and thrives best during adolescence. Although adults may find themselves indulging in it, they are less likely to be swept up by its delusions because of the improvement in judgment that comes as we mature.

Common Concepts of Romantic Love   In the United States (and throughout most of the Western world) the socially acceptable reason for getting married is *love,* and more specifically *romantic love.* Individuals who marry for other reasons, or who fail to include love in their list of reasons for marrying, are likely to be considered injudicious, misguided, or possibly suffering with a psychopathological disturbance. When "in love" the individuals find that they experience certain ecstatic feelings when thinking about or being in the presence of a specific person of the opposite sex. In its full-blown form the blissful state appears to be all-pervasive. It enhances the pleasure that the individual may derive from even the simplest everyday activities and makes many of life's inevitable pains more tolerable. The person in love comes to the conclusion that the particular party who is the object of his or her affection is the only one in the whole world capable of inducing this special state of elation. Lovers soon develop the deep conviction that these blissful feelings will last throughout their lives, even though they have never personally observed anyone—except on the movie or television screen—who has sustained this state beyond a few years. Yet, this does not deter people in love from making vows about how they will feel and behave toward one another many years hence (even the rest of their lives). Here again, the fact that the vast majority of people have not proven themselves capable of or inclined to keep these vows does not deter lovers from making them.

A type of romantic love that is particularly attractive to adolescents is the kind that I refer to as the *Some-Enchanted-Evening-Across-a-Crowded-Room* type of romantic love. In this variety, two complete strangers, merely on viewing one another (from across a crowded room is desirable but not crucial to the phenomenon), are suddenly struck, as if by a lightning bolt, from out of the blue, with intensive feelings of affection and sexual attraction for one another. I also refer to this type of romantic love as the *bifurcated lightning bolt* kind of love. Here, God in heaven decides that it is now the time for these two particular individuals to fall in love. He therefore thrusts a lightning bolt down toward earth which, just before it reaches the ground, splits into two parts, each one of which invests the lovers. So magnetized, they make a beeline for one another, stomping over people in between, and "read life's meaning in one another's eyes." I also refer to this as the *acute infectious disease* type of romantic love. Here the individuals are suddenly afflicted with cravings for one another, as if stricken with an illness. This is one of the reasons why individuals with this kind of love may refer to themselves in popular song as having been "bitten by the lovebug." In medicine we have a term: *pathognomonic sign*, which refers to that sign that clinches the diagnosis of a disease. The lovebug disease has a pathognomonic sign—a sign that differentiates it quickly from all other diseases known to medicine. Patients who are suffering with any other disease known to medicine would be quite upset if a doctor, when admitting them to the hospital, would inform them that they will have to share a bed with another patient suffering with that disorder. People with the "lovebug disease" have no such objections; in fact, they welcome being in the same bed together. This is the one pathognomonic sign that differentiates it from all other diseases known to medicine.

In all these cases the individuals view their attraction to come from mysterious, almost magical, forces that instantaneously and irresistibly draw them together. Although some view the cause of the overwhelming attraction to be external (as planned for by God, for example), others attribute it to internal factors (such as "body chemistry"). I, personally, suspect that internal psychological and biological factors are the most important elements in producing this phenomenon. The individuals enter the room predisposed to the experience, and even hoping for it, because of a lack of meaningful involvement with anyone else at the time. And loneliness may intensify the craving for such an involvement. The need for an esteem-enhancing experience as an antidote to one's pains and frustrations may also be present. Perhaps the object of the intense attraction bears some physical resemblance to an earlier love object, such as an opposite-sexed parent or a former lover. Sexual frustration is in all probability present as well. All of these cravings may be particularly great at the time—explaining thereby the suddenness with which the individuals are drawn to one another. All these factors together result in a copious outpouring of hormones into the bloodstream that enhances formidably the desire of the two individuals to spend as much time as possible with one another, both physically and psychologically. In fact, they may give such high priority to being with one another that they may ignore obligations vital to their well-being. And when the two people become more involved with one another the attraction becomes solidified by a dovetailing of both healthy and neurotic needs. (Both of these factors will be elaborated upon below.)

The risks that one takes by falling in love with a stranger are no different from those one takes when one, for example, buys a used car from a stranger or lends money to a stranger. One does better to get a little more information before entering into such transactions, and yet it is both amazing and pathetic how individuals who would never be injudicious enough to buy cars from or lend money to strangers will be willing to sign a contract in which they take an oath to live together for the rest of their lives with a "stranger from across a crowded room."

The Psychodynamics of Romantic Love   Before discussing what I consider to be the important psychodynamic factors operative in bringing about the state of romantic euphoria, I wish to emphasize that I do not necessarily equate psychodynamics with psychopathology. Most, if not all, forms of psychological behavior have psychodynamic elements, but not all psychologically determined behavior should necessarily be considered psychopathological. Each of the psychodynamic factors I describe here runs the gamut from the normal to the pathological. Each person who is "in love" utilizes one or more of these mechanisms. And each person may utilize them in either normal or pathological degrees and in any combination in between these extremes.

One factor operative in the romantic love phenomenon is compliance with social convention. In our society we consider "love" to be the most important reason for marrying another person. Of course, in other societies other criteria have been used. In some, money and power were unashamedly utilized as criteria for matchmaking. The ancient Pharaohs routinely married brothers and sisters in order to keep power and wealth within the family. Unfortunately for the Pharaohs, genes for intellectual retardation were quite common in their families—resulting in an unusually high percentage of retarded monarchs. Marrying cousins and near relatives was a routine practice among European royalty, even up to this century. Unfortunately for the European aristocracy, genes for hemophilia were quite prevalent. The presence of these defective genes, however, did not seem to deter marriages between close relatives because of the great desire to keep wealth and power in the family. And even among commoners, marriages planned by parents is an ancient tradition, the parents considering themselves to be more judicious than their children for making such an important decision. Here again, considerations other than romantic love were generally operative in the parents' decision-making process. Although I would not recommend that we resume the practice of parents deciding whom their children shall marry, I cannot say that the practice is not without its merits.

Social convention, then, deems it normal for people, especially when young, to have the experience of falling in love. In fact, people who claim that they have never had the experience are often viewed as being somewhat deficient and even unfortunate. We are much more like sheep than we would like to admit and there are many for whom the social-compliance factor is an important one. When one's friends start falling in love, then one starts falling in love as well. It is similar to the phenomenon by which anorexia/bulimia and even adolescent suicide have come into vogue in recent years. When it becomes "the thing to do" in the adolescent set, many adolescents are likely to go along with the crowd, even if it means acquiring some dreaded disease and even if it means killing oneself.

I believe that an important contributing factor to the development of feelings of romantic love is the need to provide oneself with a narcotic. Like the narcotic, it quickly produces intense pleasurable sensations and thereby provides enjoyment—practically on demand. One need not apply oneself diligently over time to gain pleasure; one merely need spontaneously induce the state within oneself and revel. (One need not even have encouragement or reciprocity from the object of one's affection; "unrequited love" can produce the same euphoric state.) In addition, like the narcotic, it makes one insensitive to pain. There are many painful feelings associated with the prospect of marriage—if one is to allow oneself to think about them. One is committing oneself to a lifelong arrangement—a decision that cannot but be extremely anxiety provoking. The prospect of living—for the rest of one's life—with the same person cannot but make an intelligent and sensitive human being shudder. And the awesome responsibility of rearing children is certain to produce further anxieties. Romantic love is an extremely potent tranquilizer for the treatment of such anxieties. Narcotics also dull one's senses and make one less discriminating about what is happening in the world around. And romantic love assists the lover in denying deficiencies in the partner, deficiencies that may be obvious to almost everyone else, deficiencies that might cause most judicious individuals to pause before making such an important commitment. As with the narcotic, the ecstatic feelings are experienced only early in its use. As time passes the drug becomes less and less capable of producing the blissful state. Alas, such is also the case with romantic love.

One of the important attractions of the romantic love experience is that it is an esteem enhancer. We generally admire most those who have the good sense to like us (and conversely, we are quickest to dislike intensely those who are stupid or blind enough to hold us in low regard). We cannot but find attractive a person who has selected us—from all the billions of other people on earth—to respect, confide in, and communicate sexual attraction to as well. Typically, the individuals bestow praises on one another to a degree not generally seen in any other situation. All stops are pulled out in the service of this goal. Even one's own mother does not hold one in as high regard as one's lover. The process may start, for example, with A bestowing on B some complimentary comment. B, thereby flattered, returns the favor. A then considers B to be quite judicious for having such high regard for him or her and thinks then even more highly of B. B, receiving even greater positive feedback, esteems A even more highly and communicates this. A mutual admiration society thereby develops with an upward spiraling of the compliments. The society is founded on the agreement that "if you'll admire, praise, respect, and find me sexually attractive, I'll do the same for you." This is indeed one of the important attractions of the phenomenon.

Unfortunately, there are only about 400,000 words in most unabridged dictionaries of the English language, only a small fraction of which are useful in the service of complimenting one's beloved. It is even more unfortunate that the majority of individuals have only a few of these in their repertoire. As a result, the praises tend to become somewhat repetitious and they thereby lose some of their efficacy. In addition, the individuals may believe that it behooves them to maintain the high frequency of compliments and this can be somewhat taxing and draining. Healthy people can allow the romantic love experience to simmer down somewhat and have ongoing experiences that enable them to supply fresh compliments. Those who do not may then become frustrated with this aspect of the romantic love experience. Last, individuals with profound feelings of low self-worth are more likely to gravitate toward this aspect of the romantic love phenomenon because the praises provide compensation for low self-esteem.

There is yet another element in this phenomenon that enhances even further the feelings of self-worth of the individuals involved. If the object of one's affections is perfect, and if one is in turn loved by that perfect person, then one must indeed be a most admirable person indeed. It is as if the young man in love were saying: "She is perfect. Among her perfections is wisdom. She loves me. If she is wise enough to love me, I must be unique, adorable, lovable, wise, and maybe even perfect like her. Why, she even tells me that 'we're a perfect match.'"

Another factor operative in the romantic love experience is reaction formation to underlying anger. All human relationships are ambivalent, and those who are in love are no exception to this principle. However, there are individuals who believe that it behooves them to have a relationship in which there is no anger expressed—lest the relationship be viewed by themselves and others as not "the real thing." In most (if not all) human relationships angry feelings are inevitably going to arise at some point, often very early. We cannot satisfy one another's desires all the time; the frustrations that ultimately result in all close human encounters must produce resentments at times. In healthy relationships, the individuals express these at the earliest possible times, in a civilized manner, in the hope that the problems may be resolved. If a problem cannot be resolved, and if there are many such problems, then the individuals usually part ways. If, however, they are successful in resolving the inevitable conflicts that arise, they may then be in a position to maintain a relationship that may ultimately mature. Individuals who are too guilty to express their resentments or who need to feel that there are none, are likely to use the romantic, loving feelings in the service of reaction formation. Obsessive love may then be used to suppress deep-seated hatred. Accordingly, romantic love not only provides a cover-up of angry feelings—for those who believe that they should not be present in good relationships—but lessens the likelihood that the individuals will work out the problems that are producing the anger in the first place. In this way it contributes to the perpetuation of difficulties in the relationship and even to its deterioration.

Romantic love can also be used to satisfy pathological dependency cravings. It is much more socially acceptable to gratify pathological dependency with a spouse than with a parent. This would be an extension of the previously described shift in which the adolescent transfers dependency on parents to dependency on peers. In romantic love, the dependency gratifications may be even greater and a marriage based on such cravings is not likely to be stable, because in any parasitic relationship the host as well as the parasite ultimately get to hate one another. The host resents the parasite because his or her blood is being sucked; and the parasite resents the host because of his or her vulnerability. At any point the host may flick off the parasite, leaving him or her with no sustenance. And such resentments may, over time, develop into hatred when the two individuals become "locked in" with one another.

Another factor that may be operative in the romantic love phenomenon is the desire to outdo one's friends and even evoke their jealousy. One can boast to friends that one is loved, adored, admired, and even worshipped by another party. When one's friends are not at that time having that fortunate experience, then it places the beloved in a superior position in the competition for success in the dating/mate-acquisition arena. One can then boast of the "good catch" and flaunt the beloved to one's friends. Again, individuals with low feelings of self-worth are more likely to utilize this maneuver.

I wish to emphasize again my point that psychodynamics should not necessarily be equated with psychopathology. Each of the above contributing factors, when present in mild degree, may very well be considered normal. To the degree that romantic love becomes obsessive and prolonged, to the degree that it becomes delusional, to the degree that it interferes with important functions (school, work, etc.), to that degree should it be considered psycho-pathological. The healthiest situation for the adolescent, I believe, is to have a few such experiences, but not to make any commitments under the influence of the romantic-love feeling. Adolescents are generally too young to marry and have children and the romantic experience may result in their taking these steps. My final advice, whether it be to the adolescent or to the adult who is "in love," is this: Romantic love is a wonderful experience. Enjoy it while it lasts, but don't make important decisions under its influence—like marriage, for example!

It would be unfortunate if the reader concluded from this somewhat cynical description that I am totally condemning the phenomenon. I believe that in moderation it can be an enriching, uplifting experience that makes life more meaningful. It has served to inspire some of the world's greatest artistic and scientific creations. The person who has not tasted its sweet fruits has missed out on one of life's most rewarding experiences, but when it is indulged in to excess, when people are so blinded by it that they enter into self-destructive involvements, I consider it a type of psychological disturbance. One can compare romantic love to the occasional alcoholic beverage. Used in moderation it can ennoble our spirits; when we are addicted to it, it can destroy us. I think that it is possible that in recent years there may have been some decrease in the tendency of people to become addicted. The "tell it like it is" philosophy that has become so popular in recent years may very well lessen the tendency of people to enter into this self-induced delusional state to such an extreme degree.

Factors Operative in a Mature Heterosexual Relationship   I believe that a more judicious concept of love between adults is to view it as a composite of many factors, each of which is on its own continuum—from a very low to a very high level. One factor, of course, would be the romantic love element. This is generally strongest when one has very little information about the other party. A number of years ago there was a movie entitled *Lovers and Other Strangers*. This title itself is a clear statement of one important aspect of the romantic love phenomenon. We can love most ardently those about whom we know least. Romantic loving feelings tend to decrease in situations in which there is ongoing close contact—such as when the two people live together. The feelings do not survive well under the competition of hair in the sink, bathroom smells, snoring, etc. Accordingly, a relationship that is based purely on this factor, and has little else, is not likely to survive long. As mentioned, romantic loving feelings may include formidable psychopathological elements, and this is a further reason for distrusting them. I am not claiming that romantic feelings have no place at all in a mature relationship, only that they be considered to be one part. Ideally residua of the initial feelings survive over time, to re-express themselves in periods of relaxation, tenderness, and sexual intimacy.

Another factor to be considered is sexual attraction. Here too sexual feelings can range from very strong to very weak, and even to the point of nonexistence. Generally, these are strongest in the earliest phases of the relationship when there is much novelty and even a "forbidden fruit" element. In the healthiest relationship, however, the sexual feelings may still remain strong over many years, even after these initial factors are no longer operative. But here too fluctuations may be present and still be considered within the normal range.

Another factor, one that is quite important, is that of genuine respect. Here, too, there is the continuum from very low to very high. In a good relationship there is a high regard for the other person's opinions in important areas—so much so that the partners are willing to take action on the basis of their respect for one another's opinions. And respect also includes respect for the other person's rights, space, freedom, aspirations, and a wide variety of other needs. Related to respect is admiration. Here there is high respect to the point of real esteem. When there is admiration the loving relationship is likely to be even stronger. However, it is important for the reader to appreciate that respect and admiration must be based on realistic qualities, not fantasized ones. They must be qualities that are genuinely considered worthy of respect, not easily attained attributes.

Another important element in a good loving relationship is the desire to share with one another. Here again there is the same continuum from very little desire to share to very strong desire. Probably the most common area for sharing is child rearing. However, there are some couples who may not enjoy this kind of sharing, but other kinds of mutual endeavors. Of course, the more areas in which the couple enjoys mutual sharing, the stronger will be the relationship. I would not consider the ideal, however, to be one of complete togetherness on practically every area of functioning. Marriage should not be a "three-legged race." I make reference here to the traditional children's game in which the children race in pairs, each tied together as if they had three instead of four legs. In such a marriage, as in such a race, the individuals are likely to fall flat on their faces. There must be opportunities for decompression and for each to have his or her own living space. They must each have the opportunity to enjoy the benefits of other relationships as well, but not to the point where the loving relationship takes second place.

Another factor that is important in a good loving relationship between adults is the willingness to make *reasonable* sacrifices for the other party. I emphasize the word reasonable because I consider an inordinate desire to sacrifice (or to be sacrificed for) to be unhealthy. Accordingly, sacrifices that are motivated by masochistic and martyristic tendencies are not what I am referring to here. Rather, I am talking about the willingness to deprive oneself and do things for the other party under circumstances of personal inconvenience and sacrifice, but not to the point of seeking or creating situations in which one can provide oneself with morbid extensions of the willingness for self-abnegation in the service of the loved one.

The reader may be wondering why I have included here such an extensive discussion of those factors that are operative in the mature adult heterosexual relationship. My reason is that adolescents are extremely unlikely to exhibit such elements. Accordingly, their loving relationships rarely satisfy these criteria and so are likely to be transient. There are rare occasions, however, when the adolescent relationship may indeed serve as the basis for the development of these more stable and mature qualities. It behooves a therapist to be appreciative of these differentiations and to recognize that it is only over time that one can tell whether the relationship will mature in the aforementioned directions.

In addition, there are the psychopathological processes that are operative in even the healthiest relationships. She claims she wants a husband and he claims he wants a wife. What she really wants is a child and what he really wants is a mother; and so the relationship takes on all the hallmarks of a parent/child relationship. He is a very quiet, uptight kind of person who is ill at ease in social situations and has little to say. She is very voluble, extremely gregarious, and enjoys speaking with others. Accordingly, he can rely upon her to "fill up the vacuum" in social situations. So we have a man with verbal constipation who falls in love with a woman with verbal diarrhea—and the match is made. She says she wants a husband and he says he wants a wife. Basically, she wants a sadist and he wants a masochist, and they "fall in love." I am not referring here to the full-blown type of sado-masochistic relationship in which the partners reach orgasm via beating and torturing one another. Rather, I am referring to the more common and less dramatic form in which there is cruelty, maltreatment, and denigration. The alcoholic man is likely to fall in love with a woman who has some kind of a savior complex, in which she believes that she is going to cure him of his drinking. Another woman is going to cure her betrothed of homosexuality by giving him a good heterosexual sex life. Schizoid or severely suppressed people may gravitate toward one another because each would feel uncomfortable with a partner who is freer to express emotion.

L. Kubie (1956) considers the need to "settle old scores" and "right old wrongs" to be an important psychopathological factor in many heterosexual relationships. A woman, for example, who was rejected by her father may involve herself with a man who is similarly rejecting in order to extract love from her husband, who is viewed as a surrogate father. What she didn't get from her own father she now hopes to get from his substitute. Finding a loving man in the first place might seem simpler and more judicious, yet it would deprive her of the opportunity of going through the process of converting the unloving to a loving man and thereby accomplishing the transformation. Another example: A man might want to make his bad mother (now equals wife) good or use her as a target for the present expression of past resentments originally felt toward his mother. For individuals to do this they must marry people who have the very same alienating qualities that they claim they never want to have in a spouse. These qualities exist as internal bad objects in the individuals themselves, and these are then projected out onto the spouse, even when they don't exist. The spouse is then viewed as a "bad internal object representation." The distorted view of the spouse, then, results from two processes: 1) a transference onto the spouse of feelings originally felt toward one's own parent in childhood and 2) a projection of one's own internal bad object parental representations that have been incorporated. The real personality of the family member then hardly exists because the individual is seen primarily, if not exclusively, as a bad object representation and/or as someone who is distorted by one's own transferences.

According to Kubie these two processes contribute significantly to the individual's desire to use the spouse to settle old scores and/or to right old wrongs. The list of such psychopathological interactions goes on and I am sure the reader can provide his or her own examples. The examiner must appreciate that one or more of these pathological types of interaction are likely to be present along with the more normal factors delineated above. Although adults will often manifest these pathological types of interaction in full-blown form, one observes them *in statu nascendi* in adolescents. Therapists do well to detect these developing pathological manifestations and do what they can to interrupt the process in its earliest stages.

Clearly, by the definition I have just presented, adolescents are not likely to qualify as good candidates to have strong mature loving relationships. And they generally don't. The romantic euphoric element is often predominant and they do not have the experiences to entrench in depth the other elements. The relationships are often transient and this lessens even further the likelihood for such entrenchment. Unfortunately, they often have the foundations for the kinds of pathological interactions that may contribute to disturbed adult heterosexual relationships. It behooves the therapist to be aware of these and to do everything possible to alleviate them in order to reduce the likelihood that these will contribute significantly to the youngster's ultimate heterosexual difficulties.

Parental Reactions to the
Adolescent's Sexual Development

Generally the greatest fear of the parents of adolescent girls is that their daughters will become pregnant. To a lesser degree, parents of adolescent boys fear that their sons will prematurely become fathers. Healthy parents take proper precautions, provide reasonable sexual education, and, at the appropriate times, provide information about contraception if they have no religious or ethical proscriptions against the utilization of such safeguards. They also inform their youngsters, at the proper time, that if a pregnancy were to occur the youngster should feel comfortable telling the parents at the very outset. Disturbed parents instill formidable fears of sex in their children, the result of which may be a pregnancy that is not disclosed to them, or disclosed when it is too late to handle it in the most expeditious fashion (again, depending upon the parents' religious values).

It is normal for parents to have a certain amount of jealousy of their adolescents' sexual freedom. Healthy parents, however, put this in proper perspective and the jealousy does not play an important role in the way they deal with their youngsters. Parents who cannot tolerate their adolescents' emerging sexuality may become punitively restrictive with regard to the youngsters' sexual opportunities. A father, for example, may be obsessively concerned with his daughter's clothing, especially with regard to how revealing it is. He may refuse to let her leave the home with low-cut blouses and be extremely punitive when she uses even occasional cosmetics and perfume. Some fathers who exhibit such concerns are actually fighting their own sexual urges toward their daughters and may be unconsciously taking the position: "If I can't have her, then I'm not going to let anyone else have her either." And the daughters, too, are not immune from having sexual feelings toward their fathers. Many would describe the feelings of such a child as "oedipal." As I have discussed elsewhere (R.A. Gardner, 1968a, 1973a, 1986a), I believe that only a small percentage of the patients I see have what I would consider justifiably to be called "oedipal problems." When such problems are present, there are usually special situations in the family that are conducive to the development of these difficulties. These will be discussed in Chapter Two.

I mention here what I consider to be a normal way for an adolescent girl to deal with occasional sexual feelings toward her father by excessive criticism, disgust, and even frequent fighting, in order to disguise (to both her father and herself) her sexual attraction. And a father may respond in kind, with regard to his own sexual feelings, by frequently bickering with his daughter. A similar phenomenon may exist between mothers and sons. I consider such fighting to be within the normal range when it is occasional and does not interfere with functioning in major areas. When, however, it becomes a deep-seated pattern, then I would view it to be pathological.

CONCLUDING COMMENTS

I have presented in this chapter what I consider to be normal developmental conficts of the adolescent. Rather than confining myself to any particular developmental theory, I have focused on those developmental conflicts that I have seen over the years to be the most important for youngsters during this stage. Nor do I claim to have covered all developmental problems. I do believe, however, that I have dealt with those that are most likely to serve as a foundation for psychopathology. Because psychopathology so often emerges from these normal conflicts, the understanding of these will place the reader in a better position to understand the psychopathological processes that I will be describing in this book.

TWO

COMMON SITUATIONS CONDUCIVE TO THE DEVELOPMENT OF PSYCHOPATHOLOGY IN ADOLESCENTS

In this chapter I will discuss those situations I have found to be most conducive to the development of psychopathology in adolescents. This chapter, therefore, should not be viewed as a comprehensive statement of the wide variety of situations that can produce psychopathology in adolescence. Rather, it describes those situations that, in my own personal experience, are most commonly conducive to the development of such difficulties in these youngsters. I recognize that others, with different patient populations, would describe different situations—some similar to mine and some not. The developmental conflicts described in Chapter One are at the foundation of the psychopathology of most of these youngsters. The particular situations described in this chapter combine with these underlying developmental conflicts to bring about the psychopathological reactions. The conflicts described in Chapter One may very well be normal; the situations described in this chapter are generally pathological and play an important role in determining whether the normal developmental conflicts will serve as the foundation for psychopathology or merely become resolved through the process of maturation.

The reader will perhaps note what may initially appear to be be an emphasis on situations that produce antisocial behavior in these youngsters. This over-representation is not related, I believe, to any particular bias on my part. Rather, it reflects my experience that antisocial behavior is the most common category of difficulty in the adolescent patients referred to me. As I have mentioned frequently in other publications of mine, when I collect data for a book, I invariably find that anger problems are the ones I am most commonly asked to treat and so the sections in my various books related to anger problems are usually the most extensive (R.A. Gardner, 1971, 1973a, 1976, 1977, 1979 and 1986a).

SOCIAL, CULTURAL, AND EDUCATIONAL FACTORS

Day-care Centers

In recent years we have witnessed a burgeoning of day-care centers. This growth has paralleled the shift of women from the home into the work place. Obviously, when women are no longer at home taking care of the children someone has to take over this role. As far back as the late 19th century, at the time of the establishment of the kibutzim in Israel, this problem had to be faced. The young pioneers who first established these settlements designated certain women, called *metapelets*, to involve themselves primarily in child rearing–thereby freeing up mothers to work in the fields, factories, etc. The day-care center is the American equivalent of this phenomenon. The success or failure of the day-care principle rests on the quality of the care given the children and the hope that it will be as good as that provided by the biological mother. On the basis of my experiences with children who have spent many years in such centers, I believe that many of these facilities are significantly deficient in providing such quality care. Of course, when the biological mother herself is somewhat impaired in maternal capacity then the day-care center may very well be a boon for her child—its deficiencies notwithstanding. But when one compares the care given in the average center with that given by the average mother, I believe that the mothers come out significantly ahead (and the children in day care, therefore, significantly behind).

In the last few years the problem of sex abuse of children in day-care centers has received widespread attention, but I believe that physical and emotional abuse are also common. It is unreasonable to expect that people who would be depraved enough to sexually abuse children are completely free from tendencies to abuse children in other ways—ways not directly related to sex abuse. Of course, it is impossible to get accurate statistics regarding the prevalence of such practices. This is especially the case for emotional abuse, for which objective criteria cannot be utilized. I believe, however, that the lower the cost of the facility, the less the regulation by the community, and the greater the number of children per care provider, the greater the likelihood that one or more of the three forms of abuse is likely to take place—especially emotional abuse. And I consider neglect to be a form of emotional abuse. It is difficult to learn exactly what is going on in these facilities because the children, most often under the ages of three and four, are ill equipped to describe exactly what has happened behind their parents' backs. It is important to appreciate that people who choose careers in these centers are not always motivated by the noble desire to provide children with loving care; many are motivated by money and some by the opportunity to find helpless scapegoats for their sadistic impulses and objects for the pedophilic gratification.

I believe that many of the children "dumped" into these facilities suffer with deprivation of affection and that such deprivation may contribute to a wide variety of psychiatric disturbances. In fact, it is reasonable to say that the vast majority of psychogenic disturbances include deprivation of affection in childhood as an important contributing etiological element. Elsewhere (1973a) I have described in greater detail the specific relationship between such privation and the development of various forms of psychogenic disturbance in childhood.

A particular form of such disturbance, which I focus on here because of its increasing ubiquity, is that of *psychopathic behavior*. I use the word *psychopath* to refer to an individual who has an impairment in the development of internal conscience mechanisms. The individual feels little if any guilt over the infliction of pain and suffering on others. There is little capacity to put oneself in another individual's position, especially an individual who is the object of one's persecution, exploitation, etc. For the psychopath the primary deterrent to such behavior is the immediate threat of external punishment. I believe that western society has become increasingly psychopathic in the last 20–25 years. I see the trend to have started in the early to mid-1960s and to be continuing. There is far more exploitation of individuals, far less honesty, far less dignity, and far less concern for the feelings of others. We are living in a much more exploitive world than we did 20–25 years ago.

I am not claiming, for one moment, that the history of mankind prior to that time was characteristically free from psychopathy. There were certainly times when psychopathy was probably even more widespread than it is now. For example, following the period of the Black Plague in the mid-14th century, when Europe was depleted of about 25 to 30 percent of its population, society became almost entirely predatory with a nearly complete deterioration of moral standards in church, government, and even family life. And there have certainly been other periods in mankind's history when similar situations prevailed. Unfortunately, we are moving with increasing frequency into such an era. In day-care centers young children are not being provided with good models for the development of conscience because their caretakers themselves have grown up in a psychopathic society and have taken on its values. In addition, a child is most likely to learn to be "good" when he or she is rewarded for goodness by loving caretakers. In Chapter One I described in greater detail how the absence of caring parental figures at the imprinting, pleasure-pain, shame, and guilt stages produces failure in the development of the internal guilt-evoking mechanisms.

It would be an error for the reader to conclude that I am condemning entirely the whole day-care concept. It would also be an error for the reader to conclude that I am condemning all day-care centers and all their personnel. Rather, I am sharply critical of many with which I have had personal experience. Furthermore, I do not believe, even under the most ideal circumstances, that day-care center personnel can provide the same kind of love and affection that the natural average, healthy parent is capable of giving. There is something about the biological tie that increases the likelihood that the child will develop a strong psychological tie. Day-care personnel do not have this foundation for the development of this important psychological bond. And the inevitable turnover of both children and caretakers makes it even more unlikely that such bonds will develop.

As women enter increasingly into the work force they are spending less time with their children. The growth of day-care centers helped fill the need for a place for mothers to leave their children during the workday. Obviously, a mother cannot be in two places at the same time; she cannot be at work and at home taking care of the children. Although these new trends certainly serve well the needs of women, especially those who consider a full-time job as child rearer to be boring and unsatisfying, they do not serve well the needs of their children. Most mothers in this situation find themselves on the horns of a dilemma. To the degree they satisfy their work interests, they neglect their children; and to the degree they satisfy their children's needs, they neglect their careers. We are witnessing an ever burgeoning growth of "latchkey children," i.e., children who carry their house keys with them to school in order to be able to enter their empty home at the end of the school day and then wait for their parents to return from work.

What is the solution then? Should mothers return to their traditional roles as homemakers? I do not think so. But even if I did think so, there would be no turning back. The answer, interestingly, I believe to be a very simple one. There are few simple answers to the problems of the world, yet I believe we have one here—as difficult as it may be to accomplish. The answer lies in restructuring society so that mothers and fathers can divide child-rearing obligations. All we need do is have each parent work outside the home half the days of the week. The mother, for example, might work outside the home on Monday, Wednesday, and half of Friday; and the father could then work outside on Tuesday, Thursday and the other half of Friday. Such an arrangement is entirely feasible. Everyone has had the experience of calling an office in order to speak with Mr. Jones. One is informed that Jones is not available that day and that he will be in the following day. However, if one wants to speak with Mr. Smith, who is equally capable of handling the situation, then he is available. All of us are expendable. There is no one whose job is so vital and/or unique that there aren't other individuals who can take over. Life goes on even when the most vital people become incapacitated, retired, or die.

Many feminists are clamoring for more money for day care. I think this is an error. Some of the more vociferous of these women are individuals who abhor child rearing and denigrate homemaking. These women would do far better to use their influence in bringing about the aforementioned changes in the work place: changes that would accommodate a 50/50 split by parents in child rearing and work obligations. This arrangement would be the optimum one for younger children, during the first four to five years of life. After the youngest child enters school, the parents would then be freer to involve themselves more extensively in the work force. I consider this arrangement to be entirely viable at the present time. The vast majority of organizations could implement it for most of their employees without formidable difficulty. Its implementation would remove one important contributory factor to the psychopathology of children and, by extension, adolescents.

Unfortunately, the seemingly utopian plan of each parent working half time and spending the remaining time at home with the children is not close to being realized. What can we do then at this point? In presenting my recommendation, I will use the mother as the example of the primary caretaking person because, at the present time, she is more likely to be the one who is providing such care. In part I believe this is a "good" thing because mothers are more likely than fathers to have a stronger psychological tie with the infant at the time of birth. However, it is also a "bad" thing because it is a statement of society's failure to provide adequate opportunities for men to participate fully in the child-rearing process. The optimum program, I believe, is one in which the younger the child the greater the amount of time the mother has with it. Certainly in the first six months or so the mother should be spending most of the time at home. I am not stating that there be no respite. She too needs some decompression and alleviation of child-rearing involvements. And most mothers probably need this daily or at least a few times a week. Such respites should be taken while the child is sleeping and/or while the child is cared for by persons such as the father, grandparents, and close relatives and friends. These people are much more likely than the strangers at the day-care center (no matter how sophisticated and devoted) to provide the child with optimum care. It is important for the reader to appreciate that the six-month figure given above may vary and that is why I stated, "six months or so."

During the second half of the first year (I know that I am being particularly vague here) I would suspect (I am not certain) that children can tolerate maternal absence for longer periods. I suspect, as well, that if a mother returned to work for one to two days a week at that time *and* the child was cared for by one of the aforementioned individuals (as opposed to someone in a day-care center) the child would probably be all right. By extension, the older the child the greater will be its tolerance for separations while mother is working. By 2-1/2 to 3 years of age children are certainly more capable of tolerating longer times away from their mothers and are more likely to profit from the group and peer experiences that are so important for healthy development. *If* the care provided is warm, humane, and tender and *if* the ratio of caretakers to children is adequate, then the day-care experience at this age is likely to be salutary. But there are very big *ifs* here because, as mentioned, I am dubious about the quality of the care provided in most centers.

Like many other things in life the rich have a much greater chance of getting quality day care than the poor. In the early grade-school period children still do better if, on returning from school, they find mother or some other well-known figure who will provide love, affection, and attention. I recognize that my position on this point would be considered "sexist" by many feminists. Many women's desire to enter the workplace is so strong that they have to blind themselves to the psychologically detrimental effects of turning their children over to the care of strangers. They have to deny the fact that no one loves our children more than biological parents and close relatives (and on occasion close friends). If one were to interpret my comments here to indicate that I want to drive women back into the home, that would be a serious distortion of my intent. Rather, I want to bring mothers *as well as fathers* back into the home. However, I want mothers to be in the home more than fathers during the infancy period. And then, by age two to three, both parents should be involved equally in the child-rearing process.

Socioeconomic Deprivation

Children who grow up in homes and neighborhoods in which they suffer socioeconomic deprivation are likely to be angry; and such anger is likely to contribute to the development of a variety of psychopathological manifestations, especially in adolescence. In childhood the youngster is generally not capable of acting out on such hostile impulses or expressing fully the symptoms derived from such deprivation. In adolescence, however, the youngster may very well exhibit psychopathology, especially in the realm of drug abuse and antisocial behavior. The drugs serve in part to provide some pleasure in a situation which is generally viewed as pleasureless. And the antisocial acting out serves as a vehicle for the expression of the rage engendered by the deprivation. The sense of deprivation is enhanced further by the inevitable exposure to situations that provide opportunities for comparison between what the youngster has in reality and what the child might very well have had under more favorable circumstances. Movies, television, newspapers, magazines, and other aspects of the mass media perenially bombard the youngster with the "good life" out there—a life which the child is continually being rejected from and which he or she may consider an impossible goal toward which to aspire.

The economic deprivation is generally apparent in the home, the neighborhood, and the schools. Such youngsters are brought up in an atmosphere in which they consider themselves to be among the "have-nots" and there is continual comparison with the "haves." Accordingly, the child grows up in an environment of ongoing deprivation, frustration, and anger. Unfortunately, the youngsters with whom the child associates during the formative years are exposed to similar privations, and they too exhibit the same kinds of psychopathology that derive from the deprivation. As a result there are few if any peer models with whom the child might make healthier identifications.

I believe that one of the most important determinants as to whether a child in this situation will develop psychopathology is the presence of a father in the home. In those homes in which a father is present, there is less likelihood that the youngster will develop antisocial behavior, abuse drugs, or manifest other symptoms derived from deprivation—the economic privation notwithstanding. Even when the neighborhood is one in which drugs and crime prevail, if there is stability within the home, especially a stable marriage between the parents, then the likelihood that the child will become involved in such activities is reduced significantly. Although there might be present healthy adult models such as ministers, recreation directors, teachers, etc. for more salutary emulation, these figures generally have far less influence on such youngsters than fathers.

The rectification of this situation obviously goes far beyond what therapists can do in their offices. It is only via changes in those factors that have contributed to the socioeconomic deprivation in the first place that one can hope to reduce significantly the frequency of the kinds of adolescent disturbances derived from such privation. The therapist does well to appreciate the formidable forces operative in producing such psychopathology and must recognize, thereby, how impotent he or she is to change such children—especially when they do not reach the therapist's office until the adolescent period.

Schools

Whereas the home plays the most important role in the child's psychological development during the first three or four years, the schools play an increasingly important role during the next decade or so (at least for most children). Those who are unfortunate enough to be provided with inadequate educational programs are likely to develop psychopathology, both in childhood and in adolescence. I believe there to have been a progressive deterioration of our educational systems (both public and private) in the last 15 to 20 years. A number of factors have contributed to this deterioration. One relates to teachers' salaries. It is unreasonable to expect that schools can attract high quality, well-educated individuals when other careers provide much greater pay. In most municipalities garbage men make as much as, if not more than, elementary school teachers. The public sector can generally afford to provide higher salaries than private and parochial schools; yet the public schools seem to be getting the poorest quality teachers. The more dedicated ones are willing to take positions for lower salaries in order to work in the more academically stimulating atmosphere of the private and/or parochial schools.

I believe there has been a general diminution in the commitment of teachers to the educational process. I am not claiming that this is true of all teachers, only that the percentage of teachers who are deeply committed to their profession has been sharply reduced in the last 15 to 20 years. One manifestation of this trend is the decreased frequency with which children are required to do homework. Giving children homework most often involves homework for the teacher. And less dedicated teachers are not willing to take on this extra responsibility. In previous years there were many more teachers generally viewed to be somewhat hard nosed and dictatorial, yet their despotism was benevolent and years later their students have looked back with gratitude on what they were "forced" to do. These days "respect" for the child often involves a degree of permissiveness and indulgence that does not serve children well in the course of their education. A good educational experience helps the child learn that there are times when one has to do things that may be unpleasant in order to derive future benefits. "Respecting" the child's wish not to suffer such discomforts is basically not in the child's best interests. True respect for children involves the *requirement* that they do what is best for them, not the indulgence of their avoidance of reasonable responsibilities. The net result of these unfortunate trends is that children learn less during their primary and secondary school years — with the subsequent result that SAT scores have dropped significantly during the last 15 to 20 years and many studies have demonstrated that the majority of children are abysmally ignorant of basic facts about history, literature, english, and mathematics.

Another factor operative in the deterioration of the educational system has been the growth of a generation of teachers who themselves have not learned very much during their own educational processes. Often, these are teachers who went to college during the 1960s when students' self-indulgence may have reached an all-time high. Grammar, punctuation, spelling, and foreign languages were dismissed as "irrelevant." Many other subjects that required self-abnegation, self-discipline, and hard work were also often viewed as irrelevant. These are the people who are now teaching our youngsters. Not only do many of these teachers serve as poor models for their students, because of their impaired commitment to the educational process, but they are compromised as well in what they can teach. I routinely ask parents to bring in my child patients' report cards. Often I see egregious errors in grammar, punctuation, and spelling. I have had secretaries whom I have had to let go after a week or two because of their ignorance of basic

English. They were not people who I felt needed time to adjust to a new job; rather, it might have taken years to get them to reach the point where they could function adequately in a standard secretarial position. They often did not even appreciate how ignorant they were. They didn't even recognize that a misspelled word looked misspelled and so had no motivation to consult a dictionary for the correct spelling.

In their book, *What Do Our 17-Year-Olds Know?*, C. E. Finn and D. Ravitch (1986) report a study conducted with approximately 18,000 17-year-olds who were selected to reflect the makeup of the population as a whole regarding region, sex, race, type of school, and type of community. Some of their findings: Thirty percent of the students did not know that Christopher Columbus reached the New World before 1750. More than 35 percent were not aware that the Watergate scandal took place after 1950. More than 30 percent believed that one consequence of the Spanish-American War was the defeat of the Spanish Armada. Approximately half of the students believed that *Nineteen Eighty-Four* dealt with the destruction of the human race in a nuclear war. Over one-third did not know that Aesop wrote fables. Over 42 percent did not know that Senator Joseph R. McCarthy conducted anti-Communist investigations. Seventy percent were unable to identify the Magna Carta. And the book goes on and on with many more examples of the abysmal ignorance of the average American teenager. But these findings should not be surprising, considering the kinds of educational programs these youngsters are being provided.

This deterioration of the educational process has extended up into the college and university levels as well. When I went to college we generally went from nine a.m. to five p.m. Monday through Friday and a half-day on Saturday. Most courses met four or five times a week and laboratory courses two to three afternoons a week. It was expected that one would do four or five hours of homework a night. School began the day following Labor Day and continued right through early June. There was a one-week Christmas vacation, possibly a one-week Easter vacation, and of course national holidays. Otherwise we went to school. This is no longer the case. Even in the so-called "best" colleges and universities the formal academic program is far less rigorous. Most students average two or three hours a day of classes while professors may only have to come in five to ten hours a week and are otherwise unseen. These days, the academic year, although it may start around Labor Day, generally ends in early May. Some institutions use the Christmas and/or Easter season as an excuse for an extended holiday (two to four weeks). Others have long vacations (lasting two to four weeks) between semesters. Many need no other excuse for a long break than the season (spring or winter vacation). These students are being short-changed. "Educations" of this kind may cost $15,000 a year or more.

Recently, a mother of a patient, who teaches at one of the public universities in New York City, related to me an incident that demonstrates well the deterioration of our educational systems, even at the highest level. The woman is a highly intelligent, well-trained, scholarly individual with a Ph.D. in a very demanding field. One day her chairman called her into his office and told her that he was having a problem with her, namely, that too many of her students were failing. He informed her that a 40 percent failure rate was unacceptable. She informed him that she was actually being quite generous, and that if she had marked in a less generous way about 60 percent of her students would fail. He told her that he had sat in on a couple of her classes, knew exactly what the problem was, and considered it easily rectifiable. He then went on to explain to her that she was not giving tests in the "correct" manner. What she was doing was to tell students on Friday, for example, that there would be a test on Monday covering the material in certain chapters of the textbook. This he considered "unfair" to the students. Rather, the "correct" way to give a test was to tell the students on Friday exactly what questions would be asked on Monday. Under the new system the failure rate dropped from 40 to 20 percent, but even then she found herself being quite generous. Such procedures are a manifestation of a bastardization of the educational system. They make a farce of education and, worse, are a terrible disservice to students. The next step, of course, is merely to tell what questions will be asked and give the answers that will be expected. If one extends this further one might as well give out (or sell) the diplomas in advance and save everybody a lot of trouble.

Things are even worse at some of the lower level colleges. Many of these merely go through the motions of providing an education and are basically a sham. Students are given textbooks that are seemingly rigorous and demanding, yet in actuality the students are only required to learn a small fraction of what is presented therein. Those in charge recognize the travesty but are party to it, even at the highest levels. The net result of all this is that students are not getting a bona fide education and are thereby entering into the workplace ill equipped to handle jobs for which they are ostensibly being trained. Also they are being deprived of the feelings of accomplishment and high self-worth enjoyed by those who have acquired skills and talents through hard labor and dedication over years. The situation, thereby, contributes to psychopathology, because feelings of low self-worth are an important contributing factor in the development of psychogenic symptoms. In addition, it contributes to psychopathic trends (I am not saying gross psychopathy) because of the sanctions the youngsters are given for "cutting corners," taking short-cuts, and otherwise doing shabby work.

Accordingly, I consider most colleges in the United States to be little more than "winter camps." Most (but certainly not all) colleges are nothing more than businesses that cater to a gullible population of parents who consider it crucial that their children go to college. Four years are spent in which the "students" indulge themselves in alcohol, sex, and drugs—with little serious attention to academics. And no one flunks out because colleges need the parents' money. (No sane businessman throws a paying customer out of the store.) Grade inflation gives students the specious feeling that they are learning something. As long as there are parents who believe it is *crucial* that their children (no matter how simple and/or unmotivated) have a college education (no matter how specious and inferior), there will be people happy to supply the "product." These educational depravities become progressively worse, because for each successive generation there is greater distance from traditional models in which healthy values were practiced and preached. Elsewhere (1973a), I have described in greater detail other deficiencies in our educational system that contribute to psychopathology.

Television and Movies

There is little question that television and movies contribute to the development of various forms of psychopathology. I wish to emphasize, at the outset, that I believe that the detrimental influences of these media can be offset to a significant degree by a healthy, stable home situation. However, even in the most healthy and stable homes, parents are still working against the nefarious influences of these media on their children's psychological development.

Prior to the early 20th century, people were required to derive their own sources of home entertainment. It was an active experience and necessitated a certain amount of ingenuity and creativity. Watching television and movies is an easy and passive experience, which deprives the individual of the gratifications to be derived from the more traditional home entertainment activities. And this passivity extends itself into other areas of life in which individuals have become accustomed to being served and catered to. This contributes to both physical and mental laziness—the latter type being much more psychologically detrimental than the former.

Although still denied by some (especially those who produce television programs), there is compelling evidence that television violence contributes to violent behavior among viewers. One of the earliest studies in this area was that of A. Bandura et al. (1963) who found that physical and verbal aggressiveness increased in nursery school children after brief exposure to violence. Over the years, many (but not all) studies have lent strong confirmation to Bandura's original conclusions. The notion that the observation of violence in movies and television has cathartic value and thereby reduces pent-up anger is now generally discredited. Whatever cathartic benefits individuals may derive are far less important than the factor of inciting the viewer to further violence. L. Berkowitz and E. Rawlings (1963) were among the earliest to discredit the cathartic value of such observations. More recently G. Comstock and his associates (1978, 1983, 1986) have demonstrated a positive association—especially for boys—between exposure to television violence and antisocial behavior. Comstock et al. consider the evidence strongest for "interpersonal aggression," that is for fighting, minor theft, and name-calling. The relationship is less obvious for the more extreme and harmful types of antisocial behavior, such as criminal activity. I consider the difference in the two types of violence to be related to the home environment, especially with regard to its degree of psychopathy and sanction for the more severe forms of antisocial behavior. N.M. Malamuth and E. Donnerstein (1982) have also found there to be an increase in sexual violence after exposure to sexually explicit movies in which women are assaulted.

Many studies have found that there are specific factors in television and movies that are likely to evoke violent reactions. One factor is the implication, either overt or covert, that the aggressive behavior is rewarded or not punished. Another is that the particular action is normal, usual, and a reasonable adaptation to real-life circumstances. Another factor is related to whether or not the violent behavior is so portrayed that it arouses distaste or disgust. If the viewer is not shown the victim's pain or suffering, the sorrow of friends, or remorse on the part of the perpetrator, it is more likely that it will stimulate antisocial behavior. If the situation is similar to one that the viewer is involved in, it will serve to increase the likelihood of violent acting out on the part of the viewer. When sexual aggression is the theme, it is more likely to be reproduced by the viewer if the woman eventually relishes the assault. If prior to exposure the viewer is already angry, the likelihood is increased that antisocial behavior will subsequently be exhibited.

Some might argue at this point that the implications of this research are that we should strictly avoid exposing our children to any kind of violent material in movies, television, etc. Some might even ask about the judiciousness of exposures to Shakespearean tragedies (*Hamlet* and *Macbeth*, for example), such classics as the *Iliad*, and even biblical passages in which violence is portrayed. Are not these works equally capable of inciting violent reactions? There is most often (but not always) a difference between the violence portrayed in these great works of literature and the kinds of violence one sees in most movies and television. The main difference is that in the great works of literature violent acts are not simply reflex responses, but are embedded in a context of deliberation. One of Hamlet's problems is that he deliberates too long; he cannot make up his mind. We are told that he is a man who "thinks too much." In the process of his deliberations, however, the viewer is treated to many "lofty thoughts" and valuable wisdoms about the world. In contrast, in most television programs the violence is impulsive and is used as the *first* method of dealing with a difficult situation. In addition, in the great works of literature there are many other redeeming elements in the story that enhance the reader; this is most often not the case in the typical movie and television story in which the violence predominates.

The ancient Roman emperors knew that the best way to gain popularity among the general populace was to give them "bread and circuses." By circuses, they were not referring to clowns and acrobats. Rather, they were referring to gladiatorial conflicts in which the combatants fought to the death or spectacles in which prisoners, political dissidents, and individuals of religious persuasions unacceptable to the emperor were fed to lions. We have our equivalents today in such sports as boxing, wrestling, bull fights, and cock fights. To the degree that we can replace the more primitive forms of hostile entertainment with the more sophisticated and humane types, to that degree will we contribute to the prevention of psychopathology derived from such exposures and, by extension, will move toward the enhancement of ourselves as civilized human beings. The Nobel laureate Konrad Lorenz once said: "I have found the missing link between the higher apes and civilized man. It is we."

The Legal System and Penal Institutions

One factor contributing to the development of psychopathology in adolescents, especially antisocial behavior, is the present structure of the legal system and penal institutions. I do not claim to be an expert in these matters and I fully appreciate that they are exceedingly complex. I also appreciate that the solutions to the problems presented herein are also complex and some of them may not have any solutions. Yet, I will make some recommendations which, if implemented, could reasonably contribute to the prevention of certain forms of adolescent psychopathology.

Our legal system is much too lenient in the way it deals with adolescent offenders. It has been said, (and I don't know who said it): "A criminal is a very old man who has committed a series of violent crimes." This statement, of course, reflects the penal system's leniency toward juvenile offenders. First offenders are rarely punished and those who have the wherewithal to hire clever attorneys are even less likely to suffer repercussions for breaking the law. Such leniency only serves to sanction antisocial behavior. Compensation to victims is rarely considered and this only lessens the likelihood that discomforting and painful repercussions will deter offenders. Many policemen do not even bother arresting many offenders, because they recognize that nothing is likely to happen to them. Even when a youngster is found guilty of a crime, the records may be destroyed after a period of good behavior. One could argue that such leniency is humane, and that a youngster should not have his or her record marred for life because of an indiscretion committed in adolescence. Whatever the merits of this argument, there is no question that leniency increases the likelihood that a youngster will commit a crime because of the knowledge that one's record may still remain clean. I sincerely believe that fewer crimes would be committed if reasonable and humane punishment were more predictable and criminal records could not be destroyed or the information expunged—no matter how young the convicted offender.

Another problem relates to the apprehension of criminals. In order to protect the rights of those who might be falsely apprehended and convicted, legislators have passed many laws in recent years that serve to protect individuals from such miscarriages of justice. Whatever benefits society may derive from such laws, there is no question that they have been so manipulated by attorneys that perpetrators have succeeded in avoiding prosecution and punishment for their offenses. Attorneys are taught in law school to protect the rights of their clients, even though they may not have conviction for their causes. Lawyers are taught that their personal convictions regarding the nature of the criminal's behavior (no matter how heinous) should not deter them from fighting for their client's cause. Although I recognize the right of a person to have legal representation, I still believe that a better system would be one in which lawyers were taught that they should not represent a person for whose position they have no conviction. Under such a system criminals would have a more difficult time getting legal protection and this, I believe, would contribute to a reduction in crime. Furthermore, clients whose lawyers do not have conviction for their positions are not being given as effective representation as those whose attorneys have such conviction. The notion that the attorney can serve equally well under both circumstances is misguided, psychologically naive, and a disservice to clients. Elsewhere (1982, 1986b, 1987a, 1987c) I have commented on this and other criticisms I have of the adversary system.

Judges, with justification, are loathe to send youngsters to penal institutions where they will be mixed in with hardened criminals and thereby made worse rather than better. This problem could be obviated by the creation of institutions designed for younger offenders. Although such facilities exist there are far too few of them, certainly not enough to accommodate more than a small fraction of youngsters whose placement there might "help them remember" not to commit crimes. Another problem relates to the overcrowding of jails. There have been times when courts have ordered jails to release criminals before their sentences have been completed, because of overcrowded conditions. Although attempts have been made to release the less dangerous criminals, the process has on occassion resulted in violent crimes and even murders being committed by such released individuals. Clearly, under such a program, prisons are going to free individuals who are considered "safer"—for example, younger criminals who have committed fewer crimes.

DEPRIVATION OF
PARENTAL AFFECTION

Examiners today generally make the assumption that there will often be found a relationship between deprivation of parental affection and the development of psychogenic pathology in their child patient. Although a wide variety of parental deficiencies may be considered, most if not all of them have in common a basic impairment in the parent's capacity to provide the child with the love, guidance, affection, nurture, and protection that is so vital to its well being. Most examiners do not appreciate that this relationship, which is viewed as being so obvious today, was not always appreciated. For example, at no point in Freud's discussion of the analysis of Little Hans does he mention the possibility that there might be some relationship between Hans' symptoms and parental deprivation of affection (S. Freud, 1909). Although Hans' phobia was termed a "psychoneurosis," Freud considered the symptoms to be basically developmental in etiology (a derivative of the "normal" oedipal phase) and even went further to point out that he considered the parents to be normal and healthy, without any evidence of impairment in their parenting capacity.

It was not until the 1930s that we first saw articles suggesting the possibility that there might be some relationship between a child's psychopathology and parental impairment in providing affection. D.M. Levy (1937) introduced the term "affect hunger" to describe this phenomenon. Using the model of the nutritional deficiencies that result from deprivation of vitamins, he considered various childhood psychogenic symptoms to be the result of such deprivation. In 1944 J. Bowlby published the results of a study in which he tried to determine whether there was any relationship between juvenile delinquency and parental deprivation of affection. His finding that a significant percentage of juvenile delinquents came from homes that were disturbed seems unsurprising to us today; however, in Bowlby's time the article was considered to be a landmark contribution. It ultimately resulted in the *World Health Organization* asking Bowlby in the late 1940s to review the world's literature and try to ascertain if there was indeed a relationship between parental deprivation in childhood and the development of psychopathology. In his monograph *Maternal Care and Mental Health*(1952) he concluded that there was indeed such a relationship. Again, his publication was considered a landmark in the history of the field of child psychiatry.

In subsequent years numerous studies have lent confirmation to this theory. The consensus has been that a wide variety of disorders can result from parental absence and/or impaired parenting capacity. The absence of the father (or deficiencies in his ability to serve well in this capacity) has been particularly linked with impaired superego development and the appearance of antisocial behavior. One of the most well known of these studies was done by A. Bandura and R.H. Walters (1958). In their study of antisocial youngsters and their families, they found a high frequency of disruption of the relationship between delinquents and their fathers. They concluded that these impaired relationships interfered with the youngsters' identification with their fathers and internalization of their values. A. Kardiner and L. Ovesey (1951), in their studies of black families, found a correlation between delinquency and the absence of a suitable male model for identification. In addition, when these absentee fathers did have contact with their youngsters they often encouraged, either overtly or covertly, the antisocial behavior of their sons. R.J. Marshall (1983) has written an excellent summary of important contributions in this area.

Another way in which parental deprivation of affection contributes to the development of psychopathology in youngsters relates to the anger engendered in children by parental deficiencies. When there is little guilt over the expression of such anger, then antisocial behavior is likely to develop. (In contrast, when the child has been taught to feel shame and/or guilt over the expression of his or her resentment then the symptoms of anger inhibition may develop.) Rage over the parental privation is another important factor contributing to antisocial behavior, a factor separate from the aforementioned superego deficiencies that are likely to be found, especially in situations where the father is absent or psychologically impaired.

There are some deficient parents who basically do not want to have children. In extreme cases they will murder their children. Body parts of infants may be flushed down the toilet, or the dead infant may be buried, or simply placed in the garbage. In less extreme situations children are brutally beaten as they serve easily as scapegoats for the venting of parental hostility. Such brutalized children are inevitably going to develop psychopathology. There are parents who want their children removed from the home, but cannot permit themselves to overtly abandon the youngster. They thereby create situations so intolerable to the youngster that he or she runs away. These children are prime candidates for becoming prostitutes (either male or female) and every large city has its collection of them. As well-meaning workers with such children know, when the families are called and told that their youngster has been found, not uncommon responses include: "Who asked you to butt in?" "If you like her so much, why don't you take her?" and "I don't know what you want. You must have the wrong number. We never heard of her." These, of course, are the most extreme examples of parental deprivation.

Separating and divorced parents are also likely to create a situation in which the youngster suffers with feelings of deprivation of affection. This is not simply related to the absence of one of the parents (usually the father) from the home. Prior to the separation the child may have been exposed to and embroiled in the parental hostilities. Most often the child is used as a weapon or a tool in the parental warfare, and this is especially likely to be the case around the time of the divorce. Often, the parents are so swept up in their hostilities that they pay little attention to their children. Elsewhere (1976, 1977, 1979a) I have described in detail the variety of psychiatric disturbances likely to arise in the divorce situation. And, if the parents are sick and/or foolish enough to involve themselves in protracted litigation (especially custody litigation) then more severe forms of psychopathology are likely to develop. Elsewhere (1986b, 1987c) I have described these disorders in detail.

IDENTIFICATION WITH PATHOLOGICAL PARENTAL TRAITS

Although I believe there to be certain genetically determined components to personality structure, and even the propensity for the development of certain forms of psychopathology, there is no question that identification with pathological parental traits plays an important role in the development of childrens' and adolescents' psychiatric disturbances. The modelling process is far more extensive than most parents (and many therapists) appreciate. Linguistic development is an excellent example of this phenomenon. Most three-year-olds are reasonably fluent in the language of their parents and will utilize with uncanny accuracy the parental intonations, pronunciations, and associated linguistic gestures. When one considers how formidable a task it may be for an adult to learn a new language, one can appreciate how much time and energy children put into this process. Yet, it is done in what is seemingly an effortless way. I believe that the impulse to mimic a caretaking figure is genetically determined, and that over the course of human evolution those individuals who were weak in this area were less likely to survive—because they did not acquire those parental traits necessary for optimum functioning.

The first-born child emulates and identifies with the parents. The second born has three models for identification: the two parents and the older sibling. I often have said that the three-year-old is the parrot of the five-year-old, especially if the two children are of the same sex. Five-year-old Billy says he wants a cracker. His three-year-old brother, Jimmy, will in all likelihood reflexly decide that he too wants a cracker. Parents may jestingly say, "I wonder where Jimmy got the idea?" The traditional game of "house" is a good example of the process by which children entrench their identification models into their psychic structure via the process of reiteration. Children most often start such a game with the assignment of roles and there may be some arguments as to who should be the father, the mother, the baby, etc. (And it may take a long time to settle the arguments over which role each child shall assume.) Once the game gets rolling, one sees an exact repetition of what goes on in the household. Typical household scenes are reenacted: serving breakfast, sending the children off to school, eating lunch, meeting the children upon their return from school, giving them milk and cookies, instructing them in their afternoon activities, feeding them supper, involving them in after-supper play, getting them to bed, and lulling them to sleep. Disciplining the children is also a common preoccupation and the "parents" are traditionally far more punitive than the real parents. I believe that this phenomenon relates to the fact that children's superegos are generally weak and a certain amount of "overkill" is necessary if they are to develop a normal level of conscience.

The list of parental traits that children identify with is long, in fact as long as the list of parental traits that exist. Parents who are committed to the educational process, who continue to learn long after their formal education has ended, are likely to have children who will similarly become committed to school. On a number of occasions I have seen youngsters with little if any commitment to the educational process who are brought by parents who similarly lack conviction for academics. Both may have been high school drop-outs and rarely show any interest in reading, expanding their intellectual horizons, and even watching programs on television that are above the level of pap. Generally the school refers the child and the parents reluctantly come, hoping that the therapist will disagree with the school authorities and conclude that the child has no problems. On occasion I have had parents in this category who have literally fallen asleep during the consultation. The chances of a therapist helping such a child develop more academic enthusiasm is extremely small.

Another common situation in which the identification process contributes significantly to the development of adolescent psychopathology is the one in which the parents are involved in vicious divorce litigation. Such youngsters live in an atmosphere of ongoing animosity between the parents. They are likely to identify with one or both parents and then exhibit antisocial behavior themselves. The antisocial behavior is not simply related to the acting out of anger the youngster feels over the privations associated with the parents' preoccupation with their marital difficulties. It is also related to the identification process wherein the child's repertoire of behavioral patterns becomes increasingly restricted as he or she is exposed continually to the parental battles. These patients are frequently brought to therapists who are asked to help them without direct work with the parents. Therapists who take on such cases are at the same time grandiose and simple-minded. The likelihood of helping such youngsters without reducing the parental animosity is almost at the zero level.

Another common situation that contributes to the development of psychopathology in children is the child's emulation of and identification with parents who themselves exhibit psychopathic tendencies. As mentioned, I believe that we have experienced over the last 15 or 20 years a definite increase in psychopathic traits in our society. The increasing crime rate is the most blatant confirmation of this phenomenon. But there are many other examples: hijacking of airplanes; terrorist attacks against innocent women and children; killing policemen (armed and unarmed); defaulting of debts to the government by students; scientists who falsify their data; and crimes committed by policemen, lawyers, and judges. There has been a deterioration of values that extends to almost every area of functioning. Doctors can no longer trust their patients to pay a bill at the end of the month; most require payment at the time services are rendered if they are to survive in practice. Most homes are not considered to be complete without burglar alarm systems. Clergymen are no longer considered unlikely candidates to commit child sex abuse. The standards for getting a job as a teacher become progressively lower, to the point where many teachers write report cards with gross errors in grammar, spelling, and punctuation. It is no surprise that SAT scores are getting lower.

Another identification phenomenon contributing to the development of psychopathology in children and adolescents is that of "identification with the aggressor." The youngster who observes a parent treating others in a cruel fashion may fear that he or she will similarly become a target of the parental hostility. One way of protecting oneself from this eventuality is to join the hostile parent as an ally. This decision follows the principle: "If you can't fight 'em, join 'em." An extreme example of this phenomenon occurred in concentration camps where Jews became Nazi sympathizers and even attempted to join the ranks of their persecuters. The records from the period of the Spanish Inquisition reveal the execution of thousands of monks and nuns, many of whom were Jews who had taken on such guise in order to protect themselves from being killed.

PARENTAL SANCTION OF
PATHOLOGICAL BEHAVIOR

The acquisition by a youngster of parental pathological patterns via the aforementioned process of identification is a relatively passive process with regard to the parent. The parent just serves as a model for the child's pathological patterns. In this section I discuss a more active type of transmission of parental pathological patterns. Here the parent consciously or unconsciously attempts to bring about the pathological manifestations in the child and receives definite gratifications from the child's behavior. Certainly these two processes can coexist; in fact, one generally finds a combination with one or the other form predominating.

Antisocial Behavior

It is in the realm of antisocial behavior that parental sanction is quite common. Although juvenile delinquency is seen in all economic strata, it is generally more prevalent in the socioeconomically deprived. Many factors contribute to this, but an important one relates to the resentment of the "have nots" toward the "haves." Adults who are chronically enraged over the disparity between their own situation and that of those who are more fortunate and/or enterprising are generally judicious enough to appreciate that direct expression of their resentment may result in serious repercussions — such as going to jail. Youngsters, however, because of their cognitive immaturity, are less likely to appreciate the long-range consequences of their acts. Furthermore, adolescents' delusions of invulnerability make them excellent candidates for acting out parental anger.

A storekeeper complains to a father that his son stole some goods. The father responds, "My Bill would never do such a thing." The parent may suspect that the storekeeper's complaint is justifiable, but may rationalize his failure to discipline or punish with the belief that only a disloyal and defective parent takes a stranger's side against one's own child. Another parent in the same situation responds, "Don't bother me. All kids do that. It's normal. I used to do the same thing when I was a kid. Get out of here. Don't bother me!" Another parent responds, "Jimmy, tell the man you're sorry." Jimmy then perfunctorily says that he's sorry. The stranger, quite frustrated, responds, "But aren't you going to do anything?" To which the father replies, "He told you he's sorry. What more do you want? Now get out of here and don't bother me!" In this situation Jimmy knows well that there will be no repercussions for his antisocial behavior, and he can rely on his father to protect him from those who might want to punish him or make him suffer other consequences for his delinquency.

I once saw a 12-year-old boy who was brought by his parents because of fire setting. When I asked the parents how they were dealing with the problem the mother replied, "Well, Doctor, what I do is this. When he comes home from school I tell him he can go into the backyard and set fires in a garbage can. I tell him he can do that as much as he wants as long as the fires are confined to the garbage can. In this way I want him to get it out of his system."

In response I said to the mother, "You told me that you also have a 14-year-old daughter. I would expect that, if you're like most mothers, you're becoming somewhat concerned about how she'll handle her sexual urges which, at this point, are probably getting stronger. If you're like most mothers you're probably wondering about whether she might become promiscuous, get pregnant, or acquire some sexually transmitted disease. Am I correct?" The mother responded affirmatively. I then continued, "Now suppose I suggested that you put up notices in local supermarkets, your church, and other prominent places in your community announcing that during a certain week all young boys in your neighborhood should come to your house and will have the opportunity to have sexual intercourse with your daughter. The purpose here would be for her to get the sexual urges 'out of her system.' What would you think of that suggestion?"

The mother replied, "Why that's insane. I would never do such a crazy thing."

To which I responded, "Well, I don't see much difference between the way you're handling the fire-setting problem and the plan I proposed for your dealing with your daughter's sexual urges. Both plans are based on the assumption that there exists a finite amount of urge that needs to be expressed, and once this amount is 'out of the system' nothing is left and the problem is then resolved." The mother was not too happy with my analogy, but did discontinue the practice of allowing the boy to build fires in the garbage cans.

There are parents who provide their children with money in order that they may buy drugs. When asked why they do this, some common replies are: "If I don't give him the money, Doctor, he'll go out and steal it and then he may have to go to jail." or "I've got to give her the money, Doctor. If I don't, she'll probably have to go into the streets and become a prostitute. How else can a girl of 15 earn $100 a day?" I have seen a number of parents who routinely cover their adolescents' forged checks. They usually justify this practice with the rationalization that they are protecting the youngster from the police and the courts. They seem not to appreciate that they are perpetuating the pathological behavior that they ostensibly want to discourage.

A common maneuver utilized by middle- and upper-class parents is to find a lawyer who will "get the kid off." They look for the shrewdest and most cunning attorney they can find, one who is well known for his or her ability to manipulate the judicial process in order to protect the client from suffering consequences for illegal behavior. Such parents may try to use political influence, contact people who can influence the judges, "pull strings," and otherwise manipulate the judicial process in order to protect their youngsters from suffering any consequences for their antisocial behavior. A far better position for such parents to take is that of asking the judge to implement the usual punishment for youngsters of that age, who have committed that specific crime, that particular number of times. They should neither ask for leniency nor request Draconian punishment, only the usual and reasonable punishment for that crime. This is the best way to help such youngsters "remember" not to repeat their offenses.

I present here an example that demonstrates well the phenomenon of parental sanction of pathological behavior. Henry, a 14-year-old boy, was referred for treatment because of delinquent behavior. His defiance of authority was ubiquitous. He was not only continually thwarting his parents but his teachers and school authorities as well. He refused to do homework, was often truant, and was failing most of his courses. He joined with friends in petty thievery and occasional mugging. He was also starting to experiment with drugs and alcohol. His father was an extremely rigid and punitive person who made Henry feel quite impotent. From ages ten to twelve he had worked with another therapist without too much success. Unfortunately, this therapist had died a year previously.

When he entered his first session he smugly looked around and said, "You shrinks are all the same...same stupid couch...same stupid diplomas on the walls...same damn pictures of your family on the desk." I understood Henry to be trying to lessen his anxiety in this new situation. By finding similarities between my office and that of his previous therapist he was reducing his feelings of strangeness. In addition, he was trying to identify me with his former therapist in order that I could better serve as his replacement. The hostile veneer was also anxiety alleviating; acting like a tough guy is a typical teenage defense against fear. Although anger displaced from his father onto me was also contributing to Henry's hostility, I considered the anxiety-alleviating factor to be the most important at that time. To have delved into the hostility at that point would have missed the aforementioned important issues and would have robbed the patient of his defenses at a time when he was very much in need of them. Appreciating his need for reassurance that his therapist and I did indeed have many similarities, I replied, "Yes, we psychiatrists often have much in common." This comment made Henry less tense and less hostile.

In spite of a promising beginning, I cannot say that Henry and

I had a very good relationship during the subsequent months. This was primarily due to my failure to identify with him when he engaged in antisocial behavior—especially when it took on dangerous proportions. I was, however, making some headway when the father angrily stated in a joint session that he was fed up with Henry's long hair and that he wanted him to cut it shorter. (This occurred in the mid-1960s when the long hair vogue its antisocial value had reached a peak.) I tried to dissuade the father from putting pressure on Henry and explained to him that it was one of the most innocuous forms of rebellion ever invented and he should be happy that Henry was resorting more to it and less to the more destructive and violent forms. The father was deaf to my advice. Following the session he took Henry to a barber shop. There he and a barber held Henry down while another barber gave him a very short haircut. Following this, Henry completely refused to attend school. (During the course of the therapy he had gotten to the point of attending most of the time.) There was also an intensification of his antisocial behavior, to the point where I was convinced that he would soon be in trouble with the police. In subsequent sessions it became apparent that Henry considered himself to have been castrated by his father. His rage was enormous.

About two weeks after this incident in the barber shop Henry came to my office with a teenage friend and asked if the latter could wait for him in the waiting room. The meeting was not particularly eventful. During my session with the patient who followed, she thought she smelled smoke. I didn't smell anything and neither of us thought it was necessary to investigate. At the end of the session, when we walked out of my consultation room, I was horrified to see that attempts had been made to set my waiting room on fire. Fortunately, the curtains were made of fire-resistant material and so did not ignite completely. The bathroom toilet tissue and paper hand towels had all burned, but the flames did not spread to the walls. Had the waiting room caught fire, my only exit would have been out the 13th story window.

I summoned Henry and his family back for a session at the end of my day. When I asked Henry about the incident, he admitted that he and his friend were responsible. When I asked him if he appreciated that I might have been killed, he smugly replied, "Doc, you gotta die sometime." I concluded that this was not a time for analytic inquiry. Since I was discharging Henry from treatment, such inquiry would have served little, if any, purpose. Besides, I was not particularly interested in spending time helping Henry to gain insight into such things as his act being a reflection of rage felt toward his father displaced onto me. At this point, "I didn't care two shits about the transference." I was just interested in getting rid of him as quickly and efficiently as possible. I called his parents in, told them about the fire incident, explained that I could not effectively treat anyone who had tried to kill me, and I was therefore discharging him from treatment. Without any particular sense of concern for what almost happened to me, they requested that I refer them to someone else. This I refused, explaining that I had too much concern for my respected colleagues to refer someone such as Henry to them. Although I recognized that this rejection might help Henry appreciate that there could be untoward repercussions to his dangerous behavior, this was not my motivation in discharging him. Nor was it my intent to provide him with any kind of therapeutic "corrective emotional experience"; rather, I just wanted to get rid of him.

Before they left I suggested the parents give me the name of Henry's friend, so I could call his parents and inform them about what their son had done. I called the boy's father, a lawyer, and told him that his son and my patient had tried to set fire to my office and, if they had been successful, my only exit would have been out the 13th story window. His immediate response was, "Can you prove it?" I replied, "You and your son deserve one another," and I hung up. A more blatant example of a parent's sanctioning a son's antisocial behavior (so often the case) would be hard to find.

Pathological Sexual Behavior

Two mechanisms are most often operative, either alone or in combination, in parents' sanctioning abnormal sexual behavior in adolescents. The first is vicarious gratification. Via this mechanism the adolescent is utilized to gratify unfulfilled parental sexual yearnings. The parent, by virtue of age and possibly marital restrictions, is generally not as free to engage in as wide a variety of sexual activities as the adolescent. The adolescent, therefore, lends him- or herself well to satisfying vicariously parental sexual cravings. It is as if each time the youngster engages in a sexual activity the parent enjoys similar satisfaction. However, in order to enjoy such gratification the parent must have information, details, and even on occasion observation of the sexual activity. Vicarious gratification may be conscious and/or unconscious.

The other mechanism is reaction formation. Here the parent is not consciously aware of the underlying desires that the adolescent involve him- or herself in the sexual activity. Rather, it is expressed as its opposite, that is, the prohibition and denial of the adolescent's sexual activities. There is an obsessive preoccupation with the adolescent's sexual life in the form of obsessive denunciation and excessive restriction. Such a parent, however, does not realize that each time the condemnation is verbalized a mental image of the adolescent engaging in the sexual activity appears in the parent's mind. Accordingly, the wish is gratified via the visual imagery that the preoccupation provides, and the guilt is alleviated via the denunciation process. It is as if the parent is saying: "It is not that I want my adolescent to have sex. No, it's just the opposite: I *don't* want my adolescent to have sex. In fact, I hate the thought and will do everything possible to prevent such a terrible thing from happening."

For example, a mother gives her daughter long lectures about the evils of sex and warns her before each date about the terrible things that can happen if a girl engages in such activities. Following each date she cross-examines the youngster—especially with regard to every single detail of any possible sexual encounters. When the youngster denies such involvement, the mother is incredulous and accuses her of lying. When, inevitably, she describes some activities the mother's facial expression changes completely. Although her words are words of condemnation, her facial expression is one of agitated excitation. She craves more and more facts and unconsciously relishes every detail. This situation is reminiscent of the name of a song that was popular when I was a teenager: "Your lips tell me no-no, but there's yes-yes in your eyes." At some level the youngster recognizes what is going on and complies with the mother's wishes, gratifying vicariously thereby the mother's desires and protecting the mother from guilt via the utilization by the mother of the mechanism of reaction formation.

While I was in residency training, during the late 1950s, I saw a 14-year-old girl, Joan, whose mother demonstrated the aforementioned phenomenon quite well. I saw the girl in the psychiatric clinic where she was referred because she had been "gang raped" by approximately 14 or 15 boys. The girl and her mother were not exactly sure how many boys it was, but it was in that range. This took place in the girl's bedroom while her parents were away one evening. On gaining further details it was clear that there was absolutely no forced entry, either into the girl's home or into her vagina. In fact, the girl had invited a few boys to come over and "have some fun" and they were even asked to bring along some friends.

When getting background history I learned from the mother that she always considered it important to impress upon her daughter the dangers of sex. Accordingly, from the time Joan was five or six she began to lecture her on how sinful sex was and the terrible things that could happen as a result of it—including pregnancy and sexually transmitted diseases. (In those days they were called venereal diseases.) However, the mother also related how she appreciated that teenage girls need "privacy." Accordingly, starting at about the age of 12, when a boy would come to the home to visit Joan, the mother would allow Joan and her friend to go into the bedroom and even close the door. But she insisted that the door not be locked. Periodically, without advance warning, the mother would charge into the room. Not surprisingly, she would often find the youngsters at various levels of disrobing, would then chide them for what they were doing, and insist they put their clothing back on and stop fooling around. She would then close the door because she knew she could then "trust" her daughter not to do it again. Of course, this trust did not extend more than 15 minutes, at which time the same scenario was repeated.

Obviously, with this programming, it was no surprise that this girl was "gang raped." This vignette is an excellent demonstration of the mother's utilization of this girl for vicarious gratification of her own frustrated sexual needs. The mother set up a situation that would insure that she would gain the gratifications she desired, namely, observing her daughter enagaged in various sexual acts. In addition, the mechanism of reaction formation was utilized in that by lecturing her daughter on the evils of sex, and reprimanding her when so engaged, she could assuage the guilt she felt over what she was doing.

The next example of this phenomenon that I present is an unusual one (as the reader will soon come to see), in that it involves a personal and professional experience of mine – combined into one person. The story begins in high school when I dated briefly a girl who attended the same school. I was 17 and Virginia (a not inappropriate pseudonym as the reader shall soon appreciate) was 16. During our first date she informed me – in very emphatic terms – that she had every intention of being a virgin when she got married. It is important to appreciate that this took place in the late 1940s when such was the official position of most girls whom I dated. Such professions, therefore, would not expose the individual to the kind of ridicule that they might in many circles these days. As the evening progressed I was surprised by how readily she brought up the subject of her virginity and how frequently she mentioned it. At the end of the second date her mother called me into the bedroom for a private conference. There she told me that I seemed to be a nice young man; however, I should know that her daughter had every intention of being a virgin when she got married, and Virginia had the mother's full support on this resolution. When she was sure that I had gotten that message, she dismissed me from the room.

Throughout the third and fourth dates it became apparent that Virginia was obsessed with this virtuous goal and it became clear that, unlike her girlfriends, she really meant it. Her peers, although they would occasionally profess such intentions, generally showed some flexibility with regard to this resolve and engaged in a variety of activities which led me to the conclusion (and hope) that they might not last long regarding their commitment to this principle. I, at that point, hoped (desperately) that I would *not* be a virgin when I got married – especially because I planned to go to college, then medical school, then internship, and then residency – training that might last until the time I was around 30. As I saw it, I was 17 and already considering myself somewhat retarded regarding "how far" I had gone – if I could believe my friends (who, of course, would never lie about such matters). As far as I was concerned the sooner I lost my virginity the better, and so Virginia and I parted ways. Clearly, Virginia and I had "irreconcilable differences."

We then went down our separate paths in life. Every few years, when the subject of compulsive commitment to the state of virginity would come up, I thought of Virginia and wondered whether she had gotten married and, if not, whether she was still a virgin. The answer came about 30 years after graduation from high school. I received a telephone call in my office one day from a woman who asked me if I would see her 16-year-old daughter on an emergency basis. She described the situation as being an urgent one because during the previous weekend, while she and her husband were away on vacation, her daughter had a "sex orgy" in the house with some of her friends. Worse yet, the male participants in this orgy were said to have been black and Hispanic (the family was Jewish). Last, she had good reason to believe that this all took place under the influence of drugs. I informed the mother of my usual practice of seeing the youngster and both parents in a two-hour consultation, during which time I see the three in varying combinations, as warranted. And so an appointment was made.

I can still remember my astonishment when I walked into the waiting room that day and saw not one, but two Virginias. The older Virginia was still named Virginia. (I had not linked the mother's name with my former high school date, especially because her last name was now different.) Although clearly 30 years older, I immediately recognized her as the girl I had dated in high school. Her daughter, whom I will call Sally, could have been a clone of the girl I had dated. After the initial introduction I informed the parents that it was my usual procedure to see teenagers first and then bring the parents into my office subsequently. However, I thought it important that we have a little chat before my interview with their daughter. I first asked the mother if she remembered me. She looked at me, somewhat quizzically, and replied that she did not. I asked if she had any recollection of ever having seen me at any point in her life, especially during the teen period. Again, she emphatically stated that I was totally unfamiliar to her and that she was quite sure she had never seen me. I then informed her that we had dated briefly while in high school. She was incredulous. She agreed that she had indeed attended the high school I named, but insisted she had not dated me. In order to provide her with further "evidence," I mentioned the names of a number of people whom we knew in common. She remembered some of them, but still insisted that she had no recollection of me. I decided not to pursue the matter further in the waiting room and came to the initial conclusion that she had probably blotted out of her awareness "sex maniacs" such as myself.

I then went into the consultation room with Sally. After sitting down, I had the feeling that a time machine had transformed Virginia back to the way she was 30 years previously—so uncanny was the similarity between the daughter and mother. The girl was a clone of her mother. It was as if she had inherited only the genes of her mother and none from her father. Perhaps, I thought, her mother was indeed a virgin when she got married and, not only that, was a virgin when she conceived, and I was dealing here with an immaculate conception. And, I even wondered whether Virginia might *still* be a virgin. Sally interrupted my musings and probably did so in part because of the strange expression I must have had on my face as I looked at her. "Doctor Gardner," she said, "my mother is a nut! As long as I can remember, she's given me this shit about being a virgin when I get married. As far back as I can remember she's been telling me about how proud she is of the fact she was a virgin when she got married, and that her grandmother was a virgin when *she* got married, and that she has every intention of me being a virgin when I get married. And my father's bought that crap. He's always told me about how proud he is of the fact that my mother was a virgin when they got married. I've often said to him: 'maybe no one else wanted her.'" As she spoke I kept thinking: "Incredible, I can't believe it. Maybe it's true what they say about truth being stranger than fiction."

The daughter then continued: "I assume she told you a story about a sex orgy that I supposedly had with black and Puerto Rican drug addicts. This is more of her crap. The woman's off the wall. What really happened was this: My girlfriend and I went out on a double date. Her boyfriend is black. He's a great kid. He's one of the best students in the class. In fact, I think I like him more than I like the boy I was going out with, but she doesn't know that. Anyway, after the movie we went back to the house. I know I promised my mother that I wouldn't bring anybody back, but what the hell! There was nothing illegal about what we were doing. Then the four of us shared *one joint*. That was it. One joint she turns into drug addiction! It was the second time I did it and I really didn't even enjoy it. My boyfriend and I went into the bedroom and fooled around a bit. I'm still a virgin and it's lucky that I still have sexual feelings. With a mother like her, it wouldn't be surprising if I ended up frigid or something like that. There's no way I'm going to be a virgin when I get married, but I'm not ready for it yet. It's crazy to marry someone that you haven't gone to bed with. I don't know where she's coming from. That's the whole story. I'm not lying to you."

There was nothing in the girl's story, either in the way she told it or about the facts that she had presented, that led me to believe that she was not being honest. Furthermore, I had "background information" that made her story quite credible. Inquiries into other aspects of Sally's life revealed no evidence of psychopathology. She was doing well in school, had many friends, and was not causing her parents difficulties at home in other areas. Apparently, she had grown up in a fairly healthy way in spite of her mother's obsession. I suspect that this was due to the influence of peers and society at large, a society in which more permissive attitudes toward sex served to counterbalance the puritanical indoctrination of her mother.

I then brought the parents in and the girl confronted them directly with the disparity between what she claimed happened and that which her mother fantasized. It was clear that the mother's renditions were fantasy and a reflection of her own problems in this area. In the course of the interview Virginia—not surprisingly—told me that she had always vowed that she would be a virgin when she got married (apparently thinking that this was news to me) and that she had always encouraged her daughter to follow in her footsteps in this regard. Virginia's husband then stated: "I'm in full agreement with my wife. I was very impressed on our first date with the fact that she felt so strongly about being a virgin when she got married. That was one of my main attractions to her." And then Virginia continued: "Yes, I knew that my husband really respected me. He never made advances like the other boys. He never pushed for sex like the others." All I could say to myself while listening to this was: "It takes one to marry one" and "For every man there's a woman."

Near the end of the interview I informed the parents that I did not consider their daughter to be in need of treatment. I recognized that a direct statement to the mother that it was she (and also the father) who needed therapy would not have worked at that moment. Accordingly, I recommended family counselling in the hope that the mother might ultimately become a patient herself. The mother was receptive to this idea and was quite astonished when I told her that it would not be possible for me to serve as the therapist. She was surprised by my statement and asked me why. When I told her that our past relationship precluded my having the kind of objectivity necessary for successful treatment, she replied, "What relationship?" I told her again that it was my firm belief that we did indeed have a relationship in the past, and that as long as *I* believed that (even if it were only a fantasy) my serving effectively as a therapist was not possible. Once again, she was unconvinced. I was not going to argue with her on this point. Also, I told her that even if there had been no previous relationship between us, I would have recommended another therapist anyway—because of my belief that in this situation a female therapist was warranted. I informed her that I believed she might be more receptive to comments about her daughter's sexuality if they came from a woman. She agreed that this would probably be the case, because both she and her husband were firmly convinced that all men—even psychiatrists—were obsessed with sex (with the exception of Virginia's husband, of course). Accordingly, I referred the family to a female colleague with whom they lasted about two sessions. My colleague informed me that the mother left claiming she would have no further involvement with therapy because all psychiatrists (regardless of sex) were obsessed with sex and she would have to find another way to insure that her daughter would be a virgin when she got married.

This vignette is presented as an example of a situation in which a parent's pathological attitudes about sex could contribute to psychopathology in an adolescent. Fortunately for Sally she somehow avoided developing psychopathological reactions to her mother's attempts to indoctrinate her. The most likely outcome for Sally would have been some identification with her mother's obsession, which she might have transmitted down yet another generation. However, as mentioned, I suspect that the more sexually free environment in which she grew up probably served to counterbalance her mother's influence and put her on a more reasonable course. Another possible outcome of such indoctrination could have been sexual promiscuity. Certainly the mother's preoccupation with sex provided her with fantasy gratifications; however, she utilized the mechanism of reaction formation to assuage the guilt she felt over her sexual cravings. Each time she told herself she would not have sex until she got married, she had to have some kind of sexual fantasy—which she ostensibly was not going to indulge in. The fantasy about Sally's being a virgin until she (Sally) got married must have involved fantasies about Sally's sexuality. Under these circumstances it would have been reasonable that Sally might have acted out her mother's unconscious wishes. We do not know more than a fraction of those factors that determine the way in which psychopathology will develop and the factors that prevent its occuring. My hope is that Sally has finally interrupted the traditional psychopathology of her family heritage.

Now to another example of how pathological sexual attitudes in a parent can produce pathological sexual behavior in an adolescent. Many years ago, while I was serving as a psychiatrist in the military, a colonel once came to me, quite depressed, claiming that this was the most painful and humiliating day of his life. The story, he stated, began 17 years previously when his wife gave birth to their oldest, a boy: "The obstetrician came out of the delivery room and told me that my wife had just given birth to a boy and that both she and the child were doing fine. The first thought that came to my mind was, 'The thing I fear most is that this boy will grow up to be a homosexual. I hope I never live to see that day.' And so, in order to prevent that terrible thing from happening, I bought him these porno books when he was three and four years old. I bought both homosexual and heterosexual porno books. I showed him the pictures in each and explained to him how the things that the men were doing to each other were *bad*, and how the things the men and women were doing together were *good*. When he was 13 years old, and started to mature physically, I told him that he never had to worry about sexual frustration, because I was going to take him to a 'nice lady' who was going to teach him about sex. So I took him to a house of prostitution where he had his first experience with a woman. I told him that anytime he wanted money to go back I would give it to him. And last night, Doctor, the thing I was most terrified of, occurred. The military police came and informed me that they had found him in bed with a sergeant engaged in homosexual activities."

This boy was almost destined to become homosexual, so great were his father's unconscious pressures on him to go in this direction. The boy's compliance was in part related to his recognition, at some level, that a homosexual was exactly what his father wanted him to be. With such programming, with such inculcation of homosexual imagery, with so many warnings to stay away, the child could not but be tempted. This father, although he had never engaged in a homosexual act himself (in fact, he exhibited disgust and anger toward anyone who had), was a man who basically had strong homosexual inclinations that he could not admit to himself. His preoccupation with the fantasy that his son might become a homosexual was basically the wish that he do so—disguised as a fear. The image that appears in a person's mind is the most important manifestation of his or her genuine wish. The words that one conjures up in association with the image can serve to deny the wish's true intent. The thought "I hope he doesn't grow up to become a homosexual" reflected the father's basic wish that the boy do so—to satisfy vicariously, through his son, his own unconscious wish to become one. Putting the desire in the negative, or in the form of a fear, served to lessen guilt over unconscious awareness of the basic wish. The boy was driven to comply with his father's wish, and allowing disclosure was most probably his way of communicating his compliance. I obtained some verification of this subsequently when I learned that the father wanted exact details of the nature of the boy's homosexual involvement. It was clear that he was then gaining vicarious gratification from these explanations.

The Divorce Situation

Parents who are actively embroiled in divorce conflicts may consciously and unconsciously sanction pathological behavior in their children. One of the more common types of pathological behavior engendered in children by divorce is the utilization of the youngster as an ally and as a weapon in the divorce war. Both parents try to enlist the aid of all the "troops" they can recruit, and children may serve as the central warriors. Elsewhere (1976) I have described in detail this phenomenon as well as a wide variety of other pathological reactions that children may develop in the divorce situation. Here, I focus on a syndrome that may develop in the course of custody litigation. Again, there are a large variety of disorders that may develop in children in the course of such litigation and I have described these in detail elsewhere (1986b). The syndrome I describe here is selected as a good example of overt and covert parental sanction of a child's symptomatology. Although the focus here is on the child, in whom the disorder exhibits itself in the most blatant fashion, much of what I describe here is also applicable to the adolescent.

Clinical Manifestations of the Parental Alienation Syndrome

Although this syndrome certainly existed in the past, it is occurring with such increasing frequency at this point that it deserves a special name. The term I prefer to use is *parental alienation syndrome*. I have introduced this term to refer to a disturbance in which children are obsessed with deprecation and criticism of a parent—denigration that is unjustified and/or exaggerated. With rare exception, the disorder arises in the context of a custody dispute, especially when the custody conflict is being litigated. The notion that such children are merely "brainwashed" is narrow. The term brainwashing implies that one parent is systematically and consciously programming the child to denigrate the other parent. The concept of the parental alienation syndrome includes the brainwashing component but is much broader. It encompasses not only conscious but subconscious and unconscious factors within the parent that contribute to the child's alienation. Furthermore (and this is extremely important), it includes factors that arise within the child—independent of the parental contributions—that contribute to the development of the syndrome.

Typically the child is obsessed with "hatred" of a parent. The word *hatred* is placed in quotes because there are still many tender and loving feelings felt toward the allegedly despised parent which are not permitted expression. These children speak of the hated parent with every vilification and profanity in their vocabulary, without embarrassment or guilt. The vilification of the parent often has the quality of a litany. After only minimal prompting by a lawyer, judge, probation officer, mental health professional, or other person involved in the litigation, the record will be turned on and the command performance provided. Not only is there the rehearsed quality to the speech but one often hears phraseology that is identical to that used by the "loved" parent. Again, the word *loved* is placed in quotations because hostility toward and fear of that parent may similarly be unexpressed.

Even years after they have taken place, the child may justify the alienation with memories of minor altercations experienced in the relationship with the hated parent. These are usually trivial and are exeriences that most children quickly forget, e.g., "He always used to speak very loud when he told me to brush my teeth," "She used to say to me 'Don't interrupt'," and "He used to make a lot of noise when he chewed at the table." When these children are asked to give more compelling reasons for the hatred, they are unable to provide them. Frequently, the loved parent will agree with the child that these professed reasons justify the ongoing animosity.

The professions of hatred are most intense when the children and the loved parent together are in the presence of the alienated one. However, when the child is alone with the allegedly hated parent, he or she may exhibit anything from hatred to neutrality to expressions of affection. Often, when these children are with the hated parent, they will let their guard down and start to enjoy themselves. Then, almost as if they have realized that they are doing something "wrong," they will suddenly stiffen up and resume their expressions of withdrawal and animosity. Another maneuver commonly utilized by these children is to profess affection to one parent and to ask that parent to swear that he or she will not reveal the professions of love to the other parent. And the same statement is made to the other parent. In this way these children "cover their tracks" and avoid thereby the disclosure of their schemes. Such children may find family interviews with therapists extremely anxiety provoking, because of the fear that their manipulations and maneuvers will be divulged.

The hatred of the parent often extends to include that parent's complete extended family. Cousins, aunts, uncles, and grandparents, with whom the child previously may have had loving relationships, are now viewed as similarly obnoxious. Greeting cards are not reciprocated. Presents sent to the child's home are refused, remain unopened, or even destroyed (generally in the presence of the loved parent). When the hated parent's relatives call on the telephone, the child will respond with angry vilifications or quickly hang up on the caller. (These responses are more likely to occur if the loved parent is within hearing distance of the conversation.)

With regard to the hatred of the relatives, the child is even less capable of providing justifications for the animosity. The rage of these children is so great that they become completely oblivious to the privations they are causing themselves. Again, the loved parent is typically unconcerned with the untoward psychological effects on the child of the rejection of these relatives.

Another symptom of the parental alienation syndrome is complete lack of ambivalence. All human relationships are ambivalent, and parent-child relationships are no exception. The hated parent is viewed as "all bad" and the loved parent is "all good." The hated parent may have been greatly dedicated to the child's upbringing, and a deep bond may have been created over many years. The hated parent may produce photos that demonstrate clearly a joyful and deep relationship in which there was significant affection, tenderness, and mutual pleasure. But all these experiences appear to have been obliterated from the child's memory. When these children are shown photos of enjoyable events with the hated parent, they usually rationalize the experiences as having been forgotten, nonexistent, or feigned: "I really hated being with him then. I just smiled in the picture because he made me. He said he'd hit me if I didn't smile." This element of complete lack of ambivalence is a typical manifestation of the parental alienation syndrome and should make one dubious about the depth of the professed animosity.

The child may exhibit a guiltless disregard for the feelings of the hated parent. There will be a complete absence of gratitude for gifts, support payments, and other manifestations of the hated parent's continued involvement and affection. Often these children will want to be certain that the alienated parent continues to provide support payments, but at the same time adamantly refuse to visit. Commonly they will say that they *never* want to see the hated parent again, or not until their late teens or early twenties. To such a child I might say: "So you want your father to continue paying for all your food, clothing, rent, and education—even private high school and college—and yet you still don't want to see him at all, ever again. Is that right?" Such a child might respond: "That's right. He doesn't deserve to see me. He's mean and paying all that money is a good punishment for him." And the child's mother may smugly agree that the child's position is completely justifiable.

Those who have never seen such children may consider this description a caricature. Those who have seen them will recognize the description immediately, although some children may not manifest all the symptoms. The parental alienation syndrome is becoming increasingly common and there is good reason to predict that it will become even more common in the immediate future if custody conflicts become even more prevalent. It is seen in younger children and adolescents. Younger children, however, are likely to develop more primitive and naive complaints than adolescents, but in both cases fabrications and exaggerations are characteristic. At this point I will discuss the pathogenesis of this disorder, with particular emphasis on three contributing factors: parental "brainwashing," the child's own contributions, and situational factors.

"Brainwashing" By brainwashing I refer to an active and conscious attempt on a parent's part to deliberately bring about the alienation of the child from the other parent. Often the brainwashing is overt and obvious. The loved parent embarks upon an unrelenting campaign of denigration that may last for years. A mother, for example, whose divorce was the result of marital problems that contributed to her husband's seeking the affection of another woman, may continually vilify the father to her children with such terms as "adulterer," "philanderer," and "abandoner." Similarly, she may refer to the father's new woman friend as a "slut," "whore," and "home-breaker." No attention is given to the problems in the marriage, especially such a mother's problem(s) that may have contributed to the husband's new involvement.

At times the criticisms may even be delusional, but the child is brought to believe entirely the validity of the accusations. The child may thereby come to view the noncustodial parent as the incarnation of all the evil that has ever existed on earth. Often the infrequency of visits or lack of contact with the hated parent facilitates the child's accepting completely the loved parent's criticisms. There is little or no opportunity to correct the distortions by actual experiences.

A mother may complain so bitterly about her financial restrictions that she will lead the children to believe that they may actually go without food, clothing, and shelter, and that they may very well freeze and/or starve to death. I have seen extremely wealthy and extravagant women utilize this maneuver—to the extent that their children have come to believe that because of their father's stinginess they are ever on the verge of starvation. There are mothers who, when talking to the children about their husbands' having left the home, will make such statements as, "Your father's abandoned us." In most cases the father has left the mother and has not lost any affection for the children. Clumping the children together with herself (by using the word "us" rather than "me") promulgates the notion that they too have been rejected.

There are parents who are quite creative in their brainwashing maneuvers. A father calls the home to speak to his son. The mother answers the telephone in the son's room. The father simply asks if he can speak with his son. The mother remains silent. Again, the father asks to speak with his son. Still the mother remains silent. After another minute or two of the father's pleading and the mother's stony silence, the mother (with the boy right next to her) says: "I'm glad he can't hear what you're saying right now" or "If he heard what you just said, I'm sure he would never speak with you again." When the father finally speaks with the boy, and explains that he had said absolutely nothing that was critical, the boy may be incredulous. The result is that the father becomes very fearful of calling his son, lest he again be trapped in this way. The father then is accused by the mother of showing no interest in his boy. A related maneuver is for the mother to say to the calling father after such a scenario (again when the boy is within earshot): "That's *your* opinion. In *my* opinion he's a *very fine boy.*" The implication here is that the father has made some scathing criticism, and that the mother is defending the child.

These attempts to denigrate a parent are conscious and deliberate. There are, however, other ways of programming children that can be equally, if not more, effective, but which do not involve the parent actually recognizing what is going on. In this way the parent can profess innocence of brainwashing propensities. A parent may profess being a strong subscriber to the common advice: "Never criticize the other parent to the child." A mother may use this advice with comments such as: "There are things I could say about your father that would make your hair stand on end, but I'm not the kind of a person who criticizes a parent to his children." Such a comment engenders far more fear, distrust, and even hatred than would the presentation of an actual list of the father's alleged defects. The parent who expresses neutrality regarding visitation is essentially communicating criticism of the noncustodial parent. The healthy parent appreciates how vital is the children's ongoing involvement with the noncustodial parent and does not accept inconsequential and frivolous reasons for not visiting. The "neutrality" essentially communicates to the child the message that the noncustodial parent cannot provide enough affection, attention, and other desirable input to make a missed visitation a loss of any consequence.

Related to the neutrality maneuver is the one in which the parent repeatedly insists that *the child* be the one to make the decision regarding visitation. Such a child generally knows that the parent basically does not want the visitation and so the child then professes the strong opinion that he or she does not wish to visit. Such a mother might say after a child refuses: "I respect your strength in standing up for your rights. If we have to go to court to defend you we'll do it. I'm not going to let him push *you* around. *You* have *your* right to say no, and you can count on my full support."

A common way in which a parent will contribute to the alienation is to view as "harassments" the attempts on the part of the hated parent to make contact with the children. The alienated parent expresses interest by telephone calls, attempts at visitation, the sending of presents, etc. These overtures are referred to as "harassments" and the children themselves come to view them similarly. In frustration, the parent increases efforts to contact the children, thereby increasing the likelihood that the attempts will be viewed as nuisances. A related maneuver involves a mother's saying to a calling father (with the child within earshot): "If you keep up this pressure to see him we're going to have one of those teenage suicides on our hands." If this is said enough times, the child learns about a maneuver for avoiding visitations with the father, thereby complying with mother's wishes. The next step is for the child to threaten suicide if the father attempts to visit, to which the mother can then say to the father: "He keeps saying that he'll kill himself if he has to visit you."

Factors That Originate Within the Child   Of course, a parent may use the child's contribution to promulgate the alienation and "get mileage out of" this factor, but it is a contribution that originates from psychopathological factors within the child. An important contributing element stems from the child's fear of alienating the preferred parent. The hated parent is only ostensibly hated; there is still much love. But the loved parent may be feared much more than loved. The fear may be that of losing the love of the preferred parent. In the usual situation it is the father who has left the home. He has thereby provided for himself the reputation of being the one who rejects and abandons. No matter how justified his leaving the home, the children will generally view him as the abandoner. Having already been abandoned by one parent the children are not going to risk abandonment by the second. Accordingly, they may fear expressing resentment to the remaining parent (usually the mother) and will often take her position in any conflict with the father.

I believe the courts have not been paying enough attention to the formidable influence of the early life influences on the child's subsequent psychological status. Early life influences play an important role in the formation of the child's psychological bond to the parent who was the primary caretaker during the earliest years. Courts have been giving too much weight to present-day involvement and ignoring the residual contributions of early bonding to present experiences. Mothers have been much more often the primary custodial parents during the child-rearing process. This produces a bond between the two that results in strong attachment cravings when there is a rupture of the relationship. Accordingly, when there is a threatened disruption of this relationship by a "sex-blind" judge or joint-custodial mandate, mother and child fight it vigorously. Commonly, the mother brainwashes the child and uses him or her as a weapon to sabotage the father's attempts to gain primary custody. And the children develop their own scenarios, as well, in an attempt to preserve this bond. I believe that residua of the early influences are playing an important role in the attempts on the part of both parties to maintain the attachment bond. Many of the preposterous, naive, and absurd complaints described above in the initial description of the syndrome are examples of the kinds of contributions and scenarios children create by themselves. These include such complaints as they only smiled for a happy, family photograph because their father has threatened to hit them, that they hate all members of their father's extended family, that they

really want to throw his presents in the garbage, that they never
want to see him again in their whole lives, etc.

Situational Factors   Often situational factors are conducive to
the development of the disorder. Most parents in a custody conflict
know that time is on the side of the custodial parent. They
appreciate that the longer the child remains with a particular parent,
the greater the likelihood the child will fear and resist moving to the
home of the other. One way for a child to deal with this fear is to
denigrate the noncustodial parent with criticisms that justify the
child's remaining in the custodial home. For example, a child's
parent dies and the grandparents take over the care of the child.
Although at first the surviving spouse may welcome their involvement, there are many cases in which the grandparents subsequently
litigate for custody of the child. The child may then develop
formidable resentment against the remaining parent in order to
insure that he or she will remain with the grandparents, the people
whom the child has come to view as preferable parents.

In one case I was involved with, two girls developed this
disorder after their mother, with whom they were living, met a man
who lived in Colorado. The mother then decided to move there with
the two girls. The father brought the mother to court in an attempt
to restrain her from moving out of the state with the children.
Whereas previously there had been a good relationship with their
father, the girls gradually developed increasing hatred of him as
their mother became progressively embroiled in the litigation. It was
clear that the disorder would not have arisen had the mother not
met a man who lived in Colorado, a man whom she wished to
marry.

We are now observing another phenomenon that is contributing to the development of the parental alienation syndrome: the
widespread attention being given to the sexual abuse of children by
parents. Heretofore, the consensus among those who worked with
sexually-abused children was that it was extremely rare for a child to
fabricate sexual abuse. This is no longer the case. A child's accusation of a parent's sexual abuse can now be a powerful weapon in the
alienation campaign. A vengeful parent may exaggerate a nonexistent or inconsequential sexual contact and build up a case for sexual
abuse—even to the point of reporting the alleged child abuser to

investigatory authorities and taking legal action. And the child, in order to ingratiate him- or herself with the litigious parent, may go along with the scheme.

The argument previously given to support the position that false accusations of sexual abuse by children are extremely rare was that sexual encounters with adults were basically outside the child's scheme of things. Accordingly, having no specific experience with sex abuse, the child was not likely to describe in detail sexual encounters with adults. This is no longer the situation. We are living at a time when sex abuse is discussed on television, in newspapers, magazines, and even in school prevention programs. There is hardly a child who is not bombarded with information about the details of sexual abuse. Accordingly, it is no longer true that the child does not possess the information to make a credible accusation. Children who are looking for excuses for vilification and/or ammunition for alienation now have a wealth of information for the creation of their sexual scenarios. And there are even situations in which there has been no particular sex-abuse indoctrination or prompting by a parent; the child him- or herself originates the complaint.

It is important for mental health professionals who are evaluating children who allege sex abuse to inquire as to whether the parents are involved in a custody conflict. If so, they should consider the possibility that the allegation has been fabricated. I am not claiming that bona fide sex abuse does not take place in families in which there is a custody conflict; I am only stating that the possibility of fabrication is increased in this situation. One of the ways of differentiating between the child who is fabricating and the one who has genuinely been abused is to observe closely the way in which the child makes the accusation. Children who have genuinely been abused are often fearful of revealing the facts. Often they have been warned by the abuser that there will be terrible consequences if the sexual encounters are divulged. They tend to be anxious, tense, timid, and shy. They may fear encounters with other adults who are of the same sex as the abuser, anticipating similar exploitation and threats. In contrast, the child who fabricates sex abuse presents with an entirely different picture. Most often these children are quite comfortable with their accusations and have prepared little speeches, which they freely provide to attorneys, mental health professionals, judges, and anyone else who will listen. Their litany should be a clue that they are fabricating.

Another way of finding out whether the child is telling the truth is to place the child and the accused parent in the same room. The adversary system does not allow itself this important method for obtaining information that could be useful to it in determining "the truth." When the accused and the accuser are in the same room together, with the opportunity for an "eyeball-to-eyeball confrontation," there is a much greater likelihood that the two individuals will be honest with one another. After all, they were both allegedly there. They know better than anyone else the details of the alleged encounter and each one is likely to pick up the other's fabrications in the most sensitive way. Of course, the younger the child, the less the likelihood he or she will be able to engage effectively in such confrontations, but they can still be useful. Last, mothers of fabricating children relish the accusation and deny conflicting evidence. Mothers of children who are genuinely abused commonly deny the abuse or react with horror and grief. Elsewhere (1987a and 1987c) I discuss in greater detail these differentiating criteria. Particularly useful in this regard is my *Sex Abuse Legitimacy Scale (SAL Scale)* (1987d).

Concluding Comments on the Parental Alienation Syndrome

The implementation of the presumption that children do best when placed with the parent who is most involved in child rearing, especially during the formative years, would reduce significantly the custody litigation that we are presently witnessing. It would result in many mothers' automatically being awarded custody. It would not preclude, however, fathers' obtaining custody because there would be some fathers who would easily satisfy this important criterion for primary custodial assignment. The implementation of this presumption would still allow those parents (whether male or female) who were only secondarily involved in the child's rearing to still have the opportunity to seek and gain custody. Such parents would, however, have to provide compelling evidence that the primary custodial parent's child-rearing input was significantly compromised and their own contributions so formidable that they should more justifiably be designated the primary custodial parent.

Elsewhere, (1986b, 1987a, 1987c, 1987d) I discuss these aspects of the disorder in greater detail.

PARENTAL OVERPROTECTION

Children who are overprotected by their parents are likely to become overdependent and, when older, less equipped to function independently at an age-appropriate level. I believe that if one compares adolescents today with those who grew up prior to the 20th century, we would have to say the vast majority are overprotected. Prior to the early part of this century, when the child labor laws were passed in most states, there was no age limit below which children could not be employed. Furthermore, because of the absence of welfare, labor unions, and other social benefits, if family members did not work they might not indeed survive. Although things became easier for children in the 1920s, they once again suffered privations in the 1930s – during the Great Depression. During World War II there was little time and money available for the indulgence of children. It was in the 1950s that we entered into an era of ever-increasing affluence. Many parents today, who suffered privations in their youth, have tried to compensate and give their children the things they did not enjoy in their own childhood. Sometimes they do this to the point of overindulgence. Moreover, we are living in a child-oriented society in which the importance of proper child care has been emphasized – often inordinately so.

In this section I describe youngsters who are more overprotected than the average, who will become thereby more overdependent than the average, and whose overindulgence then serves as a foundation for the development of psychopathology. Because parental overprotectiveness generally manifests itself most blatantly in the earliest years of a child's life, I will discuss in detail its manifestations and psychodynamics in childhood. However, residua of these influences certainly manifest themselves in the adolescent period and even later. In my discussion of parental overprotectiveness I will be making much more reference to mothers than fathers. I do not believe that this emphasis is a reflection of any sexism on my part; rather, it relates to the fact that at this time mothers, more often than fathers, are the primary caretakers and therefore the ones who are more likely to be overprotective of their children. I am not claiming that this is "good," only that this is the situation that prevails at this time.

Overinvestment in the Child's Life

There are mothers who are overprotective as a way of compensating for basic feelings of maternal inadequacy. By becoming "super-mothers" they can protect themselves from the basic feelings of incompetence that they unconsciously feel. Their own mothers may have been poor models for mothering, and so they have not acquired techniques that will insure their functioning adequately as mothers themselves. Many such mothers denigrate the maternal capacity of other mothers and view them as neglectful or incompetent. The healthy mother recognizes that she cannot devote herself 100 percent to her child's welfare and appreciates that there will be certain times when the care of the child must be entrusted to others. She accepts the fact that there will be times when, in spite of her vigilance, she will not be able to give uninterrupted attention to her child. Overprotective mothers may view these normal lapses and interruptions in mothering as manifestations of ineptitude.

Some mothers' lives are so limited that their total feelings of usefulness are derived from their children; they may have little if any other involvements that provide them with meaningful gratifications. Such mothers may be threatened by maturation of their children, whose ultimate independence would deprive these mothers of their primary source of satisfaction in life. Such mothers may utilize a wide variety of excuses to retard their children in their emotional growth and development. They may not permit their children to ride their bicycles away from the home, cross the street alone, or venture far from the home when others their age are doing so. Such mothers may view the neighborhood as far more dangerous than do other parents. They may not consider their children old enough for overnight visits, sleep-away camp, or staying at home alone—at ages when other children are doing these things.

The healthy mother has other sources of gratification and, therefore, need not retard her children in their development in order to maintain a sense of usefulness. Many women in ghettos, women without adequate education, and mothers without husbands, may have many more children than they can adequately provide for—both economically and psychologically. Yet they continue to bear them, in part because of their dread of the time when their youngest will be out of the house. When this time comes, they fear they will then be of no use to anyone. This is one of the reasons why such women may be particularly lax when using contraceptive measures. But the syndrome is by no means confined to the socio-economically deprived. There are women from every stratum of life who find themselves significantly depressed when their youngest children go out on their own. Some of these women have had deficient relationships with their husbands and have used their children to make their lives more rewarding. The "involutional depression" (a deep depression generally occurring in the forties or fifties) has many contributing factors. One is the feeling of uselessness that is experienced by people who have been so extensively devoted to their children that they have no other satisfactions to turn to when their youngsters grow up and become independent of them. Treatment of such women is predictably futile if it does not help these patients provide themselves with new and meaningful sources of gratification.

Parents' anxiety over their grown children's impending separation may be clearly seen in many parental maneuvers. Such parents may find fault with every prospective marital partner. They may engender guilt in a youngster who is preparing to leave the home: "How can you leave your poor old mother? After all the sacrifices I've made for you, how can you do this to me?" Or, they may inculcate the notion that the ideal child is the one who is continually concerned with his or her parents' welfare and that marrying is an abnegation of this responsibility.

The husbands of these overinvested mothers are often passive. They generally view the mother as a "super-mother" and are unaware of the depth and psychopathological nature of the relationship between the mother and the overprotected child. They generally support the mother's rationalization that other mothers are neglectful. They usually subscribe to the traditional view that the mother should be in complete control of child rearing and that fathers are the breadwinners. There is usually little conflict between the parents with regard to child rearing because the father typically submits to the mother's "authority" in this area. He may rationalize such submission by subscribing to the "united front" theory, which states that it is very bad for a child to observe parents disagreeing. By complying with this dictum, he justifies submitting to the mother's will and passively accepts the mother's opinions regarding what is best for the child. Sexual inhibition problems in the parents may contribute. These "super-mothers" may be so invested in their children that they have little investment in other activities, such as sex. And their passive-dependent husbands may relate to their wives in a mother-son pattern in which sex has little place. The mothers may be threatened by a sexual relationship with an adult male, but may be more comfortable with the milder sexuality of the mother-son relationship. In such situations the male child is used by the mother as a sexual-sensual surrogate. The processes by which this arrangement takes place are usually unconscious.

Fear of the Child's Anger

There are people who subscribe to the dictum: "If someone is angry at me, I must be terrible. I must, therefore, do everything possible to avoid annoying anyone." Such people do not seem to be aware that, no matter how hard we try, there will still be those who will dislike us. In their attempt to be loved by everyone, such people are ever vigilant to avoid saying or doing anything that might alienate. These people live by the dictum: "If the situation is such that someone has to end up angry, I'd rather it be the one than the other person." They go through life passive, friendly, and compliant—but inwardly hating themselves. They are not concerned with the appropriateness of the other person's anger or with the distortions that may have occasioned it; only that angry interchanges are to be avoided if one is to protect oneself from the anger of others and preserve one's self-respect.

Some people in this category are even threatened by the anger of their children and do not seem to appreciate that much of a child's anger is inappropriate and irrational. They are so conditioned to preventing or avoiding anger that they automatically react to their

children's anger by doing everything possible to prevent or interrupt it. Also, they may consider the child's anger to be a reflection
of some parental impairment on their part—subscribing to the
dictum that the good parent never frustrates the child and has a
child who is always "happy." The children of such parents become
spoiled and overindulged, because they quickly learn the manipulative value of their temper outbursts. With a screaming tantrum the
child can get just about anything he or she wants. Such children,
clearly, grow up ill-equipped to function in the adult world—unless
they find someone who will similarly indulge them, and some do.

Some parents with anger inhibition problems harbor residua of
their childhood belief that anger can destroy. Their overprotection
serves to eliminate all overt expression of the child's anger. They
may view the child's expression of anger to be a dangerous
phenomenon and may not be able to conceive of love and anger as
coexisting. They may be significantly impaired in providing proper
disciplinary and punitive measures because of their fear of the
child's angry response. The child incorporates these parental attitudes—a process that contributes to the child's suppression and
repression of hostility. When the parents do everything possible to
prevent and/or interrupt the child's anger, the youngster gets the
message that angry expression is dangerous and such feelings
should be suppressed or repressed, if at all possible. The foundation
is thereby laid for the development in the child of anger inhibition
problems and the host of symptoms that can derive therefrom, e.g.,
phobias, obsessions, compulsions, regression, and even paranoid
projection of anger.

Use of the Child for Vicarious Gratification of the Parent's Frustrated Dependency Cravings

Many overprotective mothers are basically dependent adults.
Many are still quite dependent on their own parents and inwardly
crave to revert to the infantile role and gratify thereby their
dependency cravings. Because this would be socially stigmatizing,
these desires cannot generally be realized overtly. However, they
can be gratified vicariously, i.e., by such mothers' psychologically
projecting themselves into the position of others who are enjoying

such dependency satisfactions. In many cases a mother may gratify these dependency cravings by projecting herself psychologically into the position of her child. Each time she ministers to the child, she is vicariously gratifying her own dependency needs. She is psychologically giving to her projected self. Each time she indulges and infantilizes the child, she vicariously gratifies her own desire to be the recipient of such indulgence. This is a common mechanism. It is at the root of compulsive benevolence. Many saint-like individuals are not as altruistic as they may appear. Although society may certainly derive great benefits from their benevolence, less than holy contributing factors are often present. Vicarious gratification of dependency is one of them.

Coolidge et al. (1962) described a related phenomenon in these mothers. Specifically, they fear that they will never be able to give enough to their children and are excessively guilty over minor child-rearing lapses. The authors believe that the mother's view that she can never give enough to her children relates to her identification with the child and her own dependency needs. Psychologically, she has projected herself out onto the child and her belief that the child never has enough is based on her basic belief that she herself can never have enough. In short, she projects onto the child her own insatiable dependency cravings.

Exaggerated Reactions to the Child's Physical Illnesses

One way in which a parent can compensate for feelings of inadequacy about parenting capacity is to be excessively cautious about exposing the child to potential infection and other situations that might bring about physical illness. Such parents can then look upon other parents as being neglectful and thereby feel superior. A common example of this phenomenon is the parent who views the child to be particularly vulnerable to infectious diseases such as colds. There are two common myths that contribute to the concerns of parents and entrench this manifestation of overprotection. The first is that one can catch a cold by exposing oneself to cold air without the protection of warm clothing. There are, unfortunately, even physicians who subscribe to this theory. It is indeed unfortunate that the name of the disease "the common cold" (or simply "cold") is the same as the word to describe a state of relatively low temperature. The first use refers to a disease caused by a virus and is characterized by nasal congestion and sneezing. It is rarely accompanied by fever (although at times one may feel a little "chilly"). The second use of the word refers to the temperature of an object or place. Most important, it has never been demonstrated (to the best of my knowledge) that there is a cause and effect relationship between the two. In other words, one does not "catch a cold" from cold air. One gets a cold by being infected with a particular virus. This can only occur if one ingests, inhales, or otherwise introduces into the body the particular virus (or, more accurately, one of the class of viruses) known to cause the disorder at a time when the body defenses cannot successfully fight it. (I will elaborate on this point in greater detail in my discussion of myth number two.) These viruses do not have wings, and they do not fly around like bats in the night air. They are much more comfortable in the nasal passages of our friends and relatives, and one is much more likely to come in contact with them by someone's sneezing in one's face. Exposure to the cold (whether indoors or outdoors) does not give us a cold—at worst it only may make us a little more uncomfortable and chilly if we already have a cold in the first place. Exposure to cold has no effect on the duration of the illness. There is an old medical adage that states this quite well: "A cold, if untreated, lasts a week; if treated, it will last seven days."

What I have just said is well appreciated by most physicians and is standard medical knowledge. Yet it is very hard to convince even well-educated and otherwise intelligent parents of this simple truth. Extensive studies by the U.S. Army have demonstrated that the incidence of colds is no greater among men out on winter maneuvers (with all its cold, mud, rain, sleet, etc.) than among those who remain in the warm barracks. Quoting these studies to overprotective parents has generally been a waste of words, so deeply ingrained is this myth. Parents who can rise above their misconception on this matter, and allow their children more freedom and flexibility of exposure, will have children who are not only psychologically healthier than they were before but, for reasons that I will now present, physically healthier as well.

The second myth is that the most important factor in determining whether an individual will contract a disease is exposure to it. If this were the case, our hospital beds would be filled with doctors, and there would be no room for anyone else. Practically everyone has wondered, at some time or other, why it is that doctors don't get sick very often, that they seem to be less susceptible than others to catching diseases from their patients. The answers to this question are simple—and well known among most physicians. First, physicians as a group are not the kinds of people who quickly take to bed when they get sick. If for no other reason, their livelihood depends on their being up and about. Not too many people are going to seek medical advice from a doctor who is sick in bed. Second, there are many mechanisms in the body (such as serum antibodies and white blood cells) that serve to fight off invading germs, and these defense mechanisms are strengthened by exposure to the organisms that produce disease. Each time we are exposed to disease-producing organisms, the body intensifies its production of antibodies and other disease-fighting agents. After we have successfully fought off the germ, these defense mechanisms remain for varying periods of time and serve to protect us from future infection. Sometimes we have contracted a disease and may not even be aware of it because the symptoms are so mild. Even when we have had such "sub-clinical" cases of the disorder, we have built up our protective mechanisms.

We do children a service then when we expose them—to a reasonable degree—to the variety of infections they may encounter. We thereby enable them to acquire many "sub-clinical" infections that serve to protect them from the numerous reexposures they will inevitably encounter. Parents who try to protect their children from exposure to germs (and this is difficult to do, so ubiquitous are the organisms) deprive their children of the opportunity to build up their immunity and this may result in their becoming more sick after exposure to germs than they would have been had they been allowed the usual exposures. Although some children are constitutionally very susceptible to infection, most who are considered to be in this category do not differ from others in their germ-resisting mechanisms. They are different from other children by having parents with phobias and germ preoccupations.

This type of overprotectiveness may bring about the very disorders such parents are ostensibly trying to avoid. Frequent references to sickness provide children with preoccupations they might not have otherwise entertained and introduce modes of behavior that might not have entered so readily into the child's scheme of things. The sickness adaptation enters the child's reper-toire and thereby increases the likelihood that he or she will feign or exaggerate illness (either consciously or unconsciously) to gain certain pathological gratifications. Bombarding the child with the possibility that something terrible will happen is one of the most effective ways of bringing about the feared occurrence. And the illnesses so engendered may be reinforced by indulgent treatment when the child becomes ill (either in reality or psychosomatically). The child is put to bed, fed three meals a day, entertained, and given sympathy and understanding. Such parents may subscribe strictly to the rule that a child is not to return to school until after three days in the afebrile state. Even though the pediatrician may advise the parent that such precautionary measures are excessive, the parent will not accept the advice and will continue to indulge the youngster.

The parent who frequently visualizes a child to be ill (or on the verge of an illness)—when there is no evidence for sickness or real danger of such—reveals a basic wish that the child be sick. There are many reasons why such a mother might want a child to be ill. The sick child can enable the mother to satisfy vicariously her own dependency needs, because each time she unconsciously ministers to the sick child she is ministering to her own projected self. In addition, taking care of the helpless child provides her with an enhanced sense of usefulness and may thereby provide her with an opportunity to prove her competence as a parent. This is especially likely for the parent with feelings of parental inadequacy.

Visualizing or anticipating a child's illness can serve as an outlet for parental hostility. All relationships are ambivalent, and in even the most loving relationship there is some hostility. Living in close proximity with another person must, by the very nature of living, at times frustrate us. And this is especially the case with children who may cause us more frustration and inconvenience than many adults. Infants get up at all hours of the night, wet, soil, make irrational demands, need our constant surveillance, etc. Accordingly, they inevitably produce angry feelings in us and, at times, the thought that we would have been better off without them. Some parents, however, feel very guilty about such thoughts and believe that some fine folks somewhere have no such ambiva-lence—but have only loving feelings toward their children. Because such hostility may not be admitted comfortably to conscious awareness, it is repressed and may be released via a variety of disguise mechanisms—one of which is to imagine that the child is physically ill. Each time a visual image of the child's illness appears, the wish that the child be sick is thereby gratified. However, the guilt over this wish is assuaged and/or alleviated by the associated fear that the illness will occur. In association with such fantasies, the parent is basically saying: "It is not that I *wish* my child to be ill; it is only that I *fear* that the child will be sick." I am not claiming that such parents *really* wish their children ill. Generally, their hostility is not that extreme and the loving components are still the major ones. What I am saying is that they are *ambivalent* toward their children and that they are too guilty to express openly their hostilities. The illness image is the symbolic expression of hostility toward the child; converting the wish into a fear serves to reduce and possibly eliminate guilt over such hostile expression.

There is often a realistic element in this type of overprotection. Children do get sick, automobile accidents do occur, and certain neighborhoods are indeed dangerous; it is neglectful to deny this. Overprotective parents, however, can be identified by the *degree* of precaution they exercise. Their exaggerated concerns and precautions—above and beyond what is reasonable—distinguish them from other parents and are the criteria by which one can ascertain whether such worries are inappropriate and harmful to the child. Children in such families may not only fulfill such parental wishes and become sick (thereby complying with their parents' psychopathological desires), but utilize the parents' fears to their own advantage. They may feign physical symptoms in order to avoid unpleasant tasks and obligations, and the parents may comply because the child's illness provides them with the aforementioned gratifications. The stage is then set for the development by the youngsters of a variety of psychopathological mechanisms that involve utilization of physical symptoms.

Exaggerated Protection of the Youngster from the Inevitable Pains and Discomforts of Life

Many parents, with the justification that they are protecting their children from psychological trauma, lie or evade rather than answer directly certain children's questions. Most parents no longer give the old stork story when a child asks questions about his or her origin, but many still couch their responses with euphemisms or other patent prevarications. Many are careful to avoid discussing in front of a child the impending death of a person well-known to and possibly even loved by the child. When the child is finally told, only he or she is shocked by the news. Everyone else has had the time to slowly accustom themselves to the loss. The child may then be told that the deceased is now "living in heaven" and leading a very enjoyable life—even when the parent has absolutely no belief in an afterlife. Children may not be told about an impending divorce until the actual day of separation. Again, they are thereby deprived of the opportunity to desensitize themselves in advance to the trauma. Similarly, a child may not be told about a hospitalization until the actual day that he or she is to go. And then the child may be told all sorts of absurd things about its purpose, for example, that there will be no pain, and even that there will be no operation—when the parent knows well that this is not the case.

In all of these examples the parents operate under the misguided notion that the disclosure of the unpleasant news will be psychologically deleterious to their children. Actually, children are far less fragile in this regard than most parents appreciate. Most are able to tolerate well all of the aforementioned painful situations. What they are not able to handle (and they do not differ very much from adults in this regard) is the anxiety that comes from being kept in ignorance. The child usually senses that something "bad" is taking place. When children's questions are unanswered, avoided, or responded to euphemistically, they sense the duplicity. They know that they are not being given the full story and may then only think the worst. From the child's vantage point, the issue is one that is "too terrible to talk about." Then, he or she may become preoccupied with a variety of fearful fantasies—fantasies far more horrible than the event that is not being disclosed. Such children would adapt far better to the trauma if they were given direct and honest explanations—at a level commensurate with their age and ability to understand.

Parents who lie in the ways I have just described are doing their children a serious disservice. Under the guise of protecting them from pain, they are causing them more problems than the children would have had were they told the truth. They are causing their children to lose trust in their parents and this cannot but be psychologicaly detrimental. If a child's parents cannot be relied upon to tell him or her the truth, who then can be believed? This problem may become worsened when the child's lack of trust extends to the teacher—resulting in a compromise of the youngster's ability to learn in the classroom. In addition, such parental duplicity squelches the child's natural curiosity. If important questions are continually avoided or unanswered, curiosity is dampened. And by the time such children reach school, they may have lost the interest in and the hope of learning anything from anyone.

Material Indulgence of the Youngster

Parents who have suffered a variety of privations in their own childhood may wish to compensate for their own deprivations by providing their children with the benefits they could not or did not enjoy. Such parents may commonly say: "I want to give them everything I didn't have when I was a child." By identifying themselves with their children and by observing *their* gratifications the parents partially achieve similar gratifications themselves. An uneducated parent, for example, may be willing to suffer significant sacrifices in order for a child to have a college education. And parents who were economically deprived during their childhood can, through their childrens' successes, vicariously compensate for their own earlier privations. Such experiences are ubiquitous and generally healthy. They are beneficial to both the child and the parent. They are, in part, responsible for human progress. Knowing that their parents derive so much pleasure from their accomplishments may serve as a strong impetus for children to succeed; and the parents' frustrations can be lessened through such vicarious satisfactions. The mechanism becomes abnormal, however, when it is used to excess, e.g., via indulgence of the youngster, especially material indulgence. This may be associated with an exhibitionistic aspect in which the children are used to compete with the neighbors' children with regard to who has the most expensive clothing, vacations, summer camps, college, etc. The children thereby develop pathological values and dependency problems in which they

become ill-equipped to suffer the discomforts and privations necessary to tolerate if one is to achieve goals on one's own.

A related disorder is one that I refer to as *The rich-man's son
syndrome.* In this disorder in parent-child relations the child is
indulged as an extension of the parents' own self-indulgence or as a
means of exhibiting the parents' wealth. This is well described in the
anecdote about the rich lady and her son who pull up in their
chauffeured limousine to the front entrance of an ultra-expensive
hotel. As the doorman assists the chauffeur in putting the son in his
wheelchair, he comments to the mother, "I'm sorry your son can't
walk, Ma'am." To which she replies, "Of course, he can walk. But
thank God he doesn't *have* to." The story demonstrates beautifully
the principle of the child's being indulged for the parent's own
glorification. The effects of this kind of abuse can be devastating.

I recall an 11-year-old boy who was brought to me because he
lacked motivation in school. Although basically bright, he was
doing very poorly. His father, in his mid-thirties, worked in the
business of the paternal grandfather, who was a multi-millionaire.
The boy stated that he knew that it didn't make any difference
whether or not he did well in school because, no matter what
happened, he would ultimately go into the family business. The
boy's father had been asked to leave a series of prep schools because
of poor academic performance as well as refusal to comply with the
school's routines and regulations. Although he had progressive
difficulty gaining admission to other schools, his father's donations
ultimately resulted in his acceptance. His experiences in college
(more accurately colleges) were similar. After graduation he entered
his father's business, where he had little involvement. There, he
was treated with the deference due the boss's son, but he was not
basically respected. The patient's mother, a very good-looking
woman, married her husband primarily for his money. Both were
waiting for the paternal grandfather to die in order to inherit his
fortune.

From early childhood, the father had had a recurring dream in
which he was drowning. But just as he was about to suffocate, he
would suddenly realize that he could breathe under water. The
dream clearly reflected his life situation: no matter how overwhelmed he might become over the repercussions of his laxity, and

no matter how oppressive life became for him because of his failure to effectively fulfill his obligations, he would suffer no consequences. At the last moment some magic force (his father, of course) would enable him to survive. The father had many problems. He drank in excess and would have violent outbursts when inebriated (during which he would beat his wife). He was chronically agitated and flittered from pleasure to pleasure in an attempt to gain some gratification from what was basically a very ungratifying life. The boy was already following in his father's pattern. He was deprived of nothing material and took at his whim. He had no motivation for change or treatment, and my attempts to engage him in therapy met with failure.

To want one's children to have some of the things one was deprived of in childhood is reasonable. However, to give children the idea that the primary purpose of those around them is to satisfy their every whim ill-prepares them to function adequately in reality. Such indulgence deprives them of the ego-enhancing sense of mastery that can only come from striving and accomplishing on their own. Many parents who grew up in the Great Depression tried to compensate for their own childhood frustrations by giving their children "everything they didn't have." A sad mistake. They would have done far better had they *given* their children a little privation (still possible in the midst of affluence) and prevented their the-world-owes-me-a-living attitude that is one of the effects of this well-meaning, but misguided, indulgence. The child who is overindulged with material things in order to make him or her happy brings to mind James Thurber's comment: "The world is so full of a number of things, I am sure we should all be happy as kings. And you know how happy kings are."

Parental Overvaluation of the Child

A moderate degree of parental overvaluation is normal and healthy. Parents who do not distort slightly in the positive direction regarding their children's attributes are usually somewhat deficient in providing affection. Parents who harbor absolutely no delusions about their children, who see their liabilities quite accurately, and who do not at all overestimate their children's assets, are depriving their children of a vital stimulus to growth and development.

Children require praise, reward, and other forms of positive reinforcement for their accomplishments if they are to be motivated to
repeat them and pursue other goals. Such encouragement, by the
very nature of the child's immaturity, requires a certain amount of
exaggeration and overvaluation by the parent.

For example, a four-year-old boy comes home from nursery
school with a Mother's Day card that, by most adults' artistic
standards, is certainly not extraordinary. However, the child's pride
in presenting it, the feeling of mastery he enjoys over having made
it, is clearly present. The healthy parent responds to these additional feelings on the child's part. The healthy parent is filled with
pleasure in response to the child's joy and responds with enthusiasm. These "vibrations," which are transmitted by the child as he
proudly shows his parents his Mother's Day card, contribute to the
parents' overvaluation and enthusiastic response and they exclaim,
"That's beautiful!" Intellectually, they know that the card is not
beautiful. What is beautiful is the total situation: the child's vibrations and the parents' responding resonations. These contribute to
the parents' belief that the card is "beautiful." The parent who does
not respond with such resonance is deficient in the ability to provide
the child with meaningful affection, and this particular defect on the
parent's part may play a role in lessening the child's motivation for
further creative endeavors.

There are parents, however, who go too far in this regard and
their exaggerations can justifiably be called delusions--so divorced
are they from reality. Such parents cannot permit themselves to
view accurately their children's deficits and they exaggerate their
children's assets to an inordinate degree. Because our children are
the psychological extensions of ourselves, we can enhance our
feelings of self-worth through their accomplishments. However,
there are parents whose need for this particular mode of ego-
enhancement is excessive. They have few if any other ways of
gaining a feeling of self-worth and so may develop delusions about
their children that go far beyond the normal parental exaggerations.
Such parents may then view a child as a genius or a prodigy, and
they may view others who do not show proper appreciation of the
child's unusual abilities as blind, jealous, etc. Youngsters who grow
up in such a setting may not develop an accurate image of
themselves, may select unreasonably high goals, and may lead a life

of considerable frustration. In addition, they may take a very jaundiced view of people around them and believe that they are ignorant, hostile, and unappreciative of their talents – not a situation conducive to the formation of meaningful friendships and success in life.

Engendering in the Youngster
Excessive Fear of the World

There are parents (especially mothers) whose whole lifestyle is pervaded by a morbid fear that dangerous things are taking place in the world around them. These mothers are likely to engender in their children separation anxieties and a wide variety of phobic responses, especially a separation anxiety disorder. More than anything else, these mothers are overprotective. They do not allow their children to ride bicycles on streets where peers are being trusted to do so or to swim in deep water when other children their age are permitted. Running errands to distant neighborhoods is not allowed. Summer camp may be unthinkable. The mothers may consider parents who send their children off to such camps to be neglectful: "Parents who send their kids to summer camp just want to get rid of them. I would never do such a thing to *my* child." Or they may rationalize never having sent the child off to summer camp: "He (she) never asked to go." Day camps, however, may be permitted. Some of the children with separation anxiety disorder may not even be able to tolerate this degree of separation, but others can. I suspect that those children who do go are less threatened by the day-camp situation, because it is so filled with fun and games that they may be distracted from their phobic preoccupations.

These are the mothers who are forever peeking out the window to make sure that everything is all right in the street. They may not permit their children to play at such distance that they cannot easily be seen or heard. Even going around the corner may be too threatening. Some are given even less freedom because of dangers that are seen to exist in the neighborhood. Although there are certainly dangerous neighborhoods, other children are allowed to play, and the restrictions and warnings they are provided are far fewer than those given to the child with a separation anxiety disorder.

There may be a general atmosphere of secretiveness in the home which, in subtle ways, is a manifestation of the maternal overprotectiveness. The child may not be told about disturbing events that occur in the family, such as serious illness, divorce, or job loss. The child is viewed as not being able to handle such upsetting news and a conspiracy of silence may be entered into between the mother and other family members in order to protect the child.

The basic message that such mothers are giving to their children is this: "The world is a dangerous place and only I can protect you from the calamities that may befall you if you venture forth into it. If you always stay by my side, you will be protected from these dangers and all will be well with you. If you go forth without me, terrible things may happen to you. In fact you may even die!" This is the common element that lies beneath all of the aforementioned overprotective maneuvers. The child is repeatedly being told: "Watch out for this! Beware of that! Be careful of this! Stay away from that!" The child is being programmed with the message that there are dangers all around. These children are consistently being told that mother can be relied upon to protect them from these dangers. An important reason why such children fear going to school is that, for the first time, there is an enforced separation from the mother. Although the school doors are not actually locked, there is formidable social pressure for the child to remain there. The child who wants to go home is viewed as infantile, still "a baby," and is likely to suffer social stigma. In the school situation such children are captive. They are exposed to the dangers they have been taught await them when not under mother's protection. And they cannot readily run home to reassure themselves that their mothers are not suffering some calamity if this is one of their concerns.

Most often, the fear of school does not exist in isolation. Refusal is a common concomitant. Generally, the younger the child the greater is the fear element. And the older the child, the greater is the refusal element. But even the younger, panicky child will usually exhibit a refusal element. An adolescent is more likely to present as school refusal; he or she may even rationalize what is actually fear with professions of refusal. If the adolescent stays at home when not in school, then the fear element is probably dominant. However, if the adolescent spends time with friends outside the home, then the disorder should more properly be referred to as a school refusal problem or truancy. In the latter case, the term *school phobia*, or *separation anxiety disorder*, is not appropriate in that the child is not exhibiting the characteristic dependent tie to the mother.

When leaving the home in the morning the child frequently complains of a variety of *physical symptoms:* headache, nausea, vomiting, diarrhea, fever, stomachache, low-grade fever, etc. These symptoms are usually physiological concomitants of the fear and/or anxiety. Typically they are indulged by the mother, and it is difficult, if not impossible, to convince her that no physical disease is usually present. She may accuse the physician who advises her to ignore or not to indulge these symptoms of being insensitive and even deficient as a doctor for taking such a blasé attitude toward physical illness. She may also justify keeping the child home on the grounds that she doesn't wish to expose the other children in the classroom to possible communicable disease.

Children with a separation anxiety disorder will often exhibit a wide variety of other fears. They may fear visiting other children's homes when unaccompanied by their mothers. Overnight visits may be impossible. Sleep-away camp is often unthinkable, and even summer day camps may be out of the question. These children are often afraid of the dark and will insist upon night-lights in their bedrooms. All children linger at bedtime and find a variety of excuses for keeping parents close by to help assuage the "separation anxiety" they experience before going to sleep. These children exhibit even more fears of such nighttime "separation."

Children with separation anxiety disorder may be afraid to go on errands in the neighborhood when other children their age are eager for such growth experiences. They may be afraid to stay in their rooms alone or venture alone into remote parts of their own homes, such as the attic or the basement. Many young children are afraid of dogs and other animals. These children persist in exhibiting such fears beyond the age when most children no longer manifest them. Many children, especially younger ones, are fearful when their parents go out for an evening. But these children are even more fearful of being left with babysitters and dread the prospect of their parents going out for an evening. They are usually more fearful of new situations than other children their age. And a whole list of other fears may be present, such as fear of monsters, muggers, strangers, plane travel, and dying.

In addition to the aforementioned fears, other personality difficulties are often present. These children tend to be demanding, coercive, and manipulative. This is especially the case with regard to the school situation. Upon being cajoled or pressured into going to school, a child may state, "If you make me go to school, I'll jump out of the window." Unfortunately, the parents of these children tend to take such threats more seriously than is warranted. There is a grandiosity to these children that relates to the pampering and indulgence their parents provide. Often they act as if they were the masters and their parents the slaves. Coolidge et al. (1962) emphasize these children's exaggerated sense of infantile omnipotence. Leventhal and Sills (1964) propose that a central personality characteristic of these children is their grandiose and unrealistic self-image. They too consider this to relate to the narcissism and feelings of omnipotence engendered by the parental overprotectiveness. They describe how these children's aggrandized self-image is threatened in the more egalitarian school situation, so they thereby crave to retreat home where their narcissistic gratifications can be indulged.

The mothers of these children are often phobic themselves. They may be agoraphobic, e.g., they may be afraid to drive in open places, or even drive at all. They may be afraid of crowds or airplanes. They may be afraid to travel alone and are thus tied down to their homes. Some are claustrophobics. Such mothers serve as models for their children's phobias. It is by identification with the parental model that we see another contributing factor. Eisenberg (1958) emphasizes the mother's communication of her anxiety to the child. It is not so much by word as through gestures, attitudes, and facial expressions. The mother fears the cold, impersonal attitude of the school, and she serves as a model for such fear for her child. In addition, the mother's very life style reiterates the basic message that the world is a dangerous place. The mother sees dangers where others do not, or she exaggerates dangers that others consider to be mild.

As was true of other types of overprotectiveness thus far described in this section, the fathers of children with separation anxiety disorder tend to be passive in their relationships with their wives. They tend to view their wives' overprotectiveness as a parental asset. Some will consider the mother to be the expert in the home, and they view themselves to be the experts in the workplace. Accordingly, they bow to her authority. However, they may not only defer to her in the child-rearing realm, but in other areas as well. Basically, many of these men are dependent individuals themselves and gratify their longings for a passive-dependent relationship in their marriages. The weakness of such fathers makes them poor models for identification and does not engender in their children a sense of security. This further contributes to their youngsters' separation anxieties and feelings of vulnerability in their relationship with a world that they have come to view as hostile and dangerous.

The Complementary Psychodynamic Patterns of the Mother and Child   At this point I present what I consider to be a central psychodynamic pattern in the etiology of the separation anxiety disorder. To the best of my knowledge, this formulation has not been presented elsewhere, (with the exception of my own previous publication, 1984). It comes from my observations of these children and their parents over many years. As is true for all psychodynamic formulations, it is a speculation. However, it is a speculation that I believe warrants serious consideration when one attempts to understand what is going on with these children and their families.

To understand better this somewhat complex formulation, it is best to begin with the mother. I present here what I consider to be a typical picture, a composite of many mothers I have seen whose children exhibit a pathological degree of separation anxiety. As mentioned, she is often a dependent person, still dependent on the maternal grandmother. Consciously or unconsciously, she did not wish to leave the home of the maternal grandmother, but submitted to social pressures to leave home and marry. However, she did so with a neurotic compromise in that she still maintains her dependent tie to the maternal grandmother. She may live close to the maternal grandmother or, if not, she still maintains very strong and frequent ties. Not only did she basically not wish to marry, but, in addition, she did not wish to assume the role of child rearer. Basically, she wished to remain a child in the home of her own mother. Accordingly, she resents the burden of raising her child and is basically angry at him or her. (Coolidge et al., emphasized this factor in the etiology of this disorder.) She cannot allow herself to accept these unloving feelings because of the guilt they would evoke in her. She deals with her hostility toward the child by reaction formation. Each time she envisions some calamity befalling the child, she gratifies in fantasy her basic wish that the child die. But she is too guilty to accept the fact that she harbors such death wishes within herself and so transforms the wish into a fear (an extremely common mechanism). It is not, then, that she *wishes* the child to be harmed, but that she *fears* that the child would be harmed. To fear a child's death is socially acceptable; to wish it is not. But the fantasy provides partial gratification of the wish, whether or not she views it as a wish or a fear. She tries to keep the child constantly at her side in order to reassure herself that her hostile wishes have not been fulfilled. Accordingly, she is forever peeking out the window to make sure that the child is fine and fears his or her going around the corner because from that vantage point she cannot reassure herself that the child has not been harmed. It is around the corner especially that the child may be hit by a car, mugged, raped, etc. In school, as well, she is deprived of such reassurance.

It is important to appreciate that when I say these mothers harbor death wishes toward the child, I am not saying that they actually wish the child to be dead. Our unconscious minds utilize primitive mechanisms to represent thoughts and feelings, mechanisms that often "exaggerate to make a point." Visualizing the child as dead is a way of symbolically representing the hostility the mother harbors toward the child. It must also be appreciated that the mother's "death wishes" are really only one aspect of her feelings toward the child. Like all human relations, the mother-child relationship is ambivalent. Deep loving feelings are present as well, and the mother of a school-phobic child would generally be devastated if her child were to die—the intense hostility notwithstanding.

The anger they originally felt at the prospect of rearing a child becomes intensified over the years as the demands on these mothers increase. She becomes increasingly angry at the child because of the drainage of her energy and increasingly guilty over the direct expression of such resentment. Accordingly, there is a build-up of the reaction formation mechanism that serves, as mentioned, to allow for a fantasized expression of hostility without concomitant feelings of guilt.

Interestingly, an almost identical psychodynamic pattern develops in the child. The child is basically angry at the mother for a number of reasons. Being kept from activities that other children enjoy produces social stigmatization. Other mothers are allowing their children to venture forth into areas in the community where these children are prohibited from entering. Being made more infantile is a source of anger for the child. The children's excessive dependency on the mother is a source of frustration and irritation. The basic impairments in the mother's capacity to be a parent (more of which will be discussed later) are a source of deprivation for them. So deprived, these children become angry. They are not getting the same degree of healthy attention and affection as are children being reared in more stable homes. However, they cannot directly express this anger. They are much too fearful of doing that. They are much too dependent on their mothers to allow such expression. After all, she is their protector from the dangers that await to befall them "out there." If resentment were to be expressed openly toward her they might lose her and then be exposed to the malevolent forces that ever await to pounce on unprotected children. So they must repress and suppress their hostility. And the children too come to deal with their hostility in the same way as their mothers. Specifically, they use repression, reaction formation, and fantasized gratification. Each time they envision calamity befalling the mother, they satisfy in fantasy their own hostile wishes toward her. By turning the wish into a fear, they assuage their guilt. They must be ever at their mother's side in order to reassure themselves that their hostile wishes have not been fulfilled. In this way, mother and child develop very similar psychodynamic patterns.

In this situation other difficulties develop that contribute to the entrenchment of the pathological tie. The parasite and the host ultimately come to hate one another. The host comes to hate the parasite because its blood is being sucked. And the parasite grows to hate the host because it is ever dependent on the host and, at the whim of the host, may be "flicked off" and then may die. Although the host gains the gratification of benevolence, altruism, and other ego-enhancing feelings, the basic resentment may counterbalance these benefits. Although the parasite may gain the gratifications of a "free meal," there is a precariousness to the situation that compromises this gratification. Being at the mercy of another person is not only ego debasing but frightening. And the frustrations associated with being in such a situation may ultimately produce resentment. The mother-child relationship in the separation anxiety disorder is basically a host-parasite one. And the anger so engendered in each feeds back into the aforementioned psychodynamic patterns. It becomes an additional source of anger that cannot be allowed expression in conscious awareness. It contributes thereby to an entrenchment of the repression, fantasized wish gratification, and reaction formation.

In short then the mother and child exhibit complementary psychopathology. However, more than complementing one another, the psychopathology is almost identical. It is almost as if the child's psychopathology is a rubber stamp of the mother's. Accordingly, a therapeutic approach that focuses on the child primarily, if not exclusively, is not likely to be successful. The forces in the mother that contribute to the maintenance of the pathological tie are great and are not likely to be altered significantly by a therapeutic program restricted to working with the child alone.

It is important for the reader to appreciate that what I describe as "new" in this formulation is the basic similarity between the psychodynamic patterns of the mother and child. The mechanisms of repression, fantasized gratification, and reaction formation are well-known mechanisms and have been described in a wide variety of psychogenic disorders. In addition, it is important to reiterate that when I say "death wish" here I do not believe that the mother really wants the child to die. In fact, were the child to die, it might very well be the greatest tragedy ever to befall the mother (and, obviously, the child). Rather, I am referring to the primitive unconscious impulses that exist within all of us. All human relationships are ambivalent. All have a combination of hostile wishes and loving feelings. And the hostility, on occasion, can become formidable—to the point where there may be transient wishes that the other person be removed. When all is balanced out, the mother basically does not want the child dead. The death wish is a primitive expression of the intense hostile feelings that may exist in all relationships and which exist to a greater degree in both the mother and child when a separation anxiety disorder is present.

Separation Anxieties in the Adolescent   The separation anxiety disorder is most often diagnosed in the prepubertal years. It is unrealistic, however, to expect that such programming is going to reduce itself significantly in the adolescent period. Although some reduction may inevitably accompany the child's physical growth and development, with its accompanying autonomy, residua of the early separation anxieties are likely to manifest themselves in the teen period. The refusal element may be more apparent than the phobic in such adolescents. If, when absent from school, the youngster stays at home, then it is likely that dependency on an overprotective mother is the central theme. If, however, the youngster does not go home when out of school, but rather stays with peers, it is likely that the problem does not warrant the term separation anxiety disorder. Furthermore, the adolescent is generally more embarrassed to exhibit fearful symptoms than the younger child. In fact, I have often been surprised about how little shame many young school-phobic children have over their symptoms. In their states of panic they may give forth blood-curdling shrieks that cause teachers to run out of their classrooms wondering who is being murdered. And yet, most often they are not generally humiliated by these displays. The adolescent is much more likely to cover up fearful feelings and utilize refusal as the ostensible reason for not going to school.

Another factor in the adolescent separation anxiety disorder relates to the adolescent's appreciation that adult independence is close. The younger child tends to view adulthood as millions of years away. It is so remote that for all practical purposes it can be ignored. Adolescents cannot utilize such denial mechanisms. They have the bodies of adults and are capable of procreation. They may even be physically taller and stronger than both parents. Such a situation may be very frightening, especially if they are ill equipped to deal with life at an age-appropriate level—as is often the case with school-phobic youngsters. In response, adolescents may regress and entrench the dependent tie with the mother to provide protection from venturing forth into a more demanding and less benevolent world. However, one rarely sees a separation anxiety disorder beginning in adolescence. Even when the overt symptomatology does manifest itself in adolescence, there have generally been many factors (such as those described above) that have contributed during earlier years. Some precipitating symptom may have brought the whole complex to a head, but there is generally a wealth of contributing factors that have antedated the appearance of the phobic symptoms.

Adolescent separation anxieties may manifest themselves at the time the youngster is applying to college. Procrastination in filling out applications is a common problem for these youngsters. In some cases the parents are ever on the youngster's back to get these in on time; in other cases (especially when the parents are significantly overprotective) they do not concern themselves with the application deadlines and thereby join the youngster in the neglect that will reduce the likelihood that he or she will go off to college. If such youngsters do go to college they may only attend those in their immediate area. These are the youngsters who have the greatest difficulty adjusting during their freshman year. They will rationalize frequent returns to their home by complaining about their roommates, the faculty, or a wide variety of other discomforts and inconveniences they suffer at school. They may justify returning home with the complaint that the kids in their college are primarily involved in sex, drugs, and drinking. Therapists do well not to be taken in by this latter complaint. Student preoccupations with sex, drugs, and drinking are to be found in practically every college—including the most prestigious. Healthy youngsters do not leave school because of the ubiquity of such patterns of behavior. Overprotective parents can be relied upon to agree quickly with the youngster that removal from the institution is warranted. Some of these youngsters may actually fail in school in order to return home. Many then quit college altogether, remain at home, and may ultimately get a job close to the parental household. And some may stay at home for years, not working, and supply an endless series of rationalizations for their failure to leave home.

ENGENDERING THE YOUNGSTER'S OVERVALUATION OF THE PARENT

It is important to differentiate between true respect of a parent, which is engendered in a child in response to genuinely admirable qualities that a parent exhibits, and specious respect, in which the child merely acts as if there were respect or refrains from verbalizing disrespectful thoughts. The parent who does not genuinely earn the first may resort to trying to get the second—that being better than nothing. The parent who says, "All I want is respect" is, in the very process of making the statement, losing it. In order to compensate for the lack of real admiration they detect in their children, they pathetically try to obtain respect by demanding it ("I want you to show respect around here"), or by evoking guilt ("What a terrible thing to say to a parent"). Such maneuvers can only cause the child to *lose* respect for his or her parent. How can the child respect a parent who asks to be lied to—either through coercion or by causing guilt?

In the healthy situation, the child truly admires many qualities in the parents and genuinely respects them in response to attributes exhibited by the parent and appreciated by the child, not to some nebulous inner quality. I am not an adherent of the philosophy that holds that true love ignores and transcends the loved one's deficiencies—no matter how alienating they may be. Rather, love is a response to readily observable attributes that far outweigh the loved one's deficiencies. When the latter outweigh the former, the terms *love* and *respect* have little applicability.

Parents who believe that they have to present a perfect image to their children try to hide their deficiencies with the rationalization: "I wouldn't want him (her) to lose respect for me." This is an excellent way to lose a child's respect because most children, as they grow older, inevitably discover their parents' deficiencies and the parents' duplicity in hiding their faults lessens the child's respect.

Healthy parents recognize that they have both assets and liabilities. It is hoped that the former will outweigh the latter so that the child will profit far more than suffer from the relationship with the parent. Such parents can tolerate the revelation of deficiencies because they are more than counterbalanced by their assets. Admitting one's defects (in situations where their revelation is reasonable and appropriate) truly gains the respect of the child. The child respects the honesty and the strength of character intrinsic to such admission and acquires realistic ideas about what the parents are really like, namely, that they are not perfect, but rather a composite of both admirable and alienating qualities.

Children who grow up with the notion that their parents are perfect will often have trouble in their future relationships with others, whom they may similarly expect to be perfect. Accordingly, they will inevitably be disillusioned and frustrated as each human being they encounter proves to be fallible. They may spend their lives in the futile quest for the perfect mate or be unable to adjust to marriage, where the acceptance of deficiencies in the mate is vital to survival. In work situations, they may be deprived of satisfaction because they are unable to accept fallible superiors and colleagues, and their continual disappointment and dissatisfaction with other relationships as well may result in significant loneliness.

The younger the child, the more likely he or she will be blind to parents' defects. The very young child, in the early years of the identification process, tends to accept everything parents do and say as gospel. Parental distortions about reality become the child's. Although some parental misconceptions are often rectified as the child grows older (for example, their prejudices and superstitions), others may not be (for example, "It's bad to be angry" and "Sex is evil"). Many things occur in psychotherapy. But one process that is central to the treatment of all patients, regardless of age, is the correction of the distortions about life that they have acquired from their parents. In my work with children there invariably comes a point, usually quite early in treatment, when I will tell the parents, in the presence of the child, that their approach to or ideas on a certain subject are, in my opinion, misguided, false, etc. Many parents become fearful that such confrontations will undermine their child's respect for them. This has not been my experience. Rather, the child generally welcomes these conversations and the accompanying atmosphere of openness and honesty. The child gets a more accurate view of the world, which cannot but be therapeutic; indeed, his or her respect for the parents is increased because, by admitting their defects, they are acting in a more respectable manner. I do not, in such situations, insist on the parents' revealing their every fault—only those that directly pertain to the child and come up naturally in the context of the child's therapy. The parents' lives need not be an open book to the child; they have a right to their privacies. For example, a father's impotency or a mother's frigidity are not problems that would generally come up in interviews in which the child is present.

I once treated a child who had a school phobia as well as many other fears, such as ghosts and visiting the homes of other children. The child's father was afraid to fly in airplanes, and the mother was claustrophobic. Both were overprotective and feared letting the child cross the street alone, ride her bike, and swim in deep water — when other children her age were doing so. The parents' own fears plus their admonitions to the child regarding neighborhood activities made her world a dangerous place indeed. The parents were able to follow my advice to let the patient engage in the same activities as her peers and this was helpful in reducing some of her phobias. However, their own phobias were of many years' duration and were deep-seated. I could not, therefore, remove significantly this contributing element to the child's phobias. In order to reduce its effects on her, I advised the parents to discuss their phobias with the patient. I encouraged them to communicate to her their realization that their fears were exaggerated and unrealistic as well as their helplessness to change themselves in spite of their wishes to do so. I considered it important for the patient to hear directly from them that their thinking was distorted.

The parents were hesitant to follow my advice, lest the child lose respect for them. I convinced them that it was important for the child's therapy for her to gain an accurate view of the world and that they were contributing to her distortions by not confronting her with their awareness that they themselves had symptoms that were, in part, the result of false notions about reality. Furthermore, I convinced them that their daughter was already aware of their phobias and that the very process of their hiding them from her was causing her to lose respect for them. They hesitantly agreed to follow my advice, and their doing so, I believe, played a role in the child's improvement. It is important for the reader to appreciate that all psychiatric symptoms are complex and are not merely the result of distorted ideas about reality. But the correction of false notions is a central and vital aspect of psychiatric treatment.

A common pronouncement of parents to children is: "Mother knows best" or "Father knows best." If believed by the child, this kind of remark tends to provide him or her with a distorted view of parental assets. If disbelieved, it lessens the child's respect for the parent because of the intrinsic duplicity of the statement. This kind of comment, however, has additional implications. Generally, parents who profess it mean well and hope that their children's adherence to the principle will serve them well. It is usually true that when there is a difference of opinion between a mother and an infant or very young child, the mother's position is the more prudent one. However, some parents continue to imbue this concept into their children long after it is appropriate. As a result, the children may continue to rely excessively on their parents' advice, beyond the age when they should be making many decisions on their own. They may continue to the point where their own opinions about what is best for themselves should, at least, be given serious consideration and may, indeed, be better-advised than those of the parents. In addition to fostering dependency, such comments also tend to undermine the child's self-esteem. Implied in the notion that mother is always smarter, is the idea that the child is always dumber. Resentment toward the parent inevitably arises in response to such implications, and continual advice from an omniscient parent cannot but lower the child's self-esteem even further.

For the very young child, absolute decisions by the parents are most often necessary. The child cannot appreciate the subtleties, shades of meaning, or the arguments for and against a particular decision. Even for controversial subjects, such as whether or not to allow thumb-sucking and pacifiers, the parent should weigh the pros and cons, come to a decision, and then follow through with the chosen approach. Benevolent despotism, I believe, is the best form of government for children and other primitive peoples. As children grow older, however, they can appreciate more of the complexities of life and should be told, in a controversial situation, whether or not their parents are certain about their decision. If *some* course of action is warranted, it is best taken, even if ambivalently; but the parents' lack of certainty should be communicated to the child without shame or hesitation. For example, "We don't know whether you'll be better off at Camp A or Camp B. They're different kinds of camps. Let's try Camp A this summer. If it doesn't work out, we'll try Camp B next summer." Such an approach helps the child appreciate that parents are fallible and not omniscient. It does not undermine respect because, as already mentioned, admitting occasional deficiencies and fallibilities enhances, rather than detracts from, the child's respect for a parent.

In the adolescent period, as discussed in detail in Chapter One, youngsters need to view their parents as backward, old-fashioned, pig-headed, etc. This makes it easier for them to leave their homes and go off into a world which, in reality, is never going to treat them with as much love, tolerance, and willingness to sacrifice as their parents. Perfect parents make it more difficult for the adolescent to find flaws. Denigration of the parents also serves the purpose of helping the adolescent compensate for feelings of low self-worth. Although adolescents may profess superiority over their parents, the reality is that adolescents are not capable of independent functioning in our complex industrialized society and so their feelings of independence and superiority have delusional elements. If, however, the adolescent does indeed have certain areas of proficiency that the parents do not genuinely possess, then an extremely salutary situation is present. For example, many adolescents today know more about computers than their parents. When they have the opportunity to give meaningful information and assistance in this area to a parent, they are being provided with a salubrious experience. Under such circumstances there is less need for the youngster to resort to compensatory delusional superiority. In addition, there will be less need to view the parents as having outlandish deficits (as imbeciles, village idiots, and anachronisms of the Middle Ages) because they have real "deficiencies" that the adolescent does not possess.

SEXUAL PROBLEMS

With the exception of sex abuse, sexual problems are not generally common prior to the age of puberty. My experience has been that a sexual explanation is rarely applicable when attempting to understand the psychiatric difficulties of children below the pubertal period. In adolescence and thereafter, sexual issues may be central elements in the formation and perpetuation of a patient's psychopathology. Although I believe that Freud gave too much attention to sexual factors—and thereby neglected other important elements in the development and perpetuation of psychopathology—the sexual factor is still an important one. In order for the reader to understand better my views on the sexual difficulties of adolescents, I will first present my understanding of the Oedipus complex because it so frequently is brought in when discussing sexual problems—at any age. An understanding of my views on this issue will place the reader in a better position to appreciate my opinions on the other sexual problems of adolescence to be discussed in this section. I will give particular attention to the sexual problems that may arise in stepfamilies and to homosexuality. Although other sexual difficulties certainly may appear in adolescence, the ones that I focus on here are those with which I have had the greatest experience.

Oedipal Problems

Freud's Theory of the Oedipus Complex Freud described the Oedipus complex as a normal childhood psychological phenomenon in which the boy or girl, between the ages of three and five, exhibits sexual-possessive fantasies toward the opposite-sexed parent and simultaneously views the same-sexed parent as a rival. The boy anticipates that his father will castrate him for his incestuous designs on his mother, and the girl is said to fantasize that she once did indeed have a penis but lost it or it was cut off. Freud's theory of the Oedipus complex was derived from the analysis of adult patients—most of whom Freud considered neurotic and some of whom we would today consider psychotic. To the best of my knowledge, Freud only published one article on the treatment of a child, the case of Little Hans (1909), and even here Freud was not the therapist. Rather, the boy's father treated him with Freud serving as the supervisor. In the three-and-a-half month course of treatment, Freud saw the boy only once. Freud believed that Hans' treatment confirmed his theories of infantile sexuality and the Oedipus and castration complexes. Furthermore, Freud believed that sexual attraction toward the opposite-sexed parent and jealous rivalry with the same-sexed parent appeared universally in children between the ages of about three and five.

Freud's Theory of the Resolution of the Oedipus Complex Freud believed that the healthy child resolves the Oedipus complex at about five years of age and then enters into a six-year period of relative sexual quiesence—the latency period. According to Freud, the resolution of the Oedipus complex comes about partly via natural developmental processes. He compared oedipal resolution to the loss of the milk teeth and the growth of the permanent teeth. In addition, he believed that natural psychobiological processes also contributed to the resolution, specifically that the boy's fear that his father would castrate him contributed to the development of his superego and subsequent suppression and repression of sexual fantasies toward the mother (S. Freud, 1924). By psychologically identifying with his father's superego, the boy incorporates his father's dictates against incest and thereby inhibits expression of his sexual designs on his mother. He thereby protects himself from his father's castrating him. He simultaneously carries down other elements of his father's superego and thereby incorporates other family and social rules. Freud held that the therapist's role in helping children alleviate oedipal problems was to foster resignation in the boy that he cannot gratify his sexual-possessive cravings toward his mother. However, he is consoled with the hope that someday he will get a suitable substitute, someone "as wonderful, beautiful, etc." as his mother. In short, the boy is asked to forestall gratification in this area for many years. Last, Freud believed that the failure to resolve the Oedipus complex successfully was a central contributing factor in *all* neuroses.

The Author's View of the Oedipus Complex   My own experience over the 30 years that I have worked intensively with children is that only a small fraction, less than two percent of all patients I have seen (regardless of age), exhibit oedipal problems or problems that are most readily understood as being oedipally derived or related. The remainder have difficulties that are unrelated (or only remotely related) to oedipal difficulties. And when oedipal problems are present, there are usually specific factors in the family constellation that directly contribute to the development of such. They do not arise naturally, as Freud would have us believe, but are the result of very specific family patterns that are conducive to the development of such symptomatology.

To elaborate: I believe there is a biological sexual instinct that attracts every human being to members of the opposite sex. From birth to puberty this drive is not particularly strong. Although weak and poorly formulated during the prepubertal period, it nevertheless exhibits itself through behavior that I consider manifestations of *oedipal interest*. A normal boy may speak on occasion of wishing to marry his mother and get rid of his father. These comments may even have a mildly sexual component such as "and then Mommy and I will sleep in bed together." I believe that the possessive, more than the genital-sexual, interest predominates here. The child is primarily interested in a little more affection and attention undiluted by a rival. I am not claiming, however, that there is absolutely no sexual interest at all during these early years. Such interest does exist, in mild form, and is likely to express itself toward the opposite-sexed parent, the individual with whom the child is most familiar and with whom the child feels safest. The child then has to be taught about the incest taboo: that one cannot touch parents in certain places, see the opposite-sexed parent undressed, kiss with the tongue, and engage in a variety of mildly sexual activities. To label these manifestations an Oedipal complex is to imply that they are possibly pathological and that they play an important role in the child's life. Rather, I consider them relatively unimportant phenomena in normal development, neither warranting any special label nor having any particular pathological significance. However, like all forms of behavior, they have the *potential* for becoming exaggerated and may contribute thereby to the development of psychopathological processes.

In a setting where the child is not receiving the affection, nurture, support, interest, guidance, protection, and generalized physical gratifications (such as stroking, warmth, and rocking) necessary for healthy growth and development, he or she may become obsessed with obtaining such satisfactions and develop one or more of a wide variety of symptoms in an attempt to deal with such frustrations. One *possible* constellation of symptoms are the kinds of sexual urges, preoccupations, and fantasies that Freud referred to as oedipal. The instinctive sexual urges, which are normally mild and relatively dormant, have the *potential* for intensive expression even as early as birth. Getting little gratification from the parents, the child may develop a host of fantasies in which frustrated love is requited and the rival is removed. Such fantasies follow the principle that the more one is deprived, the more one craves, and the more jealous one becomes of those who have what one desires. When this deprivational element *is combined with* specific oedipal-inducing factors (to be discussed below), then a symptom complex may exhibit itself that can appropriately be called oedipal in the classical sense. The foundation for the development of neurosis is formed not, as Freud would say, through the failure to resolve successfully one's sexual frustrations regarding the parent of the opposite sex, but through the failure to come to terms with the more basic deprivations from which the child is suffering.

But other specific factors must *also* be operative in order that oedipal paradigm symptomatology be selected. It is not simply the aforementioned deprivations. Among these other factors that channel the adaptation in the oedipal direction, I believe that the most common for the boy are sexual seductivity by the mother and/or castration threats (or the equivalent) by the father. It is important for the reader to note that the oedipal paradigm includes two phenomena: 1) sexual attraction toward the opposite-sexed parent and 2) fear of retaliation by the same-sexed parent. Although the latter is considered to be caused by the former, this is not necessarily the case. A boy, for example, might be threatened with castration without there necessarily being any kind of sexual seductivity on his mother's part. A boy might be threatened that his penis will be cut off if he plays with it, and this threat might be made in a situation where there is no seductivity on the mother's part. (This is exactly what took place in little Hans' case, Gardner, 1972a). Or there might be maternal seductivity without any retaliatory threats by the father. When either one or both of these processes are operative—on a preexisting foundation of parental deprivation—then, I believe, there is the greatest likelihood that symptoms will arise that can justifiably be referred to as oedipal. Of course, one might ascribe "unconscious" oedipal factors to a wide variety of symptoms. Psychoanalysts are famous for their ingenuity in creating a series of links between a symptom and the Oedipus complex—and these linkages range from the plausible to the preposterous. Here I confine myself to the phenomenological definition, one based on observable or accurately reported symptoms and/or behavior.

My discussion focuses here primarily on boys. I do not believe that this reflects any bias on my part; rather, it relates to the fact that Freud himself elaborated much more on oedipal manifestations in the boy and had great difficulty applying oedipal theory to girls. (It is beyond the purpose of this book to speculate on the reasons for this.) It is also important to differentiate between *sexual seductivity* and *sex abuse*. Oedipal problems may arise when there is sexual seductivity, but not when there has been actual sex abuse. When there is sexual titillation, the child develops cravings that cannot be gratified, and symptoms may then emerge which are designed to deal with these frustrations and deprivations. In sex abuse, there is usually no sexual frustration and an entirely different constellation of symptoms may emerge, such as symptoms related to distrust, fear of disclosure of the sexual activity, and generalized fear of involvement with adults who are of the same sex as the abusing parent (Gardner, 1987a, 1987c, 1987d).

The Author's Approach to the Alleviation of Oedipal Problems Freud used the term "resolution" to refer to the passing of the Oedipus complex between the ages of five-and-a-half and six. I prefer to use the term *alleviation* because I do not believe that oedipal involvements and interests are ever completely resolved. At best, oedipal problems can be alleviated. In fact, I generally go further and use the term alleviation to refer to the therapeutic aim of just about all psychogenic symptomatology. Considering the present state of our knowledge (perhaps the word ignorance would be preferable here), it is premature to use such strong words such as *resolution* and *cure*.

My therapeutic approach to the alleviation of oedipal problems reflects my concept of the Oedipus complex itself. The problems to be alleviated relate to the general problem of emotional deprivation *and* parental seduction and/or threats of castration. When addressing myself to the deprivational element I consider the improvement in the parent-child relationship crucial to the alleviation of oedipal problems in children. An attempt is made to improve the boy's relationship with his mother so that he will obtain the gratifications that are due in childhood and will be less obsessed with gaining them in psychopathological ways. A similar approach is used with girls exhibiting oedipal problems in their relationships with their fathers. In addition, such children are helped to accept the fact that they cannot completely possess either of their parents and that the affection and attention of each of them must be *shared* with other members of the family. This sharing concept is an important one to impart. The child must be helped to appreciate that no one can possess another person completely: The father shares the mother with the children; the mother shares the father with the children; and the child has no choice but to share the mother and father with the siblings. In the context of such sharing, children must be reassured that although they might not get as much as they want, they will still get something. In addition, they must be helped to gain gratifications from others during the present time. Whatever deficiencies may exist in the parent-child relationship can be compensated for to some degree by satisfactions in other relationships.

It is a well-known therapeutic principle that if one is going to take something away from a patient, one does well to provide substitute gratifications at that time, i.e., gratifications which are healthier and more adaptive. My approach does not involve suggesting to the child (as does Freud's) that he wait until adulthood. To wait for his possessive gratifications may appear to consume an endless number of years. Rather, he is told that he has the potential to gain some of these satisfactions in the present, and he is given the hope that as he grows older he will have greater autonomy to acquire the more exclusive type of possessive relationship enjoyed by his father.

I attempt to ascertain whether there has been parental seduction. If so, I inform the parents of my opinion that their behavior is seductive and strongly recommend that they refrain from such activities. At times they are consciously aware of the process and, at other times, they are not. In the latter situation, it may be very difficult to impress upon them the seductive elements in their behavior. I also try to learn whether there have been castration threats, overt or covert. Again, if present, I do everything to discourage them. Elsewhere (1975, 1986a) I have presented details of my clinical approach to the treatment of oedipal problems.

Oedipal Problems in Adolescence   The Freudian theory holds that there is a reactivation of the Oedipus complex in the early post-pubertal period. I personally have never observed this in my extensive work with adolescents. I am not simply referring to clinical and phenomenological manifestations; rather, I am referring to unconscious processes as assessed by projective tests and dream analysis. I am not claiming that I never see Oedipal problems during the post-pubertal period. Rather, I am saying that there does not appear to be any increased frequency during this phase when it is compared to other phases of life.

The therapeutic approaches described above are applicable to younger children as well as adolescents. There is one extremely important difference, however, between the therapeutic approaches to adolescents and those which I utilize with younger children. Specifically, as mentioned above, younger children must be given the *hope* that someday they will be able to get their possessive-sexual gratifications from others. The substitutes that they can reasonably be encouraged to avail themselves of during the prepubertal period are generally those of some physical caressing with mother and possibly a reasonable degree of physical contact with others. For the healthy child, this generally suffices. If the child is so charged up sexually that more is desired, it is likely that other factors are operative—such as sex abuse or an unusual degree of titillation. Even when this is the case one cannot reasonably recommend to a prepubertal child that he or she get sexual gratifications from peers. One can't suggest that the little boy play "You show me yours and I'll show you mine" with the little girl next door or take her to a secret place where they can enjoy mutual genital stimulation. Our society generally views such behavior as undesirable, and the parents of the young child who has been selected for such activities is likely to be quite upset (with justification) over such a recommendation.

In the adolescent period, however, such opportunities can be reasonably encouraged and there is a likelihood of varying degrees of gratification. Obviously, the further along the adolescent path the patient is, the greater the chance that such satisfactions will be available and enjoyed. It is important, however, for the therapist to impress upon the youngster that the best and most meaningful sex comes in the context of a relationship; however, I would not take this caveat so far as to condemn occasional transient sexual activities. Last, when Oedipal problems are present in adolescence they are likely to have been present during previous years. Accordingly, they are more likely to be deeply entrenched and therefore less likely to be alleviated. However, the prognosis is still better than that of the patient who is first seen during adulthood—by which time there has been a longer period of entrenchment.

Sexual Problems in the Stepfamily

I will begin my discussion of sexual problems in stepfamilies with some *speculations* on the origins of the incest taboo. It is reasonable to speculate that in the distant past, long before humans learned to record their experiences in writing, men and women began to appreciate that sexual relations among members of the same family tended to have a disruptive effect on family life. In fact, the jealousies, rivalries, and hostilities that such activity could result in might destroy completely the family's ability to function together as a cooperative unit. It was probably also appreciated (again this is speculative) that a coherent family produced the most stable, reliable, hard-working, and effective children. Such children then were not only more likely to produce coherent families themselves, but were more likely to contribute to the success and advancement of the society. In short, it was probably recognized that the survival of a civilized society depended upon a stable family life, and that free sexual access of the family members to one another could be a disruptive influence on family stability. Accordingly, incest taboos were created—not out of some higher moral or ethical principle, I believe, but from the practical observation that the very survival of the society depended upon them.

Our sexual hormones, however, know nothing of incest taboos. They hedonistically produce sexual cravings with little concern for whether the object that may potentially provide release happens to be a relative. We have to learn that certain people are "off limits." Lower animals learn no such restrictions. Keep a mother rat in a cage with her brood and her sons do not hesitate to copulate with her when they become sexually mature. The rats seem to suffer no guilt (like poor Oedipus did) over the fact that they may be fathers to their own brothers and sisters. But even with this long-standing history, the incest taboo is a shaky one. Even in the relatively stable, intact home the children tend not to be too strong in their adherence to the principle. In early childhood, especially, children may be quite obvious about their physical desires toward the opposite-sexed parent. Although such desires may not be specifically for heterosexual intercourse, they do include various other kinds of heterosexual activities, e.g., erotic play and the observation of undressing and toilet functions. And if there is parental seduction, then the child's sexual cravings are likely to be intensified.

In the adolescent period, when sexual desires become markedly intensified, sexual urges toward parents may become particularly strong. In childhood the likelihood of reciprocal sexual interest by the opposite-sexed parent is small (but certainly not nonexistent—as evidenced by the ubiquity of child sex abuse). In adolescence reciprocal interest by an opposite-sexed parent may be significant, because the adolescent's sexual development can be a source of strong sexual stimulation to the parent. The youngster's attraction to the parent, then, becomes even harder for the adolescent to handle—intensified as it is by the parental stimulation. It is quite common for such mutual attractions to be repressed by both parents and children. Like most repressed impulses, however, they often find release via symbolic and other forms of disguised expression.

For example, an adolescent girl may complain how "disgusting" her father is when he engages in everyday physical functions. She may become "nauseated" by his chewing at the dinner table, the sounds of his brushing his teeth and gargling, or even by an occasional burp or belch. Such disgust generally covers up and serves to repress from conscious awareness the sexual titillation that results from such primitive physical expression. Although one may not immediately consider the aforementioned activities to be typically sexually arousing, they, like sex, are manifestations of primitive animal functioning. And this may suggest sexual activity to a teenage daughter, who generally has no closer access to her father's more directly sexual forms of animal functioning. The young woman who becomes anxious when eating dinner with a date (sometimes to the point of being panicked) is often afraid of the sexuality implied by the primitive eating function. Or father and adolescent daughter may cover up their sexual attraction to one another by frequent bickering. Angry interchange can hide underlying loving feelings and serve to distract the individuals in conflict from their loving feelings that press for release. And all this may occur in the normal, intact home.

In the stepfamily the incest taboo is usually less strong on the part of both the children and the adults. Neither have had years of living together during which time there has been ample opportunity for indoctrination to the incest taboo (both directly and subtly). Also, years of familiarization lessen the novelty that enhances sexual stimulation. Stepparents and stepchildren are very "new" to one another and are thereby more likely to be sexually stimulated by one another. Accordingly, the situation becomes much "hotter" and more highly charged, and the maneuvers to decompress it more formidable. Violent arguments between stepfather and stepdaughter (as well as stepmother and stepson) are one of the more common ways in which both may protect themselves from their sexual feelings. In addition, the child, before separation, may have resigned him- or herself to the fact that the parents' bond is unbreakable and oedipal cravings futile. When the parents do break up, and a newcomer replaces one of them, the child is less likely to view the marital relationship as inviolable. A boy living alone with his mother may consider the arrangement a fulfillment of oedipal fantasies. The appearance of a stepfather on the scene robs him of the total possession of his mother that he considered himself to have had. Accordingly, the oedipal rivalry and hostility may become very intense. And a girl living with her divorced father may have similar reactions to her new stepmother. Prior to the separation the child had to come to terms with *one* rival for the affection of the opposite-sexed parent. Now that that one has been displaced, a second rival has appeared on the scene. It is as if after David subdues Goliath, a second giant suddenly appears from behind a mountain. And the child may wonder how many more giants there are behind it. Sometimes the sexual titillation, rivalries, guilt, frustration, and hostility produced by the sexual feelings between a teenaged stepchild and the opposite-sexed stepparent can become so intense that the youngster's leaving the home (to live with the other parent or go to boarding school, for example) may be the only viable solution to the problem.

Myra's situation provides a good example of how disruptive of a second marriage an adolescent's sexual rivalries can be. Myra was 16 when her parents separated because her father was having an affair with Gail, a 25-year-old woman. Following the separation Myra and her two brothers lived with her father, because her mother did not feel that she could cope with raising the three children herself. One year later her father married Gail, who had never been married before. And Gail moved into the home.

Gail was much closer in age to Myra than she was to Myra's

father, who was about 50 at the time. In addition, Gail claimed that she would prefer to be a "friend" to Myra, rather than a mother. In fact, it was quite apparent that Gail was so immature a person herself that it would have been impossible for her to have assumed a maternal role to an infant, let alone to a 17-year-old girl. Gail was demanding of her husband, kittenish, self-indulgent, and severely materialistic. She thought about little other than clothing, jewelry, cosmetics, and decorating her new home. Myra ostensibly welcomed Gail's decision that she would be a friend rather than a mother to her, but in my work with her it became apparent that she was disappointed in Gail because she was being deprived of the guidance and protection that she still basically wanted—even though she could not openly admit this. Soon after Gail moved in, she and Myra began lending one another clothing; they confided in one another (even about personal matters between Gail and Myra's father); and they often enjoyed passing as sisters.

The honeymoon, however, for all three was short-lived. Myra began to complain that her father took his wife's side over hers whenever there were differences of opinion. Myra resented bitterly when her father and Gail would go out on a Saturday night and couldn't understand why she couldn't go along—especially because she and Gail were such good friends. On a few occasions, Myra knocked on the master bedroom door and was told to go away with reasons such as "we're busy" or "we're resting." Myra was convinced they were having sexual intercourse and bitterly complained that it was vulgar of them to make love during the day. "They're just like animals," she complained, "and have no sensitivity to the feeings of others." Within two months of the father's second marriage, bitter fighting between Gail, Myra, and her father became almost incessant. Hardly an issue did not become blown up into a major battle. It was quite clear that Myra was furious at her father for choosing a "peer" over her for a wife. And she was jealous of Gail's intimacy with her father, a jealousy that was made worse by Gail's flaunting to Myra her relationship with her husband under the guise of divulging intimacies to a close friend.

It became apparent to me very early in my work that all three would probably require years of intensive therapy if there were to be any possibility of their dealing successfully with this problem. Myra was in her third year of high school at the time of the marriage and I decided that her being out of the home would probably be the most expedient way of decompressing the situation. Although this would involve her "losing" her father such a short time after she had "lost" her mother, I believed that the pains of such separations would be less than those she was suffering in this intolerable situation. Accordingly, I raised the question of Myra's going off to boarding school. Although each of the members of what had psychologically become a *ménage à trois* had mixed feelings about the recommendation, all finally agreed that it would probably be best for all concerned—which it proved to be. Although Myra's example is an extreme one, the basic rivalries exhibited in her situation are common, even though they generally manifest themselves in less dramatic and traumatic ways.

Another situation in which sexual tensions commonly arise is the one in which a man marries a divorced woman who has a teenaged daughter. In such cases there is often a greater degree of sexual expression and awareness than may occur between a father and his natural daughter. Sometimes these sexual needs are gratified through seductivity on one or both sides, although usually one or both parties will suppress such threatening feelings. Overtly, the relationship often appears to be a hostile one and they rarely have a nice thing to say to one another. However, their ongoing feelings of anger and irritation are manifestations of their deep involvement, and by considering themselves to be irritated by one another they can assuage the guilt they would feel were they to come to terms with their genuine feelings. In some cases the stepfather may be excessively concerned that his adolescent stepdaughter is dressing too seductively. He may become particularly upset when she wears tight sweaters or low-cut blouses, and fights will ensue over whether or not she should be permitted to leave the house "so exposed." Actually, the stepfather in such situations is usually unconsciously jealous of the opportunities other men have with his stepdaughter that he does not enjoy. In essence he is operating on the principle: "If I can't have her, then nobody else is going to have her either."

A boy whose father has left the home may be unconsciously unreceptive to sharing his mother with a substitute father. The hostility toward the stepfather in such cases may sometimes become quite fierce, although generally the healthy child does not react so violently to the appearance of a stepfather. If his relationship with his natural mother and father had been good, he would not be so threatened by the prospect of sharing his mother's affection with his stepfather. He would be secure enough in his relationship with his mother to know that he can still get meaningful affection at the same time that she is involved with another person. If his relationship with his parents had been poor and there was insecurity regarding whether affection would be forthcoming, the son may become excessively possessive of his mother and intensely threatened by his stepfather.

Then there is the situation in which a teenaged boy is living with his father and the latter marries a young woman, possibly closer in age to the boy himself than to the father. Even if the father's young new wife is totally uninterested in the boy and has little if any sexual attraction toward him, the likelihood is that the boy is going to find the experience titillating. On occasion, the boy's attraction is overt and conscious. More often it is primarily unconscious, with only fleeting and transient sexual thoughts toward the stepmother. Often, the stimulation is great and it may be dealt with through hostility. By constantly finding fault with the stepmother and seizing upon every excuse for an altercation, the young man can distract himself from his sexual attraction and preoccupy himself with less threatening thoughts and feelings.

Because of the weakened incest taboo that exists in families in which a teenaged youngster is living with an opposite-sexed step-parent a highly charged situation exists. The idea that therapy may bring about an alleviation of such tensions is often naive and even grandiose on the part of the therapist. A therapeutic goal of alleviating such tensions must ignore the power of our hormones as well as the conditioning of a highly sexually oriented society. But even those who have conviction that therapy can be useful in such situations will generally agree that the goal of such decompression is not likely to be achieved in a short period. By this time the youngster would have been out of the house anyway, and so one cannot be sure that the improvement in the relationship between the teenaged youngster and the stepparent was an outcome of the therapy, or simply the result of the youngster's leaving the home.

Homosexuality

The Question of the Etiology of Homosexuality   Now to the difficult and controversial subject of homosexuality. No one can say that he or she knows with certainty the etiology of homosexuality. Some claim it is a normal variation in the human repertoire. Others consider it a definite form of psychopathology. Still others would say that both genetic and psychological environmental factors may be operative to varying degrees and that individuals differ regarding the contribution of each of these factors. The subject, unfortunately, often generates strong emotional reactions that are likely to becloud objectivity. For example, if in a conference on the etiology of schizophrenia, an authority believes personally that it is organic in etiology, even those who disagree are not likely to get too heated in their refutations. Similarly, those who claim the disorder to be psychogenic are not likely to raise the blood pressures of those who disagree with them. Last, those who claim it results from a combination of both organic and psychogenic factors are not likely to be vilified by those who disagree. Similar calmness is seen when one talks about organicity vs. psychogenicity for such disorders as migraine headaches, ulcerative colitis, peptic ulcers, hypertension, etc.

But if one says publicly in the 1980s that homosexuality is a psychological disorder, the speaker may be pelted with rocks and, if well known, may be the subject of public demonstrations, angry editorials in newspapers, and heated diatribes. Even in university and academic settings, where differences of opinion are supposedly given equal opportunity for expression, those who hold that homosexuality is a psychological disorder may find themselves ostracized. I believe that such intense emotional reactions may be related to reaction formation on the part of those who respond with such strong feelings. Certainly, their anger and condemnation are the hallmark of reaction formation and suggest that it is psychologically threatening for many to accept the possibility that homosexuality may be psychogenic. (Similarly, it may be psychologically threatening to some to consider it organic.)

The position taken by most mental health professionals in the 1970s and 1980s is that homosexuality is a normal human variation and not a form of psychopathology. This is not my view. I recognize that my position on this point is atypical and unpopular; it is nevertheless my belief. To elaborate: I consider there to be a continuum with strong heterosexuality on one end and strong homosexuality on the other. No individual, no matter how strongly heterosexual, is free from homosexual tendencies. Similarly, no homosexual individual, no matter how strongly homosexual, is free from heterosexual inclinations. All individuals, therefore, are at some point between the two ends of this continuum. Although homosexuality is seen in lower animals, it generally manifests itself when heterosexual outlets are not available or as a transient phenomenon. To assume that there are human beings in whom it is the inborn preferential orientation requires the assumption that mankind has departed markedly from the evolutionary pattern. In addition, one must then believe in the existence of a natural sexual variant without the goal of direct or indirect species procreation — another evolutionary innovation, to say the least.

I believe that the person who is an obligatory homosexual, who cannot or who has no desire to function heterosexually (especially when such opportunities are available), is suffering with a psychiatric disorder that is primarily, if not exclusively, environmentally induced — although there still may be a small genetic (or constitutional) contributing factor. Such an individual has a problem that might readily be classified in many cases as a kind of phobia or inhibition. Specifically, this person is so fearful of or inhibited from functioning sexually with a member of the opposite sex that he or she *cannot* do so, even when opportunities are available and the heterosexual partner is desirous of such an involvement. I will discuss in the next section what I consider to be the more common factors that contribute to the development of an obligatory homosexual orientation. Such an individual might be viewed as similar to the person with other kinds of phobia, such as agoraphobia or claustrophobia. There may very well be a genetic predisposition in that the individual has a very low threshold for elicitation of the flight reaction. Environmental factors that engender phobic responses become superimposed upon this genetically determined foundation and the clinical phobia manifests itself.

The fact that a genetic component may be operative does not warrant our declassifying the phenomenon from the list of psychiatric disorders. And this is what has happened with homosexuality. I believe that political factors much more than psychiatric, have played a role in its removal from the list of disorders. It would be an error for the reader to conclude that my position regarding the etiology of homosexuality should justify any infringement on the civil rights of such persons. In fact, I am a strong proponent of the position that one's private sexual orientation should in no way be considered for job placement, advancement, and/or a variety of other rights and privileges—as long as the individual's sexual behavior does not impinge upon the rights and freedom of others. This principle should apply equally to both homosexuals and heterosexuals.

My views are less firm with regard to the possible psychopathology of people who are bisexual or are non-obligatory homosexuals. Such individuals appear to work on the principle: If it feels good I'll do it—regardless of the sex of my partner. Such persons may enjoy homosexual activities, even when heterosexual opportunities are available. Although I am less firm in my belief that bisexuals are suffering with psychopathology, I suspect that many (but not necessarily all) are. Lastly, because of the homosexual potential in even the strongest heterosexuals, I would not consider pathological a rare homosexual act on the part of a heterosexual person. This would especially be the case when heterosexual opportunity is not available. The inborn homosexual *capacity* allows for sexual gratification in a heterosexual when heterosexual gratification is not available. It provides a vehicle for the release of pent-up sexual tensions in a situation where such release would be difficult or impossible. Accordingly, homosexuality serves a function in certain situations. As an alternative mode of sexual release one could even argue that it is superior to masturbation because it involves human interaction rather than narcissistic self-gratification.

It is important for the reader to appreciate that I am not claiming to know with certainty that the above theory is correct. It is the view I hold at this time on the basis of my present understanding of human sexual behavior. It behooves the examiner to have an opinion on this issue if he or she is to be providing recommendations regarding the treatment of people who present with homosexual urges and are considering treatment. One cannot wait for all the information to come in (it may take hundreds of years). A mother brings a four-year-old boy for consultation because he is preoccupied with dressing in her clothing and has been exhibiting effeminate gestures. One therapist might take the position that the child's behavior is normal and/or the child is an individual who is genetically programmed to be homosexual. Accordingly, that therapist would not recommend treatment. Another therapist might consider the child to be exhibiting pathological manifestations and would recommend therapy. (I consider myself to be in the latter category.) A 14-year-old boy asks his parents to bring him to therapy because of homosexual preoccupations. One therapist may consider the boy's thoughts to be inevitable concomitants of a normal homosexual variation and might treat the youngster to help him to become more comfortable with his homosexuality. Another therapist (include me again in this group) considers the boy to be exhibiting pathological manifestations and recommends treatment for the alleviation of the homosexual tendencies. Obviously, the position the therapist takes in each of these situations may have an important effect on the total course of these youngsters' future lives. Accordingly, we *must* make recommendations, recognizing that they have been made on the basis of *hypotheses* regarding the etiology and significance of homosexuality.

Although I believe that the obligatory homosexual is suffering with a psychiatric disorder, this should not be interpreted to mean that I believe that an obligatory homosexual (or any other kind of homosexual for that matter) should be deprived of his or her civil rights. One's private sexual life should not be a factor in determining job opportunities, career choice, and so on. If a homosexual's proclivities interfere with job functioning, then that must be taken into consideration. But this same principle holds with heterosexuals. If a homosexual man has a job as an elementary teacher and encourages homosexual activities among his students, then one should limit his opportunities for such inculcation. But the same principle holds if a heterosexual teacher were to engage in similar behavior.

In addition, I consider the average male obligatory homosexual to be suffering with more psychological difficulties than the average female obligatory homosexual. This may come as a surprising statement to many readers, and I have not seen anything in the literature supporting such a statement. What I say here is my own opinion supported, I believe, by these arguments: With rare exception, the primary sexual object for both males and females is the mother. She has carried the child within her own body for nine months, has suffered the pains of its delivery, and has the capacity to feed it from her own body (although she may not choose to do so). The average healthy father, no matter how deeply involved with his newborn infant, is not as likely to have as strong a tie with the *newborn* child as the average healthy mother.

In our society, where the mother is still the primary caretaking parent in most families (recent changes in the pattern notwithstanding), the earliest primary attachment for infants of both sexes is the mother. In the normal development of the boy, he transfers his affection from his mother to girl friends and ultimately to other adult females. The progression is a relatively smooth one for the average healthy boy and does not involve the kind of shift required of the female. The girl, in contrast, must transfer her sexual involvement from a female (her mother) to male figures: boy friends and then adult males. It is reasonable to assume that residua of the attraction to the mother are likely to be present at subsequent levels of development. One confirmation of such residual attraction is the fact that many more heterosexual women are physically attracted to the naked female body than heterosexual men are to the naked male body. Many more heterosexual women purchase magazines depicting naked women than heterosexual men purchase magazines depicting naked men. (The latter are primarily purchased by homosexual males.) For a woman to become a lesbian involves a fixation at an earlier level of development: the level at which she was attracted to her primary sexual object, the mother. Her subsequent lovers are in the same mold, so to speak, and are readily understandable. Blocked from heterosexual gratification by internal psychological and/or external situational factors, it is reasonable that she may be fixated at or regress to an earlier level—but along the track of sexual attraction to a female.

The male homosexual, in contrast, has a much more complex course toward his resultant homosexual orientation. He must abrogate mother and all her derivative surrogates. He must shift toward an intense sexual involvement with a father surrogate without any continuity with his previous psychobiological track. The psychological processes involved in such a path are complex and extremely powerful. The distortions of thinking necessary to effect such a transfer are profound. It is for these reasons that I consider the obligatory male homsexual to have deeper psychopathology than the obligatory female homosexual.

Common Psychodynamic Patterns That Contribute to the Development of Male Homosexuality   It is not my purpose here to present a lengthy discussion of the various psychological factors that have been considered of etiological significance in the development of male homosexuality. Rather, I will describe those factors I have found to be operative in the patients whom I have seen over the years who have presented with this symptom. My experience with male homosexuals has been much greater than that with lesbians; accordingly, I will have more to say about the male homosexual's psychodynamics. I have seen a number of boys whose parents have brought them to me at the ages of three to four because of effeminate characteristics. I have seen boys at the elementary school level who are brought to treatment because they are teased by their classmates with epithets such as "fag" and "gay." I have seen adolescents who initiated the request for treatment because of disturbing homosexual inclinations. (Those who have not been disturbed by these, of course, have not sought therapy.) And I have seen men in their 20s and 30s who have come for therapy for their homosexuality.

I believe that an important factor operative in the development of the homosexual symptom is the craving for the love of a father. In over 30 years of experience as a psychiatrist I have not once seen a male homosexual who has had what I consider to have been a strong, healthy relationship with his father in childhood. Although there may be exceptions to this, I have not yet seen them. Furthermore, a number of male homosexual men have told me that they themselves have never met a homosexual man who had a good relationship with his father. What is often lacking is the traditional father-son relationship in which the "two guys together" do things as a team. Homosexual men have not had the experience of joining together with their fathers and engaging in a variety of activities with a sense of camaraderie. They do not have fathers who proudly show off their sons. I do not believe it is necessary that these activities be "male" or "macho" such as sports and other traditionally male activities. They could involve intellectual, artistic, and creative interests. What is important is that the two together be "buddies" and that there be a sense of pride in each other. The father enjoys showing off the son and the son is proud of his father—and thereby identifies with him and emulates him. I believe that boys who have had this experience *over time* in their childhood *can't* become homosexuals. This may sound like a very strong statement, but I believe it to be the case. The obsessive quest for the love of a man is basically a quest for the love of the father who never gave it, or who gave very little. Commonly, obligatory homosexual men search the world in an endless hunt for the man who will love them, and they equate sex with affection. But the quest is futile, because what they get (sex) is only a *symbol* for what they want (love). It is not the real thing and so it does not give them what they are really looking for. This is one of the important factors in the compulsive promiscuity of many homosexual men. I. Bieber (1962), who studied and treated homosexuals intensively for over 50 years, has come to the same conclusion. In a lecture of his that I attended in the late 1970s he stated: "I have never seen a male homosexual who had a good relationship with his father. If a man had a good father-son relationship in childhood, it is impossible for him to become a homosexual."

There are many different types of father-son impairments that may result in this deprivation. In some cases the fathers are absent, or almost entirely so. I am not claiming that the absence of a father automatically dooms a boy to become a homosexual. I am only claiming that the situation increases the likelihood that the boy will develop a homosexual problem. I believe that the ever increasing divorce rate in the last 30 years has contributed to the increasing prevalence of homosexuality. More and more boys are being brought up in homes without fathers and this, I believe, increases the likelihood that they will become homosexual. Homosexuality increased in Germany after World War II—during which almost a whole generation of German men were killed. I believe this is the most reasonable explanation for the post-war rise in homosexuality in Germany.

Fathers who are present but rejecting, denigrating, and abusive are not likely to have the aforementioned healthy relationship that will prevent the development of homosexuality. Sometimes the weakness of the father-son bond can be subtle. I once saw a homosexual adolescent youngster whose father was a mortician. The family lived above the funeral home and although described as present and available for his son, he was psychologically extremely remote. First, the kind of person who becomes a mortician is generally one who must have significant inhibition in the expression of feelings in that someone who is more emotional could not tolerate the daily emotional strains of this profession. And the same emotional inhibition reflected itself in the father's inability to serve as a confidante, comrade, and meaningful "friend" of his son. The only father-son activities they did engage in occurred in adolescence when the boy was old enough to assist his father in the funeral home. Furthermore, during the father's absences (both physical and emotional) the boy spent significant time with his mother, maternal grandmother, maternal aunt, and paternal aunts. The aunts were unmarried, doted over the boy, and he could have been considered a substitute son for them. He was basically brought up by women with whom he had identified to a significant degree.

I once saw a three-year-old boy whose parents brought him because of effeminate gestures and frequent attempts to put on his mother's clothing. One of his greatest pleasures was to sit with his mother and her women friends and chat. His father was a hairdresser as was his paternal grandfather and three uncles. (Homosexuality was denied in the hairdressers as well as any other members of the family.) The father worked six days a week and relaxed on the seventh. The boy would frequently go to his father's shop on afternoons and all day Saturday to watch his father work. On Sunday the father was "too exhausted" to spend significant time with the boy. I believe that in this case the boy was not only being deprived of a strong relationship with his father (his presence notwithstanding) but was identifying with females whom he observed received significant attention from his father.

A 14-year-old boy asked his parents to bring him to therapy because of strong homosexual fantasies. His father was an extremely domineering, controlling individual who always presented with a facade of reasonableness. However, in any discussion in which differences of opinion were expressed, he maintained a rock-like rigidity. The patient's mother was passive and submissive in her relationship with the father. Neither parent had much capacity to get involved emotionally with the patient and his older sister, then 17. During his initial evaluation, he described very early recollections of his scratching at the locked door of his parents' bedroom every Sunday morning. His parents viewed his attempts to crawl into bed with them on weekend mornings to be an intrusion into their privacy and had absolutely no appreciation of the family joys that such cuddling and horse playing can provide. Early in treatment the patient described this repetitious dream:

> My family and I were in a car going up the driveway to my school. There was a little shack next to the school. I went into the shack. There was a hand there in a white glove. It was a mechanical hand. I had to be very quiet. It was very dangerous, so I couldn't make any noise. Once I sneezed and the hand went over my mouth.

On analysis we learned that the little shack, next to the school, represented the patient's view of himself as isolated from the mainstream of his peers and possibly his family as well. The mechanical hand, covered by a white glove, represented his father who did not allow the patient to express his genuine thoughts and feelings. Even the sneeze, which the patient could not control, was suppressed by the white-gloved hand. The dream was a statement of the great pressure for expression of the patient's repressed thoughts and feelings. Viewing his father as a mechanical hand in a white glove was a statement of the patient's belief that his father was machine-like rather than human. The white glove implies sterility and cover-up of "blackness" and other undesirable personality qualities. It also symbolized the father's veneer of reasonableness to disguise inhumane (mechanical) qualities.

There are a variety of other mechanisms that may be operative in producing a homosexual orientation in a son. The father consciously or unconsciously may wish that his son either be homosexual or a woman, and the youngster complies with the father's wishes—again, consciously or unconsciously. Earlier in this chapter I described this phenomenon in the case of the army Colonel who "feared" over many years that his son would become a homosexual and did everything possible to prevent this from taking place. Sometimes the fathers of homosexual men are jealous of their sons' close relationships with their wives and this rivalry *contributes* to their hostility and rejection of their sons.

Another important factor which I have found to be operative in male homosexuality is the reaction formation to hostility that is often beneath the homosexual's obsessive love of men. Like most obsessions, the obsession with the love of a man is often a way of denying a basic hatred. Considering the poor relationships male homosexuals have had with their fathers in youth, it is more reasonable to predict that homosexual men would be antagonistic toward other males rather than be loving of them. I believe that many homosexuals deal with their anger by reaction formation. However, the hostility may still express itself in the context of the jealous rivalries that they often have in their relationships with one another. Taunting lovers with other lovers is a common phenomenon. Flirting with others in the presence of a lover is commonplace. Although there are certainly homosexual relationships that are benevolent, many are extremely malevolent—relationships in which the "lovers" treat one another quite sadistically.

In the late 1950s, during my residency days, I once spent a two-week vacation period working as a general physician at a homosexual community on Fire Island near New York City. I learned much about homosexuality during that two-week period. Most striking was the hostility these men exhibited toward one another. Although typically well mannered, gracious, and quite well groomed, when inebriated they were capable of extremely brutal behavior toward one another. In fact, the main kind of medical treatment I provided was treatment of various physical traumas that they inflicted upon one another. In restaurants and bars they thought nothing of flirting with one another's "dates." Although heterosexual men and women may have some attraction to their friends' dates, they generally suppress these out of a sense of loyalty to their friends. This was not the case among these men.

I recall being invited to a dinner party by a homosexual couple. Within minutes of my arrival it was quite apparent that one of the couple (whom I will call Ralph) was the dominant and assertive one and the other (whom I will call Paul) was the passive and submissive one. Ralph ordered Paul around as if he were a slave, and Paul did everything possible to ingratiate himself to Ralph. Ralph treated Paul with scorn, and Paul seemed not to notice how much he was being denigrated. When we sat down to eat, Ralph sat at the head of the table, while Paul was in the kitchen preparing to serve the meal. Paul served Ralph first. Ralph tasted the food, spit it in Paul's face, and picked up the plate and emptied its contents on Paul's head. He screamed: "What kind of shit do you think this is?" Paul then began crying, begging Ralph for forgiveness. Although I am sure that such a scene could take place with a heterosexual couple, I consider it far less likely. These men presented themselves as "lovers"; I think they would have been more honest if they had presented themselves as "haters." It is not difficult for me to understand why murder of the homosexual lover is not uncommon.

Another factor I have found operative in many homosexuals is the narcissistic one. A heterosexual man is attracted to someone who is quite different from himself; the homosexual man, in contrast, is attracted to someone who looks like himself. It is not uncommon for homosexuals to become sexually aroused when looking at themselves in the mirror, and I had one patient who actually masturbated when looking at himself in the mirror. He told me that this was a fairly common practice among homosexuals.

Interestingly, most homosexual men have good relationships with women. Although they may have little if any sexual desires toward women, and although they may be fearful of sexual encounters with them, they are not fearful of women in general. In fact, they often get along quite well with women because they share the same interests. They can discuss at length clothing styles, hair styles, furniture, home-making, and other topics that are usually of interest to women. This is one of the reasons why homosexuals are overrepresented in the hairdresser population. The average man would find intolerable even the prospect of spending many hours each day talking with women about the topics women discuss in their beauty parlors. This comfort with and enjoyment of women as friends often stems from a close and sometimes seductive relationship with their mothers. Many were "Mama's boys" in their childhood and even as adults are quite interested in their mothers and treat them quite well. It is not uncommon for homosexual men to ask each other about how their mothers are; however, it is far less common for them to ask each other how their fathers are. Many of the mothers of boys who become homosexual had poor relationships with their husbands and turned to their sons for a compensatory relationship. Commonly their sons became their confidantes. Often the sexual relationship between the parents is a poor one, and the mother turns to the son for some kind of physical gratification — although not generally overtly sexual. This, however, is often enough to satisfy her needs. The son may also have been titillated by this special relationship with his mother and may gravitate toward men as a way of avoiding heterosexual relationships because of their incestuous connotations. The titillation by the mother may also evoke resentment toward women in general. The homosexual orientation then becomes a statement of the homosexual male's total sexual rejection of women.

The mothers of these men are often overprotective, domineering, and interfere with the youngsters' developing strong ties with girls in the dating period. Subsequently they do whatever they possibly can to disrupt their sons' relationships with women who are potential candidates for marriage. In fact, the mother may have actually encouraged the homosexuality (most often unconsciously) because of her appreciation that a homosexual son is less likely to marry and leave her. Some mothers of homosexual men had conscious or unconscious wishes that the child be a daughter and the boy's homosexual orientation is, in part, an attempt to gratify the mother's wish. The mother's position as the primary authority and disciplinarian in the family may result in the son's view of women as harsh, hostile, and as individuals who are to be feared or avoided for intimate relationships.

For some homosexual men, an important contributing factor has been homosexual seduction in the prepubertal or pubertal years. Some of these men, I suspect, would not have developed along the homosexual route had it not been for this (or these) early encounter(s). It is as if the homosexual encounter caused them to "switch tracks." Because of their lack of sexual experience they came to view homosexuality as a source of intense pleasure and had no appreciation that heterosexuality was also a pleasurable option. And residua of this early distortion seem to have played a role in their subsequent gravitation toward homosexuality.

I am not claiming to have presented a comprehensive statement of all the psychodynamic mechanisms operative in producing male homosexuality. Rather, I have described what I have found to be some of the more important mechanisms that contribute to the development of this form of psychopathology. I. Bieber (1962) and L. Hatterer (1970) are both proponents of the view that homosexuality is primarily, if not exclusively, a psychogenic disturbance and have described in detail their studies in this area. L.C. Kolb and

H.K.H. Brodie (1982) make reference to a number of studies of identical twin pairs in which one member became heterosexual and the other homosexual. These studies lend support to the theory that the genetic loading in homosexuality may be minimal and that it is primarily a psychogenic disorder.

Common Psychodynamic Patterns That Contribute to the Development of Female Homosexuality   As mentioned, I have had less experience with female homosexuality and would prefer not to merely report here the experiences of others. In my discussion of the etiological factors operative in bringing about male homosexuality, I mentioned my experiences with consultations and therapy of homosexuality in childhood and adolescence. In contrast, I cannot recall parents ever having brought a pre-school girl to me because of masculine tendencies. Nor have I had any experiences with girls at the elementary-school level being brought to treatment because of this complaint. I have, however, seen adolescent girls who are disturbed by their homosexuality (again, those who are not upset by it do not come for therapy). And I have seen a few young adult women in whom homosexuality has been a presenting complaint; however, as mentioned, my experience with such women is limited. One reason for this, I suspect, is that such women are more likely to go to a female therapist. In addition, in recent years, both male and female homosexual adults are less likely to view their homosexuality as a manifestation of psychopathology, because of the view held by many mental health professionals today that such behavior is not a psychopathological manifestation.

However, in the course of my custody evaluations (Gardner, 1982 and 1986b) I have had many occasions to evaluate both male and female homosexual parents. Some of the women I have seen who are homosexuals have become so after varying degrees of involvement in heterosexual life. Often they have turned to homosexuality because of their disillusionment with men. Some considered themselves heterosexual in their earlier years but, after many rejections and disappointments, turned to homosexuality for sexual gratification as well as satisfaction of their needs for emotional involvements with other people. A common statement made by homosexual women is that women make much more sensitive lovers than men. They describe most men as being concerned only with their own needs and as losing interest entirely after they have had their own satisfactions. Women, in contrast, are described as being far more sensitive and empathic lovers who are more concerned with the needs of the partner. Whereas one can say with a high degree of certainty that homosexual men have had poor relationships with their fathers, I cannot make the same statement about homosexual women having had poor relationships with their mothers. Some have actually had good relationships with their mothers and are not turning to other women as part of a life-long campaign to extract love from a female. This may be an explanation of why lesbian relationships are more likely to be deep and ongoing than male homosexual relationships.

A powerful anger element, however, is frequently operative in lesbianism. Whereas in male homosexuality the anger is dealt with by reaction formation and obsessive love of men, in female homosexuality the anger is the result of disappointment with and rejections by men. Accordingly, the love of women is not particularly sought as a way of suppressing and repressing underlying hatred of them. Lesbians hate men and love women. Male homosexuals are friendly with and like women, but their love of men is often a reaction formation to underlying hatred. Accordingly, they are much worse off because there is less of a likelihood that they will have bona fide loving relationships with either sex.

Other factors may be operative in bringing about female homosexuality. A woman may find lesbianism attractive because of fears of heterosexual involvements. Some homosexual women basically would have preferred to be men and such women may gratify these desires (at least in part) by acquiring male gestures, wearing male clothing, and using dildos in sexual acts in which they portray the role of a male. Some have identified with homosexual mothers. Just as some male homosexuals are obsessively involved with loving men as a reaction formation to an underlying hatred of men, there are female homosexuals who are enraged at women and their homosexuality is a reflection of their dealing with this by reaction formation. Some have indeed been rejected by their mothers and are looking for mother love from another woman. Some rival with a male for the love of a female as a manifestation of an Electra complex. Some have parents who basically wanted a boy, encouraged them to be tomboys when younger, and may have even encouraged their becoming "dykes." An overprotective mother may contribute to a daughter's homosexuality in order to discourage marriage and keep her in the home. A father who is threatened by his daughter's heterosexuality may also encourage her homosexuality. Just as a seductive mother may contribute to a boy's development of homosexuality, a seductive father may similarly contribute to a girl's development of lesbianism. In both cases the opposite-sexed partner comes to be viewed as titillating, but not gratifying, and therefore a source of frustration. A woman who was rejected by her mother in childhood may assume a male identity in order to attract mother and derivative females, just as she observed father to attract her mother.

Considerations Regarding the Treatment of Homosexual Adolescents   It is not my purpose here to discuss at length the psychotherapy of adolescent homosexuals. Furthermore, my experience in this area is not vast enough for me to be able to present myself as an expert in this area. However, I certainly have had some experience in the treatment of these youngsters, and there are some statements I can make that I believe might be of interest and help to those who are treating them.

First, when the teenage homosexual boy comes for treatment the therapist does well to warn the youngster that an important determinant of whether or not he will be able to switch to the heterosexual track will be his ability to avoid entering into an active homosexual life. The youngster may be greatly tempted to do so because of the high likelihood that there will be little sexual frustration and frequent success. When a young teenage boy walks into a gay bar, the likelihood of his being rejected is extremely small. But even if he is rejected in the first and second encounters, it is not likely that he will continually be spurned. This is in sharp contrast to the situation for the adolescent boy in the heterosexual scene where, sexual revolution notwithstanding, the youngster is not likely to enjoy immediate success with a high degree of predictability. The heterosexual youngster, then, must have the ego-strength to tolerate rejections and recognize that they do not necessarily mean that he has significant deficiencies. Rather, he must be able to appreciate that he cannot be attractive to everyone and that a significant percentage of girls will not find him particularly desirable. However, he must have the self-confidence to move on to other girls and recognize that after a certain number of overtures he is likely to achieve some kind of successful involvement. During the course of his quest he must have a thick enough skin to tolerate occasional rejections. A homosexual youngster may not have the fortitude for such rejections and his "thin skin" results in his gravitating toward homosexual bars (or other places with a high density of homosexuals) where he is far less likely to suffer such rejections. Once in that scene he is also far less likely to go back to the heterosexual track.

In the last few years, with the increasing spread of AIDS, homosexuals have reduced significantly their frequenting gay bars, bath houses, and other places where they go for sexual encounters. Accordingly, this danger for the homosexual adolescent has lessened. However, these youngsters are still viewed as "luscious fruits" by older homosexuals and are likely to be lured into homosexual encounters by them. One or two such encounters may tip the balance significantly in the homosexual direction. As mentioned, the power of these early encounters cannot be underestimated. I have seen a few homosexual males who claim that their introduction to homosexuality took place around ages four to six when they were sexually seduced. Although other factors were certainly operative, the seduction somehow "locked" the youngster into a homosexual track.

The therapy of such youngsters must involve attempts on the therapist's part to encourage dating. Therapy is not likely to be successful as an intellectual pursuit; rather, it must be combined with actual experiences in the heterosexual realm which can be discussed in the treatment process. It is important for the therapist to appreciate that such heterosexual encounters are only a small part of the treatment. There are homosexual men who have married in an attempt to cure their homosexuality and have been unsuccessful. The youngster who is ambivalent about homosexuality and who has definite heterosexual desires as well is more likely to be helped by heterosexual encounters. Others may be frightened by them, so much so that they may withdraw from treatment.

Although there may be some exceptions, I think it is preferable for a homosexual boy to have a male therapist. As mentioned, difficulties in the relationship with the father have most often been a central factor in the development of the homosexuality. Providing such youngsters with a relationship with a therapist who is warm and understanding may help to counteract the privations the youngster has suffered in his relationship with his father. Whereas the homosexual youngster equates sexual encounters with love, in proper therapy no such gratification will be provided. Rather, the therapist provides something closer to what the youngster has been deprived of, namely, a warm, affectionate, and sensitive relationship.

If the youngster's treatment extends to the point where he goes off to college, then a new problem may arise in the treatment. Most colleges today have active gay communities which are not only quite overt about their homosexuality but involve themselves actively in various homosexual campus activities. They proselytize, seduce, and make every attempt to add to their numbers. This is a dangerous situation for the youngster who is ambivalent about homosexuality and trying to "go straight." Because I consider obligatory homosexuality to be a psychiatric disturbance, I view these groups to be a statement of misguided liberalism on campus. To me, it is as appropriate to have a homosexual club on a college campus as it is to have a club of drug addicts, people with character disorders, anorexia-bulemics, etc. If the latter clubs were formed with the recognition that we are dealing with a form of psychopathology and the groups' goal is to help one another with their problems ("self-help" groups), then I would have no difficulty supporting these organizations. However, the homosexual groups have no such philosophy. Rather, their goal is to promulgate, proselytize, educate people about homosexuality, and fight for their civil rights.

Although I have no objection to homosexuals' getting their civil rights, and although I also believe that a certain amount of education about homosexuality is useful, I believe that the kind of education these groups provide is erroneous and misguided, especially because it tries to educate others into believing that homosexuality is a normal, healthy human variation. A common maneuver for these proselytizers is to attempt to make "straight" youngsters feel embarrassed about their heterosexuality. They may try to get them to feel that they are not showing reasonable flexibility in their sexual options and that they are narrow minded. I believe that such need to convert others stems from an underlying insecurity about the stability of their homosexuality and follows the principle that "misery loves company." The more straight youngsters the homosexuals can convert, the more secure they believe they will be in their rationalization that their homosexuality is a normal human variant and not a form of psychopathology.

In recent years, many boys' colleges have gone coed, and many girls' colleges have gone coed as well. Furthermore, some formerly single-sexed colleges have merged to provide coeducation for their students. There are, however, certain girls' colleges that have remained all female. Not surprisingly, some of these have become attractive to homosexual girls. Heterosexual girls who attend such colleges, often because they may be quite prestigious, may then find themselves lured into a homosexual lifestyle. Some of these heterosexual girls had never entertained notions of homosexuality and, had they not been proselytized, would have proceeded along the heterosexual track. Accordingly, I consider these girls to have been corrupted. Many of these girls were not particularly successful in their relationships with boys and so became prime targets for conversion.

I recognize that the things I have just said about homosexuality on college campuses puts me in a particularly unpopular position in the mid- to late 1980s. I suspect that there are many others on campuses who share my views, but who fear expressing them openly lest they subject themselves to public condemnation, picketing, and a variety of wild accusations. Although most universities pride themselves on being institutions where there is freedom of expression of ideas, there are still certain ideas not freely expressed—even in the most liberal and open universities. Criticism of homosexuality is one such example. Therapists treating college-bound homosexual youngsters do well to encourage them to avoid attending universities where militant gay groups are likely to have influence over their patients. Rather, they do well to encourage their applying only to schools where the gay community is either nonexistent or plays a limited role in college life. Admittedly, such places may be difficult to find, but they do exist.

Of course, the therapist must attempt to ascertain what the specific factors are that have contributed to that particular patient's homosexuality. Earlier in this section I have presented what I consider to be some of the more common contributory elements. The danger for the therapist is to assume that his or her patient automatically fits into one or more of the aforementioned categories. It is preferable to approach the situation with an open mind and to attempt to ascertain exactly which etiological and psychodynamic factors were operative in that particular patient's life situation. These are the issues that should be primarily dealt with in the treatment. The aforementioned recommendations are general ones and should be viewed more as external and facilitating factors in the therapy.

Other Sexual Problems of Adolescence

Therapists who treat adolescents will invariably be confronted with the problem of the adolescent's sexual behavior. As I will discuss in Chapter Five, I do not believe that a therapist can conduct treatment without significant imposition of his or her own values on the patient. It is hoped that the values so promulgated will serve the patient well. And it is in the sexual realm, especially, that value judgements are likely to be transmitted. My own view is that it is normal and healthy for the adolescent to progress to increasing levels of sexual activity during the teenage period. Although one does well to try to get the adolescent to subscribe to certain principles regarding the superiority of sex in ongoing relationships over transient sex, one is not likely to be significantlly successful in pomulgating this notion with most adolescents. Boys, especially, need to prove themselves as "men" by having sexual relations. And girls, too, are increasingly viewing themselves as somehow inadequate if they are still virgins in their late teens. None of this may be particularly pathological in my opinion. What is pathological is the youngster who is so obsessed with sex—much more than the usual degree of preoccupation—that other functions are interfered with. If a girl believes that the greater the number of lovers she has the more attractive she is then she is likely to have problems. If she feels that no one will want her unless she provides sex, then her sexual behavior is likely to be pathological. Her feelings of inadequacy are likely to reveal themselves in other areas, and this lends confirmation to the view that her promiscuity has less to do with sex and more to do with a misguided attempt to compensate for such feelings of inadequacy. If a boy is merely using girls as objects, has little sensitivity to their feelings, and is compulisively trying to "lay" as many as he can in order to compensate for feelings of inadequacy, then this is pathological. Here too, feelings of low self-worth are likely to manifest themselves in other areas. This provides confirmation to the view that his compulsive sexuality is a form of pathological compensation.

Another pathological situation in the context of normal adolescent sexuality is the failure to use proper protection. As mentioned, adolescents suffer with delusions of invulnerability. A related phenomenon is the delusion that they can have sex without pregnancy and that somehow only others will get pregnant. At the time of this writing there is another reason for using contraception, namely, the increasing prevalence of sexually transmitted diseases. The most dreaded of these, of course, is acquired immune deficiency syndrome (AIDS). Many adolescents consider the use of condoms to be a sign of masculine inadequacy; unfortunately, their girl friends may go along with this. So we have two problems then that emerge from the adolescent's delusions of invulnerability: teenage pregnancy and sexually transmitted diseases. Because of these delusions, I have little faith in educational programs designed to get adolescents to be more reliable in the utilization of contraception. I am not claiming that such efforts are entirely futile, only that educators should recognize they have an "uphill fight" because of the power of adolescent denial mechanisms and their delusions of invulnerability. At the time of this writing the AIDS epidemic does not appear to have infiltrated to a significant degree into the college population. Considering the ubiquity of homosexuality and bisexuality on the college campus, and considering the freedom with which college students have multiple sexual partners, it is reasonable to predict that AIDS will start making its inroads into the college population (both homosexual and heterosexual) in the near future. When one adds delusions of invulnerability to the situation, the results are likely to be disastrous. Anything a therapist can do to encourage his patients to protect themselves from contracting AIDS (by judicious selection of partners and automatic utilization of condoms) may be lifesaving.

Occasionally, an adolescent girl will inform a therapist that she is pregnant and her parents do not know. If the therapist knows that the parents will deal with the problem in a sane way, he or she does well to do everything possible to insure that the parents learn of the pregnancy as early as possible. Such a girl has to be reassured that her parents are not going to react as horrendously as she may anticipate. Early disclosure is important because, for many families, abortion may be an option. However, the longer one waits, the less viable and the more psychologically traumatic this option becomes. In some cases the situation may warrant the therapist's not "respecting" the adolescent's confidentiality and revealing the fact of the pregnancy. As I have described elsewhere (1975, 1986a) the patient is not coming to the therapist for confidentiality; rather the patient is coming for treatment. To the degree that confidentiality serves the goals of the therapy, to that degree it should be respected. In contrast, to the degree that respecting the confidentiality is anti-therapeutic, to that degree it should not be respected. The reasons an adolescent gives for not disclosing a pregnancy to parents are, in most situations, pathological and the failure to get the parents involved is likely to cause the youngster far more trouble than early disclosure.

Another sexually related problem that one sees in early adolescence is that of stealing. I am not referring to stealing in general, but a specific kind of stealing that, I believe, is related to the youngster's emerging sexuality. I refer here to the practice among early adolescent girls of stealing certain items from department stores and novelty shops. Typically, the youngsters will steal such objects as lipstick, perfume, and scarves. Parents who learn about such thefts may be amazed and respond with comments such as, "I can't understand why she's stealing these things. We certainly can afford to buy these things for her." Often, the youngsters will steal these items, although they could well afford to purchase them from their allowances. If the parent offers to pay the youngster to buy them, the offer is often refused. I believe these thefts represent an attempt on the part of these adolescent girls to enhance their sexual attractiveness with the stolen items. They are operating on the principle that forbidden fruit is sweeter and that the perfume stolen from a department store is more likely to attract boys than that provided by a parent who, by virtue of old age and decrepitude, is viewed as sexless. Although it is obviously the same bottle of perfume, its having been stolen adds a certain allure to the scent.

Often the cure for this disorder is the youngster's being caught by a department store security guard and the parents' being informed that a recurrence will be reported to the police.

CONCLUDING COMMENTS

It has not been my purpose in this chapter to present all of the situations that might be conducive to adolescents developing psychopathology. Rather, I have described those environmental factors (both familial and social) that I have found to be frequently operative in my own experiences. I recognize that others have had different experiences and so would have provided a different presentation if they were in my place. Because many of these family and environmental factors are extensive and deep-seated, the therapist does well to have modest goals with regard to changing them. Furthermore, although the adolescent is only in his or her teens, the youngster has still been exposed to many of these influences for more than a decade and this too should produce some caution in the therapist regarding predicting therapeutic success.

THREE

THE INITIAL
DIAGNOSTIC
EVALUATION

My diagnostic evaluation is divided into two parts. The first is a two-hour consultation, during which I see the youngster and both parents in varying combinations. I refer to this section as *The Initial Diagnostic Evaluation*. If treatment is warranted then I will collect more extensive data, during which time I will see each parent once or twice, the youngster two or three times, and conduct a family interview if there are siblings old enough to contribute meaningfully to such a session. The second phase I refer to as *The Extended Diagnostic Evaluation*. In this chapter I will discuss the initial diagnostic evaluation and in the next the extended diagnostic evaluation. In both phases I am interested in assessing for both psychogenic and neurologically based disorders. However, in these two chapters I will only focus on the procedures I utilize for assessing psychogenic impairment. When a neurologically based learning disability is present or is suspected then further interviews and/or testing may be warranted. The reader interested in information about the tests I administer for youngsters with neurologically based learning disabilities might wish to refer to other publications of mine in this area (1979b, 1986a, 1987b).

WHO SHALL BE SEEN IN THE INITIAL CONSULTATION?

There are many ways to conduct the initial screening interview. Various combinations of patient and/or parent(s) in different sequences, with one or more interviewers, may be utilized. For example, the patient may be seen alone, the parent(s) alone, the patient and parent(s) together, or a total family interview may be held. There may be one interviewer for all or separate interviewers seeing one or more individuals at a time. Of all the possible approaches, I prefer the first interview to be conducted with the youngster and parents together, individually and in varying combinations—as warranted. All things considered, I believe this arrangement to have the greatest number of advantages and the fewest drawbacks as compared to the other commonly used methods. Moreover, I believe that the clinical interviews (and treatment) are preferably conducted by one person.

The three-person interview also provides the therapist with the opportunity to observe directly interactions between the parents and the patient. Seeing the parents alone in the initial interview deprives the therapist of first-hand observation of the patient. No matter how astute the parents may be in describing their youngster, they cannot provide the interviewer with as accurate a picture as the patient's actual presence can.

There are some who take great pains to keep the patient-therapist dyad completely separate from all therapeutic work and/or contact with the parents. From the outset, they will arrange for the parents to be counseled by a colleague, with whom there are occasional conferences. Proponents of this approach claim that the patient's relationship with the therapist will be diluted and contaminated by any contact the therapist may have with the parents. They hold that the patient must have the feeling of having the therapist all to him- or herself and the treatment will suffer without such exclusivity. There are some therapists who take this so far that they will have absolutely no contact at all with the parents at any time.

Many hold that such exclusivity is especially important for adolescents because of their special need for independence from their parents.

I have formidable criticisms of this approach. It deprives the therapist of the opportunity of seeing the parents first-hand. No matter how accurate the patient's description, he or she most often has distortions, which may be clarified via direct contact with the parents. And the colleague working with the parents is likely to have distortions about the youngster because information about him or her has been filtered through the parents. The patient's problems are inextricably involved with the family's, and the therapist, by isolating the dyad, removes it from the field within which the problems have arisen and taken place and within which they must be worked through. Furthermore, the arrangement precludes joint interviews with the parents that can be a valuable source of information about family dynamics and interpersonal relations. Nor does contact with the parents retard the adolescent's development of autonomy. Physical contact does not have to be equated with dependency. True independence need not preclude a close, mature relationship with one's parents.

I have not found that my relationships with my adolescent patients have suffered because of contact with parents (and these have varied from occasional interviews to actual simultaneous therapy with one of the parents, usually the mother). In fact, such contacts and involvements have most often deepened my relationship with the youngster. If the parents have respect for and faith enough in the therapist to consult him or her themselves, the youngster's involvement is likely to be enhanced. When the opposite is true, when there is little if any contact, the patient's commitment may become reduced.

There are some who hold quite strongly that the adolescent should be seen alone in the first interview, but they will work subsequently with the parents in varying degrees. They reason that such an approach communicates to the patient, from the very beginning, that *he* or *she* is the patient, and that this message is vital if subsequent work is to be successful. I do not consider this to be such an important consideration because, more often than not, I see the parents as equally deserving of my clinical attention. I prefer to communicate to all that they are each to be clinically evaluated and that the greatest concentration is yet to be determined—therefore, the three-person interview.

It is for these reasons that my initial two-hour interview is one to which all three parties are invited. During that time they are seen in any possible combination, either individually or jointly. I generally begin the interview, however, with the adolescent alone, and the parents join us subsequently. In this way, I provide the adolescent with a separate experience from the parents, which is important for youngsters of this age to have. however, the parents are still brought in, which gets across the message that I am going to involve them in the treatment as well. Some adolescents object strongly to parental involvement, usually as a manifestation of specious independence or as a way of preventing parental disclosures. There is rarely a good reason for the therapist to comply with the adolescent's request (and even demand) that the parents be excluded from the therapy. To comply with such a restriction will most likely compromise significantly the treatment.

THE INITIAL TELEPHONE CALL

Although one of my secretaries almost invariably answers my telephone, she makes no appointments—whether it be the first appointment or any other appointment in the total course of the treatment. When a person calls for an appointment, he or she is informed that I will be available to speak during certain call times when I can generally speak in a more leisurely manner. If the day is particularly tight (often the case), I will converse with the parent during the evening. I generally find a ten-minute conversation necessary before setting up the initial appointment. My purpose here is to get some information about the nature of the youngster's problems to place myself in a better position to deal with unexpected events that may occur during the initial consultation. Because of the unpredictability of adolescents, therapists who work with them must be prepared to deal with many more "surprises" than those who treat adults.

But there are other reasons for my acquiring more information before making the initial appointment. Sometimes, an appointment might not be necessary. A parent might call requesting a consultation regarding how to tell the children about an impending separation. In such cases I may refer the caller to my *The Parents Book About Divorce* (1977, 1979a) and suggest the section on telling children about an impending separation. I am careful, however, to reassure such callers that I am not turning them away; rather, I am trying to save them money in that the cost of the pocket edition of my book is far less than a consultation. I inform them also that if this does not prove sufficient, then I will be happy to set up an appointment for a consultation. On a number of occasions I have received calls from distraught parents at the time of a sudden death of a spouse, which was followed by a heated family argument regarding whether or not children should attend the funeral services and burial. Often I can provide meaningful advice in a short time, and no consultation is necessary.

Sometimes the symptoms described will be short-lived and the parent is not aware of the fact that all youngsters exhibit at times transient symptomatology such as tics, gastrointestinal complaints, or a wide variety of fears. On occasion, symptomatic reactions to parental divorce may be the reason for the parent's call. In many such situations I will advise the parents to wait awhile because such symptoms are predictable and are usually transient. The authors of DSM-III-R are most appreciative of this phenomenon, and this is reflected in the stipulation that time considerations must be taken into account before many childhood diagnoses are warranted.

Some parents who anticipate custody litigation may call requesting therapy in the hope that they can then use the therapist as an advocate in the litigation. It behooves the therapist to "smell these out" over the telephone in order to avoid sticky and compromising situations. (I consider myself to have an excellent sense of smell in these situations.) If there is any doubt about such a caller's true motives, I will inform the individual that a decision must be made *before the first interview* as to whether my services are requested for the purpose of *litigation* or for *therapy*. I inform such callers that I am receptive to following either path and have significant experience in both realms; however, once one course is chosen I will not switch to the other and I will be asking that the appropriate document be signed—*again before the first interview*—which strictly confines me to a particular path. The reasons for my rigidity on this point relate to important legal issues (Gardner, 1982, 1986b).

On one occasion a mother called and, after telling me the presenting problems, told me that I would have to promise her something before she would make the first appointment. I immediately smelled something foul, but didn't know what it would be. She then told me that her child was adopted and that I must promise her that under no circumstances would I ever reveal this to him. I told her that I would make no such promise and that I cannot imagine the child's therapy proceeding without this topic being discussed at some point in the treatment. I reassured her that I would not scream the fact in the child's face as soon as he entered the room, but I would not agree to such a restriction throughout the whole course of treatment. She advised me that other doctors had agreed to this restriction. I advised her then to consult these other doctors and that I was giving her my position on the subject.

A common problem that can easily be obviated in the initial telephone call is the one in which a divorced mother sets up an appointment and informs the therapist that her former husband will be paying her bills and that the therapist should bill him directly. In response to such callers I generally respond that I will be happy to do so if her former husband will call me and tell me directly that he will be paying for my services. Often I will get the response that he is *required* to pay all medical bills as a stipulation of the divorce decree and that if I have trouble getting the money from him, I should sue him and she is sure the courts will order him to pay. Any therapist who is naive, gullible, or masochistic enough to accept a patient under these circumstances does not get my pity.

A mother will call asking for a consultation. I inform her that my usual procedure is to see both parents and the youngster, in varying combinations, during a two-hour consultation. The mother informs me that she is divorced, with the implication that that fact in itself is justification for my not involving her former husband in the consultation. I will generally then ask if the youngster's father still maintains some involvement with him or her. If the answer is in the affirmative, I then recommend that the mother consult with the father and invite him to join us for the first interview. I generally do this before a specific appointment is made. This insures that the mother will at least invite the father (who, of course, may or may not accept). My experience is that such involved fathers most often attend. The mother may argue that it would not be a good idea to have her former husband join us because "all we'll do is fight." My response to such a mother generally goes along these lines: "It is certainly not my goal to get you to fight. However, this I can tell you: I already know that as long as you and your husband cannot be in the same room together without fighting, your youngster will continue to have psychiatric problems. I cannot imagine helping your son (daughter) with his (her) problems, as long as there is such severe animosity between you and your ex-husband. I can tell you now that one of my goals in therapy will be to try to get the two of you to reduce your hostilities. If that wasn't one of my goals, I wouldn't be qualified to help your child. Also, although the fighting is certainly unpleasant, I will probably learn some important things from it that will be useful in your youngster's treatment." Here again I have most often been successful in getting both parties to attend the initial interview.

On occasion, the calling mother may respond to my request for the father's involvement with "My husband doesn't believe in psychiatry. He told me that if I want to take Wally to a psychiatrist, it's okay with him but he doesn't want to get involved." To which I will reply, "Please tell your husband that my experience has been that the more involvement I have on the part of both parents, the greater the likelihood the treatment will be successful. If your husband refuses to involve himself entirely, I will do the best I can, but please inform him that I'll be working under compromised circumstances." I call this: *The-ball-is-in-your-court-baby principle.* I basically say to the husband that the choice is his. If he wants me to conduct therapy under optimum circumstances, he will involve himself. If he doesn't do so, there will be less of a likelihood that the treatment will be successful, and he will have thereby contributed to its failure. Again, most often husbands appear when this message is transmitted to them. Doing everything reasonable to bring both parents into the initial interview establishes also a certain precedent, namely, that their involvement in the child's treatment is important and my urging them both to be present at the outset is a clear statement of this. I might say here parenthetically, for those readers in private practice, that those husbands who do not *believe in* psychiatry are not famous for their *paying for* psychiatry.

During this initial telephone conversation some parents ask my fee. Without hesitation I give my response. At the time of this writing my answer is this; "My fee for the initial two-hour consultation will be $300. My fee for the subsequent therapy ranges from a standard fee of $110 for a 45-minute session down to $80 for a 45-minute session. The exact fee will be determined at the time of the consultation on the basis of your financial situation and insurance coverage." I know of many therapists who refuse to discuss fees over the telephone. This is not only injudicious but alienating. It cannot but engender distrust on the patient's part. It is reasonable for a patient to conclude from such an answer that "I guess he's going to try to get as much as he can." And such a conclusion is warranted. The argument that the discussion may have psychoanalytic significance is not justified. The caller is not an analytic patient; he or she is just a parent who is entitled to know what the therapist charges.

Before closing the conversation, I inform the caller that I will be sending a questionnaire that I would like both parents to fill out. This questionnaire (Appendix II) is quite comprehensive and provides me with a significant amount of "upfront" information at the time of the initial consultation. I have found my questionnaire extremely valuable for the large majority of consultations. It provides the therapist with an immense amount of information in a few minutes, information that might take hours to obtain via direct questioning. It is useful in assessing for the presence of psychogenic disturbances as well as diagnosing youngsters who suffer with what I refer to as the *Group of Minimal Brain Dysfunction Syndromes (GMBDS)*. I prefer to use this term over MBD because MBD implies a single disease entity. Rather, we are dealing here with a group of syndromes. It is unreasonable to attempt to assess for both psychogenic problems and the presence of GMBDS in a single two-hour interview. In this book I will focus only on the psychogenic problems of adolescents. For a detailed discussion of the evaluation of their neurologically based psychiatric disorders, I refer the reader to my books on this subject (1979b, 1987b). The questionnaire helps the examiner determine which are the areas that should most appropriately be focused on in the initial consultation. It tells the examiner where the "smoke" is so that he or she can know where to look for the "fires." Accordingly, it should be referred to frequently in the course of the initial consultation. The reader who plans to use the questionnaire would do well to read my detailed discussion of its utilization (1986a).

Furthermore, the questionnaire has certain fringe benefits. It is detailed and thorough, thereby creating a good impression with many parents—even before the first interview. This "good impression" helps establish a sound relationship with the parents, which can ultimately contribute to the youngster's having a better relationship with the therapist. Furthermore, it provides examiners with a well-organized format on which to base their reports. When dictating a report the examiner merely peruses the questionnaire and dictates information directly from it. The organization is already there and the examiner is saved the trouble of thumbing through notes, shifting back and forth, etc.

Attached to the questionnaire is a face letter (Appendix I) which I consider to be quite important. For parents who have not asked about the fees, they are provided this information with the questionnaire so that there is no disappointment, incredulity, amazement, and other reactions that may result in nonpayment of the fees. It also informs the parents that they will have the obligation themselves to pay me and that I will not pursue third parties for payment. (Many patients feel no guilt over doctors' doing this.)

SPECIAL CONSIDERATIONS FOR THE ADOLESCENT WHO RESISTS COMING TO THE FIRST SESSION

On a few occasions an adolescent him- or herself has called to set up the initial appointment. The parents were aware of the telephone call and had agreed to pay for the treatment. In these situations it was not that the parents did not wish to have any involvement in the treatment; rather, they were told by the adolescent that their complete removal from the treatment would be a proviso of the youngster's going into therapy. Therapists who agree to such an arrangement are making a mistake. Although there may be very rare situations in which this is warranted, I personally have not yet seen one. With the exception of these circumstances, the restriction is best viewed as a cover-up maneuver, a mechanism for preventing the therapist from finding out important information about the patient. Accordingly, in these cases I asked the youngster why the parents were being prohibited from involvement in the treatment and I did not get a satisfactory answer. In each of the cases the answers involved "privacy," "It's none of their business what goes on in my treatment," and "I don't know, I just don't want them involved."

Many years ago, when I first started my practice, I received a call from a colleague who informed me that he was referring a 15-year-old girl who stated that she wanted to have treatment, but refused absolutely to have her parents involved. The parents agreed to pay for the therapy because of the girl's insistence that she would not see a therapist if they were to be involved. Reluctantly, the parents agreed. She came in the first session, gave me her name, address, and telephone number and said nothing else. It mattered not whether I was silent or reached out to her. In both cases she was mute. At the end of the session she paid me the $15 and made another appointment. During the second appointment I informed her that I was getting very bored and I would not continue with such sessions much longer. Again various approaches, including silences intermixed with overtures, proved futile. At the end of the second session I informed her that I would try *one* more session and that after that, if she still remained mute, I would terminate the treatment. The third session was spent in the same way. Following this session I called the parents and spoke with the father. He informed me that she had agreed to treatment only if he would give her $10 for each session that she attended. Accordingly, he was paying $25 a session, $15 to me and $10 to his daughter. From her point of view it was an easy ten bucks!

On a few occasions I have received calls from adolescents who wished to set up an appointment, but had not cleared this with their parents. From the purely ethical and legal point of view, it may be risky for the therapist to see such youngsters— especially if recommendations are made that the parents may interpret as not being in the family's best interests. From the therapeutic point of view, the youngsters have invariably not wanted their parents involved and the reasons given were not appropriate. From the financial point of view, making the appointment may be a bad idea because the youngster may not have given any consideration to the question of who is going to pay for the treatment. Accordingly, on each of these occasions I have questioned the adolescent further, asked for the reasons why the parents have not been informed, and recommended that he or she get back to me after the parents have been told of the call and then an appointment would be set up. (Needless to say I never heard from any of these youngsters again.)

On occasion, the calling parent will tell me that the adolescent absolutely refuses to come for treatment. I generally advise such parents to speak again with the youngster and present the meeting as a consultation, the purpose of which is to determine whether treatment is warranted. Sometimes this works, sometimes not. On occasion I have advised parents to inform the adolescent that if he or she doesn't come for the initial consultation as well as a few trial sessions then certain disciplinary measures will be implemented. Some therapists may be surprised that I will use such coercive tactics. Adolescents often need such coercion because it enables them to "save face." Under these circumstances they are not saying: "I am a sick person who needs a therapist." Rather, they are saying "I am a healthy person who is submitting to inordinate pressures by my all-powerful parents and it is judicious of me to come to these sessions in order not to suffer the consequences of my not doing so." Inwardly, they may know they need therapy and the coercion under these circumstances is good medicine. I am merely following here my principle: *Benevolent despotism is the best system of government for children and other primitive peoples.* I am not recommending that these maneuvers be utilized throughout the course of treatment; rather, I am only recommending that they be used during the early phase. In some cases the youngster will then become less defensive about the therapy and continue on his or her own. In other cases, the required number of sessions will be utilized and the adolescent will refuse to come again. On a number of occasions even these tactics haven't worked and the youngster still refuses to come—even to the first meeting. Under these circumstances I will generally see the parents a few times and provide advice regarding how to handle the patient. Although I generally am willing to continue the counseling as long as it proves useful, my experience has been that after a few sessions we reach the point of diminishing returns and the meetings no longer prove of value. There is just so long that one can treat a patient who isn't there.

THE INTERVIEW WITH THE
ADOLESCENT ALONE

As mentioned, I generally begin the initial two-hour consultation by seeing the adolescent alone. This is my practice for youngsters over the age of 13 or thereabouts. In these circumstances I go into the waiting room, introduce myself to both the parents and the young-ster, and then invite the patient into the consultation room. I tell the parents that the youngster and I will be talking alone for a while and then the parents will join us a little later. Most parents appreciate at that point the importance of my starting off with the youngster and recognize that he or she may have to have this special time alone with me. Before leaving the waiting room with the youngster I get the aforementioned questionnaire from the parents. My experience has been that frequent reference to it during the course of the interview enriches the efficacy of the data-collection process—especially for youngsters who are shy, noncooperative, or uncom-municative.

Once the adolescent is in the room I begin with a casual discussion, the primary purpose of which is to make the youngster comfortable but which is general enough not to contaminate any "blank screen." Accordingly, I might ask the youngster if the family had any trouble finding the office and/or may make some comment about the weather or some other innocuous subject. Such inter-changes also lessen anxiety by enabling the patient to view the therapist as a human being, similar to others, rather than some cold machine. From the outset one must consider the all-important relationship that one is trying to establish.

I then proceed to write down some basic data information: name, address, telephone number, age, grade, school, siblings, names and occupations of parents, etc. The purpose here is not simply to obtain this information for my files but, more importantly, to lessen the youngster's anxiety. The youngster cannot but be anxious about the interview, and providing the "right answers" to these questions is likely to lessen anxiety. If one had an instrument for measuring tension level, I believe that it would indicate a reduction of tension with each answer provided at this point.

When I was in training I was taught that the best first question to ask a new patient was something along these lines: "So what brings you to the clinic?" and "So tell me, what's the problem?" I believe this is just about the worst possible question to ask as the *initial* question in the *first* interview with a patient. To me, the therapist who does this is similar to the physician who begins a physical examination by examining first the patient's genitalia. There is a good reason why the doctor begins the examination with the eyes, nose, throat, neck and then works his or her way down to the more private parts. These "name, rank and serial number" type questions reduce anxiety and then make it easier for the patient to answer the more anxiety-provoking questions about the nature of the presenting problems. Although less than five minutes has passed, one has an entirely different patient after asking these factual questions. Accordingly, the kinds of answers one is then going to obtain will also be quite different. Answers given in a state of tension and anxiety are far more likely to be distorted than those given when an individual is calm.

I then proceed to the more specific questions about the presenting problems. On occasion, the youngster will respond that he or she has absolutely no problems at all and that the only reason for the visit is that the parents have coerced the patient to come to the session. I may then spend a few more minutes trying to ascertain what the problems might be. I might ask the youngster to tell me what he or she thinks the parents believe are the problems. If this inquiry also proves futile I will then ask the parents to join us and tell me what they consider the problems to be. Or I might refer to the questionnaire and ask the youngster to comment on what the parents consider to be problems.

An antisocial youngster may be extremely obstructionistic at this point and maintain a facade of arrogance. His or her primary attitude toward the examiner may be one of sneering condescension. All overtures of friendliness by the examiner are rejected. The patient denies any wrong-doing and considers the interview to be a total waste of his or her valuable time. Under these circumstances I generally do not waste significant time trying to engage such a youngster. Rather, I bring the parents in and invite their participation in the interview. In some cases the youngster may drop the facade; in others it is maintained throughout the course of the two-hour evaluation. Examiners do well to approach such situations with the attitude that it does not behoove them to be successful in engaging such a youngster; rather, it only behooves them to try. At the very worst the youngster will never become a patient. We did not create the pathology—it is often generations in the making—and it does not behoove us to cure anyone. In fact, vigorous efforts to do so may defeat the goals of the treatment—because pressures on such patients only enhance their obstructionism.

In Chapter One I described an antisocial adolescent who had previously been in treatment with another therapist. On entering the first session, he sneered: "You shrinks are all the same." He then glanced around the room and, while pointing to different objects, said: "The same stupid couches and those pictures of your crazy kids on the desk." Had I addressed myself to his hostility, I would have missed the point entirely and increased his defensiveness. Accordingly, I merely commented that he was perfectly right and that Dr. X and I did indeed have a number of things in common. He needed to see us as similar in order to be more relaxed, and my response served to help him be so.

Most often, in my interviews with prepubertal children, I will utilize a variety of projective techniques, diagnostic/therapeutic games, and other instruments that enable me to gain information about the patient. In the initial interview with the adolescent, however, I generally engage in "straight talk." I am primarily interested at this point in the clinical symptomatology, not in underlying psychodynamics. My main goal at this point is to collect enough information to make a recommendation regarding whether or not therapy is indicated. And, if therapy is warranted, I want to be in a position to say something about the nature and structure of the therapeutic process. The psychodynamics provide me with information regarding *why* a person has symptoms. It does not generally tell me *whether* treatment is warranted. Everyone has psychodynamics and not all psychodynamic patterns and processes warrant therapy. The primary, if not exclusive, determinant of whether therapy is warranted is the presence of symptoms and clinical behavior. In the extended evaluation I can spend time finding out *why* a person is exhibiting psychopathology.

This is an important point. Many psychologists quickly plunge into administering instruments that enable them to acquire information about underlying psychodynamics. I defy anyone to tell me whether or not a person requires therapy simply on the basis of psychodynamics. Even people who exhibit what is obviously severe pathology in their psychodynamic revelations may not necessarily be psychotherapeutic candidates. They may be too sick for psychiatric treatment and may have absolutely no insight into the fact that they have problems. Accordingly, they have little if any motivation to do anything about themselves. And for the less obvious cases, it is practically impossible to differentiate between the psychodynamic patterns of so-called "normal" people and those whom we label as having psychopathology. All the more reason then to focus on symptoms and clinical manifestations during the initial evaluative session. Later, however, once the patient is in treatment, we can certainly use such information to help us understand better the nature of the patient's problems. I am not claiming to be totally unconcerned with psychodynamics in the first interview. I certainly don't ignore such data if it "hits me in the face." Rather, I am only stating what one's priorities should be at that point.

After the initial period in which we may focus on nonthreatening material, I will usually ask the youngster to talk with me about anything that may be on his or her mind. The purpose here is to avoid going directly and quickly into the more anxiety-provoking areas related to the presenting problems. Accordingly, I may pose such introductory and vague questions as: "Now, what would you like to tell me?" or "So, what would you like to talk about?" Many adolescents at that point (especially older ones, over 16) will talk directly about their problems. The examiner does well to appreciate that even the youngster who chooses to talk about issues ostensibly unrelated to psychiatric difficulties may still be revealing them. Even younger adolescents are still aware that they are in a psychiatrist's office and so—consciously or unconsciously—are likely to think about issues related to the difficulties. Accordingly, the youngster's initial responses to these lead-in questions are likely to result in a discussion of the primary presenting problems. If not, I may then ask more specific and direct questions such as: "So why have your parents brought you to see me today?" or "As you know, your parents have indicated in this questionnaire what they consider to be your problems and difficulties. I'd like to hear from you directly what you consider them to be."

In the course of the conversation about the presenting problems, I try to get the youngster to provide me with specific details, actual examples, and elaborations. General statements and abstractions are of little value in understanding exactly what is going on with the youngster. For example, if the patient says, "I have trouble with friends," the examiner has only the vaguest idea about the problem. It is only after a detailed inquiry into the nature of the peer problems—with at least a few specific examples—that the examiner will have a clearer picture of the problem. And one should do this with each of the presenting problems. It is not the purpose here to conduct the kind of in-depth discussion that one would embark upon in a therapeutic session. Rather, the purpose is to get enough information to decide whether treatment is warranted.

Accordingly, in my initial interview with the adolescent, I generally devote the time completely to "straight talk." On rare occasions, however, I will spend a little time on projective material. I do this in situations where the youngster is telling me absolutely nothing about him- or herself, but still might be cooperative when such instruments are utilized. In other cases, the youngster has cooperated and I have learned, in a relatively short period, about the primary symptoms and so I may then wish to go on to learn something about underlying processes. For such youngsters I will generally start with the Draw-a-Person Test. The patient is given a blank sheet of paper and pencil and told: "Here's a pencil and piece of paper. I want you to draw a made-up person and then tell me a completely made-up, self-created story about that person."

From the universe of possible things a youngster can draw, selecting a person considerably narrows the child's options. However, there is still a universe of possible drawings and associations (a universe within a universe so to speak), and so the drawing is still fairly useful as a projective instrument. One should not ask the patient to draw a person of a specific sex because that may further narrow the possibilities and restrict associations. *After* the youngster has drawn a figure of a particular sex, one can then ask for one of the opposite sex. Generally, the age and sex of the figure drawn is revealing. If a boy, for example, draws a picture of a girl and pays significant attention to such details as eyelashes, coiffure, finger-nails, jewelry, and other attributes generally of great concern to females in our society, one should consider the possibility that this boy has a sexual identification problem. This would especially be the case if most observers, not knowing the sex of the child, would consider it to have been drawn by a girl. If, however, a boy draws a picture of an older woman, it is likely that the mother or her surrogate is being depicted.

By looking at the picture, the therapist can sometimes learn some important things about the patient. However, the reader should be warned that such interpretations are highly speculative and inter-examiner reliability is quite low. This drawback notwith-standing, useful information can still be obtained. This is especially the case if speculations from projective material are substantiated by clinical assessment. Placing the feet of a figure flush against the bottom of the paper may connote feelings of instability with a need to anchor or secure the body to a stable place. Patients with marked feelings of inferiority are more likely to draw their picture in this way. Significant blackness, especially when drawn frenetically, sometimes symbolizes great anxiety and a view of people as threatening. This kind of picture is more frequently drawn by patients who are clinically anxious. Large shoulders and other accentuations of traditionally "macho" features may represent a boy's attempt to compensate for feelings of weakness. This is especially likely for the adolescent with feelings of masculine inadequacy. The way in which the youngster deals with breast outline may provide information about the patient's sexual feelings and attitudes. Family attitudes toward sexuality will often provide clues as to whether the examiner's interpretation in this area is valid. The way in which the patient draws the eyes may provide inform-ation in a number of areas. Those who are shy and prone to use denial mechanisms to a significant degree may draw a figure with the eyes averted. Staring eyes have generally been interpreted to connote suspiciousness and sometimes even paranoia. Again, the examiner does well to make such interpretations cautiously and to use clinical data for support or refutation of these speculations. Machover (1949, 1951, 1960) has written extensively on the psychological interpretation of children's drawings.

The examiner should try to get the patient to tell a story about the picture. One can begin the process by asking for specific information about the person depicted. Some examiners start with the general request that the patient tell a story, and then only resort to specific questions if the request is not or cannot be complied with. The therapist does well to *differentiate* between age-appropriate stereotyped stories (which are probably normal) and idiosyncratic ones. The latter provide the more meaningful information. But here again there is much speculation.

After drawing the first picture, the child should be asked to draw a picture of a person of the opposite sex. One should take care not to specify whether the picture should be of a child or an adult, lest the universe of possibilities be reduced. One might say, "Now that you've drawn a picture of a male, I want you to draw another picture. This time I want you to draw a female." After as much information as possible has been extracted from the pictures, the examiner should ask the patient to draw a picture of a family. Because of time limitations during the first interview, it is prudent not to require the patient to spend too much time on the details of the various family figures. Here, the therapist is primarily interested in the number and sexes of the figures chosen, their relationships with one another, and the story the youngster tells about the family. My experience has been that stories elicited from the family picture are generally less revealing than those from the individual pictures. More frequently one obtains stereotyped stories about family excursions or day-to-day activities. These are usually resistance stories and provide little if any psychodynamic information. Of course, at times, one does obtain rich and meaningful stories.

Another instrument that may provide useful psychodynamic information in the initial interview with an adolescent is a series of questions described by N.I. Kritzberg (1966). The youngster is asked the question: "If you could not be yourself and had to be changed into any human being in the history of the world whom would you choose? You can select any person, living or dead, past or present, real or fictional, well known or not well known. You have the whole range of humanity to choose from." After the patient responds, he or she is asked for the reason for that choice. Following this, the youngster is asked for his or her second and third choices, and the reasons why. Then the patient is asked what three persons he or she would *not* want to be, and the reasons why. Although there are no standard answers (and there probably never will be) that can enable the examiner to determine with certainty the relative degree of psychopathology exhibited by an answer, most examiners can develop a "feel" for whether a response is normal or abnormal. And the reasons for the various choices may be particularly useful in this regard. The greater the examiner's experience with this instrument, the more the likelihood he or she will be able to differentiate between the usual and common responses and those that are atypical and idiosyncratic. A common response such as George Washington or Abraham Lincoln is not likely to be too revealing. However, if one wants to be Adolf Hitler, then some useful information has been provided. The responses to the questions regarding which individuals the patient would *not* want to be may be more difficult to evaluate. Because one is already starting with the question who the patient would *not* want to be, one cannot quickly state that the response reveals reaction formation. In this section, the Adolph Hitler response would be normal. Here again the atypical response is more likely to be revealing. Furthermore, one does well to look for *themes*. If a repeated theme emerges from the six responses then it is more likely that pathological processes are operative.

At this point therapists should direct their attention to an issue that is second in importance only to the question of whether the patient is in need of treatment. They should ask themselves the simple question whether or not they *like* the youngster being evaluated: Can I relate well to him (her)? Does the youngster appear to be relating well to me? Have we established rapport? Is there some mutual emotional resonance? If the answers to these questions are for the most part *no*, and it does not appear that there is potential for improvement in the relationship, then the therapist should have serious reservations about treating the child. We *cannot* treat everyone. We should not expect ourselves to be able to establish a meaningful therapeutic relationship with all those who seek our help. If this is truly a "screening interview" we must not indiscriminately try to treat all those who need it. We must try to treat all those whom we think might profit from working with us. There is a vast difference.

Often one interviews an antisocial adolescent who is obnoxious from the first second of the interview and continues being obnoxious throughout its course. At no point does the youngster exhibit any manifestations of friendliness, motivation for treatment, cooperative attitude, or any of the other qualities that one hopes for in a patient. One might reason that all these alienating qualities are defensive and that beneath the scornful and arrogant facade is a loving and tender human being who is merely testing the therapist or is fearful of expressing these more human qualities. Also, one might reason that tensions in the initial interview result in the patient's appearing far sicker than he or she really is. Accordingly, one has to grant the patient the benefit of these considerations and not so quickly come to the conclusion that there is no possibility for a therapeutic relationship. However, if by the end of the interview one learns that this is the pattern with the parents, teachers, principal, and a wide variety of other individuals whom the youngster encounters, then it is extremely unlikely that the therapist is going to develop a more benevolent relationship with the patient. I cannot present specific criteria for making this discrimination, because the decision must be made primarily on the basis of the subjective feelings therapists have toward the patient and what they *surmise* the patient feels about them. If there is any possibility of the therapist's changing his or her opinion and ultimately developing a better relationship then, perhaps, other sessions should be offered. If these are absolutely refused by the patient, then the therapist need not feel that he or she was instrumental in rejecting prematurely a potential candidate for meaningful therapy.

In summary, I say this: Don't treat a child you don't like. If you cannot bring about a change in such antagonistic feelings, then recommend someone else. Generally, during the first interview I am able to come to a decision regarding this issue. If not, I may suggest a second (and sometimes a third) session. If by then I feel that there is hope for the formation of a therapeutic relationship with the youngster, I will suggest the full intensive workup. If not, I save everyone time, trouble, and money, and either refer to someone else or, if the youngster has already been given up as untreatable by a few previous therapists, I suggest no treatment at that time and discuss with the parents other recommendations.

INTERVIEWING THE YOUNGSTER
AND PARENTS TOGETHER

I will then invite the parents to join me with the adolescent. Again, I may begin this phase of the interview with some general relaxing questions in order to help the parents feel more comfortable. I might ask about whether they had trouble finding the office or whether they had difficulty because of the weather. Some parents, at this point, will make a humorous comment which may help to alleviate their anxiety. If they get a smile from the therapist, he or she becomes less menacing. It behooves the therapist, in this phase, to hear their message and comply with the parents' request for a friendly response. A poker face or austere, humorless mien will only increase anxiety and lessen the chances of obtaining accurate information. For example, as one family was taking seats, the father chose the larger, deeper chair and laughingly stated: "I hope I don't fall asleep in there. It looks so comfortable." The remark clearly revealed his desire to desensitize himself to his anxiety and avoid the anticipated threats of the interview. I smiled and replied: "I hope you don't. I usually find that I have a little more difficulty getting information from someone who's sleeping." The father laughed and then seemed more relaxed. I did not go into the sources of his anxiety nor did I psychoanalyze the remark. I responded at the exact level at which he was functioning and directed my attention to his true request. A well-selected humorous response is likely to do more to reduce anxiety at such a time than direct statements about how the interview is really not so bad. With my response he had the *living experience* that I was benevolent.

Many things can happen at this point and the therapist must be alert to appreciate their meaning and sufficiently flexible to alter the interview in order to derive the maximum benefit from what may occur. Therapists do well to appreciate, however, that the most likely reason for atypical comments and responses during this very early phase relate to the need to reduce the anxiety associated with the first screening interview.

I usually then turn to the parents and ask them to tell me what they consider the patient's problems to be. I generally look vaguely halfway between them, so as not to focus on one, but rather to determine if either tends to be more active and/or to dominate. Throughout the interview my position is that of the *ignorant interrogator*. I use the word ignorant here in the true sense of the word: someone who does not know. And I am interrogating continually in order to lessen my ignorance.

I go back and forth between patient and parents, ever clarifying, ever adding to my knowledge. If there are contradictions between what the youngster says and what the parents say (a common occurrence), I might say to the patient, "Now you say one thing and your parents say just the opposite. What about that? I don't understand. I'm confused." The question should be posed in the spirit of an honest, open desire to learn the truth and not with the implication that the therapist is trying to prove any particular person right or wrong. Such additional back-and-forth inquiry may result in agreement as to the presence or nature of a particular problem. If it does not, that line of inquiry should be abandoned for the time being, with a comment such as, "Well, it seems that you and your parents see it differently. Let's go on and talk about some of the other problems. Perhaps later I'll be able to get a clearer picture of what's going on."

Although some youngsters may suffer some embarrassment over their problems being discussed so openly, there are compensatory therapeutic benefits to be derived from such confrontation. They clarify the reasons for the patient's being in the therapist's office, and this serves to make the problems more ego-alien and more amenable to treatment. The therapist, a significant figure of authority, agrees that they are "problems" or "troubles" and by implication undesirable qualities without which the child would be better off. In addition, naming, labeling, and talking about unpleasant subjects reduces their anxiety-provoking potential. The patient often anticipates that revealing defects will result in scorn, punishment, derogation, and/or other unpleasant reactions from the therapist and/or parents. When the expected condemnation is not forthcoming, the patient has what F. Alexander and T. French (1946) and F. Alexander (1950) refer to as a "corrective emotional experience," and feelings of self-loathing and anxiety that surround the symptoms may be reduced. Generally, the advantages of the open discussion more than compensate for the patient's embarrassment. Those who avoid such confrontations deprive the patient of these benefits.

It is important to discuss also the youngster's assets, accomplishments, skills, and hobbies. This serves to counterbalance the ego-debasing material that has been thus far focused upon. By necessity, therapy must concern itself, either directly or indirectly, with the problems that have brought the patient to treatment. There is usually little in the symptoms that the child can be proud of and much that he or she is ashamed of. In the world beyond the consultation room, the problems may represent only a small fraction of the child's living experiences; in the consultation room, unfortunately, they occupy a significant percentage of the treatment time if the therapy is to be meaningful. In order to counterbalance this unfortunate but necessary emphasis, therapists do well to take every opportunity to focus on ego-enhancing material. If warranted, the therapist should compliment the patient on *meaningful* accomplishments. There is no place for gratuitous or feigned praise in therapy. Interest (only if genuine) should be expressed in any activity that is a source of gratification for the patient. This, too, can serve to enhance the relationship.

If the patient cannot think of any assets, I respond: "If you can't think of anything good about yourself, I'd say that that in itself is a problem." If the youngster still has trouble identifying admirable qualities, I enlist the aid of the parents. If they also cannot describe praiseworthy characteristics, it reflects deep inadequacy in their parental affection. I consider the healthy parent to distort *slightly* in the positive direction regarding a child's assets (Gardner, 1973a). The child who lacks such parental distortion is being deprived indeed. I am not referring to gross exaggereations which are clearly not manifestations of healthy parental attitudes. For example, to consider the mediocre piano player to be "talented" is healthy; to consider him or her a "prodigy" is a delusion, which can only create difficulty for the youngster in forming an accurate selfimage. Probably more important than what the parents *say* regarding the patient's laudable traits is their *feeling-tone* when presenting them.

Is there the smile of pride and the warm glance, which are the hallmarks of the loving parent, or are the positive qualities described in a perfunctory way, as if the parents felt it behooved them to "dig up something" to bolster the youngster's ego? Such considerations are vital to the determination of the depth of parental affection.

The concentration on assets may also reveal the pathological do-gooder, the "Momma's boy," and others with hypertrophied super-egos. The list of their assets is long. They dote over mother when she is not feeling well; they are clean, neat, bathed, and make their beds without being asked; they rarely fight with siblings; they get straight As in conduct; they may be teacher's favorite, and so on. Other mothers say to their children: "Why can't you be like Tommy?" This constellation of symptoms is often difficult to treat because it does not produce pain or discomfort for the youngster or the parents, but is rather a source of pride and ego-gratification. Nevertheless, it can reflect significant difficulties.

The information obtained during this phase of the interview is the most important for making the decision as to whether treatment will be necessary. The decision should be made on the basis of *symptoms*, not on psychodynamics. The therapist must not only know the appropriate levels at which normal behavior ends and the pathological begins, but must also appreciate that everyone has psychodynamics and that having psychodynamics is not the same as having psychopathology. Psychologists, especially, are prone to recommend therapy more on the basis of findings on the projective tests than on clinical symptoms. This is an error. The patient's psychodynamics tell us something about (but not *all* about) the mechanisms of symptom formation. But psychodynamics also tell us about the processes that contribute to the development of normal behavior as well. We should treat symptoms, not psychodynamics.

Conduct in the home is a poorer criterion of psychopathology than outside behavior. The home generally provides a more permissive atmosphere than the world at large. Inquiry into home life does not assess well the child's ability to inhibit the more primitive impulses and adjust appropriately to the demands of reality. Children generally recognize that parents are safe targets and convenient scapegoats for their pent-up hostilities. They appreciate that parents will tolerate much more abuse than anyone else.

When the patient has not acquired the skills and capacity to function properly in school or in relationships with friends, the presence of psychopathology is strongly implied. Good functioning in these two areas generally indicates that the youngster is not likely to be significantly disturbed. If not provided, I ask for information about these areas of functioning. The questionnaire (Appendix II) also provides information in these areas. How does the patient get along in school? What do the teachers say about his or her conduct? Does the youngster have a "best friend"? If so, how often do they see one another? Do other teenagers call on the patient? If so, how often? Is the patient invited to others' homes? Is the patient in the "ingroup," on the fringe, or is he or she a "loner"? Questions such as these are the most vital of the interview and provide the most meaningful data as to whether psychopathology is present.

One area of difficulty which I have not found helpful to dwell on at length is that of sibling rivalry. It is normally fierce, and to devote much time to its vicissitudes is wasteful because such inquiry adds little meaningful information. If the mother, for example, says that her son fights often with his brother, I will ask her how often. If the frequency is less than ten to fifteen fights a day and if there is no history of dangerous trauma being inflicted, I usually say something like: "That sounds par for the course. What other problems are there?" Of course, if the brother is having nightmares in which he screams out: "No, no, Jerry. Don't beat me!" then the rivalry is probably pathological. In contrast, the absence of overt manifestations of sibling rivalry suggests a family in which aggression is significantly inhibited.

At the same time that one is obtaining verbal accounts of the patient's difficulties with the back-and-forth inquiry, one should also attempt to stimulate and catalyze interaction among the members of the family. It is hoped that the exact kind of interaction which takes place in the home will be reproduced. It is the unwise interviewer who attempts to squelch or circumvent arguments between family members and tries to "cool things" when an argument threatens to erupt, because much of value can be learned from such encounters. Are feelings freely expressed or is the argument highly intellectualized? Who is dominant? Does the patient side with any particular person? Are there tears? If so, what effect do they have? The healthy family will be somewhat embarrassed and restrained in its arguments, whereas the sicker family will not be so self-conscious. The possible considerations are endless; it is a rich source of information indeed.

In the context of the family discussion it is important to look for the presence of laughter and humor. One or two humorous comments, mutually enjoyed by members of the family, speaks for a healthy element in their relationship—regardless of what pathology may be present. The ability to laugh is a vital ingredient to health, whereas the humorless family is usually a sick one. And the capacity to laugh at oneself indicates ego-strength, healthy insight, and makes one's foibles more bearable. Therapists who respond warmly, with a humorous comment at the right time, provide a setting that fosters these informative responses.

Of course, the therapist should not be party to pathological humor. The hail-fellow well met type, the back-slapping jokester whose humor is patently obsessive and defensive, should not be responded to in kind because to do so would only encourage the utilization of this ploy to avoid honesty. The parent who uses wit in the service of expressing hostility should not be encouraged by the therapist's laughing at his or her jokes. Sarcasm, verbal scapegoatism, the laughing ridicule should be noted mentally but certainly not joined by the therapist.

If, during the course of the parents' description of the presenting problems, the patient interrupts with comments such as "Don't tell him that," or "I told you never to tell him that," or "You promised me you wouldn't talk about that," one might react with surprise and say something like, "What! Keeping secrets from your *own* psychiatrist? Didn't you know that you're never supposed to keep secrets from a psychiatrist?" One might then reinforce this principle by asking the patient to think about television programs he or she has seen in which this fact has been demonstrated.

During the discussion of the presenting complaints it is important to observe the various parties. One should especially observe the patient's relationship with each of the parents. Glances and gestures, as well as vocal intonations, provide information about affection, respect, and other forms of involvement. Seat placement, physical contact, and direct statements to one another also give much information about the interpersonal relationships of the parties being interviewed. In fact, this aspect of the interview may be more important than the specific information about presenting problems that is ostensibly the focus.

At this point, one may proceed in a number of different ways. If the examiner suspects that there is much useful information that the parents can relate but have been hesitant to reveal in front of the patient, the youngster might be told, "Now I'm going to speak with your parents alone, so I'd appreciate your having a seat in the waiting room." To some youngsters this might be followed by, "I'll be speaking with them about things that are personal for them. If what they say relates directly to you, and should be your business, I'll call you back in." It is important for the reader to appreciate that I much prefer the atmosphere be one of an open pool of communication in which all things pertinent to the patient are discussed freely with both parents and the youngster. Or, the interview with all three parties may be continued, if that appears to be the most judicious approach. But most often I do set aside some time to see the parents alone, especially because it provides me with the opportunity to learn about marital problems that might not so freely be discussed (often with justification) in front of the patient.

INTERVIEW WITH
THE PARENTS ALONE

When the parents are seen alone, they should be asked if there are other problems that they have hesitated to discuss in front of the patient. Often such reluctance is ill-advised, and the parents should be encouraged to discuss these issues with the patient (who is then brought back into the room). When this is not the case, and the parents are alone, one does well to get some information about the marital relationship. Time does not permit going into great detail at this point, but the therapist should attempt to get a general idea about its stability and whether significant problems are present. When making inquiries about the parental relationship, each side should be heard; however, in the initial interview, it may not be possible to come to any conclusions regarding which party exhibits the greater degree of pathology. The examiner merely wants to obtain a list of the main problems; an in-depth inquiry goes beyond the scope of the initial consultation.

On occasion, both parents will claim that they have a good marriage and that they love one another. There are two possibilities here: One is that this is true and the other is, of course, that the parents are denying (either consciously or unconsciously) impairments in their relationship. When presented with a "happy marriage," the examiner might respond with a comment like: "Every marriage has some problems; no marriage is perfect. There are times, I am sure, when the two of you have differences of opinion. Every marriage has its fights from time to time. What are the areas of difference in your marriage?" When presented in this way, the parents will generally become more comfortable about revealing areas of difficulty. Of course, there are marriages in which the partners never fight, but in such cases one or both generally suffers with a deep-seated anger-inhibition problem, and the "peace" they enjoy is paid for dearly with symptoms and/or character traits resulting from the pent-up hostility that inevitably arises in all human relationships. Sometimes parents who deny marital difficulties in the joint session will provide significant information about their marital problems in individual sessions. Of course, the therapist would then be negligent if he or she did not go into the reasons for the cover-up during the joint session.

It is desirable to get some idea about the depth and nature of psychopathology in each of the parents. The interviewer will often have already obtained some information along these lines from general observations. The level of tension in the initial interview is generally quite high from the outset. Strong emotions are evoked. In such an atmosphere it is likely that many forms of psychopathology will be revealed. This is especially so for such character traits as suspiciousness, dependency, volatility, low frustration tolerance, strong need to control and dominate, and seductivity. One of the easiest ways to obtain information about the parents' psychopathology is to ask whether either of them has ever been in treatment. If the answer is yes, the therapist should ask about the main problems for which the parent(s) has been or is in therapy. A person who is in relatively good psychological health usually will not hesitate to discuss the major reasons for seeking treatment. Significant secretiveness may, in itself, represent a problem. One should not, however, expect a person in therapy to reveal every secret or personal problem in the presence of the spouse, although it is reasonable to expect that the major issues will be comfortably discussed. Withholding from the spouse significant information about the therapy reflects a defect in a marital relationship—even if the therapist advised against such revelations to the spouse. Time only permits an outlining of the major problems for which the parent sought therapy; more detailed information can be gained in subsequent interviews.

Before closing the part of the initial interview in which the parents are seen without the patient, they should be invited to talk about anything else they consider important. If a presented issue appears to be significant, some time should be devoted to it—to a superficial degree—reserving detailed elaboration for subsequent sessions.

CRITERIA FOR DECIDING WHETHER TREATMENT IS WARRANTED

Four areas of inquiry are useful in helping the examiner decide whether a youngster needs treatment. Before elaborating on these, it is important to emphasize that transient symptomatic manifestaions are extremely common in children and to a lesser extent in adolescents. Practically every youngster exhibits occasional tics, short-term phobic reactions, temper tantrums, occasional stealing episodes, lying, bribing, sleep difficulties, and so on. An example would be the youngster whose parents have recently announced that they are going to separate and then get a divorce. It is normal for such children to exhibit transient symptoms such as depression, impaired school curiosity and motivation, crying spells, psychosomatic complaints, withdrawal from friends, and antisocial behavior. The examiner should recognize this point and not quickly recommend therapy. Only when these symptoms persist more than a few months is treatment warranted.

Of course, some counseling with the parents may be useful during this period. It is often difficult to ascertain that level of symptomatology at which the normal frequency and intensity ends and the pathological begins. Also, it is only when atypical, inappropriate, or pathological behavior exhibits itself over time that one should consider therapy. It is difficult, if not impossible, to provide a sharp cutoff point regarding how long symptoms should be present before treatment is warranted, but a few months is certainly reasonable. This important consideration is taken into account in the latest diagnostic and statistical manual—DSM-III-R (1987).

School

The school is the most important area of inquiry for determining whether or not a youngster requires therapy. The child is born a primitive infant. It is the role of parents, during the earliest years, to make every reasonable attempt to transform these primitive human beings into individuals capable of functioning in society. The school can be viewed as the first "testing ground" as to whether they have been successful in achieving this goal—to the degree required for functioning in nursery or kindergarten. It is there that children must restrain their primitive impulses most consistently and predictably. The home is a much more relaxed atmosphere and its toleration for atypical behavior much greater. In addition, parental denial of difficulties may also leave psychopathology undetected or unappreciated. In the school, however, the teacher can compare more objectively the youngster with others his or her own age and ascertain whether atypical behavior is manifesting itself.

There are two areas of inquiry that most sensitively assess school adaptation, namely, academic performance and behavior. if the patient is not reaching what the teachers reasonably consider to be his or her academic potential, then psychopathology may be present. In addition, one wants to know about the patient's relationships to teachers, especially with regard to cooperation, respect for the teachers' authority, and general willingness to comply reasonably with classroom routine. Inquiry into the patient's relationship with classmates is also important. Youngsters who are functioning well in these classroom areas are not likely to have serious psychopathology.

However, there are occasional patients with psychiatric difficulties who do well in school, both in the academic and behavioral areas. They may be over compliant and passive youngsters who are quite fearful of any manifestations of defiance or failure to follow usual routines. They may be viewed by the teachers as "a joy to have in the classroom" and may be an immense source of pride for their parents. Their "uptightness," however, will probably get them into trouble in some areas, especially when self-assertion is warranted. But these patients represent a small minority and the basic principle still holds, namely, that the youngster who is doing well in school in both the academic and behavioral realms is not likely to be suffering with significant psychopathology.

Neighborhood

The second important area to consider when deciding whether a youngster needs treatment is that of relationships with peers in the neighborhood. Whereas peers will not tolerate more atypical behavior than parents, they will tolerate more than the teachers. Accordingly, maintaining friendships does not require a degree of integration that successful school performance necessitates. In order to maintain good relationships with neighborhood friends, children must have learned to share, consider the rights of others, wait their turns, adhere to the rules of games, and they must have developed a wide variety of other interpersonal accommodations that will enable them to maintain friendships. The therapist does well to inquire as to whether the patient actively seeks friends and is sought by them. Does the patient invite others to the home and do other youngsters come to the home in order to spend time with the patient? One wants to know the *kinds* of youngsters the patient spends time with. Are they reasonably normal, healthy, and well-integrated children or are they in the fringe groups, the atypical, the antisocial, or those who have such personality disturbances that most of the youngsters do not want to involve themselves with them? If the latter is the case, then psychopathology may very well be present in the patient. But even this patient may be healthier than those who have no friends at all.

Home

Home behavior is the least valuable area for ascertaining whether or not psychopathology is present. There, the consequences of atypical behavior are the least (when compared to school and neighborhood certainly), and the mechanism of parental denial may also operate to compromise the parents' capacity to ascertain whether or not behavior is atypical. Children normally do not behave as well in their homes as they do in the homes of their peers and in school. They often follow the rules applicable to each situation, and the rules at home are generally most lax and the consequences for breaking them most lenient. It is well to assume that children "get away with as much as they can" in each situation.

Parents will often complain that a child does not cooperate at home regarding doing the usual chores and assisting in the household routine. For example, a mother may say that she has a hard time getting Billy to take out the garbage, and he always dawdles, finds excuses, or just flatly refuses to do it. My views on this are that there has probably never been a child, in the history of the world, who ever wanted to take out the garbage. In fact, even garbagemen generally don't like taking out garbage, although they are often paid quite well for these services (most often even more than the child's teachers)! It is the child who *wants* to take out the garbage who may be exhibiting difficulties. This is especially the case if the child wants to make sure that the garbage cans are completely clean, that not a speck of dirt remains in them, and that every coffee grain is completely removed. Obviously, such a child is suffering with moderately severe obsessive-compulsive symptomatology. I would go further and say that the child who does *not* occasionally exhibit uncooperative behavior probably has psychological difficulties.

I recall, as a student at The Bronx High School of Science, a teacher named Mr. Levinson who was the school disciplinarian. If a child was sassy to him he would often respond, "Who do you think you're speaking to? Your mudda?" Mr. Levinson recognized well that children are likely to be more disrespectful of their parents (especially their "muddas") than their teachers. A youngster who exhibits similar disrespect to teachers has not "learned the rules" and is thereby atypical. Parents, like siblings, serve well as scapegoats, as targets for much of the pent-up hostilities of the day that cannot safely be released elsewhere.

The repercussions for "unloading" one's pent-up anger on one's family are far less than for directing them toward their original sources. I am not stating that this is a "good" thing, nor am I recommending it. I am only stating that it is a widespread phenomenon and that examiners do well to appreciate it when assessing for the presence of psychopathology. It is extremely difficult, however, to differentiate between normal and pathological degrees of disrespectful and uncooperative behavior in the home. The level at which the normal ends and the pathological begins is very blurred. This is an extremely weak area of inquiry for determining whether or not a patient needs treatment. However, this area that should not be ignored entirely. If the youngster *rarely* cooperates, if sibling rivalry is so fierce that the fighting is almost incessant, if turmoil and conflict is the *modus vivendi* in the home, then psychopathology is probably present.

DSM-III-R

If a youngster exhibits no difficulties in the three areas, school, neighborhood, and home, it is unlikely that a DSM-III-R diagnosis will be applicable. On occasion, however, a patient will exhibit DSM-III-R symptoms and still function well in the aforementioned three areas. This would be the case for a youngster with obsessions and/or compulsions that do not interfere significantly in daily life. Or, symptoms such as phobias, depression, and psychosomoatic complaints might be present without significant compromises in these three areas of functioning. The main reason for this is that many youngsters come to treatment with interpersonal, rather than intrapsychic, comflicts. The problems lie not so much *within* themselves but *between* themselves and significant figures in their environment, especially parents and teachers.

PRESENTING THE INITIAL
RECOMMENDATIONS

By this time about one-and-a-half hours to one-and-three-quarter hours of interviewing have taken place, and the examiner should generally have enough information to decide whether or not treatment is warranted. Although little information may have been obtained about the underlying psychodynamic factors that have brought about the presenting symptoms, it is the *symptoms* that should be focused upon when deciding whether or not therapy is warranted. This is an important point. All behavioral manifestations have psychodynamics. And sometimes the psychodynamic patterns include pathological adaptations. Treatment should only be recommended if the symptomatic manifestations are interfering *significantly* in the major areas of functioning. I have emphasized the word "significantly" because all individuals exhibit, at times, transient symptoms and even pathological manifestations that may be ongoing. Treatment should be recommended only when these interfere with the patient's ability to function in life to a significant degree. Only then is the time, effort, and expense of involvement in treatment warranted.

When Therapy Is Not Warranted

On occasion, I have concluded that treatment is not warranted. Sometimes the parents have been overly concerned about the youngster and have not appreciated that the behavioral manifestations that have been a source of concern are within the normal limits. Sometimes such parents may need some counseling themselves; other times they just need some reassurance. This is more often the case with first-born children. With subsequently born children the parents become more knowledgeable and less anxious and so are not as likely to seek unnecessary consultations. In some cases the patient has been "cured" between the time that the appointment was made and the time of the consultation. Merely informing the child that an appointment has been made may result in a significant reduction and even complete alleviation of symptomatology. It is as if the child reasoned: "I'd better stop this stuff right now. They've made an appointment with a psychiatrist, a shrink. They must think I'm crazy. I'll prove to them that I'm not crazy. No more crazy behavior." I refer to this as "threat therapy."

One could argue that treatment in such cases is still warranted because the underlying problems have not been resolved. Classical psychoanalysts, especially, would take this position. I generally do not embark on treatment or even continue therapy with anyone who is asymptomatic. The symptom gives me the "handle" for the therapeutic work. Our theories about psychodynamics are extremely theoretical and speculative. If the underlying processes that have originally caused the symptoms are still present to a significant degree, they will erupt once again and bring about symptoms once more. Then, I will be in a better position to treat. I have even had situations in which a parent will call me a few days before the initial consultation and state that since the youngster was informed of the appointment, the presenting symptoms have disappeared. I will express my pleasure and advise such a parent not to hesitate to call me again if the situation has changed. Sometimes a new appointment is set up in the future and sometimes not.

I generally take a conservative approach with regard to suggesting therapy. Recommending that the parents embark on the intensive evaluation (to be discussed in detail in the next chapter) is an expensive and exhausting proposition. I do not recommend it lightly. Furthermore, therapy may be extremely expensive and extended — even more reason to be cautious about recommending it. In spite of what I have said, the vast majority of youngsters who come for initial consultations do require treatment. One reason for this is that there may have been a long period of denial and refusal of treatment and, by the time the patient does come, things have built up to the point where treatment is definitely warranted. This is especially the case when a school has recommended therapy. Schools will generally tolerate significant degrees of atypical behavior before recommending treatment. By the time they do so, treatement is probably warranted.

When a Decision Regarding Therapy
Has Not Yet Been Made

There are times when the two-hour consultation does not prove adequate to make a final recommendation. On those occasions I will recommend one or more further sessions for data collection. I will not allow myself to be pressured into coming to conclusions and making recommendations in a specific period. When the parents are brought in, I tell them in a matter-of-fact way, without any embarrassment or apology, that the situation is a complex one and that I have not been able to come to any definite conclusion at that point. I then advise them what further data collection will be necessary. Sometimes one or two sessions with the patient and/or parents is all I anticipate will be required. On some occasions I will need more information from the teachers, and this is preferably done by speaking directly with them. Sometimes the patient has exhibited significant resistance during the initial session. Although psychiatric problems are present and warrant treatment, the resistance has been such that I cannot reasonably make a recommendation for therapy because there might be no patient to involve meaningfully in the process. Under these circumstances I may recommend one or two more sessions with the patient in the hope that I might then engage him or her. If this also proves unsuccessful, I discontinue my work with the youngster. I may provide some parental counseling, generally over a few sessions. On occasion, I might suggest that the patient might profit from some other modality or experience such as speech therapy, summer camp, organized recreational experiences, or treatment by a pediatrician or a neurologist. Under these circumstances, no further work with me is warranted.

When Psychotherapy Is Warranted

For most youngsters brought to consultation, psychotherapy is indicated. I then outline to the parents what I consider to be the major problems, at the manifest symptom level as well as the underlying family factors that may have contributed. I emphasize that these are my *initial* conclusions and that it is only with further experience with the family that I will be able to be more certain about the factors that are contributing to the youngster's difficulties. I advise them that it is going to be necessary for me to get to know each of them better if I am to work optimally with the patient. In order to do this I will need to see each of the parents once or twice individually to get background information from them. Following the individual interviews with each of the parents I will want to see them together because I will often get conflicting information about what is going on between them. If there are siblings old enough to contribute useful information, I will often recommend a family interview. I also advise them that I will want to see the patient two or three times more in order to collect more information from him or her. At times psychological tests will be indicated, and these will be administered concurrently with the intensive evaluation. I advise the parents that during the intensive evaluation I will be interviewing them as if they themselves were coming to me for a psychiatric evaluation. I then tell them that, when all the information is collected, I will review the material and present my findings and recommendations to them. I impress upon them the fact that I only recommend the intensive evaluation when treatment is warranted and that it serves as a foundation for my therapy. It is important for therapists to appreciate that the extended evaluation is not simply recommended for the purpose of data collection. Equally, if not more important, is its value in forming a relationship which serves as a foundation for therapy.

At this point it is important that the therapist invite the parents to ask any questions they may have about the proposal. They have to appreciate (if they do not already) that, in the private practice setting, the extended evaluation is expensive and time consuming but that it is the optimum way to proceed. My experience has been that many parents do not "hear" me at this point. They may have come with the idea that I will give them a recommendation and send them on their way and that is all that treatment involves. Although there was nothing in the face letter to my questionnaire (Addendum I) to suggest this, their wishes that this were the case or this misinformation about what treatment entails has led them to this conclusion. In such cases I try to impress upon the family that the youngster's problems are complex and that they cannot be understood very easily.

Some parents at this point will ask my opinion regarding how long the treatment will take. I hesitate to use words like always and never. However, I have no hesitation in advising therapists that they should *never* speculate on how long treatment will take. This is one of the most misguided things a therapist can do. One cannot know how successful one will be in engaging the child, nor can one predict how successful one will be with regard to involving the parents. One cannot predict how slowly or rapidly the difficulties will be alleviated; in fact, one cannot even know whether or not one will be successful at all. Often significant social and cultural factors were operative in bringing about the problems, factors completely beyond the therapist's control. Many patients' pathology has been transmitted down many generations. Accordingly, I firmly state to the parents that I cannot predict how long treatment will take and that it would be foolish on their part to put any circles on their calendars. I try to explain to them what I have just said about those factors that contribute to the unpredictability of the process. Such a statement also gets across the message that *their own participation* will play an important role in how rapidly or slowly therapy proceeds. I cannot emphasize this point strongly enough. If the parents view the treatment as a process involving their dropping their child off at the therapist's office, and then picking him or her up after a prescribed period of time, and then after X number of sessions, all will be well, they have a very misguided view of the process. Such a program may work well for many forms of medical treatment, but it is completely ill-suited to the treatment of psychiatric difficulties. The discussion at this time provides the therapist with an opportunity to get across this important point.

I emphasize to the parents that I would not be making a recommendation for the extended evaluation if I were not certain that treatment was indicated. However, at that point I may not be able to be more specific about exactly how I am going to proceed. I may say that I would anticipate one or two sessions per week (my usual frequency), but that I cannot say exactly who will be involved. Perhaps it will be primarily the youngster, perhaps primarily the parents, perhaps a combination of both. It will only be after I have had the opportunity to collect more data that I will be in a position to ascertain what the optimum therapeutic program will be. Here again, the examiner is foolish if he or she allows the parents to extract a specific statement regarding exactly what the therapeutic program will be. Of course, there are times when one can state it with certainty at that time and, under such circumstances, there should be no problem in doing so. My own usual procedure at this point, however, is to inform the parents that even after the evaluation, my proposed therapeutic program will be the one that seems most propitious *at that time*. It may be that new situations will arise that will warrant an alteration of the therapeutic program. Therapy is a slice of life. And like life, things are always happening that will warrant a change in one's plans.

Discussion of Fees

And now to the delicate subject of money. Although the face letter of my questionnaire (Addendum I) indicates my fee policy, the subject may still come up. This is especially the case if the parents wish to discuss with me the question of whether they should be given a fee lower than my standard. Whereas Freud's patients in Victorian Vienna were inhibited in discussing sex, most adult patients today reveal freely their sexual activities to their therapists—but are quite restrained when discussing financial matters. Some therapists may, indeed, share their patients' inhibitions in this area. The problem is complicated for the therapist treating adolescents because the person paying for the treatment is not the one receiving the treatment. The adult in therapy is available to discuss his or her reactions to the payment of fees; the parent of a youngster in therapy is often unavailable or unmotivated for such an inquiry. Accordingly, one cannot easily ask what the parents' income is. Even if one were to do so, and even if one were to obtain a figure, one is still not in a position to know exactly whether a fee reduction is warranted because gross income is only one part of the information needed to assess properly a person's capacity to pay one's fees. One must also know about expenses, debts, and other financial obligations. In many situations the therapist would have to have the expertise of an accountant to know whether or not a parent can afford the standard fee or whether a reduced fee is warranted. Even then, a question of family priorities must come into play, i.e., what the parents want to spend their money on, and the examiner is in no position to make decisions in that realm.

What I do then is to proceed as if the standard fee will be paid and ask the parents if they are clear on my policy of payment, namely, that payment is due at the time of each session and that my secretary will be available to assist with insurance forms and payments from third parties. It is important for the reader to appreciate that my policy of requiring payment for each session is the one that I utilize for parents of children in treatment, but I do not routinely use it for adults who are in therapy themselves. Asking a patient to pay for each session is essentially saying to the patient that there is no trust. Up until about five years ago I did indeed trust parents to pay each month for the treatment of their children. However, I believe that our society is becoming progressively more psychopathic and my former policy resulted in a significant percentage of defaulted payments. Accordingly, I have changed my policy and require parents to pay at the time of each session. This has not compromised my relationship with the child because he or she is generally oblivious to this aspect of the treatment. With adult patients, however, I have still maintained my original policy of their paying at the end of each month (or at some other mutually agreed-upon frequency). To require the adult to pay at the time of each session is essentially extending the "no trust" communication to the patient him- or herself. And this cannot but compromise the therapeutic relationship. If, however, a patient does exhibit difficulties in paying promptly, then I may very well, after therapeutic discussion, institute a policy of more frequent payments after each session. Under these circumstances, the patient has so acted that my distrust is warranted, and to trust a patient under these circumstances is not only naive and antitherapeutic but might be masochistic.

With regard to the question of a reduction to a lower level on my fee range (as originally described in the face letter of the questionnaire), I generally take a somewhat passive position when discussing this issue. It is preferable for the patient to step forth and make the request. And it also behooves the patient to present the information that supports his or her position. Otherwise, the examiner compromises him- or herself by becoming beholden to the parent to provide the information. In the context of such a discussion I might ask if the parents have insurance and exactly what coverage they have. (The face letter requests that this information be available at the time of the initial consultation.) If they cannot answer specifically these questions, then I reserve a decision until the information becomes available. If it is provided, but I still cannot ascertain whether a reduction is warranted, I might ask for other reasons why the parent believes a reduction would be appropriate. It is beyond the purposes of this book to go into the details of such discussions. The examiner must be aware that some parents pride themselves on their bargaining acumen, in the context of which guiltless duplicity is the rule. Others are ashamed to come forth with a statement of their difficulties in paying the higher fee. If the examiner suspects that such is the case, it behooves him or her to initiate the discussion of a lower fee. Some masochistic people may stay with the higher fee because of the self-destructive gratifications that paying it offers. Others may assess the value of the therapy with the level of the fee and would consider themselves to be getting less valuable treatment if they were to take a lower fee or even consider the therapist to be less adequate if he or she were to charge less. Some parents gain a sense of superiority from paying the "top fee." Some may be too passive to request a lower figure or may feel that the reduced-fee patients get inferior treatment. A divorcée, whose former husband is paying for the treatment, may welcome a high fee as another weapon against her former spouse.

What I have said thus far regarding fees relates to the initial fee at the outset of treatment. A fee may be reduced (even below my minimum) when a patient, in treatment for a significant period and committed to the process, suffers financial reverses which are not related to the patient's psychopathological processes (I use the term patient here to refer to an adult patient in treatment or the parents of a patient in therapy.) Under such circumstances I will discuss a reduction, but never to the point where no fee at all is charged. It may even be a few dollars taken from a welfare check, but I do not give "free therapy." If the patient is not willing to suffer some privations for the treatment, it is likely to be meaningful. Patients who pay nothing for their therapy often (but not always) get exactly the value of what they are paying for.

The Question of Payment
For Missed Sessions

The question of charging for missed sessions is a difficult one. With adults, advance notice of cancellation varies from many months to no notice at all (the patient just doesn't show up). The reasons for missing can fluctuate from the most realistic (patient in the hospital) and appropriate (household emergency requiring the patient's presence) to the clearly psychopathological and/or acting out, e.g., "I forgot," "I overslept," or "I just didn't feel like coming." The intermediate situations are probably the most common, e.g., "I had a bad cold" or "My bursitis acted up." A physical illness may not be the patient's "fault," but psychological factors clearly play a role in the degree to which the patient is incapacitated.

Some therapists do not charge for missed sessions. This is a therapeutic error. Missing sessions and/or withholding fees may be among the most common ways in which patients act out with their therapists. Not charging for missed sessions may serve to encourage such behavior and thereby entrench pathology. One approach is not to charge when the therapist is able to fill the session. Some therapists charge if the session has not been filled *and* the absence was due to pathological behavior, e.g. "forgetting," or a voluntary decision that something else had priority, e.g., "an important business meeting." This approach has intrinsic defects which led me to abandon it after using it for a few years. Its main drawback is that it opens up the possibility of conflict between the therapist and patient regarding whether a particular reason for missing the session was pathological.

My policy is to charge my patients for *nonfilled* missed sessions *regardless of the reason for the absence.* Patients are informed that the time is reserved for them. They are told that if I am given advance notice, I can usually fill the hour. In such cases there is no obligation to pay for the session. In the treatment of children and adolescents, this approach is helpful. At one time I was a proponent of the "no fee for illness policy." I would be called by a mother who would inform me that her child was sick and could not keep an appointment. In the next session the child would tell me about the wonderful time she had at a birthday party on the afternoon of the missed session. What does the therapist do in such a situation? A mother is getting over "the flu" and can't bring the child. Another says that a sibling is sick and she can't get a babysitter. It was amazing how the frequency of such missed sessions diminished once I began charging. When describing my missed-session policy, I inform the parents that I have found that when a child has to miss a session, seeing one or both parents instead has often been helpful.

When telling parents about my missed-session policy, I emphasize the fact that there is *no specific cutoff point* to determine whether or not they will be charged. I emphasize that the more advance notice I have, the greater will be the likelihood of my filling the appointment and, conversely, the shorter the notice the less the likelihood of the session being filled. I strictly avoid mentioning any numbers, even in the negative sense. To do so is injudicious. For example, if I were to say, "I have *no* cutoff point, such as 24 hours. The determinant of whether you will be charged is purely whether or not I can fill the session." It is likely that that number 24 will be branded in that parent's brain as the cutoff figure. In fact, even though I studiously avoid mentioning numbers when presenting my policy, on a number of occasions parents have quoted me as giving the 24-hour figure, and have even sworn that they heard me say it. Recently, I have prepared a written statement of my missed-sessions policy (Appendix III) that the parents can refer to if there are any differences of opinion or misunderstandings regarding what they were told about my policy.

Although my missed-session policy may appear stringent, it emcompasses a benefit not enjoyed by patients of many psychoanalysts who pay for sessions missed when on vacations that do not coincide with the analyst's. When I say sessions missed for any reason whatsoever, I include vacations—at any time of the year—as a reason. The result has been that I have never charged a patient who has given me a week's notice or more. Although some readers may not consider me such a "big sport" on this point, there are thousands of patients of other psychoanalysts who have paid dearly for sessions missed when they take a vacation—even with a year's notice.

CONCLUDING COMMENTS

If, at the time of the final discussion, the parents express ambivalence or hesitation, the examiner does well to invite them to discuss further their reactions. At times, it is advisable to suggest that the parents think over what has been said, rather than make a decision at that point. This is a most judicious policy. Sometimes, a parent will have deep reservations but will not express them at the time of the consultation. Such a parent might even then accept subsequent appointments, only to cancel them on short notice. It is unreasonable to expect people to pay for cancelled sessions after they have indicated they wish to discontinue treatment entirely. In fact, it is probably unethical, in spite of the aforementioned verbal agreement. Accordingly, for the sake of the parents as well as the therapist, it is wise to invite ambivalent parents to think about their decision before making appointments.

For those who say they wish to go ahead, I generally set up three appointments: one for the adolescent, and one for each of the parents. Whereas my initial consultation is generally two hours, my subsequent sessions are generally 45 or 60 minutes, depending upon which appears to be most useful and judicious. Some patients (adults as well as children) use the full hour quite expeditiously; others find 45 minutes to be optimum. People who travel greater distances often prefer the full-hour session. One does well to clarify this issue before closing the initial session.

At this point, the reader may conclude that it is not likely I can accomplish all that has been discussed thus far in a two-hour consultation. This conclusion is not completely unwarranted. Actually, I have tried to cover many contingencies, all of which are not likely to come up with the same family. Accordingly, I generally am able to accomplish most of what has been presented here during the initial consultation. But, as mentioned, if I cannot, I have no hesitation requesting a third or even a fourth appointment.

FOUR

THE INTENSIVE DIAGNOSTIC EVALUATION

In the Greek language, the word *diagnosis* means *to know thoroughly* or *to know in depth*. Accordingly, when we use the term as a mere label we are not using it in the true spirit of its meaning. The initial two-hour consultation may enable us to provide a diagnosis in the superficial sense, but it does not enable us to provide a diagnosis in the full sense of the word. It is the purpose of this section to describe the techniques I utilize to provide a bona fide diagnosis, in accordance with the original meaning of the word.

This is being written at a time when shorter forms of treatment are increasingly in vogue. Many time-limited therapy programs provide a fixed number of sessions, ten or twelve not being uncommon. Considering the complexity of the problems with which we are dealing, it takes that number of sessions to understand what the basic problems are. The patients, therefore, are being discharged at just about the time the therapist is beginning to understand their problems in depth. To me such treatment can be compared to the surgical procedure in which the surgeon who opens the abdomen, isolates the source of disease, and then, without doing any further operative procedure or closing the abdomen, discharges the patient from the hospital. I am not claiming that therapy cannot possibly take ten or twelve sessions; I am only claiming that one can generally not predict in advance how long it will take, and it generally takes longer than that. Time-limited therapy is appealing to those who want quick solutions to complex problems. It is particularly attractive to administrators and those who are supporting treatment for large numbers of patients. Accordingly, I consider it most often to be a rip-off of the poor; rich people (unless they are naive) generally do not have to accept time-limited therapy.

Here I present what I consider to be the judicious kind of evaluation, one that enables the examiner to learn in depth what the patient's basic problems are. The evaluation here serves as a foundation for subsequent treatment. The knowledge so gained puts the therapist in the best position to proceed most effectively with the therapeutic program.

THE EVALUATION OF THE MOTHER

I generally find it useful to begin with an interview with the mother alone. My experience has been that, of the three parties, she is the one who is most likely to give me important background information. Often the youngster is the least capable of the three because of his or her immaturity and ignorance of the processes that may be contributing to the difficulties. Fathers, unfortunately, are often less receptive to "opening up." I believe this, in part, relates to the general pattern in our society that fathers are supposed to maintain a "macho" image and not admit weakness or deficiency. Discussing problems with a therapist is viewed by many fathers as being a sign of weakness. Another factor probably relates to the fact that, in the traditional home, the father is less likely to be knowledgeable about all the details involved in the child's life. He may also be more reluctant to admit difficulties in the marital relationship. Although these reasons are speculative, I am convinced that my generalization is a valid one, namely, that fathers are less likely to provide me with important background information than mothers. Accordingly, I find it judicious to interview the mothers first in the intensive evaluation. However, I am not rigid with regard to this and, if scheduling of the child or father first is more readily acocmplished, I will certainly depart from this principle.

The Initial Inquiry

I generally begin the interview with the mother with an open-end question such as: "Is there anything special on your mind that you would like to say to me at this point, before I proceed with any questions?" The question is purposely vague and is designed to provide the mother with the greatest freedom to discuss any issue that she considers pertinent. I want to know here what is at the forefront of her mind, especially things that may be upsetting her, things that may be pressing for release. To ask a specific question at this point may deprive the examiner of this important information. Sometimes the mother's comments may suggest ambivalence for the intensive diagnostic program. It is important for the examiner to appreciate that bringing a child to treatment is generally viewed as an indication of the parents' failure to have raised a psychologically healthy child. The examiner's conclusion that treatment is warranted may then be viewed as confirmation that the parent is indeed deficient. In such cases I usually try to reassure the mother that I am convinced that she loves the child deeply and that, at every point, she did what she considered to be best for her child's healthy growth and development. I emphasize the point that her coming for treatment for the youngster and her willingness to make the sacrifices of time, money, and energy for the child's welfare, are a statement of parental strength and commitment. Comments along these lines sometimes reduce the parental feelings of failure. Of course, it is not proper for the therapist to make such a statement if it is untrue, and there is severe maternal deficiency. However, mothers willing to bring their children for treatment do not generally fall in that category.

If the mother has not offered any responses to my initial open-ended question, I will ask, "I'd like to know what reactions you had to our meeting last time." Or, if she has given no response along the lines just discussed, I might ask, "Are there any other reactions you had to our meeting last time?" In both cases, I direct my attention specifically to the two-hour consultation. This question also enables me to learn her feelings about the treatment, both positive and negative. It is crucial for the therapist to have a good relationship with the parents if an adolescent's therapy is to be successful. The answers to these questions at this point in the initial interview can provide information about the kind of relationship that is starting to develop between the mother and the therapist. It is the best opportunity for "nipping in the bud" difficulties that may already be starting to exhibit themselves.

I will then ask the mother what the youngster's reactions were to the interview. Here again there are a wide variety of responses. If the adolescent's reactions have been negative, I will try to ascertain what the issues were that caused the reactions. If positive, I will want to learn what things attracted the patient. If the mother states that she did not make inquiries in order to respect the patient's "privacy," I will impress upon her that my general therapeutic approach is to encourage all concerned parties to discuss the therapy as much as possible and she should err on the side of "invading the youngster's privacy." I do not recommend that she be intrusive here, only that she err on the side of being so and let the patient's own defenses and desire for privacy be the determinants of how much and how little he or she will reveal. Such "respect" for the patient's privacy often works against the aims of treatment in that it reduces the open communication that the therapist is trying to achieve in the family. Open communication among family members may be one of the most therapeutic experiences the therapist can provide. All too often psychological problems within families are the results of conspiracies of silence, suppressed and repressed thoughts and feelings, and other "skeletons in the closet." Therapy must open Pandora's boxes, and facilitating open communication is a step toward this goal.

The mother may, for example, say that the youngster told her something but made her promise not to divulge it to me. Here I will advise the mother that it was an error on her part to have agreed to keep a secret from me and that she would have done better to have said something like: "There must be no secrets from Dr. Gardner and I won't promise not to tell him." The mother may respond that if she were to say such a thing, the patient might not give her the information. My response to this is that it is better that the patient not provide the information than for her to be a participant in a conspiracy in which she and the child join forces to keep secrets from me. Also, I reassure her that important issues are likely to come out anyway and she need not fear that the nondivulged secret will compromise the treatment. (I will discuss this issue of confidentiality in more detail in Chapter Seven.)

I will then ask the mother what her husband's reactions were to the initial consultative interview. As mentioned, mothers are generally more candid to me than fathers, and so she might provide me with information about his reactions that the father himself might not so readily reveal. Often his comments relate to the financial aspects of the treatment, which may then open up a discussion again of the fee and the payment. If the husband has expressed negative reactions, I encourage the mother to tell her husband to state these directly to me. I use this as a point of departure to impress upon her that a common cause of disruption of treatment is parental discomfort regarding the expression of their grievances, disappointments, disagreements, and so on.

Inquiry into the Causes
Of the Child's Difficulties

Next I will make the following statement to the mother: "I know that you're coming here to get my opinion about why your youngster has problems. However, it's important for you to appreciate that, at this point, you probably know more about the reasons why your child has to come to therapy than I do. After all, you've lived with the child all his (her) life. You have been observer to thousands of events that I have not witnessed. Accordingly, I'm sure that you can provide me with very important information relevant to the question of why your child has difficulties." Most mothers will come up with some explanations at that point. And, interestingly, the issues they bring up are often extremely valuable and very much on point. Although she is not specifically trained in psychiatry or psychology, the mother's "guesses" are often valid explanations and provide the examiner with important information about the sources of the child's psychopathology.

I cannot emphasize this point strongly enough. Although the

mother may never have gone to graduate school, she knows the child better than the examiner and her hunches regarding why the child has difficulties (her denial mechanisms notwithstanding) may be better than the examiner's. If the mother cannot come up with any explanations, I will often urge her to "guess" or "speculate." I encourage her to do so with the advice that her guesses may still provide me with valuable leads as to what is going on with the child. Again, these "wild" guesses are often valuable sources of information.

Inquiry Regarding Parental Dealings with the Child

My purpose here is to get more specific information about the way in which the parents have raised the patient, with special focus on detrimental exposures and experiences. There are a number of ways of getting information in this area. I sometimes ask the mother to describe what she considers to be her strong points and weak points in the child-rearing realm. By presenting the question in this balanced way, one is likely to obtain information related to maternal weaknesses that the mother might otherwise have difficulty admitting. It is usually useful to ask questions in this area in such a way that guilt or embarrassment is reduced or obviated. For example, if the examiner were to ask: "Do you ever hit your child?" an accusatory finger is implied. But, if the examiner says: "All parents find, at times, that their backs are up against the wall and the child's behavior is so irritating that they feel that the only thing they can do is to give him (her) one. Then the child has a good cry, gets it out of his (her) system, and all is again well with the world. How often did you find this to be the case with your child?" Obviously, when the question is posed this way, the examiner is going to be in a better position to find out exactly how much (or how little) corporal punishment was utilized.

The same principle holds for questions in other areas. For example, if one says to a mother: "Did you like cuddling your child when he (she) was an infant?" the answer is likely to be yes in that the mother generally recognizes that not to have done so represents a parental deficiency. One is more likely to find out what really went on with a question such as: "When they're born, some babies love cuddling and others do not. How was Billy when he was born?" Actually, there is a small element of duplicity in this question. The realities are that there are indeed some babies who do not like cuddling when they are born, but they are relatively rare. They are mainly children born with serious physical illness, congenital defects, mental retardation, autism, and other severe disorders that manifest themselves at birth. Children who are not in these categories not only love to be cuddled at birth, but the deprivation of such may ultimately prove lethal. Because I know that Billy is in none of the aformentioned categories, I know that he would have wanted cuddling at the time of his birth. If his mother responds that he was not that kind of a child, it generally suggests that she herself had some deficiency in providing cuddling and her motivation for doing so was impaired.

One could ask the question: "Did you like to have Janie cuddle with you in the morning when she was a toddler?" Again, most mothers will say yes, even though the response may not be an honest one. However, if one asks: "Some children, when they're toddlers, love to come into their parents' bed, especially on weekends. How was Mary when she was that age?" By presenting the question in such a way that there are two categories of children, some who like cuddling and some who don't, it becomes easier for the mother to state that Mary was not in the cuddling category. Again, the implication here is that the deficiency lies in the child and not in the parent.

Another useful question: "What are your husband's feelings about the way you've raised Bobby? What does he consider your strong points to be and what does he consider your weak points to be?" It is generally easier for the mother to talk about deficiencies about herself if they originate from someone else because she has the opportunity to present disagreements if she wishes to do so. The examiner does well to review the list of the father's reported descriptions, both positive and negative.

An important area of inquiry to ascertain maternal capacity is the mother's involvement in school activities. In fact, this may be the most important realm if one is looking for manifestations of parental deprivation of affection. I first begin with an overall question about the mother's involvement in school activities and encourage her to provide me with an overall description. Following that, I ask specific questions that give me information about the mother's participation in the PTA, attendance at conferences with teachers, and involvement in the youngster's extracurricular activities such as school plays, recitals, sporting events, et cetera. The latter area is extremely important. The healthy involved mother finds attendance at such performances extremely gratifying. It is a grand moment when little Susie comes out on the stage dressed as Cinderella. Tears well up in the mother's eyes and her heart swells with pride. And the adolescent's parent beams with pride when the youngster appears on the stage. The parent who knows no such joy is not only missing out on some of life's greater moments but, for the purposes of the interview, has provided the examiner with important information regarding maternal capacity. In the context of this discussion, I ask the mother about the father's participation in school activities. Does *he* attend teacher conferences? Does *he* attend the school performances and does he exhibit joy and pride at them?

One wants to know about whom the child went to in the middle of the night when he or she woke up with nightmares, croup, or physical illness. One wants to find out about who takes the child to the pediatrician, especially during emergencies. Inquiry about what goes on during the evening, when both parents are home, is also important. One should inquire about homework and who helps the youngster with it. Does one parent do better than the other? One wants to know about parent's comfort with and patience with sitting on the floor playing childhood games, especially when the children were younger. One should inquire into who put the children to sleep at night, read them bedtime stories, and had more patience for dawdling.

A concept that I have found useful in assessing parental capacity is what I refer to as "Grandma's criteria" (Gardner, 1986b). These are the criteria Grandma's ghost would use if she were to be roaming invisibly around the house collecting data about parenting abilities. Because she doesn't have a Ph.D. in psychology she would be using more traditional criteria for assessing parental capacity, criteria related to the involvement of the parent in the everyday activities of the child-rearing process. Accordingly, the examiner does well to go through the course of a typical day with the mother, from the time the children wake up in the morning until the time they go to sleep at night, and find out exactly what each parent does with each of the children, especially the patient. One is particularly interested in who takes on the more unpleasant tasks and who has the greatest willingness to make sacrifices. Because she knows nothing about unconscious processes, Grandma will be focusing on these more valid criteria for assessing parental capacity.

The reader interested in more information about assessment of parental capacity does well to read pertinent material in my *Family Evaluation in Child Custody Litigation* (1982).

Description of the Marriage

I will then ask the mother the general question: "Tell me about your marriage?" Of course, I may have gotten some information about this during the initial two-hour consultation; however, here I want to get more details, especially as they relate to the patient's difficulties. This is an important area of inquiry. Children exposed to ongoing marital animosity are likely to be deprived, and such deprivations may contribute to the development of their symptomatology. And, if the children become actively embroiled in the parental conflict, there is even a greater likelihood that psychopathology will develop. It is reasonable to say that many (but certainly not all) children who develop psychological difficulties do so because of problems in their parents' marriages. If the mother describes difficulties, I will go into detail, especially with regard to those problems that the patient is either aware of or exposed to. Some parents naively believe that children are in no way affected by parental problems that they are not directly exposed to or aware of. I attempt to impress upon such parents that the effects of marital discord tend to filter down to children, even without the awareness of the concerned parties. I try to convince them that, if parents are depressed or otherwise unhappy over difficulties in the marital relationship, this is going to compromise the care of the children. Some mothers routinely state that their marriages are good ones. This is their automatic response, and they may consider it the socially acceptable thing to say. Along with this, they will often say, "I love my husband." In some cases the marriages are quite poor, but denial mechanisms have resulted in both parents' maintaining a facade that they have a "good marriage." In such cases, I might say,

"You know, no marriage is perfect. Every marriage, like every human relationship, has strong points and weak points. In every relationship there are things that you like about the other person and things that you don't. There is no marriage in which there aren't occasional fights. What I want you to tell me now are the strong points of your marriage and the weak points. I'd like to hear about the things you agree on, and the things about which you don't agree." When the question is posed this way, it becomes more socially acceptable for the mother to reveal deficiencies in the relationship. When one begins with a discussion of the positive aspects of the marriage, it becomes easier to talk about the negatives. Because mothers are generally more comfortable talking about deficiencies in the marriage than fathers, the information obtained here will be useful to the examiner during the interview with the father.

Some mothers will describe the marital difficulties, but state that their husbands have strictly warned them not to talk about them to me. There are many women who comply with this wish and I never learn about the marital difficulties. This, of course, compromises my evaluation. Other mothers tell me the problems, but request that I not tell their husbands that they revealed the information to me. Sometimes I am successful in my attempts to get such mothers to assert themselves and advise their husbands that they have provided me with this information. Others fear doing so and when I meet with the husband it becomes apparent that their wives have never revealed that they have disclosed the details of the marital problems to me. Sometimes I am successful in "smoking this information out" during the joint interview with the husband and the wife; and other times the mother is so frightened of "rocking the boat" that she continues to hold back. Such mothers are serving as models for passive submission to their husbands and this, of course, is likely to contribute to the child's difficulties. I believe that refusal to discuss marital difficulties is one of the most common reasons why parents do not agree to embark upon the intensive evaluation or, if they do so, it is one of the most common reasons why they interrupt it. Therapists who confine themselves to working exclusively with children, and do not delve deeply into the marital and/or family situation, are likely to attract such parents. However, I believe that the therapy they provide is likely to prove useless.

Sometimes the marital conflict may focus directly on the child.

A mother may say, for example, "The only fights we have are over how to deal with Tom. I believe that if things went well with him, we wouldn't fight about anything." There are two possibilities here. One is that the statement is true, and the marriage is basically a good one with the patient's problems the main source of parental friction. The other possibility is that the youngster is being used as a weapon or tool in the parental conflict and that differences over management are being utilized in the service of less noble goals. It behooves the examiner to inquire further into this issue in order to ascertain which of the two possibilities is closer to the reality. When parents are involved in divorce, the second possibility is generally the more likely. Because divorced parents are living separately, they do not have direct access to one another to vent their rage. The children, who move back and forth freely between the two households, become good candidates to be used as weapons, spies, and tools in the parental conflict (Gardner, 1976, 1977, 1979a).

History of Psychiatric Treatment

I will then ask the mother whether she has ever been in treatment. If so, I want details about the phases of her life when she had therapy, the types of treatment, the reasons for having entered into treatment, and what she recalls of the experience(s). This is a good way of getting into the question of the mother's own psychopathology. Simply to ask the question, "Do you have any psychiatric disturbances?" may produce defensiveness. However, a discussion of previous therapeutic experiences is more likely to provide useful data in this area. I am often amazed at how little people remember of their therapy. I am rarely surprised when an adolescent has little recollection of early childhood therapeutic experiences with me. But it does amaze me how little adults remember of treatment that took place 10 or 15 years previously, treatment that may have occurred while they were adults. They commonly do not even recall the name of the therapist. I am particularly interested in any marital counseling or conjoint therapy that the mother may have involved herself in with the father. This is another way of learning about marital problems. I often try to get information about what the therapist said, especially with regard to each party's contribution to the marital difficulties.

Background Information

Family Background   It may come as a surprise to some readers that my discussion of the acquisition of background information about the mother comes so late in this section. It is important to appreciate that we are not dealing here with the mother's psychoanalysis, but her involvement with her child—especially with regard to maternal capacity. Were we interested in psychoanalyzing the mother we might be much more interested in her early developmental life, her relationships with her parents, and the influences in her development that played an important role in shaping her present personality. Although I am concerned about these subjects (and will discuss them in this section), I consider them to be less important than the areas of inquiry discussed thus far.

I begin with questions about the mother's date of birth, place of birth, and list of places where she has lived during her life. If the mother has moved frequently, especially during the patient's lifetime, then I may have a clue to a factor that may have contributed to the youngster's difficulties. Children who shift around from location to location during their formative years, especially if this involves frequent changes of schooling, may suffer psychologically from the disruptions. I then ask the mother about her own mother, whether she is living or dead, and where she lives at the present time. If dead, I want to find out about the cause of death. If the information hasn't been obtained already, I want to know about the ethnic and religious background of the maternal grandmother. Ethnic factors often play a role in the development of psychopathological processes. I want to know about the maternal grandmother's religion and how religious she was (or is). I am especially interested here in fanaticism or dogmatic religious beliefs that may contribute to the development of psychopathology. I ask the mother to describe the kind of person her mother was and the kind of relationship the mother had with the maternal grandmother during the mother's childhood. I am particularly interested in the kind of maternal care that the maternal grandmother provided the mother.

I also want to know whether the maternal grandmother worked or was a homemaker. If she worked, I want to know about her occupation and whether or not she was mainly out of the home or was actively involved in the mother's child rearing. This may provide information about the mother's own maternal capacity, in that if the model she had as a child was a good one, it is more likely that she is providing good maternal input into the patient. And the opposite is the case if the maternal grandmother was deficient in this regard.

I also want to know about the maternal grandmother's relationship with the mother's husband. If there is dissension between the maternal grandmother and the child's father, it may play a role in the child's difficulties. I am particularly interested in how much grandparental input the maternal grandmother has with her grandchildren, especially my patient. Good grandparenting can play an important positive role in a child's psychological development. The exaggerated high esteem that grandparents often have for their grandchildren can serve as a buffer for the criticism and the undeserved negative feedback that children (like the rest of us) often are subjected to in life. I also ask about the maternal grandmother's psychiatric status, whether she has ever been in psychiatric treatment or has suffered with unusual medical illnesses. I then ask the mother if there is anything else that she can mention about her mother that might be of importance to me.

Next, I ask the mother similar questions about her father. I ask about her father's occupation, especially with regard to how much time he had for input into the mother's own upbringing. Information about the mother's relationship with the father may provide useful data about the mother's relationship with her husband. The female-male relationship patterns laid down in childhood tend to repeat themselves in our subsequent lives. Here too I am particularly interested in the relationship between the maternal grandfather and the patient. This is especially important if there are deficiencies in the relationship between the mother's husband and her child, i.e., the patient and his or her father.

I then ask the mother about the relationship between her parents. That relationship (whether good or bad), which the mother observed during her formative years, is often the model being repeated in the mother's present marital relationship. I am not saying that this is invariably so, only that it is quite a common phenomenon. If a mother, for example, frequently observed her father to be hitting her mother, it is more likely that she will marry a man who will treat her similarly—her vows never to marry such a man notwithstanding. If the mother's whole extended family operates in this way, it is even more likely that she will repeat the pattern in her own marriage. One could say that it is the only lifestyle she knows and that such a mother would be uncomfortable during the dating period with young men who treated her more benevolently. She would be like "a fish out of water" in such relationships and would find them strange and uncomfortable. She might even provoke men into maltreating her or always anticipate maltreatment—even though there is no evidence that she would be mistreated. And this pattern is likely to transmit itself to a third generation and exhibit itself in the patient, at a level commensurate with his or her level of development.

Sometimes, there may have been divorce in the mother's home during her childhood. In such cases I want to know about the reasons for the separation and whether or not there were remarriages. If stepparents were involved in the mother's upbringing, I want to know about them and the nature of the relationships between the mother and stepparents.

I then ask the mother to list each of her siblings and get brief information about their age, occupation, and marital status. I am particularly interested in whether or not any of the siblings had serious psychological difficulties and, if so, the nature of them. Because genetic factors often play a role in various psychopathological processes, I want to know about the appearance of such difficulties in the child's aunts and uncles as well as the child's maternal grandparents.

The First-Memory Question   I sometimes find the first-memory question to be useful. I generally pose it in this way: "Go back as far as you can and tell me what the first memory of your life is. I'd like you to go further back than the beginning of school if you can." Psychoanalysts, especially, are very interested in this question. Although it may not provide useful information, sometimes it serves as an epitome of many factors that have played a role in the patient's lifetime. When it does, it can often provide valuable clues about central psychological themes in the mother's lifetime, themes that began in childhood and exist to the present time. Sometimes the actual memory is false and the incident never occurred. However, because the mother believes fully that it did, the response can still be a useful source of information. At this point I will present a few examples to impress upon the reader the value of this question.

One mother gave this response:

> I was about three years old. I remember my brother and my father urinating. I wanted to do what they did and I tried, but I couldn't.

This mother was an extremely domineering and aggressive individual. She was married to a man who was submissive and passive. This memory clearly reflects the desire to assume the masculine role, and it was certainly the case that she had done so in her marriage.

One mother responded:

> I was three years old and my mother and father and sister were fussing over me because of my dancing.

This woman was an extremely histrionic, hysterical individual. She was markedly exhibitionistic. As a child, she had been an actress and a model. But throughout her life she continued to exhibit her talents, which were probably much less than she professed. She was so self-centered that she gave little attention to her son, who was significantly deprived. It was this deprivation that played a role in the development of his symptomatology.

Another mother responded:

> I was two or three years old. I climbed out of my crib, fell, and broke my arm.

The memory reveals the mother's basic feelings that if she removes herself from a protected environment (a crib) she will be traumatized. The mother was basically an extremely dependent individual who did not view herself as capable of handling many of life's situations and anticipated that if she were unprotected by her husband and her parents, she would indeed meet with disaster. One could argue that the arm fracture incident was a psychological trauma which deserved to be remembered. My response is that this does not negate the aforementioned explanation. There were probably many other falls, accidents, and psychologically traumatic incidents in the mother's life. The fact that she remembered this one—after so many years—is a statement that it lent itself well to epitomizing themes in her life that were central to her personality.

One mother responded:

> After I was two years old, if I misbehaved, I would be tied to a table and spanked and kept there. These are the earliest memories of my childhood.

This mother was an extremely masochistic and martyristic individual. She constantly reminded her children about how much she sacrificed herself for their benefit. She stated that at times she did twenty hours of work a day in order to devote every spare moment to philanthropic work. She constantly reminded those she served (her children and others) how much they were in her debt for her benevolence. The seeds of her masochistic-martyristic tendencies are clearly present in this first memory. This mother worked on the principle that the only way she could get affection from others was to suffer pain. She also used her martyrdom as a mechanism for expressing hostility. She would get people to feel guilty over how ungrateful they were for not appreciating her suffering on their behalf.

Another mother's response:

> I was about three or four years old. We were taking family pictures and I was very shy. I didn't want my picture taken.

The memory reveals the mother's fear of exposing herself and her basic feelings that if she is "seen," the observer will be critical or rejecting of her. And she assumes that others share her own low opinion of herself. These personality qualities were playing a role in her son's difficulties in that he too was shy, submissive, and excessively dependent upon the opinions of others. These were qualities that he acquired by identification with his mother.

Another mother's response:

> I was about three years old. It was in Atlantic City. We had gone there on vacation. I was all sunburned and my mother

made me put on a starched dress. It hurt my arms and I was crying.

This mother grew up in an upper-middle-class home where there was significant emphasis on propriety, attendance at the "proper schools," and appropriate manners and dress. Otherwise, her parents were not particularly interested in her, and her upbringing was given over to various housekeepers and maids. Although the memory suggests that the mother was resentful of this treatment by the maternal grandmother, she was actually reproducing the pattern in the upbringing of her own daughter. The mother worked full-time in order to send her child to the best private schools and gave little meaningful care and attention to them while she was at home.

One more example:

> Two memories come to mind. Both when I was about three or four years old. I remember being fed hot peppers by a little boy who lived next door. I thought he was giving me candy. In a second memory I remember being burned on the bottom as I backed into a gas heater.

This mother, although in analysis with another therapist, had never analyzed her earliest memories. I discussed with her their possible psychological significnce and suggested that she try to analyze them. She responded:

> I come from a long line of masochists. In both of these memories I'm getting harmed. In the first I was tricked. It really wasn't candy but pepper. I still think men are untrustworthy. When they say they're gonna give you something sweet, it turns out that it isn't. The second one makes me think that I wasn't adequately protected by my parents. I feel they should have protected me.

This mother's analysis agreed with my own guesses as to the psychological significances of these first memories. In both she is harmed. In the first she is harmed by another's duplicity (being fed hot peppers) and in the second she brings about her own misfortune (backs into a gas heater). Both suggest the propensity to being hurt either by gravitating toward those who would maltreat her or by participating in behavior that would result in her being harmed. And these tendencies reflected themselves well in her life in that she married a man who, although superficially loving and benevolent, actually turned out to be an extremely hostile individual who subjected her to vicious litigation at the time of their divorce.

My presentation of these many clinical examples was done in the hope that it would impress upon the reader the great value of this question. Although I am often critical of psychoanalytic theory and technique, it would be a mistake to conclude that my criticism is so vast that I do not appreciate the benefits to be derived from certain aspects of classical psychoanalytic theory. In fact, I believe that much in this book is still very much within the psychoanalytic model, the alterations and modifications notwithstanding.

School Life   I then ask the mother about her elementary school experiencies, both in the academic and behavioral realms. I ask about friendships during this period as well as things that might have been going on in her home that might have affected her personality. Similar questions are asked about the junior high school and the high school periods. Just as information about school and neighborhood can provide vital data about the patient, the same questions about the mother can be useful in determining whether or not she has psychopathology. With regard to high school, I am particularly interested in whether the mother dated and, if so, what kinds of experiences she had. I ask about academic and/or emotional problems.

Work History   Next, I ask the mother what she did following graduation from high school. If she went to work, I get details of her work history, particularly with regard to how well she got along with colleagues and superiors. If she had numerous jobs, I want to know the reasons for the various changes, especially if she was repeatedly fired. If she is still working now, I want to know the nature of her job adjustment. I am particularly interested in her work history since the birth of my patient. I want to know how much time she spent out of the home and in it. If she gave the child's care over to housekeepers or other caretakers, I want to know who they were, how long they remained in the home, and the nature of their relationships with the child. This is an extremely important area of inquiry because it tells something about emotional deprivation, a common cause of psychopathology.

The Premarital Relationship with the Father   I then ask the mother about the circumstances under which she met her husband and the qualities within him that attracted him to her. If there were previous marriages, I want to list each one and get information about them. I am particularly interested in any psychopathological trends that may have exhibited themselves in each of the previous marriages. Important questions in this area relate to who initiated the separation, what were the main problems in the marriage, and what criticisms former husbands had of the mother. Here again we see the question of criticisms other persons had of the interviewee. This can often be an important source of information about the interviewee's personality deficiencies, deficiencies that may not readily be revealed by the person him- or herself.

Projective Questions   Projective questions are routinely used in interviews with children. They are not as frequently used in interviews with adults. I too generally use them much more in interviews with children. However, I will occasionally present them to adults as well, when I am having difficulty getting adequate information by direct questions. In this section I will describe some of the projective qustions that I have found most useful.

Five wishes   The traditional question is to ask the person what wishes they would make if three could be granted. However, it is nowhere written that one must limit oneself to three. I generally prefer to ask for five wishes because I am then less likely to get stereotyped responses. The first two or three may very well be routine, everyday answers. When one must "scratch one's brain" and provide one or two more, then one is more likely to tap unconscious sources that may provide more meaningful information.

1. Safety and good health for all of us.
2. Equanimity for myself in daily existence.

    3. An ability to see further, to be less narrow, to compre-
hend more the meaning of the situation *while* it is happening.
    4. An ability to make and keep decisions.
    5. To be less self-absorbed—to be able to give of myself.

Superficially, the first wish appears to be normal in that most
people will include good health for themselves and their family.
However, the word *safety* does not usually appear. It suggests
unconsious hostility toward her family and then, by a process of
reaction formation, she protects them from trauma. One could,
however, argue that wishing one's family good health also implies
an initial thought of sickness and that response could also be
considered a manifestation of hostility with compensatory reaction
formation. Although this may be true, I can only say that *safety* is a
rare wish whereas *good health* is an extremely common one. This
lends support (but certainly does not prove) my belief that they have
different psychodynamics. In this case this mother did indeed
harbor formidable hostility toward her husband, a domineering and
overbearing individual upon whom she was quite dependent.

    The second wish reveals a desire for cessation of her chronic
feelings of anxiety, depression, and inner agitation associated with
her difficult relationship with her husband.

    The third wish makes more specific reference to her inability to
think for and assert herself, not only in her relationship with her
husband but with others as well. Her statement, "to comprehend
more the meaning of the situation *while* it is happening" makes
reference to her problem in considering her own thoughts and
feelings when they are contradicted by others. Subsequently, she
sometimes realizes how submissive she has been. Her wish here is
that she be more astute and less inhibited and denying when she is
allowing herself to be suppressed.

    The fourth wish also makes reference to her passivity and
dependency on authorities, especially her husband. She cannot
make a decision because she is too beholden to the opinions of
others and to keep them against resistance is extremely difficult for
her.

    Last, the fifth wish refers to her self-absorbed state which was
the result of the above-described pathology as well as her deep-
seated inhibition in giving of herself meaningfully in an affectionate

way. This mother significantly deprived her child, the patient, and described how when he was very young she refused to let him come into her bed in the mornings although he stood for hours scratching at the bedroom door. The boy came to treatment at age 16 because of marked antagonism toward his peers, especially girls. Clearly, his hostility stemmed from the deprivations he suffered in his relationship with his parents.

Another mother gave these wishes:

1. Traveling. I'd like to do a lot of traveling. I'd love to go to Europe, to Germany, Denmark, and Spain.
2. I'd like to live very long.
3. I'd like to have a lot of money.
4. I'd like to eat more without gaining weight.
5. I'd like my children to succeed. I'd like them to be as happily married as I am, to enjoy the world, the blue sky and the grass. I don't want them to marry money. I want them to be basic individuals. I don't want them to be impressed by prestige.

These wishes reveal the mother's basic egocentricism. The first four are all concerned with herself, and no mention is made of her husband and children. They all reveal the desire for self-indulgence. The fifth, although possibly a normal response, is not so for this mother. She was an extremely hysterical and histrionic individual. The most mundane subjects were spoken about with extreme enthusiasm and exaggeration. The mechanism of denial was frequently utilized, and no matter how unfortunate or miserable the situation was she tended to see it in the best possible light. Her references to enjoying "the world, the blue sky, and the grass" are all part of the hysterical picture and cannot be considered bona fide desires for her children to enjoy these aspects of living. In addition, her wish that her children not "marry money" and not be concerned with prestige in their choice of a mate was in her case simple reaction formation to her basic desire that they be most concerned with these considerations. This mother was quite involved with social status, but she denied this through frequent utilization of the mechanism of *undoing*, and spoke of her "tolerance" of social and ethnic groups which were usually discriminated against. My patient, her 17-year-old daughter, was exhibitionistic, materialistic, self-indulgent, and exploitive of her father—all qualities that she derived from her mother.

Last, one mother gave these wishes:

> **1.** I wish I could be left alone. I always feel under pressure. I'd relax. I feel under pressure from my husband to be a perfect wife. He wants gourmet cooking. He wants me to be more aggressive and I am not. He wants me to be friendly to people who might be important to him for business purposes. I just can't be that way.
>
> **2.** I'd like to travel a lot. I've never been to Europe. But we can't go now because my husband would rather spend money on cars. He gets everything he wants. He's very selfish. He always does what he wants and never what I want. I feel helpless because he has control over all the money.
>
> **3.** To be more self-assured.
>
> **4.** I wish I was more tolerant of my parents. I don't know what it is, but whenever I'm with them I cringe. I know I'm their whole life. I can't forgive them for not being more affectionate to me when I was younger. They were always working.
>
> **5.** I'd like to be completely independent so I won't have to rely on my husband for everything. If I wanted to do something I wouldn't have to ask my husband for everything. I'd like to be on my own and have my own money.

These wishes need little psychoanalysis. They describe, quite succinctly, this woman's main psychological and marital difficulties. It was no surprise that near the end of the first interview she stated: "Although I came here for my daughter, I really think I have problems of my own and I guess I want treatment for myself as well."

Verbal Projective Questions Although I routinely present children with verbal projective questions, I do not usually present them to adults. Again, when direct questions are not adequate to provide me with the information I desire, I may utilize verbal projective questions (Kritzberg, 1966). Whereas with children and young adolescents I generally ask questions about animals and objects, I most often ask older adolescents and adults about people. My usual question to the older adolescent and adult is this: "If you could not be yourself, but could live your life as any other person in history, living or dead, real or fictional, famous or not, whom would you choose?" Following the response, I ask for the reasons for having selected that particular person. I then ask for second and third choices (and reasons) and then the persons who the patient would *not* want to be. Although this question may be immensely valuable for learning about adults, it is often of little value for children because of their limited repertoire of figures from which they can select. In addition, they will often choose superheroes or other age appropriate figures. The stereotyped responses are not as revealing as the atypical. Accordingly, as will be seen below, the verbal projection question for people (as opposed to animals and objects) can be very useful for adults.

One mother gave these responses:

(+)1 Rita Hayworth. I try to copy her to a T. She led a very glamorous life. She was beautiful. She was sexy-looking.

(+)2 Maria Callas, of the Metropolitan Opera—she's not a dying thing. People adore her. People will worship her forever.

(+)3 Happy Rockefeller. She's a dream person. She's not cheap or rowdy. She's elegant. She's wealthy.

(−)1 a) A poor person. I'd never want to be poor.

b) My aunt. She was very promiscuous.

(−)2 My mother. She was very ignorant. She had a low IQ. She wasn't neat.

(−)3 The female murdered in the picture, *I Want to Live*. She kills other women. She was a murderer. She slept with men.

This mother was basically hysterical, exhibitionistic, deeply materialistic, and vain. Her vanity bordered on psychotic grandiosity. She looked upon those who did not profess adoration of her as being hostile. These cravings are well revealed in the verbal projective test. The (+)1, (+)2, and (+3) responses all reveal her desire to be adored by large numbers of people, adored for beauty and wealth. The (−)1b and (−)3 responses reflect her guilt over sexual feelings, and (−)3 also reflects her guilt over hostile feelings toward other women.

Another mother gave this response:

(+)1 Jacqueline Kennedy. She has glamor. She's respected and she's elegant. She has many intellectual interests. There is more for her in the future.

(+)2 Picasso. He lives an isolated and contented life. He has inner contentment and satisfaction. He's not dependent on others. He's uninvolved with the rest of the world.

(+)3 Jay. The man I'm now dating. He's serious-minded. He has a flair of enjoying life. He captures both worlds, the real and the unreal.

(−)1 My ex-husband's brother's wife. She has no sense of morals. She has affairs with other men and she shows no reaction, no guilt. Otherwise, she's wonderful.

(−)2 My mother. She's incapable of showing warmth. She always finds the bad side of things. She thrives on misery.

(−)3 Candy, the heroine in a book. It's a sexual satire on a foolish young girl. She has sex with her father, with an uncle, with a resident doctor, with someone in a men's room, and a hunchback in the street.

This mother was an extremely infantile and self-indulgent woman. She was sexually promiscuous and neglected her children in order to go off evenings and weekends with a series of men. She was highly materialistic and extremely exhibitionistic. She was incapable of involving herself in a meaningful way with others. All these qualities are revealed in the verbal projective responses. Her choice of Jacqueline Kennedy for her "glamor" and elegance reveal her exhibitionistic and materialistic qualities. Her inability to involve herself meaningfully is suggested in the reason she gives for wishing to be Picasso, as well as the reasons she gives for not wishing to be her mother. Some guilt over her sexual promiscuity is revealed in (−)1 and (−)3 where she denigrates two other women who themselves were quite promiscuous.

Another mother stated:

(+)1 Margaret Bourke-White. She was formerly a photographer. Now she's sick. She was well-traveled and she led an exciting life. She traveled all over the world. She was married to Erskine Caldwell but they were divorced. She was very creative. She was a very aggressive woman.

(+)2 E. Nesbitt. She wrote children's books. She wrote books on poetry, English, and wild life. She supported her husband and her husband's mistress in her own home. She entertained many interesting people. She was a very strong person. She was lively and full of energy.

(+)3 My Aunt Robb. She was always held up to me as a model. She was beautiful, charming, athletic, and always enjoyed life. She always lived in an academic world, but she was not an intellectual.

(−)1 My mother. She led a hard life. She was always mixed up. I don't like her. She has no common sense. She's done all the wrong things. She favored my brother. She was unfair to me. She gave me no preparation for life. When I had to have my tonsils out, she didn't tell me in advance. I couldn't rely on her. I've never gotten any backing from her and now I can't depend on anyone.

(−)2 My father. He's led a very unrealistic kind of life. He never found meaningful work. Although he graduated from Harvard, he always held menial jobs. I wouldn't want to be him because he married my mother. He was never happy with her.

(−)3 A man at my office. He's a no person. He's a zombie. He has no animation. He's just a dead pan.

This mother was a very intelligent, independent, self-assertive, and a fairly accomplished woman. She was married to a very intellectual man who was quite dependent on her. She was somewhat inhibited in the expression of her maternal feelings. In the (−)1 response, she reveals some of the sources of her exaggerated independence and self-assertion, namely, her own mother's neglect and lack of interest in her. Not being able to depend on her mother she had never felt she could depend on anyone and had thereby become extremely independent and self-assertive. In (+)1 and (+)2 she selects women who have these qualities. The (+)2 choice exhibits this to an extreme degree where she selects a woman who supports not only her husband but her husband's mistress. The (+)3 response is not in itself pathological but tends to support the kind of independent life which this mother considers to be ideal. The (−2)response again gives information about the reasons why this mother could have little respect for men and little belief that she could depend upon them, thereby having to depend only on her own resources. The (−)3 response also makes reference to her emotional inhibition and lack of spontaneity.

Dreams I will most often ask a mother if she has had any dreams that have repeated themselves throughout the course of her life. I am in agreement with my colleagues in the field of psycho-analysis that this can be an important question. Repetitious dreams most often reflect an ongoing theme in the individual's life. If the mother has not had such experiences, then I ask her if she can recall *any* dream in her life. This, too, may be significant, especially if it is a dream that she had many years previously. The fact that she remembers it so many years later is a statement of its psychological importance. Another kind of dream that should be given serious consideration by the examiner is one that occurs before the first session. Often this may be a rich source of information about the patient's anticipations from treatment or about fundamental life problems. Unfortunately, the dream may be presented at a time when the therapist is less capable of analyzing it because of his or her unfamiliarity with the person. However, to the degree that one can analyze it, to that degree may one learn some useful informa-tion. On occasion, one files it away and may find it useful subse-quently, when one is more familiar with the person.

One mother related this dream as having taken place just prior to the initial evaluation:

> I was in the waiting room of a dentist's office and there were three dogs there. They got into the garbage cans and the dentist was going to spray the dogs with MACE (that anti-riot stuff that makes you paralyzed).

The patient's father was a physician who spent long hours in his office. The dream reveals the mother's feelings that the father (here depicted as a dentist) sees their three children as unnecessary nuisances who have to be rejected and paralyzed if he is to be freed of the obligations of taking care of them. Their scrounging for food in a garbage can reveals her feeling that he has little to offer them. It is of interest, however, that she is passive to all of this and permits it to occur.

Another mother related this repetitious dream:

> I often dream that there is a fire in the house and I have to get the kids out.

The dream serves as an expression of the mother's hostility toward her children and her desire that she be free of the responsibilities and inconveniences associated with their upbringing. However, another part of her—a part which is genuinely concerned for their well being—salvages them in time. In summary then the dream reflects the mother's ambivalence toward her children.

Between her first and second evaluation sessions, a mother related this dream:

> A service man had to come to service the bidet. He didn't know what he was doing.

I understood this dream to mean that the serviceman was this examiner and it reflected the mother's feelings that I was incompetent. The mother had an hysterical character disorder with much repression of hostility and sexual feelings. I considered the bidet, as a cleanser of her genitalia, to reflect her desires that I might in some way alleviate her feelings that sexuality was dirty, or that I might in some way be involved in cleansing her sexuality. I did not attempt to analyze this dream in this case because I felt that she was not ready to deal with any of my surmised interpretations. Often a dream like this speaks poorly for the parents' commitment to the treatment process because of its implied distrust of the therapist. Fortunately, in this case, this did not turn out to be the case, and the child did well with full cooperation on the part of the parents. My guess is that the mother gradually became more confident in me, in spite of her initial hesitation.

One mother related this repetitious dream:

I was at AB's house. She was having a birthday party for her daughter C. It really wasn't A's house but she was having a party there. She had an old-fashioned stove there, a potbellied stove. It had a beautiful rare plant growing out of it. The plant had a beautiful odor. I said, "Please tell me where you got this." A said, "Before you leave, I'll either tell you where I bought it or I'll give you a branch to plant yourself." It had pink and white pretty flowers. I kept asking her where she got it. Oh, yes, one other thing. The stove had originally been black, but it was painted white.

The mother had previously been in treatment for a short period, was intelligent, and was interested in analzying this dream. As a result of her associations and my inquiries, we decided that the potbellied stove and plant represented the mother herself. She basically considered herself to be vulgar, inadequate (i.e., "black"), and she attempted to hide these deficiencies by presenting herself with a colorful facade. This was represented by the white paint and the beautiful flowers which everyone admired and which everyone enjoyed smelling. This may have reflected her way of dealing with her inner feeling that she "smells."

This mother was an extremely materialistic and exhibitionistic woman. She was quite wealthy and was obsessed with indulging herself with expensive clothing. She said, "I even dress up to go out for the mail." She was quite shocked after she understood what the dream meant. She subsequently went into therapy with me, and the dream served to catalyze her working on this problem.

Another mother told me she used to have this dream about once a week a few years prior to the evaluation:

A very short, ugly man came up to me. He was exactly the opposite of the kind that I like. I asked him to make love to me. He was overjoyed at the idea. He couldn't believe his luck. He then made advances to me, and I told him that I changed my mind.

The dream reveals the mother's deep-seated hostility toward men. In the dream she selects an ugly man, that is, one who is most likely to respond with gratitude and enthusiasm to her suggestion of a sexual encounter and then thwarts him in the midst of his excitation. Her hostility toward men here is obvious.

During the evaluation this mother told the following dream:

> I was with a child. I was at Columbia Teacher's College. I went back and forth from making pottery to being in the apartment of a photographer. While I was making pottery, someone said that I should do it in a particular way but I insisted that I could do it better. Which was so.
>
> This photographer was trying to take a picture of a child and he said that he was on the staff at the university. The child didn't want to let his picture be taken. I told the child that he should let the photographer take the picture. The child said that he would be nice to the photographer only until the picture was taken and then he wouldn't be nice any longer.
>
> The child and I then went through many rooms and then we went out the back door and left.

The dream clearly reflects the mother's attitude toward the evaluation. The photographer is a common symbol for the therapist who "sees through," confronts, and accurately portrays the patient. The child is depicted in two ways: first as the pottery which the mother creates, and second in the form of a child. In the dream the mother reveals her feeling that she can do a better job in molding and forming her child's personality than I can and, therefore, insists upon doing it herself. In the dream she also has the child cooperate with me until the picture is taken (that is, until the end of the evaluation) and then has him refuse to cooperate further.

The journey through many rooms signifies the complex inquiry of the evaluation and their leaving through the back door reveals their desire to remove themselves surreptitiously and prematurely, rather than through the front door which would reflect a desire to leave when treatment is completed.

The dream was a perfect statement of what ultimately happened and served as an accurate warning for the examiner. The child did cooperate until the end of the evaluation, and then both he and the parents decided not to pursue treatment. Although the dream was analyzed with the mother and she accepted its implications at the time, I was unable to alter the strong forces which compelled her to follow its dictates.

Another mother described having frequent fearful fantasies and an occasional nightmare that "my husband would lose both of his legs and I'll end up pushing him in a wheelchair."

This mother was extremely masochistic. Although she had a Ph.D. degree, she constantly berated herself intellectually and had always felt that she had to present herself as intellectually average or below average if she were to attract her husband. Her husband was a borderline psychotic who had little involvement with her and devoted himself to his academic pursuits (he was a professor at a university). He had her do most of the "dirty work," that is, boring research and typing, for his own doctoral thesis.

The fantasy reveals not only her unconscious hostility toward her husband, hostility which is expressed through the desire that he lose his legs, but also her feeling that the only way he could really need her was if he were to be helpless. When he was getting his doctorate degree he needed her. Following this he would no longer need her and the fantasy allowed her once again to play a meaningful role in his life. In addition, by burdening herself with a crippled man, she could gratify her masochistic desires.

The mother of an adolescent described this dream on the night before her first individual interview with me. (There had been a previous screening interview when I saw her in association with her son and husband):

> I was on one side of a sliding door. My husband was on the other side. I was trying to shut the sliding door and couldn't.

The dream, coming as it did on the night prior to her first interview with me alone, suggests that she would prefer to place a closed door between herself and her husband so that he would not see certain things which would be unpleasant for her to reveal to me. It suggested that she was not going to tell me freely very much about her real feelings about her husband. In the subsequent part of the interview this prediction turned out to be true. She described her relationship with him as a good one and had absolutely no complaints. Of him she could only say, "He's wonderful. He's good.

Sometimes he talks a little too much, but that's nothing that concerns me. He talks a lot of common sense."

In reality, the husband was a person who was prone to make endless speeches over inanities. He would puff himself up and pontificate over the most simplistic issues as if he was spouting forth great wisdom. Only one of his four children was consciously irritated by these lectures. One of his sons (not my patient) identified with the father and at 21 was already filled with an air of self-importance.

The dream and the mother's subsequent comments revealed her fear of coming to terms directly with this quite alienating trait of her husband's.

I generally spend two interviews with the mothers of adolescents, each one lasting 45 to 60 minutes. I hope the reader can appreciate that the information gained in the individual interviews provides me with a much greater knowledge of what is going on with her than is obtained in the initial two-hour consultation. In every sense of the word, the data collection in the initial interview is indeed superficial. The examiner who does not avail him- or herself of the more extensive interviews is being deprived of vital information—information that is crucial to have if one is to understand thoroughly what is going on with the patient.

Before closing the final interview with the mother, I may ask her how she views herself ten years from now. The answer provided can also be a useful source of information. The same question can be asked about her guesses about the patient a decade from now. I am sure that the reader has a collection of his or her own questions that can also prove useful. In this section I have presented those that I personally have found most valuable.

THE EVALUATION OF THE FATHER

My discussion of the father's evaluation will be significantly shorter than that of the mother. This is primarily because many of the questions are the same and there would be little point in my repeating them in this section. However, another fact relates to my observation that fathers generally are less willing to reveal themselves than mothers and accordingly, their evaluations are often shorter. Whereas the mother's evaluation is generally two (sometimes three) interviews, each of which is 45 to 60 minutes, fathers generally have nothing further to say to me after one (or at most two) interviews of the same duration. They often are much "tighter" when responding to the projective questions, as well.

The Initial Inquiry

As was true with the mother, I begin the interview with an open-end question in which I ask him if there is anything special on his mind that he would like to speak with me about. He may or may not have something to discuss and, of course, I follow his lead. I then ask the father about reactions to the initial two-hour consultation. We then go on to questions in which I ask him his opinion regarding the causes of the youngster's difficulties. I inform him that I recognize that his main reason for consulting with me is that I should provide my opinion regarding the answers to this question. However, I advise him that his guesses and speculations can be an important source of information to me. I then proceed with the questions regarding his and his wife's dealing with the patient, both assets and liabilities. I am particularly interested in whether the father involved himself in sports with the children when they were younger, especially such activities as Little League, soccer, and so on. When investigating this area, however, the examiner should find out whether the father was fanatical about it. If the father was having fist fights with the coaches at the Little League games, he was probably doing his children more harm than good. He was probably using the child for vicarious gratification to a degree beyond the normal. I am also interested in his involvement in school activities, curricular and extracurricular.

Description of the Marriage

We then proceed to a discussion of the marriage. Here, especially, fathers may be particularly unreceptive to revealing difficulties in the marital relationship. A common situation is one in which a mother will claim that her husband had had an affair, and he has told her that he does not wish her to reveal this to me. In the session with me he will studiously avoid discussion of this issue, even though he knows that his wife is aware of the relationship. I ask the father the same questions about the marriage that I ask the mother, especially with regard to its strong points and weak points. If the father initially presents the marriage as "good," with no problems at all, I will state that all marriages have their areas of friction, and I encourage him to discuss those areas in which he and his wife have differences of opinion. Even with this sanction, the father may insist that there are no such difficulties in his marriage. If such a response is given by a father whom the examiner knows is having an affair (by some information provided by the wife), then there is little the examiner can do. It is hoped that she will bring the matter up during the joint session, but often she does not. As mentioned, in such situations, I often let the thing rest. To "rock the boat" may cause a disruption of the marital equilibrium, which may do the child more harm than good.

History of Psychiatric Treatment

I then ask the father whether he has ever been in treatment. Most child therapists will agree that boys are overrepresented in their patient population. In contrast, most adult therapists will agree that women are overrepresented in their patient population. I believe that this phenomenon relates to the fact that boys are generally more rambunctious, assertive, and "fighters." As every teacher and parent knows, boys are "tough customers" when compared to girls. Accordingly, they have greater difficulty complying with social constraints, especially in school. I suspect that there are probably genetic bases for these character traits in that they may have been more adaptive in evolutionary development. Hunters and fighters do better if they are more aggressive, and so men who possessed such qualities survived preferentially over men who did not. However, social and environmental factors have probably played a role as well in engendering these traits. At the adult level, however, men often feel the need to maintain their "macho image" and are less receptive to therapy—a process in which they are encouraged to reveal weaknesses and failings. If the father has been in therapy, I will ask the same questions that I have asked the mother regarding the nature of the problems for which he went into treatment and what benefits, if any, were derived from the therapy. I am especially interested in marital counseling and the marital problems that brought the parents into therapy.

Background Information

The questions to the father regarding background information are essentially the same as those posed to the mother. Specifically, I ask the father about his parents, their relationship with one another, and their relationships with him. I also inquire about his siblings, especially with regard to the presence of psychiatric difficulties. Here, I am particularly interested in the kind of parenting the father received in that his parents probably served as the model for his own parenting. I also want to know about the nature of the relationships between the paternal grandparents and my patient.

Military Service   One difference between the father's and the mother's inquiries relates to military service. If the father served in the military, one does well to find out about how he adjusted there and whether he received an honorable discharge. One should ascertain whether the father had difficulties adjusting in the service and whether he warranted disciplinary action and/or psychiatric treatment. The military generally requires a degree of integration similar to (if not more than) that which is required for adjustment in school. One must be willing to comply to a reasonable degree with authority and to exhibit self-restraint under stressful circumstances. If the father was in combat, one wants to find out whether he suffered with any psychiatric disorders commonly seen under such circumstances.

The First-Memory Question   As was true for the mother, questions about the father's first memory can often provide useful information about underlying psychodynamics. I present here a few examples.

One father gave this memory:

> I was about four years old. I remember leaving my mother's and father's store. I climbed over a fence outside of the store and ripped my leg open. Then I ran back into the store.

This father, although 38 years old, was still working as an employee in his parents' store. He was extremely dependent on them and was quite passive in his relationship with them. Although he spoke on occasion of going out on his own, there was little evidence that he seriously intended to do this. Although he could not openly admit it to himself, it was clear that he was waiting for the day that they would die and then the business would become his. In his marriage, as well, he was quite dependent on his wife, who domineered him mercilessly. The memory reveals the father's basic feeling that were he to leave the domain of his parents he would be traumatized. The warning serves him well and he returns to the store where he feels comfortable and safe. The first memory epitomizes the basic theme of his life and his relationships both with his parents and with his wife.

Another father had this memory:

> I was about four years old. I was driving a little toy car and running over another kid's white shoes. He was a dandy. I was a dirty little kid. I liked to get dirty. He went crying to his mother. I don't know if after that I was chastised or what.

This father was a bright, somewhat cocky, and basically arrogant man. He was quick to anger and most of his comments about people were critical. He was in the plumbing supply business and psychologically he appeared to be "shitting" on the world. The memory reflects this life pattern. His greatest pleasure appeared to be dirtying those who were clean, that is, defecating on others. His relationship with me was in the same spirit. I felt that he saw me as a boy with white shoes and his primary mode of relating to me was hostile. He stated that in grade school his greatest pleasure came when he was head of the monitors, a position, no doubt that gave him further opportunity to be sadistic to others. After graduation from college the father was fired from his first job after six months of work. He considered his firing the result of his having been rebellious: "I didn't want to do what they wanted." He finally ended up working for his own father, with whom he described a very competitive and antagonistic relationship.

The father also stated that he feared women, saying: "I see them as aggressive birds who would want to scratch our eyes out." I considered this fantasy to be a reflection of his own hostility projected onto women.

Another father's memory:

> I was in my crib. I must have been about two years old and I was picking the paint off the iron bars and eating it.

This father's parents were quite distant from him and he suffered definite emotional deprivation in his childhood. The recollection is symbolic of the deprivation he suffered in that he had to resort to the ingestion of inedible objects in his attempt to gain symbolic affection. The psychodynamics of this memory are similar to those of children with pica who ingest inedible objects because of neglect and a craving for oral-dependent gratifications.

Another father's first memory:

> I was two or three years old and playing in my backyard. My clothing caught on a fence that I was climbing. A friend of mine came and had to lift me up and take me off.

This father had a schizoid character disorder and was severely dependent on his wife and parents. Although 31 and a law school graduate, he was still unable to function as an adult. He worked for his father, who was also a lawyer, and it was clear that he could not have been able to function independently in another law firm or in his own practice. The memory reveals his basic dependency problem. When he is confronted with an obstruction or some other difficulty in life, he is unable to get himself out of trouble and must depend on others to take care of him.

One father gave this response:

> I was about three years old and I remember trying to eat cement from a wall.

This man's father (that is the paternal grandfather of my patient) was a very intellectualizing man who devoted himself to his scholarly interests instead of spending time with his children. The paternal grandmother had paranoid and depressive episodes for which she received ECT. At times she was suicidal. It is hard to see how this father felt that the love and affection givn to him was as digestible as concrete.

School Life   I ask the father about adjustment at the elementary school level. I am particularly interested in the father's comparison of himself with my patient during this period, especially if the patient is a boy. Many fathers will say that the patient is exhibiting behavior very similar to their own during this phase of their lives. One must consider the possibility that this reflects a genetic component. However, one also wants to ascertain whether the father is sanctioning atypical behavior (antisocial) or criticizing it. Possible genetic contributions notwithstanding, sanctioning may contribute to its perpetuation.

Although things are changing, women still have less necessity to dedicate themselves as assiduously as fathers to school and career planning. I am not claiming that this is a good thing; only that it is a reality of our world, recent changes notwithstanding. Accordingly, if a mother was insufficiently motivated during the high school period, it does not necessarily reflect as much pathology as a father who was similarly unmotivated. The pressures on the father to ultimately be a breadwinner are far greater than those placed on girls during the formative years. Accordingly, a girl's lack of school and work motivation during the high school period does not necessarily reflect as much pathology as in a father who is similarly unmotivated. I am also interested in the father's social relationships throughout his school career. These lay the foundation for adult relationships, including the relationship with his wife.

Work History   It is important to go into the father's work history. A long history of difficulty adjusting in jobs generally reflects psychiatric difficulties. And the father's commitment to work will generally affect the youngster's attitude toward school. If the patient sees the father seriously involved in his work, it is likely that he will thereby serve as a good model for the youngster's involvement in school work. I cannot emphasize this point strongly enough. Many parents present with children who are unmotivated to do their school work. Yet the parents may provide an atmosphere in which work is viewed as odious and there is practically no intellectual curiosity. In such an environment the child is not likely to develop strong school interest unless exposed extensively to other models who demonstrate such commitments.

The Premarital Relationshp with the Mother   I want to find out the circumstances under which the father first met the mother and what his initial attractions were. The examiner does well to appreciate that most people do not provide what a judicious middle-aged person would consider reasonable reasons for marriage. So common are the frivolous criteria for marriage that one has to consider them to be in the normal range. For example, a father may claim that he "fell in love." When one asks what the particular qualities were that he fell in love with, he may be hard put to give other answers other than his wife was physically attractive and that she was "sweet." One should be particularly interested here in any atypical relationships that were established during this period.

Projective Questions   Because fathers are generally more reticent to reveal themselves directly, one would think that projective questions might be useful. However, even in this area my experience has been that they are more reluctant to reveal themselves. This hesitation notwithstanding, one can sometimes still get useful information by the utilization of these questions.

Five Wishes   Some fathers can only go to three wishes. When they reach the fourth and fifth wishes, they become too anxious to continue because they run out of stereotyped responses. I present here some responses of fathers to the five wishes question.
One father gave these responses:

1. That Randy be okay.
2. That I have a happy marriage.
3. That I become independent and self-sufficient.
4. I can't think of anymore.

All three wishes relate to difficulties in the family. The third wish especially epitomized the father's main psychological problem, namely, that he was an extremely dependent individual. Although in his late 30s, he was very much under the thumb of his own father, whom he was working for, who was supporting him, and who controlled almost every aspect of his life.

Another father gave these responses:

1. Wisdom.
2. Patience.
3. Charity.
4. Free access to any library I wanted.
5. The writing style equivalent to George Travelli Macauley.

This father was a highly intellectualized man on the faculty of a major Eastern university. He was most fearful of intimate involvements with others and spent most of his time absorbed in his academic work. For years he had not slept in the same room as his wife and sexual contact was rare. Three of his five responses make direct reference to his intellectual and academic ambitions (#1, #4, and #5). In addition, this man flaunted his intellectual accomplishments in an attempt to bolster a very low self-esteem. This is well shown in wish #5 where he mentions the name of a person who was unknown to this examiner. When I asked him who Macauley was, he responded with condescending incredulity that I didn't know that Macauley was a famous historian. The implication of his facial expression was one of: "How stupid can you be, not ever to have heard of Macauley?"

Conspicuous by their absence are responses that refer to any human beings other than himself.

Another father gave these answers:

1. Good health and long life.
2. To be a contented, respected millionaire. To have enough material comfort to free me from worry.
3. To have stature and power. To be a better lawyer than anyone else and to be recognized as such. To be a member of the establishment.

4. For my children to have the same luck with their wives as I have with mine and to have as much money as I have.

5. The question I wonder about is whether it would be better for my wife or for me to die first? It would be better for her if I went first, but you won't get me to say that I want her to die first. No, the best thing would be if there was an accident and we both died together.

This father was an extremely grandiose, self-centered, manipulative, and hostile individual. He actually considered himself to be uniformly admired, respected, and envied by all around him. In actual fact he had no real friends. His cruelty to his daughter (more verbal than physical) resulted in her being a very withdrawn and timid child.

Response #1 is within the normal range. Wishes #2, #3, and #4 reflect the already described grandiosity, materialism, and power fantasies. Wish #5 reveals his hostility toward his wife, which he then denied. Actually, the man's wife (my patient's mother) had significant personality problems, and the marriage was fraught with difficulties. However, he had to deny this in order to maintain the image of having a "perfect marriage." Under these circumstances there was formidable hostility toward his wife, reflected in his death wishes, but he could not allow these feelings entrance into conscious awareness.

Verbal Projective Questions   Presented below are some verbal projective questions that provided important information in the fathers' evaluation.

One father gave these responses:

(+)1 Caruso or Lawrence Melchoir. I can't sing very well, and I'd love to be a great singer, to be able to entertain people that way.

(+)2 Jacques Cousteau. He leads an active, interesting life. He's adventurous; he's in the outdoors; he does a lot of skin diving.

(+)3 Dr. H. He's a very good surgeon. He does a lot of good for the people. His hours probably aren't too bad.

(−)1 Frank Sinatra or the Beatles, or others in the public eye. They have no private life. They're mobbed wherever they go.

(−)2 A politician. Most of them are phony phonies. They lie all the time. I couldn't keep track of all the lies.

(−)3 Just plain Joe. I want to get some recognition in life.

My full clinical evaluation of this man revealed him to be relatively stable and free from significant psychopathology. Although one might find evidences of psychopathology in the above responses, I considered them to be within the normal range. The (+)1 and (+)3 responses suggest that this father might have inordinate desires to be famous. However, his life situation was one in which he appeared to be very secure and adjusted in a fairly respectable but certainly not famous position. He was an engineer who was owner of a small manufacturing company. The (−)2 reply suggests the possibility that the father himself engages in duplicity or would like to do so. However, this was not substantiated by the rest of my clinical evaluation. It is important for the reader to appreciate that repression of unacceptable material exists in all people, and projective tests reveal what is being repressed. In our culture there is probably a tendency in most people to lie at times and to crave fame. Lying and inordinate ambition are not acceptable traits and may very well be repressed. This does not mean that the person harboring such desires is suffering with psychopathology. It is only when there is acting out, obsessive preoccupation, or when these trends interfere significantly with one's life pattern that the term psychopathology can justifiably be applied.

Another father gave these responses:

(+)1 Elvis Presley. He's rich and famous. He's honest; he doesn't gamble. He's a good family man. I've always been a great fan of his.

(+)2 Mickey Mantle. I like to play ball. He's my idol. I adore his strength and skill as a ball player. He's also an upright family man. He doesn't have much of an education, just like me.

(+)3 John Kennedy. He had a close relationship with the common man, in spite of all his money. But he wasn't a big shot. He had compassion for the common man.

(−)1 Fidel Castro. He deceived people. He manhandled people. He causes a lot of pain and heartache.

(−)2 Hitler. He mistreated the Jewish people terribly. He rose to power by stepping over everybody.

(−)3 Jimmy Hoffa. He engaged in many underground activities. He's a vicious leader who robbed the union membership.

This 28-year-old father worked at the dairy counter at a supermarket. He graduated high school with mediocre grades and married at the age of 20. The paternal grandfather showed the father little warmth, and abandoned the home when the father was 18 years old.

The persons that this patient selected in both positive and negative categories could very well be within the normal range. However, the reasons he gives for choosing these people reflect certain manifestations of his personal psychopathology. In the (+)1 and (+)2 responses he introduces the "family man" theme, which are clearly personal associations to these figures, and certainly not typical. They suggest preoccupation with and cravings for a close-knit family in compensation for the deprivations he suffered as a child. In the (+)3 response he chooses John Kennedy, in part because of his "compassion for the common man." His (−)1, (−)2, and (−)3 responses are all people who in one way or another have taken advantage of, deceived, and even killed the common man. These responses reveal his father's basic feelings of impotency in a world which he sees as malevolent and overpowering. He craves the protection of a benevolent authority symbolized by John Kennedy.

Another father gave this response:

(+)1 Paul Getty, for his business shrewdness. He got the oil reserve depreciation bill passed by Congress. He had no family life, so I wouldn't want to be like him for that.

(+)2 My old hometown doctor, Dr. O. He's someone who has done a lot of good for many people. He could talk to you about anything. He was a good family man.

(+)3 Supreme Court Justice White. He's an athlete. He's smart. He leads a well-rounded life.

(−)1 Adolph Hitler. He was a killer. His super-race idea was all wrong.

(−)2 Walter Reuther. He's a legalized crook. He warps our economy with the strength of his union.

(−)3 Malcolm X. He was trying to get a job done and wasn't doing it the right way. He was using violence rather than discussion.

This father had little interest in the patient, his adopted stepson, and spent 16 to 20 hours a day, six to seven days a week at work. He had strong psychopathic tendencies as well.

The (+)1 response reveals both his psychopathic tendencies as well as denial of his disinterest in family life. In the (+)2 reply we again see the denial of his lack of interest in his family via his admiration for Dr. O, the "good family man." I considered the (+)3 and (−)1 responses to be within the normal range. The (−)2 response again relates to the father's psychopathy because I considered the father himself to be a "legalized crook." The (−)3 response as it stands cannot provide too much information. Had time been available to discuss the Malcolm X associations further, more revealing information might have been obtained.

One father gave these responses:

(+)1 Nathaniel Bowdich. He was a 19th century New Englander. He was a self-taught navigator and ship owner. He established many of the principles of navigation for whaling ships. Mariners still use Bowdich's book on navigation. He was very sharp and skilled. He taught mathematics at Harvard as well.

(+)2 Thomas Jefferson. He was a happy man. He had many interests. He enjoyed life.

(+)3 Jerry G., a colleague of mine. He's articulate, outgoing, and gets a bang out of life.

(−)1 Nat Turner. Although he was free, he was really still a slave. He had obsessions that he could not let go of. He was a double-dealing shackled madman.

(−)2 Nixon. He doesn't know what he wants. He doesn't know where he's going. He's not up to the responsibility. He has no convictions of his own.

(−)3 A psychiatrist. There's too much intimacy. They're bowed down with the inner world, which is a horrible one.

This father, athough a successful professional man, was a borderline psychotic whose main symptoms were withdrawal and obsessive ruminations. He had little genuine interest in his family and only out of a sense of duty did he make attempts to involve himself with them. Consistent with this lack of involvement is the fact that in none of these responses is any mention made of family involvement. The (+)1 person, although admirable in many ways, appears to epitomize 19th century new England independence and self-assertion. He is the kind of a person who rises above hostile forces in nature and the hardships of life in a determined and single-minded manner. The choice of the navigator probably relates to the father's feelings that he himself needs some navigation and direction if he is to weather the storms of his life, especially those associated with the welling up of feelings (as represented by the ocean waves) which are so threatening to him. In the (+)2 and (+)3 responses the father reveals his desire to get some pleasure out of life, something he was not getting because of his psychiatric disturbances.

The (−)1 response reveals the father's basic feelings about himself. He, like Nat Turner, is enslaved by his obsessions and his duplicity (which was associated with his contrived and artificial involvement in his family) and cause him to think of himself as "a double-dealing shackled madman." In the (−)2 response reference is made to the father's indecisiveness related to his obsessive doubting and massive ambivalence. The (−)3 response again makes reference to the father's psychic conflicts and fears of relevation of his primitive eruptions from the unconscious.

One father was asked the animal questions in addition to the person questions. These are the responses he gave:

(+)1 A poodle dog. It gets good treatment.

(+)2 A black panther. It's shrewed and it's cunning. It's fast.

(+)3 A turtle. It goes on slowly but looks back to see if it's right or wrong.

(−)1 A cat. It's too self-reliant. It doesn't give. It just takes.

(−)2 A pig. It's only here to be eaten.

(−)3 A reptile or snake. It's misunderstood. People kill them and don't realize that they're just doing their own thing.

This father was an extremely psychopathic person. He had little interest in the patient, his adopted stepson, and spent most of his time away from the home at his job. He was a very conniving and materialistic individual who used people ruthlessly in order to obtain his own ends. His primary attraction to his wife, who was 10 years his senior, was that she was a good cook.

The (+)1 response reveals his strong impulses to passively lead a life of luxury. The (+)2 response reflects his admiration for psychopathic qualities. The (−)3 response suggests unconscious respect for the psychopathic personality type who is most circumspect, calculating, and reflective of his behavior.

In the (−)1 response the father's criticism of the cat who "doesn't give, just takes" is a clear statement of his denial of these qualities within himself, because he was a most taking person. The (−)2 response relates to the same attitude in that the father, seeing the world as a place where one is "eaten," chooses to be the "eater." The (−)3 response is a clear-cut rationalization for psychopathic behavior. The reptile and the snake are highly symbolic of the devious, the unacceptable, the cunning, and the surreptitious. The father cannot provide a logical justification for accepting such behavior but merely requests that these animals be accepted because they are "doing their own thing," and that in itself should be enough for people to accept them.

The verbal projective questions can also be used with adults to describe other family members. Just as the child is asked to select animals and objects that will suit his or her mother and father, the parent can be asked to present people, animals, and objects that will suit other family members, especially spouse and children. This father gave the following responses when asked to select animals that suited hs wife's personality:

> (+)1 A mynah bird. It's like a parrot. It's always jabbering.
> (+)2 A rhinoceros. It goes where it wants. It doesn't have much of a brain. It tromps over everything in order to get what it wants.
> (+)3 A Pekingese house dog. It has no worries. It's fed, then taken out to shit, and then put to bed.
> (−)1 A mallard. It's graceful; she's not.
> (−)2 A leopard. It's quiet and stealthy. She's loud. She has no tact. She's noisy.
> (−)3 An alligator. He lives in the water and she's afraid of the water.

This father had very little respect for or involvement with his wife and the verbal projective associations clearly reflect this. The responses illustrate the massive feelings of disdain and disgust he had for her, and each response reveals a different type of deprecation. Here we see how all of these derogatory attitudes are on the conscious level.

Another father gave these responses when asked to select animals that suited his wife's personality:

> (+)1 A lion. It's majestic. It's a leader. It's quiet and unassuming. It has perseverance. It likes to get things done in a quiet way. She's respected like the lion by the rest of the animal kingdom.
> (+)2 A Mastiff dog. It protects the house. It's a strong animal yet it's gentle. It's respected by everyone.
> (+)3 A deer because of its beauty and gracefulness. It's shy except when protecting its young and then it becomes very forceful. It's clear. It leads a quiet life. It's a choice food of carnivorous animals.
> (−)1 A cat. They're nice until you go against them. Then they will turn against you. She won't do that.
> (−)2 A snake. She's not repulsive. She doesn't instill fear in anyone.

(−)3 A bat because it's a spreader of disease. It's repulsive. It's a scavenger. It hides away from view.

This father was extremely passive and submissive in his relationship to a remarkably domineering masochistic-martyristic wife. She was extremely controlling and coercive to all members of the family, but her manipulations were rarely overt. She played on their guilt through her martyristic self-sacrificing tendencies. Both the father and the children were very much in fear of her.

These qualities are reflected throughout the verbal projective responses. She, like the lion, is the "leader" and gets things done in a "quiet" and "unassuming" way. The "respect" that the lion enjoys from the "rest of the animal kingdom" is clearly the fearful subservience she has extracted from the members of her family.

The Mastiff dog, of course, exhibits qualities similar to the lion. The mother, like the Mastiff, is the "protector of the house" and is "respected" (= feared) by everyone. In the (+)3 response the statement that the deer is "the choice food for carnivorous animals" reflects the father's primitive and repressed hostility toward the mother. By identifying himself with a carnivorous animal for whom the deer is "choice food," he can vent the rage he feels toward her. In addition, the fantasy probably represents a desire to acquire her strength through primitive incorporative, cannibalistic maneuvers.

The (−)1 response is denial pure and simple. The mother is a person who will turn against the father if he turns against her, and he lives in fear of her retribution. The (−)2 response reveals his true feelings towards the mother, namely, that she is repulsive and he lives in fear of her. The (−)3 response is again a clear statement of the real feelings the father feels about the mother. He sees her as "repulsive" and "a scavenger." The subtle and somewhat surreptitious coercive maneuvers that the mother utilizes are reflected in the comment that the bat "hides away from view."

Another father gave these responses:

(+)1 A tiger. She's ferocious at times. She yells and screams a lot.

(+)2 A horse. She likes horse races. She watches many on TV. She loves all sorts of gambling, but not to excess. She's a $2.00 better.

(+)3 Dogs, any kind of dog. She loves them and I despise them. She'd want to be a dog. (What kind?) A brown Scotch Terrier. I can just associate her with dogs. I don't know why.

(−)1 A cow. It's fat, cumbersome, and odd. She's not like that.

(−)2 A giraffe. It has a high neck and long strides. She doesn't have a high neck and she takes short strides.

(−)3 A snake. It's slimy. She's not.

The 12-year-old daughter of this man was constantly bickering with her mother, whereas he tended to indulge his wife. The mother was not a very strongly maternal person, and the patient turned to her father where she felt she could get greater affection. An hereditary loss of hair was a source of serious concern to the mother, although the father denied that it in any way lessened his attraction for her. When first seen, the family was going through what I would consider an "oedipal crisis," with the father and daughter strongly attracted to one another and denying their attraction with intermittent bickering. The mother was quite jealous over the relationship between the father and daughter and directed much of her jealous rage toward the daughter.

The (+)1 response refers not only to the father's awareness of the mother's overt hostility expressed toward the daughter but, in addition, probably reveals his sensitivity to some of the mother's additional hostilities as well. The (+)3 response reveals the father's inability to overtly express his anger and his lack of physical attraction to his wife. He could only go as far as saying that he "despises" dogs and he somehow associates his wife with a dog. Denial and reaction formation were strong defense mechanisms in this man. In the (+)1 response he reveals his basic feelings about her lack of attractiveness, and there is also suggested his awareness that she is not a very maternal person in that the cow lends itself well to being viewed as a powerful maternal symbol. Although the (−)2 and (−)3 responses could also reveal his lack of attraction to her, they also could be considered to be within the normal range of responses.

Dreams   One father reported the following repetitious dream:

> I dream that I am submerged under water. I think that I can't breathe and that I'm trying to get to the surface. I then discover that I can breathe under water and I feel much better.

The father was completely dependent upon his own father who owned a large business. As he grew up he always knew that no matter how poorly he did in school he would ultimately end up owning the business. He never applied himself and each time he failed out of prep school or college, his father managed to buy him into another. He had many psychopathic qualities and felt no obligation to spend time with his children, be faithful to his wife, or commit himself in any way to anyone.

The dream reveals his basic life pattern—that he will be magically saved from catastrophe. Actually others would have suffered the consequences of such a life of self-indulgence, but he seems to feel that he has come away unscathed. Others get drowned; he can breathe under water. The dream epitomized his life pattern, especially his relationship to his overprotective father.

This father described the following repetitious dream:

> I was taking a test and I never had time to finish it. I felt pressured and pushed. I kept feeling that I wasn't going to finish.

This is a common repetitious dream of people from homes where the academic pressures have been great. In analyzing this dream with both parents and patients, I have most often found it to reflect a feeling that the people will not be able to live up to the standards of their parents, both in the academic as well as in the nonacademic areas of life. Because so much emotional investment has been directed to the academic realms, it serves as a general symbol for success in life. I have also found the dream to reflect ambivalence on the person's part toward successful achievements in life. Failing the test is not simply the academic test, but the test of life's success as well. Often the parents of such a patient have been ambivalent themselves with regard to their children's successful performance.

This father was a borderline psychotic who was a highly educated and moderately successful professional man. However, his extreme psychopathology prevented him from getting anything but the slightest gratification from his professional and nonprofessional life.

Another father related this dream:

> I was reading one of my competitor's private reports. He walked in and I was ashamed. I put the papers down.

Although this father did not exhibit specific psychopathic trends in the clinical interview, he was a fiercely competitive, materialistic, grandiose, and coercive individual. Although he was ostensibly ethical in his business dealings, the dream reflects an aspect of his personality that was not apparent in the clinical evaluation, but would certainly be consistent with his character structure. This dream demonstrates how a parent's dream may provide the examiner with added information about character structure—information that may be useful in understanding the child's psychopathology. In this case, some of the child's antisocial behavior could be considered the result of identification with his father's psychopathic traits and the desire to fulfill the unconscious wishes of the parent.

Throughout his life, one father had this repetitious dream:

> I had a gym all to myself. I spent a lot of time there with kids, teaching them to play basketball. I have no problems there when I am in the gym.

The father, although 38 years old, was still very much a child. He was still employed by his parents in their small store, and he was very much under the domination of his wife. He spent much time out of the house coaching young boys in various sports. This activity not only served as a way of removing himself from the domination of his wife, but also provided him with a feeling of authority and competence—which he lacked in his relationship with both his parents and his spouse. Furthermore, sports enabled him to express vicariously much of his pent-up hostility. Last, the dream enables him to engage in childish activities beyond the extent to which he involved himself in reality. It is a dream of an adolescent dreamed by a man who psychologically was still an adolescent.

Concluding Comments

My goal here is to show that the individual, whether mother or father, who is reluctant to give information directly may provide meaningful data with projective tests. However, analyzing such material can be risky. I am certain that many examiners may have come to different conclusions regarding the interpretations I have given to the material presented. In my defense, I might say my interpretations are made on the basis of my direct clinical experiences with the families. Analyzing the material in isolation from such clinical data is extremely risky and is generally a poor idea. But even when one does have clinical information, there is no question that there is still a certain amount of speculation. These drawbacks notwithstanding, I find such projective material useful, especially for the parent who is not comfortable revealing him- or herself in the direct clinical interview.

THE EVALUATION OF THE PATIENT

INTRODUCTION

I generally devote three 45- or 60-minute sessions to the intensive evaluation of the adolescent. With regard to this phase of the evaluation, one can generally divide adolescents into two groups. The younger adolescents are usually unreceptive to direct discussion of their problems. They are similar, therefore, to pre-adolescent children in this regard. However, they differ from such younger children in their receptivity to storytelling and other projective games. They generally appreciate that such instruments are vehicles for the revelation of their innermost thoughts and feelings—revelations that they are not willing to provide. We find ourselves in the position, then, with such youngsters of having a patient that is too old to utilize the old standby, storytelling and other projective material, and too young to reveal him- or herself directly. Such youngsters, accordingly, are not comfortable sitting in a session for 45 to 60 minutes with the therapist's "beady eyes" staring at him or her asking for intimate revelations. With these youngsters I will often spend more of the evaluation sessions utilizing verbal projective questions, dream discussion, the Draw-a-Person test, the Draw-a-Family test, and other instruments described in this section. With older adolescents, generally those over the age of 15, I am usually more successful in engaging them in direct discussion which, in itself, provides useful data. However, this does not preclude my utilization, to a lesser degree, of the other instruments described in this section.

When purely psychogenic problems are present, I generally devote three sessions to the intensive evaluation of the youngster. And this is the kind of evaluation I will be describing here. If, on the basis of the information I obtained in the initial two-hour evaluation, I concluded that neurologically based difficulties are present, then a longer, extended evaluation is often warranted. I not only have to assess for the presence of the neurologically based problems, but for psychogenic problems as well. And the latter may fall into two categories. The first are those psychogenic problems that are secondary to the neurological impairment. They are derivatives of such impairment and would presumably not be present if the patient did not have a basic organic disorder. The second are those that are independent of the neurological disturbance and often result from family problems and/or improper child-rearing practices. Of course, the two categories may overlap and each contribute to the intensification of the other. Obviously, the evaluation for these difficulties is much more complex and generally takes five to six meetings with the patient.

It is important for the examiner to appreciate that the purpose of the extended evaluation is more than simply data collection. An equally, if not more, important goal is to lay the foundation for a good therapeutic relationship. This is not likely to be accomplished in one or two pressured interviews. The more relaxed the circumstances, the greater the likelihood the therapist will be able to engage the child meaningfully.

Direct Verbal Inquiry

When engaging adolescents in direct verbal discussion, it is important for the examiner to appreciate that most adolescents, especially the younger ones, do not have insight into the fact that they have "problems" and the examiner is well advised not to attempt to get such patients to develop what we call "insights." Although younger adolescents are cognitively capable of creating linkages between their symptomatology and the unconscious (and even conscious) psychological processes that are producing their symptoms, their denial mechanisms are often so formidable that they will be unreceptive to inquiries designed to bring to conscious awareness these associations and linkages. Accordingly, the examiner should not be looking for any kind of testimonials from these patients. Furthermore, what we call "problems" are not generally viewed as such by adolescents, especially the younger ones. To them the problem is often the people who are "on their backs" trying to get them to do things they don't want to. But even those youngsters who have differentiated clearly the behavioral patterns which their parents consider pathological from those which their parents deem acceptable and desirable are not likely to be motivated to direct themselves to alleviating the "unhealthy traits."

Therapists working with adolescents do well to appreciate that if the parents and they have been successful in getting "the body in the room" they are very much "ahead of the game." It is important for examiners to appreciate that if the adolescent *really* doesn't want to go for treatment, there is nothing that either he or she or the parents can do about it. Therapists also should refrain from trying to analyze defensive rationalizations that give the youngster a face-saving excuse for attending the meetings. For example, when a 16-year-old fullback on his high school's football team (six feet 2 inches tall and 200 pounds of solid muscle) tells you that the only reason he comes is that his "mother (four feet eleven inches, 98 pounds) makes me come here," the therapist does well to respond with such comments as: "Yeah, many mothers are kind of pushy," or "I know how you feel, my mother used to coerce me into things when I was your age." The worst possible response is to say some-something along these lines: "Now look, you know and I know that your mother cannot make you come here if you really don't want to. You could pick her up off the floor by her collar, look her squarely in the eyes, and say something like 'Look, Ma, if you don't get off my back about seeing that doctor, I'm going to carry you over to the window and drop you out.' Once you start accepting the fact that you're here because you really want to be here and that, at some level, you recognize that you have problems, then you'll be making the first step toward doing something about them." Therapists who talk this way are going to lose their patients and, if in private practice, are not going to have many child and adolescent patients. Such a response loses sight completely of the fact that the adolescent needs the rationalization to protect him- or herself from the ego-debasing realization and appreciation that they have weaknesses, deficiencies, and areas of imperfection. Accordingly, the therapist does well to accept, gloss over, or sidestep the rationalization and proceed with the discussion with comments such as: "Well, as long as you're here, what would you like to tell me?" or "Well, as long as the money's being spent and the session paid for, we might as well use up the time. What would you like to talk about?" With such reassurances, the youngster is more likely to reveal him- or herself.

A good example of this phenomenon occurred a number of years ago during the course of a custody evaluation. A 13-year-old girl entered the interview and stated firmly: "Let's get something straight right now. I know why you want me here. You want me to tell you who I want to live with. You want me to say things about which parent I prefer over the other. Well, you're not going to get a word out of me on that subject. My best friend's parents are also splitting and they're seeing a shrink and their shrink wants to see her also and ask her who she wants to live with. We're very good friends and we made a vow. We promised each other that we'd never tell you shrinks who we want to live with. We're blood sisters. We cut our fingertips and mixed the blood. We made a vow that we'll never break that promise. I'll talk about other things, but I won't talk about that subject."

I recognized that the girl's comments revealed an attempt to protect herself from the feelings of disloyalty she would have if she were to make a direct statement about which parent she preferred. She recognized that such a revelation might compromise her relationship with the non-preferred parent. However, I also suspected that a part of her probably did wish to divulge her preference in order to protect herself from being assigned by me and the court to the non-preferred parent. Her statement that she would be willing to talk about other subjects lent support to this suspicion. In addition, from previous experiences in such cases, I knew well that such youngsters often need to have the feeling that the decision was imposed upon them by a "crazy judge" and they can thereby protect themselves from the feared alienation of a non-preferred parent. Following the decision, they can complain to the non-preferred parent how they repeatedly expressed preference for that parent and it was only the insanity of the legal process that resulted in the youngsters' being assigned to the other parent.

With this understanding I responded to the girl: "I want you to know that I fully respect your thoughts and feelings on this issue and I would not consider it proper of me to use any kind of coercive techniques to get you to talk about that subject. Accordingly, I promise you that I will not ask you that question, so you can breathe freely and rest assured that we will consider that issue "off limits." I then said to her: "Accordingly, in line with this respect for your wishes, I will be willing to talk with you about anything else that you wish to discuss. We have almost the full session so you'll have ample opportunity to tell me about anything *else* that you wish to talk about."

With such reassurance the girl began to speak: "Well, I don't know what to speak about. Nothing much has really been happening with me . . . my mother and I went shopping today. There's nothing really to say about that. You know, doctor, I can't go shopping with my father. He doesn't know anything about lipstick, cosmetics, things like that. Also, girls my age really can't confide in their fathers. I can talk to my mother about my periods and my feelings about boys. I could *never* talk to my father about things like that. He just wouldn't understand. . . ." The girl continued to "roll" and tell me about the other manifestations of the close relationship she had with her mother, continually contrasting it with the more distant relationship she had with her father. There was no question that she was telling me her parental preference without consciously realizing that she was doing so. She constructed the interview, however, in such a way that she did not have to feel disloyal and yet could provide me with this vital information. Her statements played an important role in my decision to recommend that she remain living with her mother. Following the court's decision that she remain with her mother she vociferously denigrated me to her father with such statements as: "That Dr. Gardner is an idiot. I told him that I wanted to live with you. I told him about all the terrible things that my mother did with me. But he didn't listen. And then he told the judge to have me live with *her*, the bitch." Of course, with her mother, she plays me for my judiciousness, sensitivity, and appreciation of the importance of her remaining living with her mother.

These reservations about insights notwithstanding, I will usually start the interview with the traditional open-ended question: "So what's doing with you?" or "So what would you like to talk about?" If this question proves unsuccessful in getting the youngster to open up (the usual case), I may then ask a more specific question such as: "I'd like to know what your reactions were to our last interview" (referring here to the initial two-hour evaluation).

As I will elaborate in Chapter Five, abstractions and conceptualizations are of far less therapeutic value than concrete examples. Accordingly, questions beginning with "Why?" and far less valuable than questions beginning with "When, Where, What, or How?" Of course, as therapists we are interested in knowing *why*, but we are less likely to learn the reasons *why* from *Why* questions than we are from questions utilizing other interrogatory words. For example, to ask a youngster why he or she misbehaves in school is generally not productive. To ask the same patient a series of questions about when, where, with whom, and under what circumstances there is trouble in school is more likely to provide useful data. Even here, due to the youngster's defensiveness, one may not get reasonable answers because the questions are related to the patient's "problems"—a touchy subject if there ever was one. Under such circumstances one might lead into revelations about academic problems, for example, by asking specific concrete questions such as: "What grade are you in?" and "How many boys and girls are at that grade level?" Then one might go on to ask such questions as: "Who's the smartest kid in the class?" "What do you like about him (her)?" "What don't you like about him (her)?" "Who is the poorest student?" and "Do you like him (her)?" Such questions may ultimately result in the youngster's talking about his or her own attitude toward academics. Other questions that might lead into a discussion of the patient's academic problems are: "What subject do you like the most in school?" "What subject do you like the least?" "What subjects are you best at?" and "What subjects are you worst at?"

In order to discuss behavioral problems one might lead into the issue with questions such as: "Who are the kids in your class who get into trouble?" "What kinds of things do they do?" "What does the teacher do when they get into trouble?" The reader will note that I am talking here about *other* parties, not the patient. "Does the teacher yell at them?" "What does the teacher say to them when they get into trouble?" "What do the other kids feel about those troublemakers?" "What kinds of punishment do they get?" "Who's the best person in the class in conduct?" "Do you like him (her)?" From this point one might say, *"All* kids get into trouble once in a while in class, what kinds of things do *you* do that get *you* into trouble?" By stating first that "all" youngsters get into trouble, at times, it becomes easier for the patient to describe the situations when he or she has behavioral difficulties. The reader will note also that I rarely ask yes-no questions. These are most often of little value because, after one has received an answer, one does not know if it is really valid. Questions requiring specific answers are much more likely to be useful.

In order to learn more about peer difficulties, one might start off with specific, nonthreatening questions, for example: "Tell me the names of some of the kids who live in your neighborhood?" "Who are the ones you spend the most time with?" "Who is your best friend?" "What is it about that person that makes you like him (her) so much?" "What kinds of things do you like doing most with him (her)?" "Of all the kids in the neighborhood which one do you dislike or hate the most?" "What is there about that person that makes you dislike or hate him (her) so much?" "What do you think are the things that a person can do that will turn off other kids?" For the patient who is teased and/or scapegoated, one might ask what are the specific things other youngsters say to him or her when taunting is occurring. These patients might also be asked what things their parents and siblings tell them they do that get them into trouble. One might also talk here about the various activities the youngster involves him- or herself in and, if there are difficulties, the details regarding why.

With regard to pathological behavior in the home, again, the examiner does well to follow the aforementioned principles. Some good lead-in questions: "What do you like doing most with your mother (father)?" "Of all things you like doing in the house, what things are the most fun?" "What are the things you don't like doing with your mother (father), the things that are no fun at all?" "All kids get scolded sometimes. What kinds of things do your parents scold you over?" "All kids get punished sometimes. What kinds of things are you punished for?" "Who punishes you?" "What kinds of punishments does your mother (father) give you?" "How long do they last?" "Are these fair punishments?" "I want you to tell me the best things you can about your mother?" "Now tell me the worst things about your mother?" "Now I want you to tell me the best things you can about your father?" "Now tell me the worst things about your father?" "What's the best thing that ever happened to you in your whole life?" "What's the worst thing that ever happened to you in your whole life?"

One can question the patient, as well, to get information about parental capacity. This can be done by going through the events of the day, from the time the youngster gets up in the morning until the time he or she goes to sleep at night. In association with each event, one tries to find about which parent is involved and the nature of the involvement. For example, one might ask which parent gets the patient up in the morning and whether there are difficulties, and continue with such questioning about the whole course of the day. Particular emphasis should be given to those times when both parents are available. Most often, this is during the evening. In the discussion one could ask about homework—who helps with the homework, who has the most patience, and whether there is any conflict and fighting over it.

The examiner must appreciate that most adolescents generally have weak egos and will utilize a variety of maneuvers to avoid direct confrontation with their deficits. They commonly utilize such phrases as "I don't know." Accordingly, the examiner should pose questions that circumvent embarrassing confrontations. To say to an adolescent, "Tell me about the things you're scared of?" or "What are the things that frighten you?" is an injudicious way of finding out about fears. A preferable way of getting information in this area is to say: "Most people have some things that scare them once in a while. What things scare you?" By presenting fears as a normal response, the patient is more likely to divulge what his (hers) are. Also, by starting off with the positive, easily admitted aspects of an issue, it is often easier to get into the embarrassing opposite. For example, one might ask, "What are the things about yourself that you are most proud of?" I will then go into a detailed inquiry of the sources of the child's pride. With ego enhancement as a buffer, one is in a better position to ask the question: "All people have times when they do, say, or think things they're ashamed of. I'd like to hear one thing that you're ashamed of." Again, the question is so posed that shame is presented as a normal phenomenon and all I'm asking of the patient is to mention one thing that has caused him or her shame.

Some patients are particularly fearful of expressing their feelings. On occasion, feelings are relegated to the unconscious, and questions about them prove futile. However, there are some youngsters who can verbalize their feelings but are uncomfortable doing so. The worst way to elicit the expression of feelings from a repressed child is to ask the question: "How do you feel about that?" or "How does that make you feel?" One could ask the question, but should not be surprised if the repressed child does not answer. In such cases, the examiner might say, "You must have felt really sad when your parents told you they were going to split up." "You must have *really* felt lonely when the other kids didn't want to be with you." Even then one might get the answer: "It doesn't bother me!" One might respond then with, "Well, I find that hard to believe. I believe that you *do* have feelings about it but that you're not comfortable talking about it now. I hope the time will come soon when you'll feel more comfortable talking about these things."

There are occasions, however, when the aforementioned kinds of catalytic questions do serve well to precipitate an emotional response. They serve to fan and enlarge sparks of feelings that were only dimly appreciated by the patient. Another way of facilitating the expression of such feelings is to precede them with comments that make them socially acceptable: "Most kids get very upset when they learn that their parents are going to get a divorce. What were the kinds of feelings *you* had?"

A discussion of the youngster's interests and hobbies can be very useful. Sometimes, the examiner does best to start the interview with this topic, because it is the least threatening. At other times, it may be useful as a way of decompressing a situation and diverting a patient from a particularly difficult area of inquiry. One might ask very simply: "What are your hobbies?" or "What are your favorite games?" or "What do you like doing after school?" "What's your favorite sport?" These can serve as a point of departure for a discussion in which the therapist discusses his or her own knowledge of this area. Such discussion can serve to entrench the therapist-patient relationship. Sometimes the discussion may reveal pathological trends. One boy may say that his hobby is computers. However, the discussion of computers reveals that he has such a massive preoccupation with the subject that he spends little time on anything else. When asked about his favorite TV program, one child responded, "Divorce Court." A very common "hobby" of many youngsters at this time is the game "Dungeons and Dragons." This game facilitates group discussion of a wide variety of often morbid and hostile fantasies. It is particularly attractive to children who have rich fantasy lives, some of whom are borderline and others even psychotic. Recently, there have been reports in the newspapers about youngsters who have acted out these fantasies, even to the point of attempted murder and I know of at least one homicide reported in association wth the game. Examiners do well to investigate the depth of involvement with this game and discourage it for those who are excessively involved.

Three Wishes

Whereas I generally ask adults for five wishes, I usually ask children for only three. My main reason for this is that I have found this question to be less useful for children. Most often children provide so much stereotyped responses that are age appropriate and not particularly valuable sources of information, e.g., "a million dollars," "all the money in the world," or "all the toys in the world." Adolescents are somewhere in between. Some will give five meaningful, idiosynchratic responses that can be a useful source of information. This is especially true of older adolescents. Younger adolescents, in contrast, may often provide the stereotyped wishes and for them, I will generally quit after three.

A very mature ten-year-old girl (she could easily pass for 13) presented with symptoms of depression, stuttering, poor relationships with peers, and generalized tension. Her mother was extremely punitive and her father passively permitted the mother's sadistic behavior. Her first wish: "To have magical powers to make someone exactly like me. We'd then go and live in a big mansion in

Florida." I considered the first wish to reveal her desire to have a "clone," someone just like herself. She would then have a playmate to compensate for the deprivation she suffered in her household. The playmate, of course, would be kind to her, unlike her mother. She would also remove herself from the home and go to Florida, which represented, I believe, a climate of emotional warmth, ease, and relaxation. Her second wish: "I'd have a farm of horses." Although this might be a normal response, in this girl's situation I suspected that it related to her desire to be in the company of animals because her experiences with human beings had been so difficult. In addition, the horses probably had some sexual connotation for her. Her third wish: "To grow up fast and get married to a man who would love me a lot and take good care of me." Considering this child's background, the meaning of the wish is obvious. It is another reflection of the patient's general unhappiness in her home situation. Although ten, she was preoccupied with sexual fantasies involving teenage dating, seductivity, and kissing. This was partially derived from her mother who, in addition to her hostility, was a seductive woman, preoccupied with sex, but was basically a sexually inhibited person.

First Memory

An adolescent's first memory is generally a less valuable source of information than that of adults. One might argue that the adolescent's first memory is more likely to be a useful source of information because the time gap between the event and the time the question is posed is much shorter than the time lag for adults. When adults are asked this question, however, they are reaching back into the distant past and are selecting the event from a much larger storehouse of recollections, and thus it usually has a much greater psychological significance. One cannot label an adolescent immature or regressed if he or she remembers being in a crib, being fed a meal, or being taken care of in bed when sick. As is true in all projective information, one must take care to differentiate the age-appropriate from the idiosyncratic and atypical.

A very bright 11-year-old boy had great difficulties in his relationships with his parents. His mother was an extremely cold, critical, coercive, and controlling individual. His father did not protect the boy adequately from his mother's maltreatment of him. When asked for his first memory, the patient responded: "I was being put into a crib a few minutes after I was born." I believe that the patient was being honest with me; however, I also believe that the fantasy had a reality for him because it was so deeply entrenched in his psychic structure and so well lent itself to symbolizing his life situation with his mother. It reflected well his feelings of having been separated from his mother a few minutes after he was born and placed where he could not enjoy any contact with her.

This 12-year-old boy's parents both had minimal involvement with him. His father was a hard-driving businessman, a workaholic, who was often absent from the home because of long business trips. His mother was a frustrated, angry, embittered woman who ranged from tolerance of the patient to utilization of him as a scapegoat. This was the first memory he provided: "I was in kindergarten. The school nun was there. The milk she gave me was frozen and I was scared to tell her that the milk was no good. The other kids told her for me. I was afraid that if I bothered her, she would yell at me." The fantasy needs little analysis. The frozen milk is a clear statement of the patient's view of his mother as unmaternal. In addition, he fears complaining about her lack of affection because he might then be traumatized in retaliation and thereby add to the difficulties he was already suffering in association with his emotional deprivation.

A 14-year-old girl was referred because of severe outbursts of rage. She described this event occurring when she was five:

> My mother went down a one-way street in a car. She went the wrong way. A policeman stopped her. I didn't like police at that time. I thought they were mean. I was scared of them. I cried a lot and said, "Don't hurt my mother." I was screaming and crying and yelling. It got him so frustrated that he said, "The heck with it," and he got rid of us. And he didn't give us a ticket.

The patient's mother was a woman who felt overwhelmed by the world and was often confused about where she was heading and what her future would be. One manifestation of this was her poor sense of direction, which prevented her from adequately driving distances more than a few miles from her home. The patient's recalling mother's going down a one-way street is a statement of her view of her mother as a woman who doesn't know which way she is going in life. The patient's recollection of avoiding the consequences of her behavior by having a violent outburst of rage epitomizes her life pattern. The patient's temper outbursts did indeed enable her to avoid the consequences of her unacceptable behavior. Early in life she had learned that if she were to rant and rave long enough, she would get her way. In this case the policeman, the symbol of the punitive authority, is dissuaded by her tantrums from administering appropriate punishment.

Draw-a-Person and Draw-a-Family

I generally confine the Draw-a-Person and Draw-a-Family tests to the initial two-hour evaluation. On occasion, I will administer the instruments again during the course of the extended evaluation. The examples presented here were derived from that phase.

An 11-and-a-half-year-old girl came to treatment because of antisocial behavior both at home and at school. She was very resistant to the idea of coming for treatment, told this to her family, but not to the therapist. This is the story that she told about the family she drew:

> This family was very happy. They had one dog, but he didn't get his picture taken. He wanted to be in he picture, but the family wouldn't let him be in it.
>
> The next-door neighbors, they were snooping around trying to find out why the family wouldn't let the dog have his picture taken. They found out that the dog kept jumping on the cameraman all the time. They had to shut the dog up in a closet so that he couldn't get on the cameraman.
>
> The reason the dog was always jumping on the cameraman is because the dog thinks that every time the cameraman would take a picture, a gun would come out of the camera and kill the family. Finally, one day the neighbors told the family why the dog was doing that—because he thought the cameraman had a gun. The family laughed and said, "There's nothing. There is no gun."

But then the cameraman did shoot the family. He was a robber and he wanted jewelry. Then the neighbors called the police and the police put him in jail and gave the dog a medal for capturing the cameraman.

The dog, of course, represents the patient. In the beginning of the story the dog's failure to get his picture taken reflects early treatment anxieties in which the patient does not want to be seen by the eye of the camera, that is, by the therapist. Depicting herself as a dog also reflects her feelings of low self-esteem. She sees herself as being rejected by the family and "locked in a closet." The cameraman's murder of the family represents her own hostility toward her family members and the cameraman is used as the perpetrator of the crime, thereby assuaging her own guilt over the act. The dog has little remorse over their demise. By having the cameraman jailed she further assuages the guilt she feels over her hostility. Providing the dog with a prize serves further to reinforce suppression of hostility.

Verbal Projective Questions

The verbal projective questions of N.I. Kritzberg (1966) can provide useful information about the adolescent's underlying psychodynamics. As mentioned, questions about the people whom the patient would like to be transformed into are not generally useful for pre-adolescent children in that their repertoire of individuals from whom they can choose is somewhat limited and they tend to select ego-appropriate stereotyped people. Younger children, however, do better with the animal and object question. In the adolescent period youngsters begin to expand significantly their repertoire of individuals from whom they can choose and the question thereby becomes more meaningful. And, the older the adolescent, the more likely the question is going to prove valuable. This does not preclude, however, utilizing animal and object questions for the adolescent, nor does it preclude asking the adolescent questions about which animals and objects would most suit the parents if they had to be so transformed.

This 11-year-old boy came to treatment because of severe conflicts with his father, a shrewd businessman who prided himself on his business acumen. However, he was insensitive to others, to the point of being psychopathic. The mother was passively submissive in her relationship with her husband, thereby abandoning the boy to her husband's maltreatment of him. These are the responses he gave to the question regarding which persons he would choose to be changed into had he to be so transformed:

(+)1 The actor who played "Oliver." He was an orphan boy. He lived in an orphanage. He had very little food. He unknowingly meets his grandfather, and then he lives happily ever after with his grandfather.

(+)2 Mr. Robinson. He's the father in the TV program *Lost in Space*. It's a space family and they go around exploring space. In one program the father was drifting from the ship into space, and they catch him just in time. They catch him just in time to get away from monsters. He's the pilot. He's the leader of the family.

(+)3 President Johnson. He signs civil rights bills, making sure that all races have equal rights.

(−)1 Mary Martin. I saw her in that play, *The Sound of Music*. She makes this mean father into a nice man. He was very strict to his kids and she changes him so he isn't strict. I would not want to be there in the beginning of the picture when she was married to the mean father.

(−)2 My sister Ruth (age 14). She's a real kook. She thinks of love all the time. If the house was on fire and she was talking to her boyfriends, she wouldn't make an attempt to get out.

(−)3 My sister Jane (age 16). She's a big shot. She thinks she's real great. She bosses everybody around all the time. She snitches on me to my parents.

Response (+)1 reveals the patient's feelings of having been abandoned and rejected by his father and his desire to be protected by him. The (+)2 response reflects the patient's ambivalence toward his father. On the one hand, he would want him separated and removed (drifting into space) and exposed to the dangers of monsters. On the other hand, he would want him retrieved. In the (+)3 response, his desire to be President Johnson stems here from the wish to be assured equal rights, that is, to be given humane treatment from his parents.

The (−)1 response reflects the patient's desire that someone come into his home and transform his father into a benevolent and loving person. The (−)2 and (−)3 responses are, in part, normal responses for a 12-year-old boy and reflect usual sibling rivalry problems. However, in (−)2 the introduction of the house burning down theme reflects the patient's hostility toward his family. There is possibly a sexual element here as well: the fire repressing his sexual desires which he harbors toward his sister and the devastating results should he express such.

Both of this 14-year-old girl's parents were extremely rejecting and angry people. The patient herself harbored deep-seated retaliative hostility toward her parents which she was unable to express. I considered such feelings to be playing a role in the anxiety attacks which she presented for treatment.

> (+)1 A bird, a small one, a bluejay. It's sweet. It can sing and fly. They care for their children even though they are animals.
>
> (+)2 A deer. It's gentle, sweet and pretty. Deers care for their children.
>
> (+)3 An otter. It's playful. Their main objective is not to kill.
>
> (−)1 A lion. All animals are scared of you. Lions kill, and I wouldn't want to do that.
>
> (−)2 A snake. They're mean and ugly and horrible.
>
> (−)3 A bug or spider. They're horrible. They're so horrible and creepy, but I couldn't kill it. I can't kill any insect.

In (+)1 and (+)2, the patient admires birds and deer because they "care for their children," a quality which she does not enjoy from her parents. The(+)3 choice, the otter, whose main objective is "not to kill," reveals the patient's desire to repress her own murderous rage.

The same holds true regarding her desire not be a lion (−)1 because a lion kills, that is, she wishes to disown her own hostility. The (−)3 response clearly reveals her basic feelings that she is like a bug or spider, prone to be obliterated by overwhelming forces. In addition, her inability to kill small insects reveals her great conflict about the expression of hostility.

This 11-year-old boy came to treatment because of severe passive-aggressivity in the home and at school. His obstructionism was a constant source of irritation to his teachers and school personnel. The patient's father was an extremely insecure and inadequate man who compensated with a pathetic pseudo-intellectuality. He fancied himself an arm-chair philosopher and as a man who was exquisitely sensitive to the deeper processes and workings of the human mind. His seemingly erudite pontifications were most often fatuous. When frustrated, he exhibited severe rage outbursts. These are the responses the patient provided to the question regarding which animals would most suit his father if his father had to be so transformed:

> (+)1 Half-gorilla and half-lamb, because sometimes he yells and sometimes he's nice.
> (+)2 Half-cat and half-lion, because sometimes he yells and sometimes he's nice.
> (+)3 Half-tiger and half-playful dog, for the same reason. Sometimes he screams a lot and other times he's nice.
> (−)1 A gorilla. He doesn't always yell.
> (−)2 A tiger, because he doesn't always yell.
> (−)3 A lion, because he doesn't always yell.

When providing answers to these questions, it was clear that the patient was not going to exert himself or in any way inconvenience himself to think of elaborate answers. The easiest thing for him to do was to perseverate the same reasons for his choices. However, his resistance notwithstanding, he provided meaningful material. The perfunctory way in which he gave his responses, as well as their repetitious similarity, revealed his basic passive-aggressivity. His (+)1, (+)2, and (+)3 responses all indicate that the patient appreciated his father's dual personality. On the one hand, the father is "half-gorilla," a reflection of the patient's appreciation of his father's rage outburst problem. On the other hand, his father is "half-lamb," a reflection of the patient's appreciation that his father is basically a weak person. The gorilla is also a facade and serves to compensate for the basic feelings that his father is a lamb. The $(-)1$, $(-)2$, and $(-)3$ answers are basically repetitions of the gorilla, tiger, and lion themes, given without much thought and deliberation. Nevertheless, they reveal his appreciation of the compensatory personality traits of his father.

At this point, I present in detail (with many verbatim vignettes) an adolescent's responses to the verbal projective questions. I will demonstrate here not only the use of the child's responses as a source of information about underlying psychodynamics, but as a point of departure for the acquisition of additional information and therapeutic interchange. Charles was brought to treatment at age 13 because of destructive behavior in the classroom, poor academic performance in spite of high intelligence, defiance of his parents at home (especially his mother), and alienating behavior toward peers. He was fiercely rivalrous with his nine-year-old brother who was more successful in the classroom, in the neighborhood, and in his relationship with their parents.

During the initial consultative sesson I was not able to determine the sources of Charles' difficulty in the family. Charles' mother was a housewife and, to the best of my knowledge, was dedicated to his upbringing and showed no manifestations of significant psychopathology. His father, however, was a somewhat "uptight" individual who was inhibited in expressing his feelings. In spite of this he did devote significant time to the boys, especially on weekends, and involved himself extensively in their recreational activities which he served as a coach for a variety of sports.

Charles' problems are said to have started when he was three-and-a-half years old, following the birth of his younger brother. By the end of my two-hour consultation I concluded that fierce sibliing rivalry was probably playing an important role in Charles' difficulties, and I could not ascertain any other significant family problems that might have contributed to his antisocial behavior. In addition, Charles had a weight problem from excessive eating—a problem for which he was frequently criticized by his parents (especially his father).

In the second session, the first of my extended evaluation, I asked Charles the first animal question. His response: "A tiger because I would be able to defend myself from other animals. Also, they're very fast."

Charles' second choice: "A bird." Consistent with the principle that one does well to ask for species in that there are a wide variety of birds that can symbolize many different things, I asked Charles what bird he woud like to be. He responded, "A robin because they can fly wherever they want." I then asked Charles where he would fly to if he were a robin. He responded, "To Florida. I've never been there. I want to go there with my family."

Charles' third choice: "A seal because everyone likes them. They can swim wherever they want."

Before we had the opportunity to go on to the animals Charles would *not* want to be, he asked me if it was all right to change his first choice from a tiger to a chimpanzee. I told him there would be no problem there, but asked him why he wanted to be a chimpanzee. He responded, "Because they're smart and intelligent. They're active and people love them because they're cute." He then told me he would like to leave the tiger answer as his fourth choice. Again, I told him there would be no problem with that.

We then went on to the animals he would not want to be. His first choice: "A rhinoceros because everyone hates them because they're strong and they kill other animals. People are afraid of them because of the way they look with their big horns."

His second choice: "A hippopotamus because they're big and ugly. People are scared of them because of their looks."

His third choice: "A shark because everyone is scared of them. No one wants to be near them. They're killers."

I believe that Charles' request to substitute the chimpanzee for the tiger was a reflection of his strong desire for the chimpanzee response to take priority over the other three. His reasons for selecting the chimpanzee related to the problems for which he entered treatment. He described the chimpanzee as smart, intelligent, active, and "people love them because they're cute." Doing poorly in school, Charles did not consider himself smart or intelligent. Both he and the chimpanzee are "active." Charles' "activity" was associated with antisocial behavior and resulted in his being alienated from others. The chimpanzee's activity, however, does not result in such alienation; rather, "people love them because they're cute." The response reveals Charles' desire to be loved in spite of his alienating behavior. The robin and the seal responses share in common the desire to be free from constraints. At times this is a normal response, given by many children who view school and home restrictions to be constraints from which they wish to free themselves. Last, Charles' original first choice, the tiger, was chosen because of its capacity to defend itself from other animals. The response suggests that Charles sees himself as vulnerable to attacks by outsiders and would like to be strong enough to defend himself.

The three animals that Charles chose not to be share in common the hostility element. The rhinoceros "kills animals." People are "scared of" the hippopotamus. And sharks are "killers." In addition to the hostility there is the appearance element described in the rhinoceros and hippopotamus responses. Of the rhinoceros Charles stated: "People are afraid of them because of the way they look with their big horns." And with regard to the hippopotamus: "People are scared of them because of their looks." The hostile elements in the undesired animals may very well be in the normal range. However, they may also reflect inordinate hostility which Charles wished to disown. One cannot justifiably come to this conclusion from these three responses taken in isolation from other data, especially because they were given in response to the question regarding what animals he would *not* want to be. Not wanting to be an animal that is ferocious is within the normal range. Bringing in the element of appearance, however, is definitely idiosyncratic and suggests that Charles has special feelings about how he looks. This may have related to his mild obesity problem in that Charles was frequently criticized by both of his parents (especially his father) for being overweight.

Charles was then asked what objects he would want to be changed into, if he had to be so transformed. His first response: "I'd want to be a computer. It knows a lot of stuff. It knows more than a man. It's smart and intelligent. People like to use them." We begin to see here a theme emerging on the issue of intelligence. The responses suggest that Charles has feelings of intellectual inadequacy associated with his academic underachievement. His revised first choice on the animal question was the "smart and intelligent" chimpanzee and now his first choice on the object question again relates to intelligence.

Charles' second choice of object: "A pen because people would use me a lot and I'd have a lot of people around me." Charles was then asked what was the paritcular value of that and he replied,

"People *need* them. People need them to write and writing is important." The responses here not only reflect Charles' need for others to respect him for his abilities, but the particular quality for which he wants respect: writing. And writing, of course, is best done by those who are "smart and intelligent."

Charles' third object: "A stereo. People love to listen to music. I'd be used a lot." The response reflects Charles' desire that he be liked and be needed by other people, probably a reaction to the alienation he suffered from parents and peers because of his psychological problems.

The first object Charles would not want to be: "A box for corn flakes because once people are through with it they throw you away." Again we see the theme of being needed and the fear of being viewed as useless.

His second choice: "A baseball bat. You're always getting hit with a ball and someone can break you. People don't treat you well. You're just a piece of wood to them. They just throw you around." The response again reveals Charles' feelings of being rejected by others and being viewed as subhuman, as someone whose feelings are not considered. In addition, there is the element here of maltreatment from others, and this response is similar to one of the reasons why he did not wish to be a tiger, namely, because it is unable to defend itself from other animals.

The last object he would not want to be: "A gun because I wouldn't want to be used to hurt anyone else." Although one might ascribe hostility here, it is also possible that the response reflects a humane attitude toward others. Of course, both needs would be gratified by this response.

Charles was then asked what animals would suit his mother if she had to be so transformed. His first response: "A chimpanzee. They're nice, but when you get on their bad side they won't be nice to you." I then asked Charles how he gets on his mother's bad side. He replied, "If I don't listen to her she gets mad." I asked him what he could do about this and he responded, "By stopping myself from being on her bad side." I next asked him why he was still continuing to be on her bad side and why he couldn't stop doing so. His reply: "I know I shouldn't. If I get into my moods I just think 'Who does she think she is bossing me around like that?' " I finally tried to elicit from Charles information about what factors contributed to his getting into one of his "moods." He was unable to provide me with any meaningful response and so we proceeded.

Charles' second choice of animal that would suit his mother: "A bird." Again, I generally do not accept readily such a response and asked him what specific *kind* of bird would most suit his mother's personality. He replied, "A bluejay because she is a nice person. Bluejays keep on coming back if you are nice to them and give them food. If you are nice to them, they'll be nice to you, and it's like that with my mother. I've got to stop being on her bad side." I asked Charles if he thought he could do so and he replied, "Yeah, I've got to try harder. If I put my mind to it. The problem is, I've got to put my mind to it." When asked why he had not done so in the past, he replied, "I don't know. I just get into one of my moods." Again, Charles was asked what situations get him into one of his moods. He replied that when he has trouble with other children, he gets moody. Although I was able to get him to see that his difficulties with peers related to provocative behavior on his own part, I did not feel at that point that my message was sinking in. And so we proceeded.

The third animal that Charles considered to suit his mother's personality: "An owl because they're smart. She's smart. She knows a lot of things I don't know. She knows a lot of math and she can help me with my math." Again, the issue of intelligence emerges and Charles is stating here that he views his mother to be a smart woman, as someone who could help him with his studies. Children generally view their parents as smarter because that is the reality of the situation. Parents do help children with homework and generally have a much vaster fund of knowledge. I suspect, however, that Charles' response here is not simply related to this reality. Rather, it probably relates to feelings of intellectual inadequacy resulting from his academic underachievement.

Charles was then asked what animals would not suit his mother's personality. His first response: "A shark because she isn't a mean person. A shark is." His second animal: "A pig, she's a neat person and she's smart. A pig isn't." His third animal: "A gorilla, because she's not like a savage." The first and third responses could very well be considered to be within the normal range. The pig, however, again reveals the theme of intelligence, lending weight to the conclusion that this issue is very much on Charles' mind.

I then proceeded to ask Charles what animal would suit his father if he had to be so transformed. His first response: "An owl, just like my mother. I have the same answers for my father as I do for my mother." At this point I urged Charles to come up with different responses for his father in that his father and mother were two different people and I was sure that he could think of animals that indicated these differences. Giving the same answers is a common avoidance maneuver, and the examiner should encourage children to ponder the question a little longer before taking the easy route of giving identical responses for both parents. In response Charles replied, "Okay then, a cheetah. He's fast and he can defend himself."

At that point, Charles interrupted and asked me if he could give me another animal that would suit his mother because one had just come to mind. Of course, I agreed and he responded: "A dog and a cat." I suggested that we start with the dog and that he name a specific kind of dog. I cannot emphasize this point strongly enough to the reader. There are a wide variety of dogs, each breed of which lends itself well to symbolizing a different personality characteristic. And, as the reader will see in just a few seconds, my asking Charles to select a specific kind of dog provided useful information. His response: "A Saint Bernard, because you can depend on them. If you have a problem, you can tell them and they'll help you. They're famous for rescuing people in the snow." The response reveals Charles' view of his mother as nurturing and protective. However, it also suggests that he feels himself in a situation of emotional deprivation (lost in the snow). Perhaps this relates to his father's problems in expressing feelings and his mother's capacity to provide him with the affection that his father cannot.

Because Charles had stated that his mother resembles a "dog and a cat," I asked him then why he had chosen a cat. He responded: "You can also depend upon them. If you need a friend it's always there, and they're always by your side." The response again is a statement of Charles' view of his mother as warm, nurturing, and reliable. It is important to appreciate that this response, coming as it did as an interruption, must be given extra attention and credibility when assessing a child's responses. Just as the chimpanzee interruption provided useful information earlier in the inquiry, this interruption did so as well. The examiner does well to view these interruptions as reflecting significant pressure by unconscious processes to express important issues. The comments about Charles' mother's warmth, protectiveness, and affection came in the midst of descriptions of his father. They suggest that his descriptions of his father's coldness was anxiety provoking and that he needed his mother's warmth and protection as an antidote.

We then continued and Charles gave as the second choice of animal that would suit his father: "A dog, a Saint Bernard." Again, I asked Charles if he could give me a different animal because I considered the Saint Bernard response to be a manifestation of resistance in that he had just given that animal as one that would suit his mother. Without much delay he stated, "A Dalmation, because you can depend on them for help." It is difficult to assess his answer, coming as it did immediately after one that described Charles' mother as being someone on whom he could depend. I believe that Charles' father *was* dependable in certain areas such as involvement with Charles in sports. What he could *not* depend upon from his father were open displays of emotion, intimacy, and warm tender feelings. His father could, however, *do* those things that were necessary for adequate child rearing.

The third animal that would suit Charles' father: "A beaver because it works hard." Charles' father's work occupied him for long hours during weekdays; however, he was available to a significant degree on weekends to devote himself to his sons. From the ensuing discussion I could not be certain whether or not Charles felt any deprivation in association with his father's midweek work obligations. He denied such feelings. I suspect that the reality was that Charles did not consciously experience his father as depriving because he was there to a significant degree on weekends. The deprivation that he was not consciously aware of was emotional, which is more subtle—but deprivation nevertheless.

In answer to the question as to which animals are not similar to his father, Charles replied: "A lion because he is not mean or savage." The second animal unlike his father: "A fox because he is not a con artist." And the third: "A snake because he is not a slippery snake that goes around biting people." I considered the first and third responses (the lion and the snake) to be within the normal range, not only with regard to the animals chosen but the reasons why. However, the second response is, in my experience, atypical. And atypicality is one of the criteria for ascertaining psychopathology. It certainly is an unusual response and suggests that the patient, at some level, may consider his father to be duplicitous. It may be of interest to the reader to learn that on the day following this interview I did have an individual interview with the father. There was no question that he was not candid with me. He described the marriage as always having been a good one and denied that there were any problems. Charles' mother, however, during the interview prior to the one with Charles in which the verbal projective test was administered, described a number of serious marital problems, among which were infidelty on her husband's part. Although Charles' response here created only a mild suspicion that his father was duplicitous, and although such a view was not supported by subsequent responses on the test, there was indeed "fire beneath the smoke," and the initial suspicions engendered in me by this response proved to be verified in the next interview with his father.

Charles was then asked questions regarding the objects that would suit his mother's personality. His first response: "A bandaid because she helps me heal." His second response: "A chair because she is comfortable." And his third response: "A computer because she is smart and so intelligent." The first two responses, of course, make direct reference to his mother's nurturing and protecting roles. The third again is another example of the theme related to intellectual functioning which, as we know, was an area of difficulty for Charles.

When asked what objects would not suit his mother's personality, his response was, "A knife because she's not a dangerous person." His second response: "A machine gun because she doesn't go around hurting people." And his third: "A camera because she doesn't spy on people." As is usually the case, it is more difficult to make firm statements about the meaning of the negative responses than the positive. Negative responses do not necessarily indicate unconscious material that the patient is guilty and/or anxious about and must thereby relegate impulses to unconscious awareness.

They can also be explained simply as age-appropriate negative attitudes that the child has derived from the environment. Here again, one looks for atypicality for leads to psychopathology. The knife and machine gun are, in my experience, normal responses, although the machine gun may be a little strong in that a simple gun is more often chosen. The camera serving as a vehicle for spying, however, is a more atypical response and suggests feelings that the patient has that his mother spies on him. However, most children have these feelings, and so I cannot consider this response to be significantly representative of psychopathology, especially because there was no repetition or pattern of such imagery throughout the assessment.

Charles was then asked what objects would suit his father's personality. His first response: "A computer because they're smart." Once again, we see the concern with intellectual capacity.

His second response: "A thermostat because it keeps you warm and cool." This was an unusual and somewhat confusing response and so I questioned Charles for further details. Accordingly, Charles was then asked to elaborate on the point that his father, like the thermostat, keeps one "warm." In response he stated, "If I have a problem, he'll say don't worry about it and that makes me feel better." When asked to elaborate on the association between his father and the thermostat helping someone become "cool," he replied, "He's comforting and he helps you." When I tried to understand better what Charles was referring to here, the best I could determine was that he was using the word *cool* in the sense that many adolescents use it, that is, to refer to one's being unemotional and not taking upsetting experiences seriously. To the degree that this response implies improper suppression and repression of feelings, to that degree it is pathological. In my subsequent interview with Charles' father, I found him to be quite inhibited in expressing his feelings and suspected that Charles' response here related to this aspect of the father's personality.

Charles' third response: "A car." Again, just as I asked Charles to tell me the specific *kind* of dog and bird he had selected, I asked him to tell me the specific *kind* of car that would suit his father's personality. There are many different kinds of cars and they lend themselves to different kinds of symbolization. In response, he stated, "A Ferrari, because he has one and he's interested in cars."

The response suggests that Charles' father may be swept up in the common materialism of our society. This is not to say that every person who buys a Ferrari is necessarily exhibitionistic; only that there are many purchasers of this car who certainly are so, and the response should alert the therapist to look into this issue.

Charles was then asked to name those objects that would not suit his father's personality. His first response: "A hand grenade because he doesn't kill people." His second response: "A knife because he doesn't stab people." His third response: "A match because he doesn't burn people." Although the level at which normality ends and pathology begins may be difficult to ascertain with the negative questions of the verbal projective test, I believe that the responses here go beyond the normal frequency of danger-ous implements that one gets in response to these questions. They suggest Charles' view of his father as inordinately hostile—hostility that Charles is trying to suppress and repress. Considering that Charles had an acting-out problem, the responses here suggest that a contributing factor to this symptom related to Charles' relationship with his father, especially with regard to hostile elements that often contribute to such difficulties.

As mentioned, the interchanges derived from my administra-tion of the verbal projective test with Charles are presented in detail in order to familiarize the reader with the administration of the test and its utilization not only for learning about psychodynamics but for providing material that may serve as a point of departure for further inquiry, both diagnostic and therapeutic.

Dreams

Children are less capable of analyzing their dreams than are adults. The dream may nevertheless be a rich source of information about a youngster's underlying psychodynamics. The ability to utilize the dream metaphor probably exists at about the age of two or three in most children. However, the ability to appreciate the process, that is to separate cognitively the symbol from the entity that it denotes, is a later phenomenon and for the average child does not take place until the age of ten or eleven, the age at which the child reaches what Piaget refers to as the stage of formal operations. Accordingly, I do not generally spend much time attempting to help children below the age of ten or eleven gain insight into the dream's meaning. Adolescents, however, are often capable of analyzing their dreams and this is especially the case for older adolescents. I generally ask the youngster to tell me any dreams he or she can remember and inform the patient that I am particularly interested in repetitious dreams. These often provide valuable information about basic themes that pervade the patient's personality structure. Here I describe and analyze some dreams that adolescents presented me during the intensive evaluation. I will offer my understanding of the dream, but I will not go into detail about any discussions I may have had about the its meaning. My primary purpose here is to demonstrate how a youngster's dream can often be a rich source of information about underlying psychodynamics. Even when the youngster is not interested in or capable of analyzing the dream, the examiner's hunches and speculations can often be useful in the patient's treatment. Elsewhere (Gardner, 1986a) I discuss in detail my views on dream analysis and their utilization in treatment.

An 11-year-old girl presented with psychosomatic complaints, especially headaches, nausea, vomiting, and occasional diarrhea. She had a variety of allergies as well. Her mother, who was an extremely tense and angry woman, had little meaningful capacity for child rearing. The mother openly stated that she should have never become a parent. Her relationship with her husband was a difficult one because he too felt frustrated over his wife's tension and rejection of him. When either he or the children (the patient had a 14-year-old sister) would express any anger toward the mother, she would have violent rages which were extremely frightening to both the children and their father. The patient related this dream during the extended evaluation:

> I was at the beach with my friend at Atlantic City. I was in the water. A giant wave came. I had to duck under. Another big wave came and it drowned me.

This is a common dream. I consider the most likely explanation for a dream in which a patient is being drowned or submerged by waves to reflect the feeling that suppressed or repressed emotions are going to break out of the unconscious into conscious awareness. The emotions, however, are viewed as dangerous and even lethal.

Often patients will wake up from the dream relieved that they have not been drowned. And I believe that this explanation was applicable to this girl. The feelings here represent the massive hostility she felt toward her mother—hostility that could not be expressed overtly lest she suffer even further rejection and retaliation. Her feelings overwhelm her and she will drown in them. I considered many of her symptoms to be manifestations of the tension she felt in association with her attempts, both conscious and unconscious, to suppress and repress her anger toward her mother. Her dream confirmed my clinical speculations.

This 14-year-old boy asked his parents to bring him to therapy because of strong homosexual fantasies. His father was an extremely domineering, controlling individual who always presented with a facade of reasonableness. However, in any discussion in which differences of opinion were expressed, he maintained a rock-like rigidity. The patient's mother was passive and submissive in her relationship with the father. Neither parent had much capacity to involve themselves emotionally with the patient and his older sister, then 17. During the extended evaluation, he described this repetitious dream:

> My family and I were in a car going up to the driveway to my school. It was a school day. There was a little shack next to the school. I went into the shack. There was a hand there in a white glove. It was a mechanical hand. I had to be very quiet. It was very dangerous, so I couldn't make any noise. Once I sneezed and the hand went over my mouth.

I considered the little shack, next to the school, to symbolize the patient's view of himself as isolated from the mainstream of his peers and possibly his family as well. I considered the mechanical hand, covered by a white glove, to represent his father who did not allow the patient to express his genuine thoughts and feelings. Even the sneeze, which the patient could not control, is suppressed by the white-gloved hand. It is a statement of his great pressure for expression of the patient's repressed thoughts and feelings. Viewing his father as a mechanical hand in a white glove is a statement of his belief that his father is machine-like rather than human. The white glove implies sterility and cover-up of "blackness" and other undesirable personality qualities. It also symbolizes the father's veneer of reasonableness to disguise inhumane (mechanical) qualities.

Concluding Comments

The kinds of inquiries and assessment instruments described above are the primary ones that I utilize in the extended evaluation of the adolescent. They generally provide me with a wealth of information. However, on occasion, I may utilize *The Talking, Feeling, and Doing Game* (Gardner, 1973b), especially with the younger adolescents. My main purpose here is not simply to gain some data. Rather, I am interested in ascertaining how successful I will be in engaging the younster. By the mid- and late adolescent period, youngsters will generally be more comfortable talking directly and do not need this vehicle for helping them express themselves.

JOINT INTERVIEW
WITH THE PARENTS

Following the individual interviews with each of the parents alone, I will conduct a joint interview with both parents together. It is extremely important that the examiner conduct this interview as part of the extended evaluation. At times, parents may object because they will claim that each has already provided information. Sometimes, they will even claim that the information has already been given twice, in that the mother has related it during her individual interview and the father during his. When I explain to them that I often get different renditions of what is happening in the home, they will become more receptive to the joint interview because they recognize that it is important that any distortions which have been introduced into the evaluation should be corrected. Besides utilizing this interview to gain the most accurate data, the examiner is able to observe interactions between the parents. This is truly a situation in which the whole is greater than the sum of the parts. It is a rare situation in which I do not learn new things from the joint interview. This relates to both the acquisition of new information as well as the things I learn from the interactions. During the initial two-hour consultation, only a limited time is spent in the joint interviews so that the opportunity for observation of interactions is small.

The Correction of Distortions and
Other Kinds of False Data

It is extremely important for the reader to appreciate that all human beings distort their perceptions in situations of stress. At the Columbia University School of Law, it is not uncommon for a professor to stage a totally unanticipated interruption in the class. Specifically, a group of young men and women may suddenly charge into the classroom. There is screaming, a scuffle, shouts, shrieks, and angry words. Feigned gun shots, knife stabbings, and other forms of violence are likely to ensue. Then, as quickly as it began, the group suddenly leaves the room. The professor then asks each member of the class to write exactly what he or she observed. He advises them that they have been witness to a crime and that they will be asked to testify under oath regarding what they have seen and heard. The class is generally around 300 young people, just about all of whom have been extremely high in their college classes and have performed extraordinarily well on the Law School Aptitude Test. Presumably we are dealing here with a very bright group of young men and women. The professor generally receives 300 different renditions of what occurred. And each of these young people is being honest. Such is the nature of the human mind. So great is the capacity to distort under situations of stress.

Another example of this phenomenon. As the reader may know, I lecture extensively throughout the United States and occasionally abroad. Most often, I give a full-day of presentations, generally three or four lectures. The most common format is four one-and-a-half hour presentations, two in the morning and two in the afternoon. Frequently, a person will ask me a question in which there is a misquotation and/or a misunderstanding of what I had previously said. When I inform the person that I have been completely misunderstood and that I said exactly the opposite of what he or she is attributing to me, the individual often responds with incredulity. I have often had the thought that a wonderful experiment would be to make a videotape of the first presentation. Then, I would hand out an objective test (such as one with multiple-choice questions) that would be based *entirely* on the material just presented during the previous hour and a half. I am convinced that most people in the audience would give some incorrect answers and would, in addition, swear that their recollection of what I said was accurate. Then, we would get the videotape's opinion regarding what I said. These individuals would react with amazement that they could have so misunderstood me.

Our memories play tricks on us, especially if the topic is emotionally charged. And when one lectures in the field of psychiatry, one is likely to touch on emotionally charged situations. If I am lecturing on the subject of divorce, there are likely to be many individuals in the audience who have been or are going through the process of divorce, making this a charged subject for them. Under such circumstances, distortion is almost inevitable. I am not being critical of these individuals who distort or misinterpret what I say. I myself would be likely to make such errors occasionally were I in their situation. And when one is interviewing parents about their marriage and the ways in which they deal with their children, especially in a psychiatric interview, it is inevitable that distortions will arise. The joint interview can serve to correct these for both the parents and the examiner.

It is extremely important for the examiner to appreciate that one's interpretation of any situation is determined by two factors. One is the actual facts, the actual reality, and the other is what one brings to it, what one interprets it to mean, what one *wants* to understand about the significance of the events. I often say that life is like a Rorschach test. In fact, one could view this as a fundamental dictum of human experience. All phenomena can be divided into two factors: the reality and what the human being brings to the reality. The viewer's hopes, anticipations, denial mechanisms, et cetera, are all going to play a role in determining what the individual sees and how he or she reacts. Both the external entity and the viewer's thoughts and feelings about it are realities in their own right, and both play an important part in determining how one will react in a particular situation. There is a glass with water in it. One person sees it as half full, another sees it as half empty. And when parents are talking about their marriage and their children, the likelihood of these superimposed attitudes playing an important role in their discussions is very high. In fact, it is so great that I consider it to be universal. Accordingly, distortions, misrepresentations, and exaggerations are inevitably going to be present, and it is in the joint interview, especially, that the examiner is in the best position to determine what these are.

Accordingly, the examiner must recognize that the information gathering process in this interview occurs at two levels. An attempt must be made to ascertain, to the degree possible, exactly what is happening. Sometimes this can happen if the two individuals come to some kind of a compromise or when one's credibility is clearly greater than the other's. At other times it may not be possible and the examiner does well to go on to the next issue. In such cases, I might say, "Well, you say one thing and your husband (wife) says just the opposite. We've gone back and forth a few times and you each stick to your own position. I suggest we go on to another issue. Perhaps in the future, I'll learn what's really going on."

The other level, and possibly the more important, is the attitudinal. It relates to the thoughts and feelings of the individual about the particular event. Shakespeare's Hamlet said it well: "There's nothing either good or bad, but thinking makes it so." A father, for example, may put his three-year-old son on his lap while driving the car, and while both of their hands are on the steering wheel, the father gives the child the impression that he is helping drive the car. Early in the marriage, when there was a loving relationship between the parents, the mother may have considered the father's act to be a benevolent one, one designed to help the child feel like "a big man." In contrast, at a time when the marriage has deteriorated, she may complain vehemently to the examiner about the kinds of dangerous things her husband used to do with the boy, and she may give this as an example.

In the individual interviews, one may get diametrically opposed stories resulting in a complete inability to find out what has really gone on. In the joint interview, one can sometimes "smoke out the truth." For example, in the individual interviews, each parent might describe attendance at all school functions to which parents are invited, both curricular and extracurricular. However, during the joint interview the mother may say, with regard to the father, "Yeah, he came, but I always had to pull him. It was a big struggle. And when he finally got there, he used to fall asleep during the plays and recitals." The father may then sheepishly admit that he "sometimes" did fall asleep for short periods, but that his wife is exaggerating the frequency and the duration of the time spent sleeping. In the subsequent discussion, the father may admit reluctance and occasional sleeping. Although the two may differ regarding the degree of reluctance and the frequency and duration of sleeping episodes, the examiner has still learned about the father's lack of enthusiasm for these events. And this I would consider to be a parental deficiency.

"The Whole May Be Greater Than the Sum of Its Parts"

The joint interview with the parents is one of those situations in which the whole may be greater than the sum of its parts. In fact, in most of the interviews, I find this to be true because information is derived which was not or could not have been obtained in the individual interviews. This phenomenon is the result of the interaction between the parents. Because of the shortness of the joint interview during the initial two-hour evaluative session, time often does not allow for the emergence of this additional information. It is only under more relaxed circumstances, during the extended evaluation, that there is a greater likelihood that this additional data will become available.

Let us take the example of a passive and somewhat quiet man who is married to an assertive and more talkative woman. In the short joint interview, during the two-hour screening evaluation, one may sense that this is the nature of the relationship, but questions are still being directed toward both parties. In the individual interview(s) with the father, the examiner is spending most of the time posing questions (as described in detail in the above section on the interview with the father). More than 95 percent of the time is spent with the father's talking. He is a "captive audience." The individual interview should not be conducted like a classical psychoanalytic session in which the examiner sits back silently and waits for the patient to talk. (This does not preclude, however, an occasional open-ended question.) Rather, the examiner is generally concerned with obtaining answers to a whole series of questions. In the joint interview, however, one may observe directly how the mother may actually consume 99 percent of the time, while the father sits silently, allowing her to "roll." Now that he is no longer a captive audience, now that the examiner is not posing one question after another, now that he is being permitted to either talk or remain silent as he chooses, his severe problem in verbal inhibition becomes apparent. In addition, his passivity problem also manifests itself, especially when he remains silent on issues of disagreement with his wife. The father may say, "I was never one who had much to say in social situations. I never had the 'gift of gab.' I guess one of the reasons why I was attracted to my wife was because she always had something to say at all times." And, with this lead, the examiner may also learn about the father's passivity in his relationshp with the mother and his fears of asserting himself. A derivative of this would be a discussion of the patient's identifications in these areas, with the father and/or the mother.

A father may claim in the individual interview(s) that the marriage is a good one, that there were never any difficulties, and that there was never any talk of separation. In her individual interview(s), however, the mother may claim that on two occasions during the course of the marriage, she found love letters from other women. She suspects that there were probably more infidelities that she cannot be certain of. She claims also that when her husband was confronted with these letters he admitted to her that he had been unfaithful and that he would discontinue the affairs. In some circumstances I will recommend that the mother bring up the issue of infidelity in the joint meetings with her husband, and on other occasions I will not. On the one hand, I may consider it important for the child's treatment to do so, especially if the mother has good reason to believe there is an ongoing affair taking place during the time of the evaluation. On the other hand, I may consider it antitherapeutic to do so in that it might cause additional marital discord which I suspect both parents would rather avoid. One just doesn't go after the truth, no matter what the consequences. One goes after the truth in the service of doing what is best for the child's treatment. In order to determine whether or not this issue should be brought up, I will ask the mother her opinion on the subject, and her input here will be very important. Of course, I too will have input into the decision. All marriages involve a certain amount of acceptance and resignation of qualities in the other party that one would prefer did not exist. The examiner must respect such equilibria and not attempt to change every single source of marital difficulty. If one is going to "rock the boat," then one should be sure that one is in a position to deal completely with the repercussions of such a disruption of the marital equilibrium.

Let us say that both the mother and I decide that it would serve the best interests of the marriage and the patient for her to bring up the affair in the joint session. In the joint meeting, the mother confronts the father with her supsicions about ongoing infidelity. She expresses incredulity that his "business meetings" so frequently go on until two in the morning. She also expresses her disbelief that they always take place where he cannot be reached and cannot call her to tell her that he has been detained. She expresses her belief that he is with other women, either at their homes or in hotels. In response the father somewhat sheepishly and unconvincingly gives various explanations. At this point the mother may say, "Doctor, I've been living with this man for 15 years. I know him inside out. Right now he's lying. Look at that shit-eating grin on his face. That's how he looks when he's lying." The father might still hold to his original story and claim that his wife has a vivid imagination and that she has "delusions of jealousy." On occasion, under such circumstances, the mother may turn to me and ask my opinion on the subject. My response, under these circumstances, has been along these lines: "Well, I can't be 100% certain. Your wife, however, is certainly giving some very convincing reasons why she suspects infidelity, and your responses don't seem to have much credibility to me. Although I'm not sure at this point – pending more convincing information from you – I'm inclined to believe that your wife has good reasons to be *very* suspicious."

However, I do not stop there. I will then say something along these lines: "Regardless of whose version is valid here, there is no question that you and your wife have some serious marital difficulties. However, you are not candidates for marital counseling at this point, at least on this issue. Either she is delusional and believes her delusions or you are lying. In either case, people like yourselves, with this kind of a conflict, are not candidates for marital counseling." I then proceed with other issues. My point here is that the joint interview enables the examiner to learn better about a parent's personality characteristics. In the example cited above, I learned about the father's probable duplicity. On other occasions, under the same circumstances, I have learned something about the mother's delusional system. In both situations, the confrontation by the spouse provided important input in my determining what was most likely the situation.

Many other forms of interaction can be observed in the joint interview. For example, sado-masochistic tendencies that may not have been apparent in the initial screening interview may manifest themselves. As the joint interview progresses, a father may become increasingly hostile toward the mother, speak in a condescending way to her, and denigrate her. Rather than asserting herself and expressing her resentment that her husband is treating her so shabbily, she may passively sit and accept his deprecations. These personality traits of the parents are likely to be playing a role in the child's difficulties. Or, a mother may continually interrupt her husband with nitpicking and hairsplitting corrections. Rather than tell her how offended he is by her behavior, he passively explains himself repeatedly, continually trying to justify himself. Again, these patterns are not likely to have manifested themselves in the individual interviews.

The Marriage

It is in the joint interview, with both parents together, that one is likely to learn much more about the marriage than in the individual interviews. Confrontations between the parents not only enable the examiner to correct distortions but to make observations in which the interactions often provide more information than actual statements. Because marital difficulties are such an important factor in bringing about psychogenic pathology in children and adolescents, I will often devote a significant portion of the joint interview to the details of the marital relationship. Although some parents who bring children to treatment will not have any difficulties in this area, my experience has been that this is uncommon. Accordingly, I most often have little trouble getting parents to discuss the marital problems; often each has discussed them at some length during the individual interviews.

On occasion, a parent who has discussed the marital problems in individual interview will show hesitancy in discussing them in the joint interview. Most often, I consider such discussion warranted. Therefore, in order to catalyze the discussion I may make a comment such as: "Each of you has told me at length what you consider to be both the assets and the liabilities, the strengths and weaknesses, of your marriage. I would now like to discuss them here with the two of you together. Why don't we start off with the strong points." At this point, I do not specify which parent I would like to start; rather, I leave it open because I would like to ascertain which parent is going to be the more assertive and forthright with regard to the marriage, both its assets and liabilities. Suggesting that they talk about the assets first generally "breaks the ice" and makes it easier to discuss the liabilities thereafter.

On occasion, one or both parents will be reluctant to discuss the marriage and say that they don't understand how their marital difficulties have anything to do with their youngster's problems. Others will go further and state that my delving into the marriage is improper and that if they wanted marital counseling, they would have asked for it. I try to explain to such parents that their view of child therapy as a process which is focused on the child primarily, if not exclusively, is improper and injudicious. I explain to them that I cannot separate their child's difficulties from their own, that there are therapists who would be willing to treat their child without any contact with them, but I am not that kind of therapist. I try to explain to them that children exposed to and/or embroiled in marital problems are likely to develop psychological difficulties themselves. The parents may respond that they have been completely successful in protecting their children from any knowledge of their marital difficulties. In such cases I try to explain to the parents that this is practically impossible. I try to get across the point that if the parents are unhappy this is going to compromise their parenting, even if the children don't know exactly what the parents are unhappy about.

I also advise them that my view of therapy involves my counseling parents on how to take care of the children and deal with their problems, and I hope that they will be receptive to this part of the therapeutic program. It is the rare parent who is unreceptive to this; in fact, I cannot recall a parent saying that he or she did not want my advice regarding how to handle the children's problems. I also advise them that treatment for their own problems is an overlapping but separate issue. If they *wanted* treatment for their problems, I would be happy to discuss with them the question of whether I should do such counseling or someone else should. In such discussions I point out the advantages of my doing it, but try to avoid giving the impression that "I am looking for extra business." Rather, I impress upon them the fact that by having one therapist treat the whole family, I will be more in touch with those issues that are affecting the child than I would be if another therapist were to do the marital counseling.

On occasion, it will become apparent that the youngster's problems are a small and incidental spinoff of the parents' difficulties and that the main thrust of the therapeutic approach will have to be with the parents if there is to be any hope of alleviation of the patient's problems. (I will discuss this issue in the section devoted to the final presentation of my findings.) On occasion, it has become apparent that one of the parents is basically using the youngster's symptoms as an "admission ticket" for marital treatment. At some level the parent recognizes that the major problems lie within the marriage, and the hope was that by bringing the child, the parental difficulties would surface and perhaps a reluctant parent would be more motivated for therapy. My experience has been that this is a common situation and that the mother, much more than the father, is likely to have been the initiator in such a process.

On a number of occasions, it has become more apparent during this joint interview that the marital problem must be considered a fixed constant in the youngster's treatment. Sometimes one of the parents is adamantly against any kind of counseling. My experience has been that the person who is most often resistant to the counseling is the father. On other occasions, a parent may recognize that there are serious problems in the marriage but may be afraid to "rock the boat." My experience here has been that it is the mother, more than the father, who is often in this position. One has to respect defenses in a marriage. One has to respect the equilibria and the benefits of maintaining the status quo, the drawbacks of such silence notwithstanding. All marriages involve a delicate balance between healthy and pathological forces, and the examiner must respect these balances and not bulldoze the parent into "putting everything out on the table." The likelihood of people gaining anything for such tactics is small, and the therapist, under such circumstances, may do the family much more harm than good.

Dealing with the Children

The second important area that I generally focus on in the joint interviews is the parental dealings with the children. Generally, I have asked each of the parents in the individual interviews to describe him- or herself and the other parent with regard to this area. Here I want to get feedback from each parent regarding the other's comments. I generally encounter far less reluctance and resistance in the discussion of child-rearing practices than I do in the discussion of the marriage. I usually start with a broad question such as: "Now let's talk about the children and how each of you has handled the various problems that have arisen." This is generally enough to get things moving. Sometimes I will have to be more specific with questions such as: "Although we've covered child-rearing practices to some degree in the individual sessions, I'd like to go into further detail here, especially with regard to how you see each other in this area. So why don't we talk first about what you see as your own strong points and the other party's strong points in dealing with the children." Again, I do not ask a particular parent to start speaking. Rather, I want to see who initiates the discussion.

Following a discussion of the strong points and assets, I then shift to the more difficult subject of liabilities. Again, I want a statement by each person regarding how he or she sees his or her own weaknesses and how the other party sees them. Sometimes I will divide the liabilities issue into specific areas of inquiry. For example, I may ask a mother what she suspects her husband's criticisms of her have been with regard to disciplinary techniques and/or what she recalls him to have said in this area. Then, I will turn to the husband and ask him directly what his criticisms are. I will then repeat the procedure with the father's stating first what his recollections are of the mother's criticisms of his disciplinary techniques and then ask the mother directly to state them.

In the course of the discussion on child-rearing practices, I may give advice. Although my primary goal in the extended evaluation is to collect as much data as possible, this does not preclude my spending time providing recommendations. I am not referring here to the kinds of recommendations that can only emerge from extended experience; rather, I am referring to those that are simple, short, and do not detract significantly from the time spent in the data-collection process. But such *en passant* recommendations can also serve the purpose of data collection in that parents' reactions to my suggestions often provide additional information that may be useful. I am particularly interested in the parents' degree of receptivity to my advice. And there is a whole range here from the parents who passively and gullibly accept every bit of advice to those who are completely resistant and antagonistic to it. The ideal is that they be at some point close to the receptive end of the continuum, but not to the point of blind acceptance of everything I say. I would like them to have conviction for my recommendations because when they do, it is far more likely that they will implement them effectively. In addition, parents who are too passive in their relationship with me serve as poor models for their children. The children should not view me as their parents' "boss"; rather, they should view their parents as receptive to my advice but retaining the final decision-making power.

Concluding Comments

The joint interview with the parents not only serves the goal of data collection but, if successful, can help entrench the parents' relationship with the therapist. The establishment of a good relationship with parents is one of the cornerstones of effective therapy with the youngster. It is here, more than in the other interviews, that one may learn about criticisms each has about the therapist, criticisms that may not have been revealed in the individual interviews. Here, one parent may bring these criticisms up in the presence of the other. And it is crucial that they be discussed. Otherwise, the parents may harbor their resentments silently, and this can compromise the treatment and even bring about its cessation—without the therapist's knowing exactly what has gone on to compromise the treatment.

Before closing the joint interview with the parents, I discuss the family interview. Generally, I want teenagers present and those younger children who can be relied upon to contribute significantly. My experience has been that a good cutoff age is five or six. Although one may learn from the observations of interactions between the parents and the preschool nonpatient sibling, the disruptions of their presence throughout the course of the interview may outweigh the advantages of such observations. Furthermore, even children of five to eight may not be valuable contributors and may just sit there quite bored during the course of the family interview. After eight or nine, the older the youngster, the greater the likelihood of meaningful input. (The reader should not view these ages as fixed guidelines; rather, they are approximate.)

Once the decision has been made regarding which children shall participate, we discuss the issue of what to tell the siblings regarding the purpose of the family meeting. I generally advise the parents to say to them that it will be helpful to me in my work with their brother or sister to get information from them about what is happening in the family. I advise the parents to reassure the siblings that they want them to be open and honest and that there will be no repercussioins for their divulgences. On occasion, parents are reluctant to tell the siblings about the patient's treatment because they fear that the siblings might taunt the patient, tell others, or involve themselves in other inappropriate reactions to the disclosure. Most often, I advise the parents to tell the siblings about the treatment and to deal with any inappropriate reactions if and when they arise. I impress upon them that keeping the patient's treatment a secret is likely to contribute to and even intensify the patient's feelings of low self-worth, because such withholding implies that the patient is suffering with a disorder that he or she should be ashamed about. There are occasions when a sibling is so sadistic and disturbed that the divulgence might indeed work against the patient, but this has been a rare situation in my experience.

THE FAMILY INTERVIEW

Elsewhere (Gardner, 1986a) and in Chapter Twelve I discuss in detail the family interview techniques that I utilize. Here I discuss only some basic principles of the family interview in the extended evaluation. It is important for the examiner to appreciate that both the patient and the siblings may be quite tense at the beginning of the family interview. The patient is likely to be uncomfortable over the fact that his or her siblings are now going to discuss embarrassing issues. And the siblings may be fearful of criticizing their parents or may appreciate that what they say may be upsetting to the patient. Accordingly, I generally do not sit silently at the outset of this session and wait for someone to open up. Rather, I myself begin with some reassuring statement to the various parties. I will turn to the siblings and say something along these lines: "I appreciate your coming here today. I want you to know that my experience has been that brothers and sisters can often provide me with very valuable information that helps me in the treatment of their brother or sister. I know that this is probably uncomfortable for you. But I know that I speak for your parents when I say to you that they want you to be open and honest with me and that you shouldn't be afraid that there'll be any terrible consequences afterwards if you say critical things about them." At this point, I may actually ask the parents to make some statements along these lines. I will also say to the siblings: "I want you to know, also, that I understand that I am placing you in a difficult position with regard to the things that you're going to say about your brother or sister. However, I hope you'll appreciate that it's important for me to have this information and that you, probably more than anybody else, can provide it to me."

I will then turn to the patient: "I know that this is difficult for you, as well. I know that I'm asking your brother and/or sister (or whatever the number and sexes are) to say things about you that may be upsetting and embarrassing. I hope, however, that you're big and strong enough to appreciate that it's important for me to get this information if I'm to help you." When I make this statement, I generally do not expect the child to agree with me that such divulgences are likely to be in his or her best interests; I make the statement, however, in the hope that some of it does get through, and the child does appreciate my sensitivity to his or her situation.

I will then ask the siblings why they think their brother (sister) is coming to see me. This is an important base from which to operate. The derivative questions make more sense if this issue is brought out first. On occasion, the siblings do not know of the basic problems, but most often they do. In addition, their opinions regarding the problems may be at variance with the parents and this can also be useful as clarifying data. Furthermore, their confrontations may help the patient gain some insight into the fact that he or she has problems although, as mentioned so many times previously, I don't push for this.

At this point I may ask the siblings to talk about the parents. I may ask them to say good things about their parents and things about their parents that they do not like. I start with the parents here because I want to take the focus off the patient and discuss criticisms of the parties who have "thicker skins." Often, the information about the parents that the children provide me proves quite useful. They frequently come up with parental characteristics that were not previously brought to my attention. I may then go on to the subject of exactly how they see their parents' personality problems and difficulties to have contributed to the patient's. Sometimes siblings will give me very insightful information about this relationship. For example, a teenage sister might say, "I think Billy's main problem is my mother. She spoils him sick. He's the big baby of the family. She doesn't know how to say no to him like she used to say to me and my brother." Although I may recognize jealousy as an element in such criticism, there also may be significant truth to the allegations. I will then use this as a point of departure for family discussion. For such a criticism, I may turn my attention to the mother and ask for her response. I may ask Billy himself what he thinks about this criticism. The likelihood is that Billy (age 14) does not consider himself to be too indulged; in fact, he may believe that his mother is too withholding from him and indulging of his sister.

The general principle I follow when conducting family interviews is that I use each issue as a point of departure for further back and forth confrontations and discussion. Usually I ask each party what he or she thinks about what the other party has just said. Sometimes I will ask an individual what he or she thinks about what has been said previously by a few members on a particular point. I try not to let things become chaotic; rather I try to come to some tentative conclusions on each issue raised. Getting input from the other family members serves to clarify as well as generate family discussion, interaction, and information about their various relationships. Last, the family interview may have direct therapeutic benefits in that it may open up, sometimes for the first time, the kinds of discussions that have taken place previously—and this cannot but be therapeutic for the patient. I cannot emphasize this point strongly enough. The data collection interviews are often stressful to the patient and other family members. To the degree that one can help the family derive therapeutic benefits during the course of these interviews, to that degree will the therapist be compensating the family for these negative elements in the extended evaluation.

I generally do not set aside a standard 45-minute interview for the family. Rather, I will take an hour to an hour-and-a-half, depending upon how much information I suspect will be emerging. It is not my intention during this time to follow up every issue to its limit. Rather, I want to focus on major problems and collect some information about each of them. I am not conducting family therapy here; rather, I am collecting data about the family, my patient, and the various interactions of the family members. On occasion, a second family interview may be warranted. Also, on occasion, the initial family interview may have served as a breakthrough for them, and ongoing family therapy may be agreed upon. What was originated, then, as a diagnostic data-gathering procedure, ends up being an important therapeutic experience.

PREPARATION OF THE PRESENTATION

I recognize that the extended evaluation I conduct is probably more time-consuming and involved than that employed by most examiners. In fact, I myself do not *routinely* conduct such extended evaluations. On occasion, on the basis of the two-hour initial consultation, I sense that all the aforementioned interviews may not be necessary. For the purposes of this book, however, I have described in detail the full evaluation and recognize that the reader (like myself) will find situations in which it is not warranted. Similarly, the preparation of the final presentation may not necessarily be as intensive as that which I describe here. Again, for the sake of this book, I present the full preparation procedure.

The ideal way of organizing the formidable data that the examiner may have accumulated is with the use of a word processor. The examiner who has one available will save much time. Those who do not have one must utilize the more primitive procedure that I used prior to my acquisition of this valuable instrument. Accordingly, I will first describe the method I use with the word processor and then describe the more painstaking method that I utilized previously. In addition, if the examiner enjoys the indulgence of a secretary, this can obviously save time. If not, then the examiner must perform these procedures him- or herself. Fortunately, I have both a word processor and a secretary and can indulge myself in these shorter and more efficient procedures.

I begin the dictation by instructing my secretary to set up on the word processor a series of basic topics. Then, I will go through my material—from beginning to end—and dictate comments and quotations within each of these categories. The secretary scrolls up and down the screen inserting the material within each of the topics. The topics are: Basic Data, Presenting Problems, Mother's Assets, Mother's Liabilities, Father's Assets, Father's Liabilities, Patient's Psychodynamics Derived from Patient Interviews, Patient's Psychodynamics Derived from Parents and Family Interviews, Conclusions and Recommendations. When dictating the material, I do not concern myself with organization of the material *within* each of the categories. Rather, it serves the purpose of the final presentation to the parents to have just the aforementioned degree of organization. If I want to use this material in the preparation of a written report, then I will reorganize (again by word processor) the material *within* each category, but utilize the aforementioned outline as my starting point. On occasion, when the question of the child's having a neurologically based learning disability has also been raised, I will include a section in which the results of special tests in this area are also presented. I place this immediately after the section on the child's presenting complaints. I generally entitle it: Evaluation for the Presence of the *Group of Minimal Brain Dysfunction Syndromes* (GMBDS) (Gardner, 1979b, 1987b).

The basic data material is often taken directly from the face sheet of the parents' questionnaire (Appendix II). It generally includes the patient's name, age, date of birth, grade, and whether in a regular or special class. It also includes the names and ages of the parents and their occupations. In addition, I include the names and ages of the siblings and what grades they are in. Stepparents also are included.

With regard to the chief complaints, I most often start with those that have been presented by the parents (and sometimes the patient) at the beginning of the two-hour consultation. I select here only those problems I consider to be psychological difficulties and not those mentioned by the parents which I have decided are not. I include here, as well, those problems described on page 2 of the questionnaire where I request the parents provide me with a three-line summary of the main difficulties. I will then scan pages 9 through 12 of the questionnaire and select those symptoms that I consider worthy of therapeutic focus. I do not generally include here every single item checked off by the parents because some parents will list as a symptom atypical behavior of normal frequency, my warning to this effect in the introduction on page 9 notwithstanding.

In the section on parental assets and liabilities, one does well to include quotations. These enhance the accuracy of the presentation and may also prevent inappropriate antagonism toward the therapist. If one takes care to quote criticisms from the opposite parent, one is likely to prevent such occurrences. Such quotations are especially important if a written report is to be prepared. In these days of burgeoning malpractice, one wants to be certain that the written report is not used to one's disadvantage in any possible subsequent litigation. And accurate recording of quotations can serve this end in that it is not the therapist who is making the critical allegation but one of the family members. (It is a sad commentary on our times that this must be mentioned here, but not to do so would be a disservice to the reader.)

When dictating the section on the patient's psychodynamics, I not only describe each observation, but the meaning that I ascribe to it. This might include a behavioral manifestation and then an interpretation, or it might refer to some verbal projection and my interpretation. For example, I might quote certain key statements from the story that the patient told in association with a human figure that was drawn, and then I will dictate my understanding of the meaning of the story. The same is done with the verbal projective questions. With regard to the verbal projective questions about those people, animals, and objects that would suit the parents, I make sure to state that this is my interpretation of how *the child* sees the parents and emphasize to the parents that this may not necessarily be the way they are, but the way the child sees them. This is not only a more accurate way of stating things, but also can assuage the pains and discomforts of more defensive and/or insecure parents.

In the conclusions and recommendations section I will summarize the major themes in the family that are contributing to the child's difficulties. This generally ranges from two or three to about ten or twelve elements. It may include genetic predisposing factors and psychodynamic issues, both interpersonal and intrapsychic. This summary statement can also be useful in the course of therapy in that I may refer to it from time to time to refresh my memory about the variety of problems for which the patient has presented as well as to assess progress. I then state the recommended treatment program with regard to the number of sessions per week (generally one or two) as well as who shall be involved in the treatment. If the reader does not have a secretary and word processor, then the aforementioned must be done by hand. One generally writes the titles on separate sheets of paper and then skips back and forth from page to page inserting the proper information under each category.

PRESENTATION OF THE FINDINGS
TO THE PARENTS

I generally set aside an open-ended session for this presentation. It takes about two hours, sometimes longer. I make it open-ended in order to insure that we are not rushed. The adolescent and both parents are seen together during the interview, which I usually begin by explaining to them how I prepared the presentation. I directly show them the computer printouts and enumerate the various categories within which I have placed the information as it has been dictated. I then go step by step, from one section to the next, reading and commenting on what has been written therein. I advise the parents to interrupt me at any point if they have questions or wish further discussion. I prefer that the issues raised serve as points of departure for limited discussion, but not the kind of extended discussion that might be more appropriate during therapeutic interviews. Sometimes, I may have been in error with regard to a particular point or quotation and I invite the parents' correction. I inform them that my goal here is not to be "right" but to be "accurate." Unless there are a formidable number of such errors, the parents will generally appreciate my receptivity to corrections. I invite the patient's participation as well.

On occasion, I will have ordered psychological tests. I make a photostatic copy of the psychological report, give the parents one copy, and we read them over together in detail. This report is their property and they take it with them at the end of the meeting (regardless of whether or not they have chosen to have a full written report prepared by me). Examiners who do not give the parents a copy of this psychological report are asking for trouble. The parents are entitled to it and not to give it to them exposes one to justifiable criticism. They are also entitled to discuss the report in detail with the examiner, especially because such reports are often confusing and anxiety provoking to parents. Obviously, when such a report is discussed in the final presentation, it is going to add to the meeting's length.

The discussion of the final treatment program is quite important. Because it comes last, I want to be sure that we have the time to discuss this in depth. And this is one of the main reasons why my final presentation is open-ended. Parents will often ask how long the treatment will take. I generally advise them that I cannot know in advance and that the most important determinants relate to how successful I will be in engaging their youngster and how receptive they themselves will be to involvement in the therapy. Of course, by this time I have definite information in this area and will make comments on it. It is a serious error for the therapist to even proffer a guess with regard to the number of weeks, months, or years treatment will take. No matter how many qualifications he or she may give, the parents are still likely to put a circle on their mental calendar (if not their real calendar). Only the number becomes branded in the parents' brains; the qualifications never seem to have reached their ears. Even if accused of being vague, obstructionistic, or hostile, the therapist should not speculate about how long the treatment will take. It would be a rare situation in which he or she would not regret having made such a speculation.

I also discuss the nature and degree of the parental participation in the youngster's treatment. The exact degree of parental participation in an adolescent's treatment presents certain technical difficulties. When working with younger children I generally utilize the parents to a significant degree during the child's sessions. I refer to my treatment of these younger children as *individual child psychotherapy with parental observation and intermittent participation.* The parents serve very much as my *assistant therapists.* In the treatment of adults, I obviously do not have parents actively involved although this does not preclude my seeing the parents of my adult patients once or twice (generally along with the patient) if the situation warrants it. Parental involvement in the adolescent's treatment is somewhere in between these two extremes. As mentioned previously, I will not accept into treatment an adolescent who refuses to have me involve the parents. Nor is it warranted that the parents actively participate in every session. The adolescent requires a certain amount of autonomy during this transition phase from childhood dependence to adult independence. The adolescent must have a sense of separateness and keeping the parents in the room too frequently may compromise this healthy process.

I generally advise the parents that I will be expecting them to remain in the waiting room throughout the course of the youngster's session. Often, I have the parents join me at the outset with the quieter and more reticent patients, because they are similar to pre-adolescent youngsters in this regard. When the youngster is more talkative, I will generally not begin with the parent but reserve the right to bring the parent in as warranted throughout the course of the session. This is especially useful when the youngster runs out of things to say. Generally, the parent who then joins us can be relied upon to bring up issues that can serve as points of departure for discussion. Because mothers are the ones most often available to bring the youngster, I advise the fathers that they should make attempts to bring the adolescent from time to time and to join us (no advance notice required) when available. I also inform the parents that I will be recommending sessions where both the parents and the youngster will be present and that if situations arise which warrant their requesting such a session, I am most receptive to scheduling it. One wants to maintain ongoing relationships with both parents; otherwise, the youngster's treatment is going to be compromised. One wants to create a setting in which the various family "Pandora's boxes are open" and family skeletons are taken out of the closet. Joint interviews are often the most efficacious way of doing this.

I will also talk about the difference between counseling the parents on dealing with the patient vs. treating the parents for marital difficulties which they may have. It is important that the examiner not coerce the parents into treatment regardless of how formidable the marital problems are. Rather, the examiner does well to ask questions like: "Do you consider yourself to have marital problems?" "Have you ever given thought to having therapy for such problems?" and "What do you think about obtaining therapy for these problems?" It is crucial that the examiner take a passive attitude here and merely sound the parents out on their receptivity. To use coercive or guilt-evoking tactics is contraindicated, for example: "If you want to salvage your marriage, you're going to have to go into treatment. I can't imagine the marriage surviving without it" or "For the sake of your child, it's important that you people have treatment for your marriage. If you don't, it's going to be extremely difficult, if not impossible, for me to help your youngster."

People who enter treatment in response to such threats are not likely to be helped. If the parents decide that they want therapy for the marital problems, then the therapist does well to make a statement along these lines: "Well, as I see it, you have two choices here. One is to work with me and the other to work with someone else. As you know, I do treat parents of my child and adolescent patients and have often found the combination useful, but recognize that some parents feel more comfortable working with someone else on their marital problems, while being counseled by me regarding how to deal with their child. I am interested in your thoughts and feelings on this; however, it's important that you be direct and honest with me and not hold back your true feelings from fear that I might be offended. Many parents have chosen to see others and I respect that choice." This approach, I believe, protects the therapist from the parental reaction that "he (she) is looking for business." It does, however, provide the parents with an option that they may not have appreciated they had and helps them clarify both the pros and cons of each alternative—information they are entitled to have.

If medication is warranted, I will discuss this with the parents at this point. Here again, one must leave ample time for such discussion in order to assuage unnecessary or irrational fears that the parents may have. It is likely that they have some unrealistic ideas about what medication can do and cannot do, and the therapist must give them the opportunity to express their ideas if he or she is to correct distortions. For parents who are very reluctant to have their child on medication, I will emphasize that I am only suggesting a *trial* on medication and that they not commit themselves to a full course of treatment before knowing about the drug and ascertaining empirically whether or not it will prove helpful. Often, by reassuring them that a few pills are not likely to produce lifelong damage to the youngster's body, they will be more receptive to the trial.

Before closing this meeting, the therapist should invite the parents to ask any further questions. Often they may have heard of quicky-type treatments that promise results in a shorter perioid. I will generally ask them about the particular form of treatment and present them my views on it. When contrasting psychotherapy with these other forms of therapy, the examiner should be cautious with regard to making any claims about the efficacy of psychotherapy. The examiner does well to emphasize to the parents that there is no "proof" that psychotherapy works but that the examiner has definite convictions that it can be useful for certain children and their families, especially those who involve themselves with commitment to the process.

Finally, before closing the session, I ask the parents if they would like a full written report prepared. Examiners who charge for the extra work involved in the preparation of such a report should have told the parents about this much earlier. I make mention of it in the face sheet to my questionnaire so that the parents know about it even prior to the first meeting. Examiners who do not use such a document do well to mention this charge during the initial consultation. Otherwise, I believe parents have a justifiable complaint when they are advised of this new extra expense at such a late point. Even here many parents have "forgotten" about this charge and will express surprise (and even resentment) that it will cost them more money for me to prepare this report. If the parents choose to have a written report, I prepare a copy for them, give it to them directly, and let *them* decide whom they wish to give it to. This is an important point; in fact, it may be the most important point I make in this book. In these days of burgeoning malpractice litigation, the safest course is to give the parents the report themselves and let them decide whom they wish to give copies to, whether it is the school, the child's pediatrician, or anyone else. In this way, the examiner cannot be accused of having sent out critical and/or personal information to parties to whom the parents did not wish to have this information available.

Sometimes parents will ask me to prepare a modified report for certain parties, such as a school. I generally refuse to do this. I say to them, however, that if they wish to delete certain parts of the report before turning it over to the school, that is their privilege. However, I strongly urge them to make a copy of the report, cut out the deleted paragraphs, and advise the school of such deletions. Some may do this, some may not. I tell them about the injudiciousness of not telling the school that the report has been altered. But, if they do not follow my advice, I cannot be considered to have been at fault. The therapist does well to appreciate that we are living in a time when there is approximately one lawyer for every 850 individuals in the population. With such a ratio, there are many hungry lawyers who view malpractice litigation to be a very promising livelihood. (Remember the bumper sticker: *Become a Doctor, Support a Lawyer.*) Giving parents the report and letting them make copies for distribution to others is an excellent way of protecting oneself in this unfortunate atmosphere.

FIVE

CENTRAL ELEMENTS IN THE DEVELOPMENT OF PSYCHOGENIC SYMPTOMS AND PRIMARY FACTORS IN THE PSYCHOTHERAPEUTIC PROCESS

The theoretical principles presented here regarding the origins of symptoms and the central elements in the psychotherapeutic process are applicable to children, adolescents, and adults. Although the general principles presented here apply to all three age categories, there are differences in the therapeutic application of these principles regarding the degree to which the therapist relies on the patient to make active contributions to the treatment. The younger the child, the more it behooves the therapist to actively elicit, encourage, and even suggest the ways in which the child should respond to particular life situations that are causing difficulties. The older the patient the more the therapist should encourage (and at times require) the patient to contribute the solutions to these life problems. But even with the most mature and healthy patient, an occasional suggestion and the judicious introduction of recommended solutions are warranted. Here I will focus on the ways in which these principles apply to the adolescent.

THE ORIGINS OF SYMPTOMS

I view symptoms to represent maladaptive and inappropriate ways of dealing with the problems of life which confront all of us. The patient's selections of solutions to these problems have originally been devised because they appeared to be the most judicious. What we refer to as psychodynamics are basically the pathways and processes by which these problems produce symptoms. Symptoms then can be viewed as the "tip of the iceberg"—the most superficial manifestations of the disease process. At the base of the iceberg are the fundamental problems of life for which the symptom represents an injudicious solution. Between the base and the tip of the iceberg are the processes by which the symptomatic solution is created. These processes are called psychodynamics.

The iceberg analogy holds because most of the etiological processes operative in symptom formation are not apparent to conscious awareness; it is as if they were submerged. (In the case of the iceberg, six-sevenths is under water.) What is above the surface is well viewed to be the conscious material (what is readily observable), and what is below the surface is well considered to be subconscious (not immediately in conscious awareness, but readily available to such scrutiny) and unconscious (not readily available to conscious awareness, but potentially so via such procedures as psychoanalytic therapy, especially dream psychoanalysis).

As an example of the above let us take Bob's situation. Bob is 14 years old and in the ninth grade. His social studies teacher has informed the class that there will be a big test the next day. Bob is quite upset about this because he was looking forward to watching his favorite television program. The problem then for Bob is whether he should watch his program or study for the test. If he indulges himself and watches the TV program he may get a low grade on the next day's examination. A good grade might only be obtained by his depriving himself of the television program. Bob is being confronted here with one of the common dilemmas of just about all school children. Bob is facing one of the fundamental problems of life which, like all such problems, lends itself well to the utilization of maladaptive solutions.

Bob decides to watch the program in the hope that he will be lucky enough to know the answers to the questions his teacher selects to give on the test (already we sense trouble, that is, a maladaptive solution). The next day, as luck would have it, Bob finds that he doesn't know the answers to most of the questions. In order to protect himself from the embarrassment and discomfort of getting a poor grade, he decides to copy from the paper of the girl sitting next to him. Such behavior is called *cheating*, a symptom. Like all symptoms, it is an inappropriate adaptation and may result in more trouble and discomfort for Bob than that which he would have suffered had he studied for the test and deprived himself of the gratifications of watching his favorite television program.

Now let us consider the possible outcomes of Bob's symptomatic resolution of this conflict. One outcome is that the teacher will catch him cheating, reprimand him, give him a failing grade, and possibly report the event to his parents. He may then suffer further disapprobation at home. Perhaps the teacher won't catch him but his classmates observe what he is doing. He may suffer from them a certain amount of criticism and alienation. Or, the girl from whom he is cheating may get angry at him, cover her paper, and then may reject him subsequently as a "cheater." Perhaps none of these occur and he appears to be "successful." However, when the grades come back, and Bob sees that he has gotten a high one, if he has anything approaching healthy superego development, he is likely to feel less proud of his high grade than he would have had he come by it honestly. In his heart he knows that it was not deserved and so he cannot enjoy the gratification he otherwise would have had he achieved his high grade by honest effort.

The possibility still remains, however, that Bob could have cheated and *not* suffered any of the above difficulties. Let us suppose there was no negative feedback from any of the aforementioned individuals (that is, "he got away with it") and his superego development was so limited that he suffered no guilt or remorse over his behavior—behavior that would generally be considered unacceptable in the classroom. But even then there would be the untoward effect of his not having gained the optimum benefit from his educational process. His failure to study would have deprived him of the information learned by those who had studied. Although this outcome might not have caused Bob any immediate discomfort, in the long run, especially if this pattern were repeated, Bob's education would suffer. Thus, the aforementioned principle still holds.

All of these outcomes are examples of the principle that the selection of the symptomatic solution generally results in the individual's suffering with more difficulties than he or she would have if the more judicious and healthy solution had been utilized. In this case it would have been Bob's deciding to forego the pleasures of television and appreciating that such deprivation would ultimately be less painful than the discomforts and embarrassments associated with the consequences of his cheating.

Another example: An adolescent boy doesn't have friends because of personality problems. However, he learns that he need not suffer loneliness very long if he provides peers with cash and other presents. His utilization of *bribery* (the name of the symptom) is seemingly successful in that he now finds himself more popular. He enjoys thereby an alleviation of his painful feelings of loneliness. However, his pleasure is compromised by the inner knowledge that his friends are being bought and that they would not be there if he did not have the wherewithal to pay them off. In addition, his position is a precarious one because he does not have a steady supply of bribes to insure that he will not once again be lonely. And this unstable feeling also compromises his pleasure. At some level he probably senses that his "friends" do not basically respect him, and this cannot but lower his feelings of self-worth. Last, if and when he does run out of bribes (the usual case), he cannot but feel "used." Bribing, the psychopathological symptom, was devised in an attempt to deal with the common human problem of loneliness. Ostensibly, it served its purpose of providing friends; however, it was an injudicious selection. As is usually the case when psychopathological symptoms are used to resolve a problem, the individual usually ends up being worse off than he or she was before.

Jim is afraid to try out for his high school's basketball team. He fantasizes public humiliation if he misses a basket or drops a ball in the course of the game's action. Jim is a well-coordinated boy, and there is no reason to believe that he would humiliate himself. He chooses to take the safe course, doesn't try out for the team, and thereby protects himself from his anticipated humiliations. The solution that Jim has chosen does "work" in that he doesn't suffer the tensions he would have experienced had he joined. However, he suffers even worse repercussions as a result of his withdrawal. He becomes somewhat lonely in that when his friends are playing basketball he has little to do. But more important, he has deprived himself of the ego-enhancing gratifications that he would have gained as the result of his participation. He has deprived himself of the joys of playing well in an area in which he has every reason to believe he would have been competent.

There is an extremely important principle demonstrated here that pervades many aspects of living. Most new things are anxiety provoking. The healthy person tolerates such fear with the knowledge that it is usually transient and that the benefits to be derived outweigh the loss of joy and ego-enhancement to be suffered from failure to act. The philosophy is epitomized in the aphorism: *Nothing ventured, nothing gained.* All individuals can choose the safe course and avoid risk and anxiety. In the extreme, the individual psychologically digs a hole in the ground, hides therein, thereby protecting him- or herself from the vast majority of life's inevitable rejections, disappointments, indignities, and traumas. However, a heavy price is paid for such "safety." One leads an extremely boring existence, and one is deprived of the ego-enhancement that comes from accomplishment. Again, the psychopathological solution to this problem causes the individual more difficulty than he or she would have suffered had the healthier course been pursued.

Another example: While playing alone with a ball, Jane, age 13, accidentally breaks a neighbor's window. To the best of her knowledge, no one has observed the incident. A conflict is immediately set up. On the one hand, she would like to run away as fast as she can and thereby avoid any responsibility or repercussions for the damage. On the other hand, part of her appreciates that such flight would be "wrong" and that she would not respect herself for doing so. Furthermore, she might be observed and then would suffer punishment for having "run from the scene of the crime." Jane decides to take her chances and run as fast as she can. She gets home and breathes a sigh of relief. To the best of her knowledge she was unobserved, and she feels that she has "gotten away with it." However, there is some lingering guilt as well as fear that she might have been seen and that word of her misdeed will ultimately get to her parents. So even at this stage the pathological course is not without its negative repercussions. She is enjoying the pleasure of not having to own up to her responsibility for her transgression, but her pleasure is compromised by her guilt and fear of disclosure. Of course, if her superego development has been impaired, she will not suffer this guilt and she truly will have "gotten away with it." Last, if she were observed, and the incident is reported to her parents, then she is likely to suffer repercussions for her flight.

Had she gone to the neighbor and reported the incident, she would probably have been respected and even praised for her honesty, even though the neighbor might have been angry as well. If she offered to pay for the window, she would have to suffer the privations attendant to such payment. However, this negative element would have been more than offset by the ego-enhancement that comes with the knowledge that one is doing the "right" thing. In addition, she might have been praised by others for her honesty, and this could further enhance feelings of self-worth. She would have avoided the guilt and fear of detection that she might have suffered following the commission of her "crime." The ancient aphorism *honesty is the best policy* is not trite. There is great wisdom in it. The honest course usually (though certainly not always) is the best course because its advantages usually outweigh its disadvantages. People who utilize psycho-pathological mechanisms for resolving disputes may not be aware of this ancient truth.

Mary, at 15, finds herself quite lonely. Because of shyness and passivity, she has few friends and has not developed the repertoire of information about her adolescent world that makes her an interesting person to be with. She learns that providing boys with sexual gratifications enhances her popularity immensely. Whereas prior to her "liberalization" she got little attention from them, afterwards the telephone hardly stopped ringing. Although she obtained little if any gratification from sexual intercourse, she did enjoy somewhat the carressing and even more the enhanced popularity she was now experiencing. Mary's promiscuity (the name given to this symptom), like all symptoms, has many draw-backs which she may not wish to recognize. She may not appreciate that the boys are attracted to her primarily, if not exclusively, because of the ease with which they can obtain sexual gratifications and basically have little or no respect for any other aspect of her personality. This cannot but be humiliating. And, when she allows herself to appreciate the basic reasons for her popularity, she cannot but feel "used." Furthermore, she has to come to recognize the fact that once she starts to preserve her sense of pride and withholds the sexual favors, she may find herself lonely as she is depriving her so-called boyfriends of the one and only thing they want from her. And, not incidentally, she may pick up a sexually transmitted disease or become pregnant as a result of her pathological utilization of sexual behavior.

Jim, an 18-year-old, is very dissatisfied with his boss at the fast-food restaurant where he is employed. The situation has reached the point where he often dreads going to work because of the indignities he suffers while on the job. Jim is a somewhat timid person who fears expressing resentment. He feels that if he were to assert himself with his employer he might lose his job. In addition, even if he were not to lose his job, he is afraid of his boss's anger. These fears contribute significantly to his failure to assert himself and to discuss in a civilized manner the problems he has with his employer. Most often (but not always) such failure to assert oneself is pathological. It is a heavy price to pay for job security and protection from the possible resentment of the person to whom a complaint is directed.

A healthier course for this boy would be to assert himself and make reasonable attempts to resolve the conflict with his boss. If he is successful in this regard, he will have accomplished his goal of a better work relationship with his boss. In addition, he will have reduced, if not eliminated, his loathing of work as well as the self-loathing that comes with repression and suppression of pent-up resentment. He will enjoy the sense of well-being that comes with successful resolution of a problem. However, such assertion could conceivably result in his being fired. This repercussion will have to be taken into consideration before he decides to assert himself. Having made the decision to act, he must bear this risk. He might even have to suffer the discomforts of trying to find another job, and he might not even be able to find one. He has to consider the discomforts and loss of self-worth that come with unemployment. Although these are certainly formidable negative repercussions of self-assertion, he would at least be free from the self-loathing and the painful effects of not expressing his resentments.

Ruth, a 19-year-old teller in a bank, makes an error. Although some discrepancy will ultimately be detected in the accounting process, the person who caused the error may not readily be identified. Ruth knows that if she reveals the error, there might be some criticism and reprimand. However, her position is such that it is extremely unlikely that she would lose her job. Moreover, if she says nothing, there may be no repercussions because the process of detecting the person who made the error is so cumbersome that the company accountants may not wish to go to the trouble. Or, another person might be falsely implicated. She decides to say nothing. During the ensuing days she hears talk about the repercussions of her mistake and the resentment felt by her superiors toward the individual (still unknown) who could have been so careless. Although "innocent," she suffers with the fear of disclosure and some guilt. Had she admitted the error, there would have been criticism, but no job loss and no ongoing fear of being caught. The pathological way seemed easier at first but ended up being the more difficult course.

I do not claim that the examples given above explore in great depth all the ramifications of a psychopathological act. They focus on the symptom as a manifestation of the individual's attempt to find the solution to a common, if not universal, life problem. They demonstrate how the pathological solution causes the person more trouble than the healthy one. The examples have not focused on the complex psychodynamic factors that play a role in determining whether the individual chooses the healthy or pathological adaptations to the conflict. Nor have I elucidated the psychodynamic pattern by which the fundamental conflict brings about symptomatic solution.

THERAPY AS A WAY OF
OPENING UP NEW OPTIONS

Therapy involves helping people learn better ways of dealing with life's inevitable conflicts and problems. Therapy must open up new options—options that may not have been considered by the patient previously, options that may not have been part of his or her repertoire. The utilization of these more adaptive solutions *over time* lessens the likelihood that the patient will have to resort to the maladaptive, symptomatic solutions. Let us take Bob's case, for example, the previously discussed boy who cheated on tests. If Bob were in therapy, it would be important for the therapist to help Bob appreciate the various consequences that might result from his cheating. He would do well to help Bob figure out *himself* the variety of discomforts and inconveniences he would suffer as a result of the symptom. We would do well to ask Bob first to try to predict what these would be and then, after Bob could not provide any more, the therapist would suggest others for his consideration. Between the two of them, they should be able to come up with a list of the various consequences previously mentioned, such as alienation of the child from whom Bob was copying, alienation of those who observed the cheating, actions taken by the principal, measures possibly taken by his parents, the loss of the opportunity to enjoy the esteem-enhancing experience of a high grade, and the compromise of his education. Furthermore, if Bob were exhibiting psychopathic tendencies, then the therapist would do well to make attempts to fan any sparks of superego development that might nevertheless be present. Here the attempt would be to help Bob appreciate *in advance* how short-sighted was his decision to indulge himself in television viewing without giving serious consideration to the potential consequences of his utilizing the cheating solution. The hope here would be that the next time he is confronted with such a conflict, his knowledge of the consequences might play a role in his choosing the more judicious course.

In the course of such a discussion, the therapist might have asked Bob if he could think of any other solution to his dilemma. If Bob's family owned a video cassette recorder, then the option of making a videotape of the program and studying at the same time could have been discussed. Then, he could watch the program on the weekend and so both television watching and studying would have been accomplished. Or, if Bob himself doesn't own a videocassette recorder, he could be asked if he had a friend who might be prevailed upon to tape the program for him. The video tape recorder resolution, then, becomes a new option—an option that may not have previously been considered by Bob. Once utilized, this solution might become an automatic consideration for Bob when confronted in the future with this conflict. Although this new option originated in treatment, it can now become a part of Bob's repertoire.

In each of the other examples, the therapist could have helped the patient consider healthier options. The boy who used bribes to gain "friendships" could have been helped to appreciate the precariousness of his situation and the lowered feeling of self-worth that comes from being so utilized. Jim, the boy who was afraid to join the basketball team, could have been helped to appreciate the wisdom of "nothing ventured, nothing gained"—that those who do not venture forth will often lead very lonely and unrewarding lives. Jane, the girl who accidentally broke a neighbor's window, could have been helped to appreciate that it was ultimately to her benefit to take the initially painful but more courageous course of admitting her guilt. And the youngster who was dissatisfied with his boss could be helped to appreciate that the security and ego-enhancement potentially derived from healthy and civilized self-assertion are much more likely to outweigh the risks and disadvantages associated with passive submission. Ruth, the teller in the bank, could have been helped to appreciate the widsom of the "honesty is the best policy" aphorism.

COMMENTS ON
TIME-LIMITED THERAPY

I do not believe that one can tell in advance how long therapy will take. One cannot know whether or not the patient will be receptive to the therapeutic messages and experiences, and, even if so, how long it will take until they become incorporated into the psychic structure. Therapy is best viewed as just another life experience, having much in common with the kinds of experiences one has outside the therapeutic situation. Although there are some differences, there are more similarities. The main difference is that the therapist (it is hoped) is sensitive to psychological processes that the average person is not appreciative of. If the therapy does indeed turn out to be short, then I am quite pleased. But one cannot know in advance how long it will take. Anyone who claims to know is, in my opinion, simple-minded and/or grandiose. There are certain things in life that cannot be quantified in advance, and therapy is one of them.

Furthermore, the imposed time limits are likely to compromise significantly the nature of the work accomplished in each of the sessions. If the patient is watching the clock, is pressured into working quickly, and is trying to figure out a solution to a particular problem within time limitations, it is likely that the solutions so derived will be injudiciously selected. The patient who is involved in time-limited therapy is likely to be watching his or her watch during the course of each session and counting the number of sessions until "cure." This counting process is inevitably going to reduce the likelihood that the therapy will be successful. While preoccupied with the ticking clock, the patient is being distracted from focussing on the problems for which he or she is being treated. And the therapist, too, may also be involved in the same process.

If a boy were to call up a girl and ask her in advance to go out with him for ten dates and then break up, he would be considered strange. If a man asked a woman to marry him for 12 days, weeks, months, or even years—and then to divorce—he would probably be considered by the woman to be insane. Yet the same kind of arrangement is frequently made between therapists and patients, and there are many who do not consider this absurd. Sometimes the figure regarding the number of allotted treatment sessions is derived from some statistical analysis of the number of sessions that patients in the same clinic received for the treatment of that particular disorder. To me, this is like saying that the average marriage in a given community lasts 12.5 years; therefore, it is recommended that people commit themselves to a marital union of exactly that duration.

It is not that I do not do brief psychotherapy. I do it all the time, but I only do it in situations where happily it takes place. It occurs in situations where I cannot know beforehand how long the treatment will take, and in some cases it does indeed turn out to be brief. But I have never promised it would be brief at the outset because I could not know the degree to which the parties would cooperate, whether or not a relationship would be estblished, whether there would be receptivity to what I had to say, and what things would come up in the course of the treatment.

Psychotherapy in which a patient is told at the outset that a specific number of sessions is all that will be required is basically a "rip off" by clinical administrators on a gullible public. Such therapy is an administrative maneuver that satisfies those who are funding the clinic and who are often quite naive regarding what therapy is all about. It is one way of rationalizing giving a little therapy to a lot of people rather than a lot of therapy to a select few. If one is going to do this, then one should at least be honest and let people know that they are getting a watered-down form of treatment. Time-limited therapy is mainly for the poor, who often have little choice. People who are in better financial positions most often get as much treatment as they need. And those rich people who do opt for brief psychotherapy are often the naive and gullible ones, those who, despite their financial positions, are still simple-minded enough to be attracted to this absurd form of treatment.

Unfortunately, there are therapists who recognize the validity of what I have said here, but appreciate that their job security rests on their adherence to the time-limited therapy concept. Even worse, there are others who actually believe that such therapy is as good as long-term treatment because of their desire to bring about quick cures or to satisfy other pathological needs. Last, and most important, the main flaw in time-limited therapy is that it loses sight of the importance of the development of a good therapist-patient relationship as the foundation upon which treatment is built. Relationships must evolve *over time;* they cannot be expected to develop in accordance with a fixed schedule.

The reader may have noticed that in the above discussion on therapy as a way of opening up new options, the words *over time* are italicized. My purpose here is to emphasize the point that meaningful therapeutic changes are not likely to take place quickly. Although there are rare occasions when a brief encounter with the therapist can bring about long-term therapeutic results, such situations are unusual. Therapy first requires the establishment of a meaningful therapist-patient relationship. In the context of such a relationship, therapeutic messages are received by the patient with receptivity and therapeutic experiences take place that, when repeated over time, bring about personality change. Freud feared that psychoanalysis would degenerate in the United States because of the lack of patience that Americans had for solutions that might require a long-term investment of time and energy. He feared that the method would be bastardized by a wide variety of quick and seemingly attractive short cures. And he was right. Short-term methods of treatment have sprung up everywhere and promise better, more rapid, and less expensive results than long-term psychoanalytic therapy or psychoanalysis. I consider this to be a deplorable development. It is not that I do not have criticisms of psychoanalytic treatment (many have been and will continue to be presented in this book); it is only that I am critical of quick methods of treatment, especially those that promise results in a prescribed period of time, even before the patient's problems are known.

Short-term and brief psychotherapies are very much in vogue. Often a specific time limit is imposed upon the patient from the outset. Ten to 15 sessions is a common figure. The selection of such a number demonstrates complete ignorance of what I consider to be a crucial requirement of meaningful psychotherapy. One cannot possibly know how long it will take to develop the kind of relationship in which meaningful therapy is most likely to be productive.

THE THERAPIST-PATIENT RELATIONSHIP

If patients are to experience an alleviation (the reader should note that I did not use the word *cure* here) of the presenting symptomatology, it is highly desirable that both the therapist and the patient possess certain qualities. The importance of the therapist-patient relationship in therapy is often spoken of. However, the specific personality qualities that are important for each to possess and the ways in which these bring about symptomatic alleviation and therapeutic change are not often elaborated upon. The main reason for this, I believe, is that these issues have not been studied to the degree that is warranted. I present here a few of the important elements that I consider necessary to be present in each party if therapy is to be meaningful. Only basic principles will be presented here. In Chapter Six I will discuss these in greater detail.

Genuine Respect vs. Idealization and/or
Idolization of the Therapist

The patient should be reasonably respectful of the therapist because of *actual* qualities that the therapist has that engender such respect. Idealization (viewing the therapist as perfect) and idolizing (viewing as God-like, worthy of worship) of the therapist is anti-therapeutic in that it creates unfavorable comparisons with the therapist that are ego-debasing to the patient. Such a view of the therapist reduces the likelihood that the patient will relate realistically to other human beings who will inevitably reveal qualities that will be considered deficiencies by the patient. The classical analytic model, especially, is likely to result in such distortions of the therapist. One might argue that the kind of "blank screen" created by the analyst sitting behind the couch will provide him or her with the "purest" kinds of free associations, which are less likely to be contaminated by input from the analyst. However, whatever benefits there are to be derived from this approach (and I do not deny that they exist), there is a heavy price to be paid for them—a price that far outweighs the benefits. As stated, one of the prices is that the patient, having been studiously deprived of vital information about the therapist, is likely to view him or her as being perfect or close to it. This is intrinsically ego-debasing because it produces unfavorable comparisons between the patient and the therapist. Feelings of low self-worth are intrinsically associated with most (if not all) forms of psychogenic psychopathology. Idealizing and idolizing the therapist only adds to this disparity. Furthermore, this unreal atmosphere interferes with the patient's relating to others in the world who will inevitably reveal their deficits (real or so-viewed by the patient) and who will not provide the patient with the same kind of accepting and tolerant environment that the therapist provides.

We live in a world where certain conspiracies of silence are prevalent. When speaking with someone in a social situation it is generally considered inappropriate to criticize directly the individual's spouse or analyst. A woman, for example, may meet someone at a cocktail party who tells her that she has marital problems and that she is in treatment with Dr. X. The listener may know that Dr. X's general reputation at the hospital is that every one of his five wives despised him. In addition, two of them might have been personal friends of hers so she knows first-hand that this is the case. Yet, she may not reveal any of this information to Dr. X's patient, lest she "rock the boat" and/or compromise the treatment. I believe that it would be far better for the listener to present the information that she has about Dr. X, even at the risk of its being somewhat distorted. The information would certainly serve as "grist for the mill" during the next session. As a result of the patient's confronting her therapist with this information, there could be one of two outcomes. The patient might decide to leave the therapist, from the recognition that his personality deficiencies are so grave that it is not likely he can be of help to her—especially in the treatment of her marital problems. Or, she might decide to stay in treatment because of the appreciation that Dr. X still has enough on the positive side to warrant his remaining an effective therapist. ("No one is perfect.") In either case she is less likely to view him as a perfect person, and this cannot but be therapeutic.

Receptivity to the Therapist's Messages

The patient should be receptive to the therapist's comments, but not to the point of gullibility. If there has been no idealization or idolizing of the therapist, then there is less likely to be gullibility. If there is a good relationship and genuine respect, that is, respect based on genuine qualities that the therapist actually possesses and exhibits (as opposed to fantasized ones), then there is a greater likelihood there will be healthy receptivity. Respect must be earned, and healthy respect is not likely to be earned in a fantasized relationship; it is based instead on knowledge of both a person's assets and liabilities. When there is healthy respect, the balance tips in favor of those qualities that engender respect in others. In such situations people recognize another's liabilities but consider them small in comparison to assets. It is only by judicious revelation of deficiencies that such genuine respect is likely to evolve.

Identification with and
Emulation of the Therapist

There should be a reasonable desire to emulate qualities in the therapist that would serve the person well in life. (This may be conscious or unconscious.) As a result of such emulation, there will be some identification with the therapist's traits and values. I do not believe that there is any psychotherapeutic interchange that does not involve some attempt on the therapist's part to transmit his or her own values to the patient. It is hoped that the values and qualities so taken on will be in the patient's best interests.

There are many who take issue with what I have just said about identification with the therapist's traits and values. Many have been taught in their training that one should strictly avoid doing or saying anything, either implicity or explicitly, that involves the communication of, let alone imposition of, the therapist's values on the patient. I believe that this is well-meaning but injudicious advice. I cannot imagine a psychotherapeutic interchange that does not involve, at some level, the process of transmission of the therapist's values to the patient. Even in silence such imposition is taking place. Implicit in the therapist's silence is the message: "What you're saying is all right with me. I don't think it warrants any comment on my part. I don't have any books that say it is unhealthy, inappropriate, unreasonable, or otherwise maladaptive."

When we use the word *values* we refer to that which we consider to be good and bad, right and wrong. The therapist is continually making such judgments. At times, however, the terms sick and healthy may be utilized. But even here, values are intrinsically present in that what we refer to as psychopathological is basically an opinion regarding whether or not the behavior is good or bad, right or wrong. And this is very much determined by the "eye of the beholder." Parents bring a 14-year-old youngster to the psychotherapist with the complaint that, although of superior intelligence, he shows little academic motivation or curiosity. The therapist, after detailed inquiry into the family life, decides that the child has psychological problems that stem from family difficulties. The therapist recommends a therapeutic approach in which the child is treated individually along with active work with the family. The goal here is to reduce those family tensions and pressures that are contributing to the child's difficulties. The goal, as well, is to help the child himself deal with these family stresses in such a way that academic performance returns to the expected level.

By the therapist's agreeing to treat this patient, he or she is implicitly subscribing to the value judgment that education is a "good" thing and that those who do not avail themselves of their educational opportunities are doing a "bad" thing. One could argue that this is only the therapist's personal opinion. One could say (as many in our society do) that all one needs to do in life is to learn how to sign an X on one's welfare check. Under these circumstances, one will receive (in cash, goods, and services) almost as much as the average working man or woman (especially woman) or perhaps 10% to 15% less. By agreeing to treat this child and help this child reach his academic potential, the therapist is implicitly subscribing to the parents' value judgment that education is a "good" thing. I personally happen to share this value, but I am very clear that it is a value nevertheless.

Another example: A 35-year-old man enters treatment with complaints of depression and excessive drinking. He fears that he may become an alcoholic. In the course of the history taking, the therapist learns that the man's father died when he was in grade school and that he is an only child. Although 35, he still lives with his mother. He does not consider this to be a problem; rather he states that he and his mother have agreed that both would be unreceptive to a therapeutic approach that might ultimately result in his leaving home. It may be the therapist's opinion (supported by many books in his library) that this man has an "unresolved Oedipus complex" and that he is far too old to be living with his mother. Consistent with this opinion, one of the aims of therapy should be to help this man "resolve his Oedipus complex," move out of the house, meet a woman, get married, and have children—like other normal, healthy human beings. Although I am in agreement with this goal (even though I might not agree that the man's problems relate to the so-called "Oedipus complex"), I recognize that my position on this subject is still a value judgment. An anthropologist might say that there is an island in the South Pacific where people do this routinely. (There is always an island in the South Pacific where one can justify practically any conclusion regarding human behavior!)

Another therapist might think: "He's right. Stay there living with your mother. You'll never meet anyone who'll treat you as well—no matter how long you live." Still another might take the position: "You're doing a smart thing. Never get married. Women will just take advantage of you. Go out with them; have a good time; enjoy sex with as many as you can; but don't tie yourself down." Yet another says: "Homosexuality is where it's all at. My goal will be to get this guy out of that house into a good relationship with a man who will give him the kind of real love that a woman just can't provide." Yet another thinks that communes are the only sane arrangements and plans to lead the patient in that direction. Last, and certainly not the least common, is the one who says: "I will make no value judgments whatsoever about this arrangement. If he and his mother are happy with this arrangement, who am I to judge it as bad, wrong, sick, or sinful. Unless he expresses some kind of dissatisfaction, I will say nothing at all about it throughout the course of his treatment. I'll just stick to the things that bother him, namely, the depression and drinking. All of these people would be imposing their values on the patient. Even the one who claims to be strictly neutral and nonjudgmental is still going to have an effect on the patient. Under the therapist's influence the patient will maintain the status quo, which is still an option that presents a value. Neutrality is no less a position than advocating either side. It is still a statement; it still has its effects on those who are looking for input from the allegedly neutral person.

One last example. A number of years ago I saw in therapy a man who requested treatment for insomnia, tension, and depressive episodes. He commanded an extremely high salary working for a large and famous advertising agency. He spent most of his day making up songs, jingles, and clever sales pitches. He was viewed by his superiors and clients as one of the most creative men in the business. After working with the patient a few weeks, I informed him that he had to make an important decision. I told him that I considered him to have a formidable problem into which he had practically no insight. Specifically, I considered him to have a deficiency in guilt-evoking mechanisms which, if they were to be present, would produce guilt over the way he was spending his life, namely, trying to engender in people cravings to buy things that they would have little or no use for. I told him that if he were to continue in treatment with me I would try to instill in him guilt and embarrassment over the fraudulent life he was leading. And, if I were successful, he might quit his job and thereby become unemployed. In short, if he were to continue with me he might have to think very seriously about finding another career, one that was more honest and less exploitive—either within or outside of the field of advertising. I was not surprised that the man quit. He told me that he considered me out of touch with the real world and that he would find a therapist who could help him with his problems and not tamper with what he considered to be a healthy life style and ethical (because it was not illegal) career. I fully appreciate that my own personal values were operative here when I confronted the patient; however, I also believe that the next therapist who promised not to tamper with his career (and I am sure he found one) was also operating under a different value system and transmitting *his* value to the patient (in this case by silence on the career issue).

Again, my point here is that the therapist cannot take a position on a therapeutic issue without an implicit attempt to impose his or her own values on the patient. In short we must be honest about the fact that we are "brainwashing" our patients. We must also accept the fact that in the context of such brainwashing, many patients have been done terrible disservices and much grief has been caused by such impositions. In contrast, many have been exposed to healthier values—for some it may have been for the first time in their lives—which have enriched them and made them better human beings, to themselves and those who have the good fortune to encounter them.

Accordingly, therapy is a very "risky business." This problem of value imposition is further compounded by the fact that whether or not one sees something as good or bad is highly individualized and strongly determined by what the therapist brings to the situation, that is, his or her own anticipations, hopes, and even neurotic distortions. The point is well made by the anecdote of the rabbi who dies and finds himself in the hereafter, but he doesn't know whether he's in heaven or hell. He's not experiencing very much pain, so he decides he's probably not in hell. But he's not enjoying very much pleasure either, so he concludes that he's probably not in heaven. As he's groping about, trying to determine where he is, he suddenly sees coming out of the distant cloud none other than Rabbi Isaac Cohen (his mentor from the Talmudic Academy, dead now these 30 years). Rabbi Cohen, he well recalls, was one of the most religious and pious men he ever knew. In his 87 years in life he never broke one rule, so pious was he. Happily, he runs toward his mentor. He then notices that standing next to the old, stooped man's side is a beautiful, young, voluptuous woman—obviously the old rabbi's companion. The two rabbis embrace, tears running down their cheeks, happy to see one another after all these years.

At this point, the younger rabbi states: "Rabbi Cohen, it's so good to see you here. I've been roaming about, lost. I didn't know whether I was in heaven or hell. But it's obvious that if you are here, this must be heaven! A more religious and pious man never lived. It's obvious, also, that this beautiful, young voluptuous woman is God's reward to you for all the good works you've done on earth."

To which the old rabbi replies: "I'm sorry to have to tell you, rabbi, two things. First, this is not heaven, this is *hell*. And second, this beautiful, gorgeous, voluptuous woman is *not* God's reward to me. I am her punishment!"

The anecdote demonstrates my point that the aspirations and hopes that one brings to a situation are going to be an important determinant of how one interprets it. Shakespeare's Hamlet put it well: "There's nothing either good or bad, but thinking makes it so." The point is demonstrated again in a wonderful scene from the Woody Allen movie, *Annie Hall.* In a split-screen vignette, Woody Allen is on one side complaining to his psychoanalyst; and Diane Keaton is on the other side, complaining to her analyst. Woody is complaining bitterly about Diane's lack of sexual receptivity to him. He complains about how "up tight" she is and how painful is his ongoing state of sexual frustration. The deprivation is driving him crazy and he's practically tearing his hair out so distraught is he over his sexual privation. When the analyst asks him how often he is having sexual relations, he replies, "Imagine, only two or three times a week."

At the same time, Diane Keaton is complaining that Woody is continually bothering her with his sexual advances, from the moment he gets up in the morning, throughout the course of the day, until the moment he goes to sleep at night. He rarely gives her any peace. In the course of her complaining she refers to him as an animal. After further complaints about Woody's insatiable lust, her analyst asks Diane how frequently she is having sexual relations. To which she replies, "Imagine, two to three times a week, the beast." It is indeed "the eye of the beholder" that determines whether something is good or bad, right or wrong. Therapists are no exception. Our value judgments are colored by our own experiences, anticipations, and aspirations. And these inevitably will be transmitted to our patients. Let us hope that we don't do too much damage.

Most have heard at some time or other anecdotes about people who are looking for "the secret of life"—the one great wisdom under which is encompassed all the meaning of life's experiences. The jokes and/or stories often involve seeking the secret from some guru, often seated in some mountain cave in India or high in the Himalayas. Finally after a long circuitous route, during which time the individual may be exposed to many dangers, the wise man is finally confronted with the question: "What is the secret (or meaning) of life?" Well, I have the answer here for the reader. (Remember, it was I who told it to you.) The secret of life is this: *Life is a Rorschach test!* Yes, that's it. Life is a Rorschach test. Under this dictum one can subsume all psychological experiences of life. In every experience there is the reality and there is the interpretation that we make of it, depending upon our own psychic structure. There is the Rorschach inkblot, and there is the patient's projection which gives meaning to the inkblot. There is the external reality, and there is the interpretation we give to it. And there is yet another level here, namely, the *interpretation* the psychologist gives to the patient's projection. This reflects his or her values (whether the projection is "sick" or "healthy") and must also be considered part of the reality. There is the glass of water, and there is our interpretation as to whether it is half empty or half full, or whatever other meaning we want to give to it. The reality then is not simply an external entity. Rather, it is a *combination* of an external entity and the meaning and interpretation that our internal psychic structure gives to it. The two together then determine our thoughts, feelings, and actions. Let us hope that our projections and our interpretations of what is good and bad for our patients will serve them well.

Trying to Help Patients vs. Helping Patients

The therapist should have a genuine desire to help the patient. There should be a reasonable degree of sympathy (an intellectual process) and empathy (an emotional resonance) with the patient.

Therapists should have a reasonable capacity to identify with their patients, that is, put themselves in their patients' positions to view situations from their vantage point. The therapist's goal should be that of *trying* to help the patient, but he or she should not feel that the failure to do so represents a failure in him- or herself. I have emphasized the word *trying* because many therapists consider it their goal to "cure" patients or to bring about significant improvements. Many such therapists suffer with what I call *The Statue of Liberty syndrome.* This name is derived from a poem, written by Emma Lazarus, and placed at the base of the statue when it arrived in this country in 1886. It says:

> Give me your tired, your poor,
> Your huddled masses yearning to breathe free,
> The wretched refuse of your teeming shore,
> Send these, the homeless,
>   the tempest-tossed to me.
> I lift my lamp beside the golden door.

These lines are certainly inspiring. With the exception of those who are North American Indians and those who otherwise trace their heritage to pre-Columbian days, all of us are either immigrants ourselves, or are the descendants of immigrants, either recent or remote. And these forebears of ours did not generally sail away from foreign shores in their yachts. Rather they often fled a variety of persecutions and other indignities because of their religion, political beliefs, skin color, or poverty. This principle, however noble, is extended by many mental health professionals to:

> Give me your chronic hebephrenic schizophrenics,
> Your alcoholics, your drug addicts, your criminals,
> Your psychopaths, your prostitutes, your criminally insane,
> And all your other rejects from society.
> I will give them sympathy, empathy, and understanding.
> With analytically oriented psychotherapy,
> I will help them gain insight into the underlying psychological
>   processes that cause their disorders.
> And with such treatment I will raise them to new heights of
>   mental health.

Those therapists who exhibit manifestations of *The Statue of Liberty syndrome,* whether they realize it or not, are placing formidable demands upon themselves. They are doomed to suffer frustration because their claims are impossible to achieve. The pathology that we deal with (even the less severe types) is generally generations in the making, and it is therefore grandiose on the part of anyone to believe that he or she can help more than a small fraction of those who come our way.

We generally interview parents of our child patients, and often get information about grandparents. But we rarely get information about earlier generations. Yet, it is naive to assume that the influences of these ancestors have not played a role in our patients' pathology. Furthermore, we are often impotent to change the formidable social and cultural factors that are likely to have played a role in the development of our patients' psychopathology. Accordingly, therapists do well to have very modest goals in regard to the treatment of their patients. We should be comfortable with small changes. To believe that we can do more is to impose upon ourselves goals that may be extremely frustrating for us. The therapist's goal should be that of *trying.* The therapist should be able to say, after a failure, that he or she has worked to the best of his or her ability. That is all that we can ask of ourselves and that is all that our patients should be asking of us.

Those who are afflicted with *The Statue of Liberty syndrome* are welcomed by various individuals in our society. Jails are overcrowded and judges are happy to learn about people who claim that they will bring about the prevention of criminal recidivism. School principals are happy to "get off the hook" by telling complaining parents that a troublemaking child is "in therapy." Even worse is the principal who tells parents that if their child does not go into therapy he or she will be discharged from the school. (This is an extremely misguided statement and compromises significantly the likelihood of the child's being helped by treatment.) Last, therapists who try too hard are likely to defeat their own purposes because the pressures placed on the patient are apt to lessen the likelihood that treatment will be effective.

It is important for the therapist to appreciate how deep-seated the psychopathological patterns can be and that they are often generations in the making. In fact, they may be so formidable that their alleviation or cure might result in the individual's becoming a pariah from the family, so different will the person become. I do not believe that therapists give proper appreciation to this factor in explaining therapeutic failure. If, as a result of the treatment, the individual becomes entirely different from his or her extended family, it is not likely that the therapy will be successful. The so-called "cure" is too heavy a price to pay—entailing, as it will, total removal and isolation from one's family.

This phenomenon was well demonstrated by a 22-year-old young woman I saw a number of years ago. Her presenting complaint was that she found herself gravitating toward young men who would maltreat her; when treated more benevolently, she became tense, anxious, and even found herself provoking her dates into treating her hostilely. She suspected that something might be wrong with her, but wasn't sure. The girl grew up in a blue-collar home in northern New Jersey (pertinent to this discussion). When she was 14 years old, she told her parents that she wanted to go to college. Her father responded by beating her, while accusing her of trying to be superior to the rest of her family. He claimed that no one in their extended family had ever gone to college and there was no reason why she should do so.

Over the next few years she continually prevailed upon her parents to let her go to college and, finally, with some minimal assistance from her mother, her father agreed to let her go with very stringent provisions. The most important of these was that she would have to pay her entire school expenses by working in his gasoline station, which was on the West Side of Manhattan (across the river from New Jersey) in an extremely rough and dangerous neighborhood. Accordingly, she began work at 5:00 in the morning, when he opened the gas station, and worked there until about 8:00 A.M., when she then went off to school. He always paid her the minimum wage and this was the source of the financing of her education. There was hardly a day when she was not propositioned, physically mauled in a sexual way, and even exposed to a few attempted rapes. When she would complain to her father about these indignities, he invariably scoffed and told her that it was her imagination, even though the advances were often made in situations when her father could easily have overheard or even seen what was happening. At the time that I saw her, the girl had graduated college and was working as a secretary in a typical white-collar position.

It is my usual practice to invite the nearest of kin of all of my patients for a family interview, regardless of the age of my patient. In this case, as she was their only child, I invited her parents to join us in one of our early sessions. Her mother accepted the invitation but her father rejected it, claiming that he did not "believe in" psychiatry. Besides, he is reported to have said that he did not think his daughter had any psychiatric problems anyway. Accordingly, I saw the girl and her mother. Early in the interview I asked the mother what problems she considered her daughter to have. She replied, "Doctor, my daughter is perfectly fine. She doesn't have any problems, I don't know why she's coming here." When I asked her what her daughter had told her about the reasons for her visits, she replied, "I know that she thinks she has a problem with boys. She says that she often finds herself trying to get them to treat her badly, and even to hit her. I don't know why she's talking about that as if it was a problem. All men hit their wives. That's normal."

I then asked the mother if she was quite sure that "all" men hit their wives and that there were no exceptions. She replied, "Doctor, my husband's always hit me, all my sisters are beaten by their husbands, and all my brothers beat their wives. My father beat my mother, all my uncles beat my aunts, and all my aunts were beaten by their husbands. My grandfather beat my grandmother, etc., etc." I then asked her if she could conceive of the possibility that there might be marriages in which husbands did not beat their wives. She responded that she would not believe any man who claimed that he didn't beat his wife, nor would she believe any woman who claimed that she wasn't hit by her husband.

With this family background it is not difficult to see what was happening with this girl. When she went to college, she found herself in what was for her an entirely unique environment— different from any she had ever experienced. She found herself with young men who treated her benevolently. With them she was like a "fish out of water." And, when she went into the business world, she found herself in a similar situation. In order to make her relationships with boys more familiar, she would provoke them in the hope that they would treat her badly and even hit her. This is what she knew, this is what she was used to, and this was familiar. What is strange is often very anxiety provoking.

This girl's situation reminded me of the comment of Tevye, the father in the movie and play *Fiddler on the Roof*. In one of his moving soliloquies, dealing with his shock on learning that his daughter is going to marry a Gentile young man, he looks up to the heavens and says, "I could understand, God, how a bird might fall in love with a fish. But where would they live?" This girl was basically a masochist. All known females in her extended family, back as many generations as one could go, were masochists. And all of them found sadists for husbands. One could almost predict at the time of her birth that she too would become a masochist. Certainly, other factors were probably operative in bringing about her masochism. However, what I have described above was, I believe, the most formidable and significant component.

I describe this patient's situation here because it demonstrates so well my point that a patient's symptomatology, although presented as an individual problem, may be deeply rooted in family processes—processes that may go back many generations. With such a heritage, with such powerful contributing factors, the therapist must have very modest goals in the treatment of such symptoms. And even when close work with the family is possible, the chances of alleviation may be minimal.

It is important for the reader to appreciate that pathological modes of interaction between and among family members are not 100 percent detrimental. They are derived in an attempt to establish some kind of an equilibrium and generally provide benefits in spite of the pains and discomforts attendant to their perpetuation. They may contain constructive and cohesive elements—the patient's complaints about them notwithstanding. Such appreciation should lessen therapeutic fervor and reduce also the therapist's tendency to develop manifestations of *The Statue of Liberty syndrome*.

An example from my military experience demonstrates this point quite well. An elderly couple once came to me for consultation, at the initiation of the wife. He was 86 and she 83, and they had been married 63 years. They lived near a central military hospital in Frankfurt am Main, Germany, where I was stationed. (Retired military people often choose to live near military hospitals where they can receive free medical care and live close to other military retirees.) The wife described things as having gone well during the first 61 years or so of the marriage, stating that her husband was a good man, and did not gamble, drink, run around with other women, or engage in other behavior traditionally disruptive to a marriage. Furthermore, he was a devoted husband, father, grandfather, and greatgrandfather. Accordingly, they had never sought counseling before. (I always like a "fresh case," so that I don't have to deal with statements like, "Well, Doctor so and so said . . ." and "You know, Doctor, the other person we saw has a very different opinion.")

The wife then went on to tell me that during the previous two years her husband had become progressively more preoccupied with accusations of infidelity. It was not simply that he was perpetually accusing her of being unfaithful, but he was accusing her of having a special attraction for young recruits, ages 18 to 20. His suspicions reached the point where he would hardly leave her alone and when with her his allegations were continual. When she would go shopping at the PX, for example, on her return he would confront her: "Well, as I figure it, it should have taken you an hour and a half. It should have taken you a half hour to get there, a half hour to shop, and a half hour to get back. It's taken you an hour and three-quarters. I know you had a 'quickie' in the alley with one of those young soldiers." No amount of reasoning on the wife's part was successful in dispelling her husband's delusion. Her argument that she had no such inclinations proved futile. Her attempts to prove that her absences did not take longer than necessary were again responded to with incredulity and accusations that she was lying.

By the end of the interview it became apparent to me that if I had a pill that could magically dispel this old man's delusions, I would have done both him and his wife a disservice. Both of them were deriving important psychological gratifications from the symptom, their ostensible complaints notwithstanding. From the husband's point of view, it was not that he had a wife who was old and less attractive than she was 63 years previously. Rather, his wife was still so attractive that young men in their late teens would prefer her over far younger women who were clearly available. The symptom, therefore, enabled him to deny the unpleasant reality of his wife's aging. It also provided him with the enhanced self-worth associated with his belief that at his age he had such an attractive wife. And there were similar gratifications for the wife. Her protestations notwithstanding, she was flattered by her husband's belief that she was still so pretty that young men would prefer her over their peers. And both of them utilized the discussions over the delusions as a way of filling up the vacuum of their empty lives. Accordingly, as mentioned, if I indeed had a pill to dispel this delusion I would have deprived them both of valuable psychological benefits. It was from this recognition that I advised them to try to fill their lives more meaningfully by taking advantage of the many services that the military had available for such individuals. Furthermore, I advised them to involve themselves in various programs for the elderly back in the United States where they were soon planning to move.

Therapy—An Educational Experience

In the context of a good therapist-patient relationship, the therapist helps the patient learn better how to deal with the fundamental problems and conflicts of life with which we all are confronted and must deal in the course of our existence. After a detailed study of the factors operative in bringing about change in psychoanalysis (one form of psychotherapy), H. Strupp (1975) concluded that the most important elements in bringing about therapeutic change were the "lessons in constructive living" that the patient learned. I am in full agreement with Strupp on this point. The more judiciously and intelligently a person deals with the problems of life, the less likely it is that the individual will resort to pathological modes of adaptation. Therapy, more than anything else, should enhance one's capacity to deal with life's challenges. Therapy, more than anything else, involves helping people learn how to deal with these inevitable problems. The younger the patient, the more guidance, advice and instruction the therapist should be willing to provide, and the older the patient, the more the therapist should facilitate the patient's finding his or her own solutions to these problems. However, even with the most mature adults, some guidance and instruction is warranted *after* the patient has made every reasonable attempt to resolve the problem him- or herself. Accordingly, the therapeutic process is very similar to the educational.

The Therapist as Teacher

This similarity between the educational and therapeutic processes goes further. An important determinant of whether a student will learn from a teacher relates to whether the student will identify with the teacher. Teachers who are bored with teaching or unmotivated and watch the clock throughout the day are not likely to teach their students very much. In contrast, teachers who are enthusiastic, who genuinely enjoy learning and teaching what they themselves have learned, are much more likely to impart knowledge to their students. The former teach little, the latter are likely to create an atmosphere in which their students are swept up in the learning process. An important factor in this process is that of identification with the teacher. Children in the classrooms of the enthusiastic teacher want to "join in on the fun," and they thereby imitate the teacher in order to derive similar enjoyments. We learn best from those we admire and respect, and we are going to learn little from those who produce little desire for identification and emulation. Worse yet is the teacher who is feared. She not only teaches her students little, if anything, but may contribute to a generalized revulsion for the educational process and the development of psychopathology as well.

The Levels of Therapeutic Learning

Intellectual and Emotional Learning   The therapeutic learning process occurs at many levels. I believe that the *least* efficacious is the intellectual. An intellectual insight acquired by the patient is, however, more useful than one provided by the therapist. Classical analytic treatment focuses heavily on the intellectual. It is based on the theory that the primary way of bringing about clinical change is to help the patient gain conscious insight into the unconscious processes that are bringing about the psychopathology: "Where there is unconscious, there shall conscious be." As will be discussed in detail throughout this book, I believe that this focus on intellectualization robs both the therapist and the patient of more predictably therapeutic experiences. When emotions are associated with intellectual learning, there is a greater likelihood of change. Classical analysts appreciate this and recognize that an emotional loading adds clout to an intellectual insight and increases the likelihood that it will be remembered. However, classical psychoanalysts focus excessively on the role of emotions in enhancing the insight-gathering process (an intellectual endeavor) and do not give proper attention to their value as therapeutic facilitators in other areas— many of which do not rely on the development of conscious insight. I describe these below and throughout the course of this book.

The Metaphor   Metaphorical communications are especially potent. Aristotle recognized this long ago and considered the metaphor to be the richest and most valuable form of verbal communication (*Poetics*, 1459a):

> The greatest thing by far is to be a master of the metaphor; it is the one thing that cannot be learned from others; and it is also a sign of genius, since a good metaphor implies an intuitive perception of the similarity in the dissimilar.

A metaphor is basically a figure of speech in which two entities, which have no intrinsic relationship with one another, are equated. An example of a metaphor would be: "He is a rock!" There is no intrinsic relationship between a rock and a particular man. However, when one equates them, one provides a statement that is richer than the two separate entities that are being equated. The whole here is indeed greater than the sum of its parts. "She is a flower" is another example of a metaphor. Probably the greatest creator of metaphors in the English language was William Shakespeare. One of my favorites is from *Macbeth*. One could say that life is transient and that before you know it, it's over. However, one could also say, as does Macbeth (v, 5):

> Out, out brief candle!
> Life's but a walking shadow, a poor player
> That struts and frets his hour upon the stage
> And then is heard no more: it is a tale
> Told by an idiot, full of sound and fury,
> Signifying nothing.

The same message, but obviously Shakespeare's way of putting it makes the initial statement weak and sterile. I do not believe that the creation of metaphors can be taught. The ability to see linkages where others do not and to make the proper selections so that rich metaphors are formed is a talent that I believe to be inborn. It is a testimony to Shakespeare's genius that he was able to discover a relationship between the course of life and the mundane: a candle, a shadow, an actor, and the tale. Of course, we therapists do not have the creative capacity of William Shakespeare, and our ability to form metaphors is far more limited. However, to the degree that we can utilize them in our work, to that degree we will enhance the efficacy of our therapeutic communications.

Metaphors become even more enriched when incorporated into the context of allegories, anecdotes, and other narrative forms. This is not only true of children who traditionally enjoy stories, but of adults as well in that they will often learn better from a well-selected anecdote or the relating of an experience by the therapist. M. Erikson (J. Haley, 1973) was especially appreciative of the value of the metaphor in therapy. My main criticism of his work, however, is that the metaphors he would present to his patients appeared to be "pulled out of the sky" and were not, I suspect, as carefully tailored to the needs of the patients as he professed. I say this because the information upon which he would select his metaphor was often miniscule and, accordingly, his metaphorical presentations often had a high degree of speculation.

Conceptualizations and Abstractions vs. Concrete Examples
Conceptualizations and abstractions are far less potent vehicles for clarifying issues than specific concrete examples, especially examples that relate to the patient's immediate experiences. Many therapeutic interchanges are quite sterile and therapeutically unproductive because the therapist and the patient are speaking at abstract levels. It is much harder to pay attention to an abstraction, which cannot be visualized, than a concrete example, which can. One of the reasons why philosophy textbooks are so boring to students is that they dwell to a significant degree on abstractions. In contrast, the traditional detective story is very specific and concrete regarding the details it provides and is therefore much more likely to maintain the reader's interest. If a patient, for example, talks

about being depressed, the patient is speaking at a conceptual level. The therapist does well, in response, to ask the patient what he or she is specifically depressed about, what in concrete terms are the exact thoughts and feelings that the patient is experiencing and, even more important, to focus on the specific situations that have brought about the depressed feelings. The best way to alleviate the psychogenic components in the depression is to focus in detail on the specific concrete events that have contributed to it. In this chapter, as well as throughout this book, I follow this principle. I present general theoretical principles (abstractions) and then provide concrete clinical examples (readily visualized) that enhance, I believe, the likelihood that the reader will recall what I have written.

The Experience   The most potent mechanism for modifying behavior is the experience. The old proverb, "A picture is worth a thousand words," is well known. I would add to this, however, that "An experience is worth a million pictures." To the degree that the therapist can provide experiences, to that degree will he or she be able to bring about clinical change. This hierarchy of the efficacy of the various forms of learning is well epitomized by the following comparisons. Let us take, for example, the experience of reading a play. Reading the play is purely a visual experience, both at the level of reading the written page and the visual imagery that is engendered by such reading. It is primarily an intellectual experience, although some emotions may certainly be engendered. Let us compare this with attending a theatre and observing the play being acted. It is likely that the individual will be more affected by the play because an auditory modality of input has now been added to the visual experience associated with reading the play. If one becomes an actor in the play, then one is even more likely to remember its messages. The reason for this is that one is now adding physical action to the visual and auditory modalities of input. With each additional modality, there is a greater likelihood that the story will have an impact. However, the emotions being exhibited in the play are feigned. No matter how convincing the actor is, the emotions are still turned on and off in accordance with the dictates of the script. The actor is still playacting. Compare this with emotions that are caused by an actual experience. Here, the reactions are engendered by reality and even more likely to be recalled in the future.

Therapy, more than anything else, should be an experience. It is an experience that is one slice of life. It is a living experience in which one has an ongoing encounter with a person who is more honest than any other individual with whom one may be involved in one's lifetime. Our best friends may hesitate to criticize us, lest they hurt our feelings. Therapists criticize benevolently with the purpose of helping remove those behavioral manifestations that alienate others and that interfere with our dealing most effectively with the problems in life with which we are all confronted.

Although the therapist's specific knowledge and experience may increase the likelihood that an involvement with him or her will be therapeutic, such encounters were taking place long before Sigmund Freud was born. Let us take, for example, a young woman, in her late twenties, who comes to therapy because she is not yet married and is concerned that she may never meet a man with whom she will have a satisfactory marital relationship. Let us assume that the therapist is a man in his late fifties, approximately the age of her father. Let us assume further that she reports early in treatment that her father was particularly cruel and rejecting and that she learns in therapy that her anticipation of similar rejection from young men is playing a role in her avoidance and rejection of them. In the course of her treatment she discusses with the therapist her male relationships, and this insight helps her avoid a repetition of her childhood experiences. The therapist is sympathetic, understanding, sensitive, and kind. At no point does he treat her in a way similar to her father. Let us assume that her treatment was successful and she ultimately marries a man with whom she has a stable and rewarding relationship.

I believe that the *insights* this woman gained in her therapy were far less important in bringing about the therapeutic change than the *experience* she had with the benevolent and sympathetic therapist. Without necessarily having any conscious insight into the process, the experience with the therapist enabled her to reduce and possibly even remove her generalization that all men would treat her badly. Similarly, the therapist's discouraging her from involving herself in the same pathological pattern with other young men increased the likehood that she would have *experiences* with men who were more kindly disposed to her. In short, then, I believe that the major elements in bringing about change in this woman had less to do with intellectual insights and more to do with the quality of the therapist and the men that she subsequently encountered. Had the therapist been aloof, cool, and unsympathetic, she probably would not have changed—all her insights notwithstanding. I would speculate further that this experience was had by a multiplicity of women long before Sigmund Freud's birth. With similar upbringing they too had difficulties in their relationships with young men. However, if they had the good fortune to form a relationship with an older man (an uncle, teacher, or mentor, etc.), then this might have modified their views of men and lessened the likelihood that they would carry the generalization over into their courting patterns. All this may have occurred without conscious awareness and was certainly much more likely to have taken place outside of conscious awareness in the days prior to psychoanalysis. In short, it was the experience that was the best teacher, not the insight.

WALT DISNEY'S PINOCCHIO AS A METAPHOR FOR THE PSYCHOTHERAPEUTIC PROCESS

I consider the story of *Pinocchio* to be an excellent metaphor of the therapeutic process. I suspect, however, that it is not generally recognized as such. A powerful statement of what goes on in psychotherapeutic treatment may be found especially in the Walt Disney version of the original Carlo Lorenzini (pen name, Collodi) story written in 1883. It begins with Geppetto, a woodcarver, who makes a wooden boy puppet he calls Pinocchio. As he looks at his creation he begins to wish that his Pinocchio could be turned into a real boy. He goes to his window, gazes up at the heavens and prays:

> Star light, star bright,
> First star I've seen tonight.
> I wish I may, I wish I might,
> Have the wish I wish tonight.
> I wish my Pinocchio were a real boy!

Geppetto's prayer is overheard by Jiminy Cricket who feels sorry for the old man because he knows that Geppetto's wish could never come true. However, much to the surprise of Jiminy Cricket, a shimmering light suddenly fills the room, a beautiful lady dressed in shining blue appears, raises her wand and says:

> Wake Pinocchio, and live.
> To you the gift of life I give.
> Be good and give Geppetto joy.
> And grow to be a real live boy.

Suddenly, Pinocchio blinks his eyes, raises his wooden arms, and joyfully exclaims, "I can move! I'm a real boy!"

"No," says the Blue Fairy sadly, "You have life, but to become a real boy you must prove yourself, brave, truthful, and unselfish."

"But how can I do that?" asks Pinocchio, discouraged.

"You'll have a Conscience to help you!"

Looking around, the Blue Fairy beckons Jiminy out of his hiding place. "Sir Jiminy Cricket," she says, "I dub you Lord High Keeper of Pinocchio's Conscience!"

Basically, what is happening to Pinocchio is that his transformation from a wooden boy into a real boy is a two-step process. The first step, enabling him to move, has already been accomplished by the Blue Fairy. However, he is still essentially made of wood; he is not yet a real, live boy. In order to accomplish this final goal he must "be good and bring Geppetto joy" and he must prove himself "brave, truthful, and unselfish." In short, he must develop human virtues. To help him accomplish these goals Jiminy Cricket will assist him in forming a conscience. Jiminy's purpose will be to help him develop internalized guilt-evoking mechanisms that will help him deal in a civilized way with his primitive impulses. This, of course, is what therapy is all about for the vast majority of people. Some, for example those with antisocial problems, have weak consciences and so they do not properly suppress their primitive impulses. Others have consciences that are so rigid that they inhibit themselves inordinately when suppressing and repressing their primitive impulses. The goal of the therapist (here symbolized by Jiminy Cricket) is to provide the patient with help in developing a reasonable conscience—neither too repressive nor too lax.

The next day Geppetto tells Pinocchio, "But now, Pinocchio, you must go to school . . . Study hard! Then you'll soon become a real boy!" Basically, Geppetto is telling Pinocchio that another thing that must be accomplished if he is to develop into a real boy is that he become an educated individual. And so Pinocchio goes off to school, trailed by Jiminy Cricket. En route Pinocchio encounters a fox named J. Worthington Foulfellow and his cat friend Gideon, who have the reputations for being "the worst pair of scoundrels in the whole countryside." They tell Pinocchio that he is much too talented to waste his time in school and that he should join a theatrical troupe. They recognize what a find they have in a spontaneously moving puppet. Pinocchio is easily taken in. Jiminy implores him not to become involved and asks, "What will your father say?"

Pinocchio rationalizes his going off with the scoundrels, "Oh, father will be proud of me."

Foulfellow and Gideon then sell Pinocchio to Stromboli, the owner of a marionette theater. At the end of his first day of extremely successful performances Pinocchio is ready to take leave of Stromboli. Before he realizes what is happening, however, Stromboli locks him in a bird cage. As Pinocchio is sitting in the cage, while being lectured to by Jiminy Cricket on the errors of his ways, the Blue Fairy suddenly appears. She asks, "Pinocchio, why didn't you go to school?"

Pinocchio responds, "I *was* going to school until I met someone . . . two big monsters!" At this point Jiminy claps both hands to his head and frowns. At the same time Pinocchio's nose begins to grow longer. Pinocchio then continues and tells the good fairy that the monsters tied him in a big sack. His nose grows even longer. Pinocchio notices what is happening to his nose and becomes upset.

The Blue Fairy then says, "Perhaps you haven't been telling the truth, Pinocchio. You see, a lie keeps growing and growing until it's as plain as the nose on your face."

Pinocchio is *ashamed.* "I'll never lie again—honest, I won't."

"Very well," says the Blue Fairy. "I'll help you this time, because you are truly sorry. Be good now, Pinocchio."

This interchange is worthy of analytic scrutiny. It is probably the most famous part of the story. Many Freudian psychoanalysts consider the interchange between Pinocchio and the Blue Fairy to be basically an oedipal one. The nose, as a projection from the anterior surface of the body, lends itself well, they claim, to symbolizing the penis. The Blue Fairy, as an "older woman," lends herself well to symbolizing Pinocchio's mother. Geppetto, we presume, is a bachelor, in that no wife ever appears in the story. The idea that Pinocchio is being sexually turned on by the Blue Fairy is certainly possible. However, I consider another explanation to be more likely. We are told that Pinocchio is "ashamed" and that his lying is apparent to everyone about him. I believe that reference is being made here to the experience children have that when they lie adults generally can see through their duplicity. Many children are startled by the apparent wisdom of adults in this area. Pinocchio's change here, I believe, relates to the shame stage in the development of conscience that I described in Chapter One. In this phase, the child is deterred from engaging in antisocial behavior by the fear of invoking the alienation and rejection of significant figures who observe or learn of the transgression. Pinocchio has not yet internalized the mechanisms that will deter him from engaging in unacceptable behavior. The Blue Fairy is serving as another therapist (in addition to Jiminy Cricket) and provides Pinocchio with information which will serve him in his maturation into a real boy. Because he is "truly sorry" (as opposed to using the sorry excuse as a manipulative device to exonerate himself from punishment), she excuses his transgression, waves her wand, and removes him from the cage. Jiminy and Pinocchio proceed again along the open road.

Soon afterwards, Pinocchio and Jiminy once again encounter those low-life characters, Foulfellow and Gideon, who symbolize primitive drives which press for gratification and ignore potential future consequences of wanton self-indulgence. The sly fox and sleazy cat feign sympathy when Pinocchio tells them about his tribulations at the hands of Stromboli, and they persuade him to take a "rest cure" on *Pleasure Island*. Again, Pinocchio rejects Jiminy Cricket's warnings not to get involved with these unworthies. He replies to Jiminy, "Foulfellow says I need a rest after my terrible experience. Just think of Pleasure Island. Bands, circuses, ice cream mountains!" Pinocchio appears to have forgotten his promise to the Blue Fairy and happily anticipates the opportunity to indulge himself in primitive pleasures.

Pinocchio then boards a coach bound for Pleasure Island. The coach is pulled by small donkeys and is filled with impudent, noisy boys. The Coachman surreptitiously gives Foulfellow a bag of money in return for his passenger. Again, unbeknownst to Pinocchio, the fox has sold him to an individual who ultimately exploits the naive boy. After a long journey they finally arrived at Pleasure Island. "Here were bands playing, streets paved with cookies and lines of donut trees, and fountains spouting lemonade. And always the Coachman kept urging the boys 'Have a good time–while you can!'" All the bad boys are encouraged by the Coachman to indulge themselves. However, there is the ominous warning of future consequences implied in the "while you can" comment. The seed is being planted here that unbridled self-indulgence is not without its penalties. The boys continue their wanton and hedonistic lifestyle: "They climbed the Ice-cream Mountains and sailed down the Lemonade River. They smashed windows, burned school books, and teased the poor little donkeys. Pinocchio made friends with the very worst of the boys, a young bully called Lampwick, and he was always in the middle of the mischief." Lampwick epitomizes the juvenile psychopath who serves as a model for those who wish to engage in a life of guiltless self-indulgence. He is the antithesis of Jiminy Cricket and the Blue Fairy. As the fun at Pleasure Island progresses the boys become increasingly rowdy and antisocial. One day Jiminy Cricket finds Pinocchio shooting pool in Tobacco Lane. Lampwick is smoking a cigar and Pinocchio a corncob pipe. Jiminy exclaims, "Throw away that pipe! Come home this minute!" At Lampwick's prodding Pinocchio mocks Jiminy and blows a puff of smoke in his face.

Soon afterwards the bad boys are suddenly afflicted with "donkey fever," an illness characterized by rapid transformation into donkeys–starting with the sprouting of donkey ears. The Coachman starts rounding up the boys who have been newly transformed into donkeys to do slave work in the coal mines and other kinds of donkey labor. With Jiminy Cricket's help Pinocchio narrowly escapes–with only his ears turned into those of a donkey. Fortunately, the rest of his body is still intact.

After an arduous journey they finally reach home. Unfortunately, the house is empty and inside they find a letter from Geppetto informing them that he had learned that Pinocchio had gone off to Pleasure Island and he had left home to find Pinocchio. It also informs Pinocchio that while he was on a small boat headed to Pleasure Island the giant whale Monstro gobbled him up, boat and all, and that he is now living in the belly of the whale. Pinocchio then decides that he is going to save his father, even though Jiminy warns him about the dangers. This time Pinocchio's failure to heed Jiminy's warning is a healthy sign in that he manifests a willingness to take risks and suffer pain on behalf of another person. After a series of adventures, Pinocchio and Jiminy finally encounter the whale Monstro. Soon thereafter Monstro swallows Pinocchio, Jiminy Cricket, and their boat in one massive gulp. Inside the whale's huge stomach they find Geppetto, and Pinocchi devises a plan for their escape. He builds a fire, which forces the whale to sneeze. This results in the ejection of them all. But escape from Monstro is not so simple. The angry whale relentlessly pursues his former captives, obsessed with destroying them. At one point it is Pinocchio who saves his father from drowning—helped by the enhanced flotation power of his wooden body. Although finally safe from the jaws of Monstro, the ordeal so incapacitates Pinocchio that he is brought to the point of lying still, cold, and motionless.Geppetto is heartbroken, weeps bitterly, and is sure that his son is dead. He carries the boy's limp body back to his cottage and prays for him. Suddenly a ray of starlight appears and the voice of the Blue Fairy is heard. She repeats her earlier prophecy: ". . . and some day, when you have proven yourself brave, truthful, and unselfish, you will be a real boy. . . ." Pinocchio suddenly recognizes that he has been changed. Joyfully he realizes that the Blue Fairy's promise had come true. Pinocchio was no longer a puppet. Pinocchio was a real, live, flesh-and-blood boy! The Blue Fairy then presents Jiminy Cricket with a reward for his labors. It is a badge of gold on which is stated:

> Awarded to a Good Conscience
>   Who helped make
> A Real Boy out of a Wooden Head

And this is the role of the therapist, to make real boys out of wooden heads. They do this primarily by contributing to the development of the internalized guilt-evoking mechanisms, commonly referred to as the conscience. But such development does not occur quickly. It takes place only after a long series of adventures in life—both painful and pleasurable—in which lessons are learned and there is a gradual process of internalization of those dicta, values, and principles which society considers crucial for the perpetuation of a civilized world.

As mentioned, the story outlined here is taken from the Walt Disney adaptation. Disney took many liberties with the original, the most important of which—for the purposes of my analysis—relates to what happened to Jiminy Cricket. In the Disney version, Jiminy's work is successfuly completed and he enjoys the ego-enhancement of having contributed significantly to the transformation of a wooden head into a real boy. In the Collodi version, Pinocchio kills Jiminy by crushing him to death with a mallet! I leave it to the reader to decide which rendition he or she prefers.

CONCLUDING COMMENTS

The material presented in this chapter represents a statement of my views regarding the basic factors that contribute to the development of psychogenic symptoms and the fundamental elements operative in the psychotherapeutic process. This "blind man" sees the elephant this way in the late 1980s. It was not the way I saw things in the 1950s, 1960s, and 1970s. I have learned things over the years, and I suspect some modifications of my present position by the 1990s. My purpose here has been to present a relatively short statement of my views on these issues. Throughout the course of this book, however, I will be elaborating on all of these points with many clinical examples. Throughout this book, as well, I will be making reference to these principles because they are the basic foundation of just about everything that is described herein.

There is an old Hasidic saying: "A good man is one who knows what he feels, says what he means, and means what he says." The statement could very well serve as a central therapeutic goal in that it epitomizes the kinds of qualities that therapy attempts to engender in patients. We want our patients to know what their feelings are and to be able to use them judiciously. We want them to be forthright and express themselves honestly. And we want them to be viewed as credible human beings who have the courage to follow through with their convictions. Therapists who possess these qualities themselves are more likely to engender them in their patients.

Passive therapists, those who hide behind "blank screens," those who are fearful of appropriately revealing themselves, and those who are vague and/or indecisive, are not likely to be of much assistance in helping their patients reach these goals.

SIX

THE THERAPIST-PATIENT RELATIONSHIP AND THE PSYCHOTHERAPEUTIC PROCESS

In this chapter I discuss in specific detail the ways in which the therapist-patient relationship contributes to the changes that may be brought about in adolescent psychotherapy. The material here is an elaboration of the therapist-patient relationship discussion in Chapter Five—with particular focus on elements relevant to adolescent therapy. As emphasized previously, I consider the good therapist-patient relationship to be at the foundation of treatment; without it there can be no meaningful psychotherapy. There will be no identification with the therapist, emulation of him or her, or receptivity to what the therapist has to say. The orientation here is psychodynamic and the kinds of problems focused on will be those that I consider to be psychogenic. Thus the term *psychotherapeutic* in the title of this chapter. This is a comprehensive chapter and will cover, in depth, the important basic principles of treatment for a wide variety of adolescent psychogenic disturbances. It is presented as a foundation upon which the treatment of specific disorders, and specific patients, may rest.

Some readers may consider my failure to discuss in detail the

395

treatment of a wide variety of disorders to be a deficiency in this book. My response is that I am not presenting a comprehensive statement of treatment details of *all* the forms of adolescent psychopathology. I do not believe that one individual can possibly claim to be competent enough to write such a volume. Because I have had significant experience working with antisocial patients, I have devoted a chapter to their treatment. However, as the reader can readily see, both in this chapter and elsewhere, I do discuss in some detail the treatment of many other common disorders seen in adolescents. Readers interested in works that cover the wide variety of treatments for the various disorders of adolescence do well to refer to such collections as *American Handbook of Psychiatry* (1974), *Basic Handbook of Child Psychiatry* (1979), and the more recent *Psychiatry* (1986).

THE ADOLESCENT PATIENT'S PERSONALITY

Insight and Motivation

Psychotherapists generally hold that the patient must exhibit insight and motivation before meaningful psychotherapy can be engaged in. The patient must have insight into the fact that the problems are indeed psychogenic and that their psychological pain is not merely the result of external factors or physical illness. Furthermore, the patient must have the motivation to deal with these problems via psychotherapy. But this is not all. The therapist as well must have the conviction that the problems are indeed psychogenic, that the patient is properly motivated for psychotherapeutic inquiry, and is willing to suffer the pains, embarrassments, and discomforts attendant to the process of self-inquiry. The more analytically oriented the therapist is the more likely he or she is going to subscribe to these *desiderata* of effective psychotherapeutic treatment. Some therapists even recommend an initial preparatory phase in which the patient is groomed for therapy. In this early phase an attempt is made to help the patient gain the insight that he or she has psychiatric problems. Next the patient is helped to become motivated for the treatment.

My experience has been that very few adolescents (especially early adolescents) have such insight and motivation. Those who ultimately do get to us represent a small fraction of all those who have difficulties. And even those who are willing to come to our office are not generally committed to the aforementioned principles of insight and motivation. Rather, most who come to us must often find a rationalization to justify their being in treatment. The most common such rationalization is that the youngster is being coerced into therapy and is submitting to irrational and punitive parents who are forcing him or her to see the therapist. D. Holmes (1964) is well aware of this phenomenon and speaks of it frequently in his superb book *The Adolescent in Psychotherapy:* "The adolescent...is so desperately aware of his need for help that he dare not call it by that name. He must represent it to himself and to others as an abominable infringement upon his personal rights by a meddling adult (p. 209)." The adolescent often needs what Holmes refers to as "a face-saving show of resistance (p. 186)." In fact, Holmes goes further and states that when the adolescent professes motivation for psychotherapy it is generally wise to be somewhat incredulous: "A youngster's direct request for psychiatric treatment, his sincerely expressed wish to cooperate in psychotherapy even before he has the least idea what it is, or his sober appraising of the therapist's abilities, are all representative of the kind of resistance which sends shivers of apprehension through the therapist who is experienced in treating adolescents (p.117)."

With regard to the adolescents' claim that their parents are forcing them into therapy, the realities are that no parent can actually force an adolescent to come to treatment. In fact, a parent cannot even force a younger child to attend treatment on an ongoing basis. Younger children may be physically carried into the consultation room but even then, if the child is adamant enough in his or her refusal, the likelihood is that the therapist will ultimately give up. And the adolescent cannot even be physically brought into the consultation against his or her will. Even if the parent is sick enough to physically overwhelm the adolescent and bodily coerce the patient into the therapist's office, the therapist is not likely to go along with this method of bringing the youngster to treatment. The therapist does well to accept the patient's excuse and not attempt to help the youngster gain insight into the fact that it is a rationalization. To do so may result in losing the patient.

Dealing with the Adolescent
Who Refuses to Attend the
Initial Visit

On a number of occasions I have received telephone calls from parents stating that they want their youngster to go into treatment, but that he or she refuses to come. Often I have told the parents that they should inform the adolescent that an appointment has been made and that if he or she does not come at least two or three times there will be repercussions such as disciplinary measures and various kinds of privations. Sometimes this is just what the adolescent needs and then, after a few sessions, the youngster finds that the anticipated repercussions of coming to a therapist were not realized and then he or she can more comfortably continue the treatment voluntarily. On other occasions this approach has failed and either the youngster hasn't even come to the first session (the punishments notwithstanding) or has gone through the motions of attending the required number of sessions and then promptly refused further involvement with me. Under such circumstances I have generally seen the parents a few more times, provided some counseling, and then discontinued the treatment with the understanding that they would return on a request basis in the future. I cannot recall having conducted ongoing treatment in a situation in which the youngster was threatened with punishments for non-attendance throughout the whole course of the therapy. Although I recognize the possibility that there may be rare situations in which this is warranted, I believe that it can easily result in the youngster's using the therapy as a way of expressing hostility toward the parent. By coming, and not cooperating and not using the sessions meaningfully, the youngster knowingly wastes the parents' money. Therapists who are party to this hostile maneuver are not only contributing to the perpetuation of the patient's psychopathology but "ripping off" the parents as well.

Using Anger as a
Vehicle for
Self-Revelation

Sometimes the adolescent needs the vehicle of anger to reveal him or herself. D. Holmes states: "If given the opportunity to rear up on his hind legs a little, he is able to confide much information about himself without experiencing the serious loss in self-esteem which would come from submitting helplessly to an omnipotent adult and poring out his heart like a baby (p. 109)." Holmes continues: "When arguing, he (the adolescent) is able to reveal things about himself which he could not possibly speak of in a quiet, expository tone." However, Holmes also recommends that the therapist, in response, argue with the patient: "Getting into arguments with the adolescent, patient or not, is both inevitable and useful. It does not signify either a loss of dignity for the therapist or a disruptive lapse in treatment (p. 109)." Although I am in agreement that adolescents may need anger to reveal themselves, I am not in agreement that therapists do well to argue with their angry adolescent patients. Although such arguments may prolong the adolescent's self-revelatory anger, I believe that arguing back with the adolescent does produce a "loss of dignity for the therapist." A therapist's arguing implies that the therapist has some strong need to convince the adolescent that the therapist is right and the youngster is wrong. Such responsive arguing suggests that the therapist's self-esteem will be lowered if the adolescent is not convinced of the wisdom of the therapist's position. However, a therapist's arguing would be justifiable in a situation where the therapist does indeed have something to lose if the argument is not won, such as the situation in which there is a threat to the therapist's life, property, etc. But under those circumstances meaningful therapy may no longer be possible.

Final Comments on the
Adolescent's Personality

Throughout the course of this book I will be making many comments about the adolescent's personality traits and how they affect the therapist-patient relationship. Furthermore, in the next two sections I will also be commenting on adolescent personality patterns that are likely to improve or work against the development of a good therapist-patient relationship. Before closing this section I would like to focus on the personality pattern of the psychopathic youngster. As I have described in detail in Chapter One, patients with a fully developed psychopathic personality pattern are not likely to be candidates for meaningful therapy. They have not developed the capacity to relate meaningfully to significant figures in their environment, and so it is not likely that they are going to relate to the therapist. Accordingly, the therapist does well to recognize the unsuitability of such prospective patients at the outset. We cannot relate therapeutically to all human beings; we cannot help patients with every psychiatric disorder; and it behooves us to differentiate between those we can help and those we cannot. Not to do so is to cause both patients and ourselves a significant waste of time, effort, and in many cases money.

THE THERAPIST'S PERSONALITY

Here I discuss those elements in the therapist's personality structure that I believe are desirable for him or her to possess if a good therapist-patient relationship is to develop. It is important for the reader to appreciate that these personality qualities all exist on a continuum from therapists who have little capacity in any of these areas to those who are significantly strong. To the degree that the therapist exhibits these to a significant degree, to that degree is it likely that the therapist-patient relationship will be a strong one. In the next section I will describe exactly what the factors are in the therapist-patient relationship that bring about therapeutic change.

The traditional view of psychotherapy is that it is a process in which the patient comes into the therapist's office and speaks voluntarily about his or her problems. Hollywood movies, especially, have promulgated this notion of the psychotherapeutic method. Typically, the patient is highly motivated to speak to the therapist who is continually kind, sympathetic, understanding, and rational. Like many other things depicted on movie screens, this is a myth.

Many therapists (including this author), when seeing such movies, are often envious of the motivation and cooperation of such patients and may even suffer with feelings of inadequacy when they compare themselves with the therapist on the screen. These screen therapists often exhibit a degree of sympathy, empathy, and toleration that we therapists in the audience are not likely to possess. And their patients often eagerly involve themselves in treatment and pour forth their innermost secrets from the outset. The realities are that the vast majority of adolescents who come our way do not profess any particular interest in unburdening themselves. In response we generally become impatient, discouraged, and even wonder whether we are defrauding the parents by continuing a therapeutic process that is so far below what we may consider to be the ideal.

Liking Children and Adolescents

The first, and possibly most important quality, is that of genuinely liking children. I cannot imagine someone's involving him- or herself meaningfully and effectively in the field of child and adolescent therapy without basically liking young people. I am not suggesting that the therapist should like children *all* the time; in fact, I would be distrustful of those who claimed that they did. Children and adolescents inevitably cause us periods of resentment and exasperation. Rather, I am only suggesting that a significant percentage of the therapeutic experiences with them should be benevolent and moderately enjoyable.

Projection of Oneself
Into the Patient's Position

Therapists must have the capacity to project themselves into the patient's situation, to see the world through the patient's eyes— and probably to feel the way the youngster feels. We know little of this phenomenon. Why is it easy for some and for others impossible? Piaget's panoramas (in which the child is asked to determine which card shows the view that the little model man in the center of the panorama sees as his position is changed) could give us information about this quality. Some would easily be able to see the view of the model, and others would have trouble. But this is only part of the phenomenon. It describes only a *visual-mechanical* aspect of the projective process; the *human elements* are far more complex. We use such terms as *sympathy* and *empathy* in our feeble attempt to describe this quality, but we still have much to learn about it—its mechanics, its psychodynamics, and the factors that play a role in its development. Does an accurate memory of one's own childhood play a role in this capacity? I think so, but as far as I know this has not been tested. And, indeed, it might be hard to evaluate accurately. Egocentricism inhibits this quality. Therapists who lack this capacity to a significant degree are ill-equipped to help their patients. If they cannot view the world through their patients' eyes (not necessarily agree with their patients, however), then they are handicapped in helping them. (Gardner, 1973c).

Frustration Tolerance

Adolescent therapists must be willing to tolerate certain frustrations that their adult counterparts need not contend with. One potential source of frustration is the youngster's parents. They often feel threatened by the therapeutic process. Having a child in therapy may be considered proof of the parents' failure, and many defenses may be utilized to avoid coming to terms with this notion. Many parents come not because they have seen the problems themselves (they have often denied them for months to years), but because some outside agency (most often the school) has suggested psychiatric consultation. Such parents often hope to hear that the youngster is completely normal and the referrer was in error. Once the youngster is in therapy, their ambivalence may manifest itself through forgotten appointments, lateness, cancellations with meager excuses, withholding payment of bills, failure to follow through with recommendations, hostility toward the therapist, and other gambits that are consciously or unconsciously designed to undermine the treatment. Sudden withdrawal of the patient is therefore common.

At any particular time the therapist who works with adolescents has to keep three people involved: a youngster who would prefer being with friends; a mother whose life is hectic enough caring for the house and other children without having to bring the patient to the therapist; and a father who could find much better ways to spend his money. If, at any point, any one of these three develops significant psychological resistances, the others are dragged down and the project fails. I often feel as if I'm juggling three greased balls and that when one of them drops, the whole act is over. Some therapists get fed up and gradually confine themselves to adult work. In residency, one of the definitions we had of a child psychiatrist was: "someone who used to do child psychiatry." The humor stemmed from the recognition that many of our supervisors were no longer doing child and adolescent therapy, merely supervising it. The consensus was that people got tired of doing such therapy after the age of 40 or so. I passed that landmark uneventfully (with regard to my enthusiasm for child and adolescent therapy) and also passed the age 50 landmark. As I write this, I am 56 and starting to get tired. Perhaps it's my age, perhaps the frustrations of the field are finally getting to me. At the same time, my interest still appears to be quite high. Then once every week or two, I have a really good and valuable session and it all becomes worthwhile again.

The frustrations of doing child and adolescent psychotherapy may be more than counterbalanced by certain gratifications that the adult therapist may not so frequently enjoy. The satisfactions of therapeutic success are more easy to come by in child and adolescent work than in adult therapy. These patients' problems are generally of shorter duration than the adult's and may be less deeply imbedded in the psychic structure. In addition, more change can be effected in the patient's environment. The deleterious influences to which the youngster is being exposed can be altered more readily: parental attitudes modified; misconceptions rectified; management advice provided; and schools, clubs, and camps recommended. Adults who come for treatment are usually deeply entrenched in their life situations. They may be locked into a bad marraige from which it is difficult to remove themselves because of children and the financial privations attendant to a divorce. And their work situation may be similarly rigid in that quitting a job or changing one's field may not be viable for them.

The Therapist as Parent

The question is sometimes raised as to whether it is necessary for child and adolescent therapists to have had children of their own. It is certainly possible to be an effective and accomplished child psychotherapist without having had such experiences, but I believe that the lack may compromise one's therapeutic abilities. The child, when seen in an office setting, is in an artificial situation. The childless therapist has not had the experience of living and growing with children in their natural setting; fathering and mothering; worrying and scolding; changing diapers; seeing them through physical illness; handling their fights with siblings and peers; and involving themselves in the thousands of other activities that enrich one's knowledge and appreciation of children. Childless therapists, no doubt, gain many of these experiences vicariously through their patients. They may, indeed, be able to involve themselves with their patients to a greater degree than therapists who have children of their own. These considerations notwithstanding, I still hold that having one's own children enhances a child therapist's efficacy.

Memory of One's Own Childhood

The ability to remember one's own childhood experiences deserves emphasis. There are people who will say with all honesty that they cannot remember a thing about their lives before the age of eight, or ten, or even twelve. People who are so repressed regarding memories of their childhood experiences are not likely to be effective child therapists. If they are to appreciate optimally the youngster's situation, therapists have to be able to recall how it was when they were the same age as their child or adolescent patient is at the time of treatment. Child and adolescent therapists have to be able to put themselves in the positions of their patients if they are to be successful. They need to be able to project themselves back in time. In addition, child and adolescent therapists must be able to involve themselves in both processes, i.e. present and past projections. Their task, therefore, is much more difficult than that of the adult therapist.

Comfort with Patients' Anger

One of the complaints I have about the people who taught and supervised me during my training period is that they didn't warn me about one of the most important stresses attendant to practicing psychotherapy. I am referring to the stresses of continual bombardment with patients' anger. Therapists must indeed have a thick skin. And those who work with children and adolescents must have even thicker skins. Children generally don't want to be in the therapist's office and express their irritation directly at their therapists for their central role in requiring them to be brought (often dragged, coerced, and bribed would be better terms) to the therapist's office. And the parents who bring their youngsters would much prefer spending time doing other things as well as spending money elsewhere. And then there is the anger that the parents have toward the therapist for not living up to their expectations for quick and magic solutions to their problems. Most parents have such expectations and most parents blame the therapist for not bringing about rapid change. And the parents most likely to do this are those who are most uncooperative in the therapeutic process.

Then there is the obvious fact that we are dealing with sick people. Under such circumstances there should be no surprise that people are going to be angry at us, often irrationally so. Therapists must appreciate that when they go into practice (whether it be in a clinic or private practice setting) they are basically putting a sign outside their door which says: *Welcome crazy people! If you are insane, disgruntled, bitter with life, frustrated over your lot, feeling rejected, isolated, lonely, or have any other dissatisfactions with life, come in here and tell me about it. If all others reject you, don't worry, I will accept you. All others may find your behavior noxious and alienating, I will not.* When one puts out such a sign, one shouldn't be surprised if one becomes the scapegoat of irrational people who are going to do irrational things. The therapist who takes most of this personally is in the wrong field. But even people such as myself, who believe that we have not made an incorrect professional choice, find it wearying. I often find myself drained at the end of the day and am envious of those who have the opportunity to work with more congenial individuals.

Comfort with Therapeutic Failure

It is important that therapists be comfortable with therapeutic failure. Therapists who think that it behooves them to alleviate the difficulties of all (or most) of those who come to them, will suffer significant frustration and a deep sense of failure. Children and adolescents often present with a total life of exposure to the detrimental influences that have contributed to their difficulties. Their parents generally have been living with their own problems for many years as well. But things do not stop there. Not only may the pathological processes have been transmitted down numerous generations, but social and cultural processes have usually contributed as well. It is therefore grandiose of therapists to consider themselves capable of rectifying all these pathological influences, and they are assuming unrealistic obligations if they consider it their responsibility to do so. The best attitude therapists can take is to commit themselves to the therapeutic process and try their best to do what they can. If they can say to themselves, with regard to the unsuccessful case, that they have tried their best and possibly learned a few things that will serve them in good stead in the future, they should be able to accept therapeutic failure without undue guilt and self-recrimination. I have spoken previously (Chapter Five) about *The Statue of Liberty syndrome* . Therapists should ask themselves whether they are exhibiting manifestations of this disorder. If they are, they do well to cure themselves as soon as possible; otherwise, they are doomed to lead very frustrating lives.

The Therapist's Sex

The sex of the therapist is sometimes given significant attention. I believe that in most cases this is a minor factor, less important than the personality qualities of the therapist and whether or not they dovetail with those of the patient. Also more important is the skill of the therapist and his or her insight into the patient's difficulties. This is not to preclude the possibility of the therapist's sex having some importance in certain situations. For example, a youngster whose father has been out of the home might do better with a male therapist. Girls in early adolescence are sometimes quite uncomfortable with a male therapist, and they probably do better with a female during this period. Most (but not all) adolescent boys who are dealing with homosexual problems probably do better with a male therapist because, as discussed in Chapter Two, I believe that most of these youngsters have had significant impairments in their relationships with their fathers and a male therapist may be useful to help rectify this difficulty. But these examples (and there are others) represent a small fraction of patient needs. More important than the therapists's sex are the therapist's talent, skills, and personality.

Therapists Who Are Still Adolescents Themselves

In the 1960s and early 1970s many therapists who treated adolescents considered it useful if they took on the attire that would be appealing to adolescents. These gurus often sported beards, hung beads around their necks, wore fancy shirts, and sat yoga style on the ground when conducting therapy. They generally espoused the same philosophies as the hippie adolescents of the times and even went so far as to smoke pot and use other drugs with their patients. These were often people who had difficulty with the aging process and were fixated at or had regressed to the adolescent level of development. I consider the youngsters who went to these "therapists" to have been shortchanged. I believe they did them more harm than good. Although they were attractive to the young-sters and thereby may have drawn them out more quickly than more conservative therapists (such as this examiner), I believe that they also fostered antisocial acting out and deprived their patients of what I consider to have been a healthier adult model. I am not claiming that every philosophical position held by these people was unhealthy, only that many of them were so. The adolescent needs a traditional (I am not saying slavishly traditional) parent figure against whom he or she can rebel but who, at the same time, can serve as a healthy model. These therapists provided neither oppor-tunity. Fortunately, at the time of this writing, they are not very much in vogue, but they still can be found. They may not wear the same "uniforms" as their contemporaries in the sixties and seven-ties, but their reflex idealization of and identification with adoles-cent values in vogue at the time have the same detrimental effects on their patients.

Concluding Comments

I do not claim to have covered all the factors in the therapist's personality that are important for the establishment of a good therapeutic relationship. There are many subtle factors that we know little about. When we say that the therapist and the patient have "established rapport" we are being quite vague. However, this vagueness relates to our ignorance of the process. We say that they are "on the same wavelength." Again, we cannot define exactly what we are talking about when this term is used, but it does have significance. When this rapport is referred to in a male-female romantic relationship we say that the "chemistry" between the two individuals is very good. We cannot define what these particular chemicals are, but obviously they have something to do with the sex hormones. And this factor may be operative in some therapist-patient relationships when the parties are of the opposite sex. Pretty girls are likely to get more attention from their male therapists than those whose male therapists consider them less attractive. And pretty mothers are likely to get more attention from male therapists of their children and adolescents. And there are many other factors—conscious and unconscious, healthy and pathological—which may have a profound influence on the relationship.

FACTORS IN THE THERAPIST-PATIENT RELATIONSHIP CONDUCIVE TO BRINGING ABOUT THERAPEUTIC CHANGE

Possessing certain qualities requisite to doing effective work with children is of little value if these qualities are not utilized in building a good relationship with the child. A good therapist-patient relationship is crucial to successful therapy. It is the focal point around which the various therapeutic experiences occur, and it is difficult to imagine successful psychotherapy if the relationship between the patient and therapist is not a good one.

A meaningful relationship with other human beings is vital to survival. Provide a newborn infant with food, clothing, and shelter, but deprive it of the tender loving care of a mother (or her substitute) and the child will lose its appetite, become unresponsive to the environment, and may actually waste away and die. Others similarly deprived may survive infancy but may develop such severe withdrawal from others that they become effectively non-functioning individuals, living in their own mental worlds, and gaining whatever little gratification they can from their fantasies. The parental deprivation need not be overt (such as physical abandonment) but can result from psychological rejection in the form of parental withdrawal, hostility, lack of interest, or other kinds of detrimental interaction with the child. In short, it is only through meaningful and gratifying involvement with others that we develop into human beings; without such exposure we may survive, but we cannot then be called truly human.

Meaningful relationships with others are the stuff of life. More than anything else they enrich us; without them we become shells—mere imitations of living individuals. From the moment we are born until the time of our death we need others—necessary times for solitude notwithstanding. The child in treatment has generally suffered some difficulties in the ability to form and gain gratifications from involvement with others. It is hoped that therapy will help the child accomplish this. But I cannot imagine its being successful if a meaningful relationship hasn't been accomplished between the therapist and the patient.

The Therapist's Affection for the Patient

The therapist's affection for the child can serve to compensate for some of the privations the patient may have experienced in relationships with others. However, there are significant limitations in the degree to which the therapist can do this. Although the parents may exhibit formidable deficiencies, they most often are providing the child with food, clothing, shelter, protection, and guidance. Even though they may have serious psychological problems, they are in all likelihood more bonded with the child than is the therapist and they probably will always be. The youngster who has been severely deprived—so much so that there are and there never will be any bonds established with any human being—is not likely to benefit from the therapist's affection. The youngster who has suffered some (but not formidable) deprivation in this area is more likely to profit from the therapist's affection. Such affection can be ego-enhancing to the child and therefore therapeutic. In a way, it is easier for the therapist to provide the patient with the unadulterated affection that the parents and others may not be able to give. The therapeutic situation is so structured that therapists need not have to do much of the "dirty work" entailed in raising children. Therapists don't have to change diapers, get dawdling children dressed in the morning, bring them to emergency rooms in the middle of the night, worry about them when they are not home on time, etc. They, like the grandparents, can enjoy children in the most relaxed situations—when few demands and restrictions are placed on any of the parties—and so there is less chance that there will be conflicts, power struggles, and other difficulties.

I am not suggesting that the therapist should like the child all the time. It is unrealistic to expect anyone to like anyone else more than a significant percentage of the time. Children will do things at times that will irritate their therapists, bore them, and alienate them in a variety of ways. It is hoped that the therapist will use these negative reactions in constructive and therapeutic ways. I do not agree with those who hold that therapists should have "unconditional positive regard" for their patients. Those who claim that they do are either lying or just not in touch with the inevitable frustrations and irritations we experience in our relationships with all human beings—patients included. Patients who are told that the therapist "accepts" them (a condescending remark if there ever was one) regardless of what they do or say, will distrust the therapist (and justifiably so). They will recognize the duplicity inherent in such an attitude and this must be antitherapeutic. I will elaborate on the concept of "unconditional positive regard" in the next section. Accordingly, the optimum experience youngsters can have with regard to their therapist's affection is that they view the therapist as someone who likes them most of the time and that when they do things that alienate the therapist, the latter will use his or her negative reactions benevolently in the service of helping them.

Intimately associated with the affection the therapist has for the child is the feeling of pleasure that the therapist may experience with the child. The child's appreciation, at some level, that he or she is capable of providing another individual with pleasure on a continual (but not necessarily uninterrupted) basis is gratifying and ego-enhancing. And this is yet another element in the therapist-patient relationship that can be therapeutic.

There are some therapists who actually believe that they can provide children with significant compensatory affection for that which they have not received from parents and other caretaking individuals. I believe that this is unrealistic. The amount of time the therapist spends with the youngster is an extremely small fraction of that which even the more deficient parents spend with the patient. Most therapists generally see their patients once or twice a week. But even classical psychoanalysts, who see their child patients four or five times a week, are still involving themselves with the youngster a smaller fraction of the time than the parents are. Only if the therapist is willing to go to court and litigate for transfer of the child to him or herself, adopt the child both legally and psychologically, provide the child with food, clothing, and shelter, and then over years provide significant love and affection, perhaps then will the bond between the patient and the therapist be stronger than that which the child had with the parents—even the more deficient ones. Also, the therapist has not generally seen the child during the earliest years of life when the deepest bonds have been formed. And, as discussed in Chapters One and Two, if there has been significant deprivation of parental affection, the therapist, no matter how loving and giving, is not likely to be able to compensate the child anyway. The child has gone beyond what I consider to be the critical period for the development of the capacity to gain from the affection of others.

It is also important for the therapist to appreciate that children do not generally develop the kinds of deep bonds with their therapists that many adult patients form. Let us take the example of children's relationships with their teachers. Although children may spend five to seven hours a day, five days a week for approximately 180 days (the duration of the school year) with their teachers, and although they may miss their teachers somewhat at the end of the school year, they generally are not devastated by the disruption of the relationship. It is a rare child who goes into mourning or depression over the fact that he or she will no longer have a particular teacher. If this is the nature of the bond a child can form with a teacher—a person with whom the youngster spends much more time than with the therapist and a person with whom the child may have much more benevolent experiences than enjoyed with the therapist – then it is unlikely that the youngster is going to mourn or grieve after the disruption of the therapist-patient relationship. Most of the children and adolescents I see do not have any strong, painful reactions after the termination of the treatment – whether the termination be appropriate or premature. This is another statement of the weakness of the depth of the bond between therapist and patient and another reason why I believe that the therapist's capacity to provide significant compensation for parental deprivations is limited. This does not mean, however, that no therapeutic work can be done. It only means that the relationship I am discussing here, the relationship that is the foundation for the youngster's treatment, at best is weaker than that which the patient has with the parents. But this does not preclude effective therapy taking place within its context.

"Unconditional Positive Regard"

Related to the issue of the therapist's affection for the patient is the concept of "unconditional positive regard." The term was introduced by Carl Rogers who considered this attitude by the therapist toward the patient to be central to his therapeutic approach, which he referred to as *nondirective therapy* or *client-centered therapy*. I have always considered the term *client centered therapy* to be somewhat condescending in that it implies that other therapists are less concerned with their patients than Carl Rogers. It reminds me of those individuals who have bumper stickers which state "I brake for animals." Again, the implication here is that the driver of a car bearing this sign is somewhat superior to others who couldn't care less if they ran over an animal. Probably the most well known therapist to apply Rogerian techniques to children was V. Axline (1947, 1964). The basic assumption of Rogerian theory is that there resides within all of us fundamental knowledge about what is best for us, but that social inhibitions suppress and repress the expression of these healthy forces. The primary goal of treatment is to help people bring about a state of "self-actualization" via which the blocked impulses are given free expression. The optimum atmosphere in which to realize this goal is one in which the therapist is basically nondirective and provides the patient with "unconditional positive regard." Technnically, this is best accomplished by the therapist's serving a catalytic role in which the last fragments of the patient's statement are repeated back to him or her. If one looks at psychology textbooks of the 1950s and 1960s, and turns to the chapter on psychotherapy, Rogerian treatment is often presented as psychotherapy per se—often with few alternative psychotherapeutic methods described. At the time, psychoanalysis was viewed as the supreme form of treatment by psychiatrists and Rogerian therapy as the optimum form of treatment by psychologists. One element in this development probably related to the fact that the classical psychoanalytic institutes were not permitting psychologists admission—a situation that still exists, to some extent, to this day. However, this too is changing as fewer physicians are demonstrating interest in psychoanalytic training. This new receptivity to psychologists' entering psychiatric psychoanalytic training programs has not been brought about by true insight into the contributions psychology can provide; rather, it stems from the desire for self-preservation. Without such input from the realm of psychology, most analytic institutes would be defunct from lack of new recruits and acolytes.

Although Rogerian therapists claimed that the treatment was quite complex and not a simple one in which the therapist, in parrot-like fashion, repeated the last fragments of the patient's statement, in practice that is what generally went on. I recall an anecdote that was making the rounds during my residency about the man who goes to a Rogerian analyst. The following interchange takes place:

> *Patient*: Boy, I'm feeling depressed today.
> *Therapist*: So, you're feeling depressed today.
> *Patient*: I'm feeling so depressed, I feel like killing myself.
> *Therapist*: So you're feeling so depressed, you feel like killing yourself.
> *Patient*: I'm feeling so depressed, I could jump right out of that window, even though we're on the 23rd floor.
> *Therapist*: You're feeling so depressed, you could jump right out of that window, even though we're on the 23rd floor.

Patient: Yes, that's how I feel. (At this point, the patient gets up, walks to the window, opens it up, and stands on the window sill.)

Therapist (Now looking at the patient, who is standing on the ledge of the open window): So that's how you feel.

Patient (Now leaps off the ledge and a few seconds later the sound of his body—splat—is heard as it splatters on the sidewalk.)

Therapist (Now walks to the window and peers out, looking down at the sidewalk): Splat!

The reader may view this anecdote to be a mockery of Rogerian treatment, consider it a *reductio ad absurdum,* and argue that only the most simple-minded therapists would respond in this manner. I am in agreement that most Rogerian therapists would not go so far as to let the patient jump out of the window. However, I do believe that the overwhelming majority of Rogerian therapists were not doing much more than "splat therapy."

Not only am I in disagreement with the technical maneuver of catalyzing the patient's comments by repeating the last fragment, but I have other disagreements with the Rogerian approach as well. First I do not have the conviction for the existence of an inborn pool of knowledge and feelings which is basically healthy, and that it is the suppression of these thoughts and feelings that brings about psychopathology. And I do not believe that simple release of these pent-up feelings—whether by nondirective therapy or any other approach—is the primary therapeutic ingredient (although it can help a little). In fact, when people who have completed such treatment are "self-actualized" they appear to be quite similar to others who had self-actualized themselves at the same time. In the 1960s this often took the form of going to Vermont, joining a commune, and engaging oneself in eating natural foods and weaving baskets.

Furthermore, I am not in agreement with the notion that a therapist should provide a patient with "unconditional positive regard." I consider this to be a disservice in that it ill equips the patient to function in a world where this is rarely if ever provided. In fact, one's mother does not even give one unconditional positive regard. For the therapist to do so must involve some fabrication and/or suppression of the therapist's thoughts and feelings in that there must be times when the patient's behavior is irritating and alienating. Allowing the patient to believe that his or her farts smell like perfume is not providing the patient with a healthy life experience. The rest of the people in the world generally remove themselves from us when we alienate them and do not give us the reasons why. I believe that the therapist—rather than being nondi-rective and providing unconditional positive regard—should be more directive and should provide "negative regard," when such is warranted. One must differentiate between criticism given benevo-lently and criticism given malevolently. Patients need benevolent criticism and direction to help them in life. If they cannot obtain these from their therapists, then who else is going to provide them in as objective and benevolent a way.

Treatment of the Projected Self

This phenomenon has broad implications for many aspects of treatment, for both the patient and the therapist, and has not been given the attention it deserves. For example, adults in individual therapy who tend to view most of the people they encounter as harboring or exhibiting certain alienating qualities are usually deny-ing these same characteristics in themselves by projecting them on to others. Similarly, those who do group therapy frequently observe patient A suggest an interpretation of patient B's behavior that is totally irrelevant to B, but a clear statement of A's difficulties. This defense is well known to therapists and we most often have little difficulty detecting it. When we ourselves utilize the mechanism, we are less likely to be aware of it. I believe that all of us use it to varying degrees. When properly utilized, it can enhance the efficacy of our work; improperly used, it can seriously interfere with it.

Practically every therapist has been asked, at some time or other, "How can you listen to that shit all day long?" If the question is benevolently asked (and it often isn't) and if the therapist is inclined to respond seriously (and he or she is not often so inclined), one of the completely honest answers is: "In treating my patients, I treat vicariously my projected self, and this is an important deter-minant of my interest." Although many factors certainly contribute to one's choice of psychotherapy as a profession, one that is central for most, if not all, is the desire to cure one's own psychopathology. Rarely is personal analysis, or other forms of therapy which the therapist may have engaged in, enough to accomplish this goal. We are still at too primitive a level in our knowledge to use the word *cure*; at best, we usually strive toward significant *alleviation* of our own and our patient's difficulties. And whether previously treated or not, the therapist, I believe, continually attempts to alleviate his or her own psychological problems through psychotherapeutic endeavors in which the vicarious treatment of the projected self is operative. The pathological processes within us are disowned and projected onto the patient. It is as if each time we ameliorate the patient's problems, we are vicariously alleviating our own. Without this factor operative, I do not think the therapist would maintain for long interest in the psychological minutiae that patients in treatment can often endlessly discuss. In fact, if one could indeed *cure* a prospective therapist of all psychopathological problems (whatever that really means), then I question whether he or she would continue on as a therapist—so vital do I believe this mechanism to be as a motivating factor for those who do psychotherapy. There are certainly other motivating factors operative—and many of these are far less self serving—but it is a vital one that is not given the attention it deserves. The child therapist is, in all likelihood, treating vicariously his or her own childhood problems that have yet to be resolved.

If therapists are using patients to treat themselves vicariously, may this not be detrimental to the patient? Doesn't this interfere with the patient's therapy? Couldn't this be considered exploitive? Doesn't this tendency result in the therapist's seeing things in the patient that do not exist? The questions are rhetorical. They describe real dangers in the therapeutic situation—dangers that we have not studied enough to enable us to avoid them effectively. Yet, if what I have said is true—that a certain amount of this factor is necessary if the therapist is to be meaningfully interested in the patient—what is the solution to this problem? It lies, I believe, in determining that level at which the salutary use of the therapist's treatment of the projected self ends and the pathological begins. How can we learn then to make this important distinction between the helpful and detrimental use of this mechanism? It is not within the scope of this book to discuss in detail possible methods that we might utilize to make this important distinction. Elsewhere (1973c) I have proposed some techniques by which we might be able to differentiate between healthy and pathological treatment of the projected self.

Taking the Patient's Side in His
Or Her Conflict with the Parents

Some therapists believe that taking the patient's side against parents or other authority figures is a good way of engaging the youngster in treatment and entrenching the therapeutic relationship. One of the earliest and most well-known proponents of this approach was August Aichhorn, a Viennese schoolmaster who tried to apply Freudian psychoanalytic techniques to the treatment of delinquent boys. In his classic *Wayward Youth* (1925) he described the difficulties that arose in such boys' treatment because they were very defiant of authority and tended to see him as another authority against whom to rebel. He found, however, that if he looked at the world from their vantage point and identified with them in their antisocial attitudes, he could gain their admiration and thereby form a relationship with them. In words, but not in acts, he expressed sympathy for their antisocial behavior. He would become a psychological ally in order to win their confidence. Once such a relationship was established, he would gradually shift his position and attempt to bring about a stronger superego in the youngsters. An intrapsychic conflict would thereby develop, in short, a psychoneurotic process. His hope was that their desire to maintain their relationship with him would then motivate the youngsters to follow along with him as he encouraged them to remain in the treatment and tolerate its pains and frustrations. His hope also was that he would then become a model for prosocial behavior.

There is an obvious duplicity involved in such an approach, and I myself would not be comfortable utilizing it. I think that most youngsters would sense the therapist's artificiality when supporting antisocial behavior and would thereby lose respect for him or her — and this could not but be antitherapeutic. Most therapists today would not utilize this approach.

There are therapists, however, who consider themselves to be the protectors of their child and adolescent patients against the indignities they suffer at the hands of their parents. Such a position has a divisive effect on the family. It puts the patient between the therapist and the parents in a tug-of-war and is thereby antitherapeutic.

I believe that the ideal therapeutic situation is one in which children come to view their therapists as impartial, as criticizing them benevolently when such criticism is warranted and equally ready to criticize the parents when the therapist considers them to be in error. In the context of such impartiality, the therapist can still serve to protect youngsters from irrational and inapropriate attitudes and reactions they may be exposed to. In such situations youngsters may feel quite helpless; having someone whom the parents respect and who can bring about a reduction and even elimination of parental detrimental exposures can be most salutary for the patient. It reduces tension and anxiety, takes a heavy burden off the child, and removes environmental influences that may be significantly contributory to the patient's symptoms. Similarly, such an impartiality makes it more likely that the therapist will be in a position to protect the parents from the youngster's irrationality and indignities they suffer as a result of it.

Ideally, the therapist's position should be one of providing information and advice to both parents and children. It is hoped that the parents will be receptive to the therapist's recommendations. If not, therapists should listen with receptivity to the parents' disagreements. If modification is justified, the therapist should be comfortable doing so. If the therapist remains unconvinced that his or her suggestions should be altered, the following statement should be made: "Well, this is what I think would be in the best interests of your child. Perhaps one of us may change his or her opinion in the future."

Children should not view the therapist as someone who controls the parents, but rather as one who provides advice and information and leaves it up to the parents to decide whether or not they wish to accept the therapist's opinions and implement his or her recommendations. If the therapist is seen as the manipulator of the parents and if the patient sees the parents as being unduly dependent on the therapist, as people who hang on the therapist's every word and put them into action, the parent-child relationship is likely to be compromised. In addition, such a situation may produce in the child some discomfort with the therapist because he or she is jeopardizing the respect that the patient has for the parents.

Ideally, both parents and patient should come to view the therapist as truly impartial, as attempting to be as objective as possible, and as not favoring anyone. They should come to view the therapist as someone who sides with healthy behavior—regardless of who exhibits it—and benevolently criticizes unhealthy behavior—regardless of who manifests it. Generally, the criticisms tend to balance out and no one tends to feel that the therapist is prejudiced against him or her. In such an atmosphere, both the patient and parents will generally come to respect the therapist. In contrast, when therapists routinely attempt to favor the youngster, they will alienate the parents and lose the respect of the child, who senses the duplicity—a situation that is definitely antitherapeutic.

The Resolution of the Transference Neurosis

Of the innumerable patterns of human interaction each person tends to select a few favorites. From earliest childhood (primarily as the result of our interaction with our parents) we develop a constellation of patterns of relating to others that are unique. As we grow older these patterns become strengthened and we tend to utilize them in preference to others that may be either absent from our repertoire or have lower priority for utilization. Some of these patterns of interaction are healthy and enhance our effectiveness in life. Others are maladaptive and often cause us significant difficulty, both personally and in our interaction with others. These patterns are strongly repetitive—almost reflexly so. Accordingly, in new situations we tend to use the old patterns, even though we may suffer significantly because of our injudicious reactions.

Using psychoanalytic terminology, we tend to *transfer* onto others reactions that we had toward our parents in infancy and childhood. We tend to interact with others in a manner similar to the way we interacted with our parents. When these modes of interaction are neurotic—and they exhibit themselves in the therapeutic relationship—they are termed *transference neuroses*. Specifically, patients try to involve the therapist in the same pathological patterns with which they were involved with their parents and with which they try to involve others as well. Those who comply with these requests (because of their own pathological needs) maintain their relationships with the patient (they may call such individuals their "friends"); those who do not comply with the psychopathological overtures for involvement, avoid or sever ties (and may be regarded as "unfriendly"). When the therapist refuses to involve him or herself in the pathological pattern, the patient will generally react with resentment, anxiety, or other divisive thoughts and emotions. At such a point the patient may leave therapy and consider the therapist uncaring, unloving, uninterested, hostile, etc. Or, the patient may choose to try to gain insight into what is going on and attempt to change the maladaptive pattern. Such working through is referred to as the *resolution of the transference neurosis* and is an important step in the alleviation of the patient's difficulties. It is to be hoped that once the pathological pattern of interaction is alleviated in the context of the patient's relationship with the therapist, he or she will more readily develop healthier modes of interaction in relationships with others as well.

Although child analysts differ regarding whether a child can exhibit what can justifiably be termed a transference neurosis (M. Klein, 1932; A. Freud, 1965), I believe that most children will do so if they get involved with the therapist. In other words, the deeper the child's relationship with the therapist the greater the likelihood the child will exhibit the pathological patterns of interaction and the greater the chance the child will try to involve the therapist in them. For example, a 13-year-old girl, who uses coyness and seductivity to get her way with adults, may try to involve the therapist similarly. In response to the therapist's failure to react with the expected "affection," she may become angry, consider him or her to be mean and unfriendly, and refuse to return. However, if such a youngster can be engaged (and it is the purpose of this book to help the therapist accomplish this), she may be helped to appreciate and experience that there are more effective and predictably gratifying ways of relating to others. If a good relationship is not established, the patient will be less willing to tolerate the frustrations attendant to the therapist's refusal to comply with pathological requests. And the youngster will thereby be less likely to gain this important therapeutic benefit that can be derived from the relationship.

Last, I wish to emphasize the point that the aforementioned changes relating to the resolution of the transference neurosis are less accomplished from insights and more from experiences within the therapeutic relationship. The insights the patient gains into the fact that the transferential patterns are often replays of early childhood involvements is less important than the *experience* the patient has with the therapist. *Learning* that the neurotic overtures will not be successful with the therapist is less important than having the *experience* that the neurotic goal will not be accomplished. When these therapeutic involvements are expanded into the world outside of the consultation room, a similar process occurs.

The Transference Cure

When patients, very early in treatment, exhibit a sudden and dramatic alleviation (and even cure) of presenting symptoms, they are described by psychoanalysts as having exhibited a *transference cure*. Specifically, because the patient hasn't delved into the unconscious roots of the pathology and worked out the basic problems that underlie it (something that generally takes a long time to do), the therapeutic change is usually considered specious. When this occurs extremely early in therapy (such as after the first or second session), it is understood to reflect the patient's resistance to entering into treatment:

> *Patient* (at the beginning of the second session): You are, without doubt, the most brilliant doctor I've ever met. Since I saw you last time, I'm one hundred percent better. I'm feeling so good that I'm wondering whether I need any more treatment.
>
> *Therapist*: But all I did last time was ask you some questions about your problems and get some background history.
>
> *Patient*: Oh, it was much more than that, doctor. There was something about the way you asked me those questions— I don't know what it was—that made me feel so much better. In fact, I don't know what I'm going to talk about today. I don't even know why I came. I'm feeling so good.

When the "cure" occurs a little later in treatment, it often relates to an attempt by patients to get the therapist to like or even love them. After all, if the primary goal of the therapist is to cure the patient, then it is reasonable to assume that the therapist will love someone who helps him or her achieve quickly this goal. Of course, both of the aforementioned factors may be operating simultaneously, and others as well. Rarely is there a simple explanation for anything that occurs in psychoanalytic treatment—or any other kind of psychotherapy as well.

These specious kinds of cures are well known to most psychotherapists. Because they are generally manifestations of a pathological pattern, the term *transference cure* is generally spoken of with a certain amount of derision. This, I believe, is unfortunate because there is a useful, and often unappreciated, element in the transference cure. All patients, I believe, change partly in the attempt to ingratiate themselves to the therapist. From the very first encounter the patient has with the therapist he or she wants to be liked. (This doesn't differ in any way from all other first encounters with nontherapists.) The anxiety the patient experiences in the first session is, in part, a manifestation of the fear that he or she will be considered loathsome and unworthy by the therapist because of the things that will be revealed. As the relationship intensifies, there is usually an even greater need to be liked by the therapist. The patient has invested much time and (often) money in the project and the reliance on the therapist to help the patient alleviate his or her difficulties is great.

I believe that *one* element that plays a role in patients' exhibiting therapeutic change is the desire to get the therapist to like them. Others are certainly operative. But this factor is, I believe, an important one in the early phases of alleviation of a symptom. Patients know that when they tell their therapists that improvement has occurred, the therapists cannot but feel good about themselves for their contribution to the success. (Some therapists, in accordance with their theoretical position, deny having any such gratification. I don't believe them.) If the patient has it within his or her power to make the therapist feel good, then it follows that the therapist will like the patient who provides such gratification. After all, we generally like most those who have the good sense to provide us with the pleasures we seek. It is to be hoped that the new mode of adaptation will subsequently become more deeply entrenched as the patient gains greater insight into the causes of the symptoms and has the experience that the newer way is the more judicious and gratifying. Then, the patient is likely to maintain the healthier adaptation because, through knowledge and/or experience, he or she will have developed the inner conviction that it is the preferable alternative. Ideally, the patient will then no longer need to maintain the improvement for the purpose of pleasing the therapist (whom he or she will probably never see again anyway after the treatment is over—psychological ties, fond memories, gratitude, and other positive feelings notwithstanding).

The younger the patient the greater the likelihood he or she will change behavior in order to please the therapist. Children are constantly concerning themselves with the approbations of parents, teachers, and other authorities. They are constantly being told about whether what they do and say is "good" or "bad," "right" or "wrong." And the therapist is just another authority from whom they usually wish to gain acceptance. It behooves the child therapist to make use of this phenomenon. It can enhance significantly the efficacy of the treatment. Accordingly, the therapist does well to praise the patient for newly gained healthier modes of behavior. Such praises, however, must be genuine; if they are artificial and/or contrived, the patient will sense this and they are not likely to "work." It is hoped that the earlier experience with the somewhat artificial venture into healthy behavior will help the youngster reach the point where he or she engages in the healthier adaptations— both from the inner conviction and the *experience* that life is much more gratifying when he or she does so. Although adolescents are less desirous of pleasing the therapist than younger children, they are still not immune to the process. Accordingly, the therapist can still rely on the benefits ultimately to be derived from the transference cure phenomenon.

The Corrective
Emotional Experience

In the process of working through or resolving the transference neurosis a particularly effective therapeutic phenomenon that may occur is the *corrective emotional experience* (F. Alexander and T. French, 1946; F. Alexander, 1950). Essentially, the patient has a living experience (often associated with a significant upheaval of emotional reaction) that alters significantly a previous pattern. For example, a 14-year-old girl whose father has been very punitive may generalize and expect similar treatment from all men, including her male therapist. The therapist's telling such a youngster that he will treat her differently will not generally be very effective because intellectual processes only are involved in the communication. However, if the girl has the living experience— over an extended period—that the therapist indeed does not react punitively, then her view of men may indeed change. Her fearful reactions lessen and relaxation and trust gradually replace them. It is this combination of insight, feeling, and experience that brings about some of the most meaningful changes that can occur in psychotherapy.

When a boy cheats during a game I may say: "You know, it's no fun for me to play this game when you cheat. If you do that again I'm going to stop playing and we'll do something else." To simply discuss why the patient cheats may have some value. However, if this discussion takes place in a setting in which the patient experiences some frustration over the alienation his symptom causes, the conversation is more likely to be therapeutically meaningful. In such a discussion we might talk about whether this may be one of the reasons why others don't like to play with him, or about the futility of this way of trying to compensate for feelings of inadequacy, or about other aspects of the problem which may be of psychological significance. But, without the emotional reactions attendant to the threat of alienating the therapist and/or interrupting an enjoyable experience, such discussions are not likely to be very effective.

The Patient's Identification
With the Therapist

Just as children imitate their parents and acquire many of their traits (both adaptive and maladaptive), they will tend to identify with the therapist if the relationship is a good one. It is to be hoped that the personality qualities that the patients acquire in this way will serve them in good stead. There are, as stated earlier, those who believe that what I am saying is risky business—that such a process is dangerous and antitherapeutic. They hold that therapists must do everything possible to present themselves as a blank screen upon which the patient's fantasies can be projected. Some believe that the therapist should encourage the patient's realizing his or her "true self." Central to such a theory is that there exists such an entity — that each individual has within him- or herself a personality pattern that is blocked from free expression by environmentally induced inhibitions and that such blockage is central to psychopathological behavior. They hold that an important aspect of treatment involves helping the individual express freely these hidden personality characteristics.

Although I certainly agree that many people in treatment are repressed and need to be helped to express themselves (although there are many who need some repression more than anything else), I believe most people usually need to express some *specific* pent-up thoughts or feelings. I am somewhat dubious about the concept of a whole personality being hidden inside, knocking for release. Rather, I believe that some aspects of our personality may be genetically determined (such as activity level, assertiveness, passivity, and curiosity); most, however, are environmentally induced (and even the genetic ones are subject to significant environmental modification). I see core *potentials*, not core personalities. Most of our character traits, I believe, are derived from the environment — more specifically from what we learn from those in the world around us and what we acquire by imitation of significant individuals in our lives. The therapist becomes another in the series of individuals whom the child may imitate, emulate, and identify with. Even the kind of therapist described above, who tries to provide the patient with a neutral atmosphere to facilitate "self-actualization," sends many subtle cues that encourage the patient to proceed in specific directions. In addition, the therapist still has a personality, and no matter how much he or she may try to suppress and hide it, much is still revealed — much that the patient may identify with.

As mentioned, it is obviously preferable that the qualities of the therapist that patients identify with will serve them well. For example, a 15-year-old boy's father may have operated in accordance with the principle that admitting any deficiencies to his children will lessen their respect for him. The boy, then, may take on this similar maladaptive pattern and find himself having trouble with his classwork because he cannot tolerate admitting errors. If his therapist, however, is the kind of person who can, without discomfort, admit errors when they naturally arise, the patient may come to appreciate that this is a desirable and effective pattern and may take on the quality him or herself. However, the therapist's admission of errors must be genuine. To do so in a contrived situation is not only therapeutically worthless but may be antitherapeutic because it is basically dishonest. Another example. A 14-year-old girl may have acquired the pattern of lying (in both subtle and overt ways) as a significant part of her interactional repertoire. In the course of treatment, she observes the therapist to be a person who is consistently honest. As a result, she recognizes that the therapist's life becomes less complicated and that such honesty enhances the esteem the therapist enjoys from others. As a result of the process of identification and emulation, she may acquire this valuable asset herself.

Therapists traditionally encourage their patients to express their pent-up thoughts and feelings from the appreciation that such expression, properly directed and utilized (not often the case), can be therapeutic. However, many therapists attempt to do this in a setting where they exhibit little if any such expression themselves (Gardner, 1968b, 1973a). They thereby serve as poor models for their patients and so impede the process they are attempting to achieve. Therapists who express themselves in situations where such expression is appropriate, and in the best interests of the patient (as mentioned, without artificiality), have a much better chance of getting their patients to do so as the latter identify with them. Therapists who assert themselves and do not allow themselves to be taken advantage of serve as good models for patients who are inhibited in these areas. And it is only in the context of a good patient-therapist relationship that such salutary identifications can occur. As mentioned in Chapter Five, such identification with the therapist's values can be risky. It is to be hoped that such values will be healthy; otherwise the therapy will do the patient more harm than good (a not uncommon occurrence, unfortunately).

The Therapist as Educator

We learn best from those whom we respect and admire. Disliked, hated, or disrespected teachers will teach their students little of educational value (although they may teach them something about having to tolerate a despised person in certain situations). Therapists who are basically respected can teach patients much that can be of therapeutic value. One does well to compare the relationship between a therapist and a patient with that which exists between a teacher and a pupil. Teachers who are enthusiastic about their work and genuinely enjoy teaching will communicate to their students the message that learning can be fun. The student will thereby emulate the teacher and attempt to gain the same gratifications. In such a setting, the youngster will be willing to endure the frustrations and drudgery that are necessary if one is to truly learn. The identification with the teaching person is a central element in the healthy educational process. A teacher who basically dislikes the work is not likely to serve as such a model and is not likely to teach her students very much. Even worse, a teacher who instills anger and fear in children not only is going to teach them little, but may very well contribute to the development of psychopathology.

I believe that therapy is, more than anything else, an educational process. Although we certainly try to help our patients learn as much as they can on their own, we are also providing a significant amount of information in the course of the therapeutic process. Good teachers try to get their students to derive as much information as they can on their own. It is only after their students have reached the limits of their capacity to acquire information and expand from the foundations they have built that the teacher supplements that which has been self-acquired. We don't want to spoon feed our patients and entrench their dependency; we want to help them become self-sufficient human beings, who learn how to learn, but who still can supplement the knowledge they have acquired with input from others with more knowledge and experience in a particular area.

A. Freud (1965) strictly warned therapists against submitting to the temptation to provide child patients with information and educational communications. Such advice is like warning an internist not to submit to the temptation to provide patients with penicillin. I am in full agreement with H. Strupp (1975), who considers the central element in adult psychoanalytic therapy (and other forms of psychotherapy as well) to be what he calls "lessons in constructive living." The more competent one is in dealing with the problems in life, the less likely one will be to form symptoms in an attempt to resolve the inevitable conflicts and problems with which we are all confronted. Whether therapists provide such communications directly, symbolically, or through insights into the unconscious they help their patients gain, the educational element regarding more effective living is ever there. When therapists are admired and respected, their patients will be receptive to what they have to say and treatment is more likely to succeed. When the therapist is bored, just putting in time to get payment, or otherwise going through the motions, little is likely to happen.

The Correction of Distortions   As part of the educational process the therapist helps the patient correct distortions. For example, all of us carry into adult life distorted concepts of the world that we blindly accept. Adherence to these dicta may cause us many difficulties, yet they may never be questioned. It is one of the purposes of treatment to help patients examine (sometimes for the first time in their lives) these premises that guide their behavior. Some of the more common ones that adult (and often adolescent) therapists must deal with are: "No one is to be trusted," "Sex is bad," "Fun is sinful," "I must do everything to avoid criticism because all negative comments about me must be correct," "I must do everything possible to avoid anyone's getting angry at me," and "If there's a choice between another person's being inconvenienced and my being so, rather it be me." Some common dicta of childhood (which may continue into adolescence and even throughout life) are: "Mother and father are always right," "Nice boys and girls never have hateful thoughts toward their parents," "Thoughts can harm, i.e., wishing that something bad will happen to someone can make it happen," "If my mother and/or father doesn't love me very much, I can't be very good and no one can ever love me," "One fault makes you totally worthless," "There are perfect people who never make mistakes and never do anything wrong or bad," and "An unacceptable thought is as bad as an unacceptable act."

I believe that emotions related to fight and flight follow cognition and that many feelings of guilt, fear, anger, etc. can be alleviated if notions such as the aforementioned are corrected. A. Ellis (1963) holds that the correction of such cognitive distortions are the basic issues to be focused upon in psychotherapy and has coined the term *Rational-Emotive Psychotherapy* for this type of therapeutic approach. I am in agreement with Ellis that emphasis on this element is important in practically everyone's treatment, regardless of age. However, I believe that things are more complex and that many other factors contribute to symptom formation. (Although Ellis admits to other factors, he considers them far less important than cognitive distortions.)

Decreasing or Increasing Guilt From the earliest days of psychoanalysis S. Freud and J. Breuer (1895) considered reducing the patient's guilt to be one of the analyst's most important tasks. With less guilt, there is less repression and hence symptoms are less likely to develop and persist. Although Freud's subsequent experience convinced him that things were far more complex (some have yet to read his later work), the concept is certainly still valid if one considers it to be *one* of the possible contributing factors in *some* patients' difficulties. Partly by virtue of the therapist's position of authority and his or her experience in matters of things such as guilt, patients become convinced that their unacceptable urges are very common, if not universal, and that the difference between themselves and others is not so much that they have the particular thoughts and feelings, but that they feel more guilty over them. In essence the analyst communicates to the patient: "You're still acceptable to me, even though you have those ideas." (Condescending elements in the communication notwithstanding, the message is often helpful.)

In my work with youngsters who need some loosening up of their superegos, I will make such comments as: "Most people I know would get very angry when something like that happens. I guess you must have been pretty mad also," "I can't believe that somewhere, someplace, you weren't a little bit angry when that happened," or "So what's so terrible about *wanting* to do that? You know wanting is not the same as doing."

Many adolescents I see, however, do not need any loosening up of their consciences. They have what A.M. Johnson (1949, 1959) calls "super-ego lacunae," i.e., like Swiss cheese they seem to have holes in the part of the brain where the superego is (I speak figuratively, of course). If their treatment is to be useful, attempts should be made to increase such youngsters' guilt. Some comments that I may make in the service of this goal: "That's terrible. She really must have felt bad after you ripped up her new kite," and "I really don't think you could have felt very good about yourself getting 100 percent on that test after copying most of the answers from the kids around you."

To the 14-year-old bully I might say: "I know you think you're quite a big shot when you beat up those little kids. But deep down inside, you know that there's nothing so great about it and that must make you feel kind of bad about yourself. You think the kids think you're hot stuff when you go around beating up lots of kids. Some of them may; but others, I am sure, don't like you at all. They feel sorry for the children you're hitting and I'm sure you've noticed how they stay away from you." Although these comments can be very bitter medicine to swallow, they are accepted if the patient has a good relationship with the therapist. In addition, as mentioned, the therapist's attitude is more important than the content in determining whether his or her comments will alienate a patient. When benevolently communicated in the context of a firm relationship the most painful confrontations are likely to be accepted.

Acquiring a More Accurate View of One's Parents   All patients, regardless of age, have to be helped in treatment to gain a clearer view of their parents. As children, we tend to operate on the principle: "If it's good enough for them, it's good enough for me." We tend to incorporate most if not all of their traits—healthy and unhealthy. We swallow the whole bag, without separating the good from the bad. Therapy, in part, involves making (often very belatedly) these vital discriminations. The child and adolescent therapist has the opportunity to provide these corrections at a time when it can do the most good, at a time before the deleterious results of such indiscriminating incorporation and acceptance have had a chance to become deeply entrenched. Children and adolescents have to be helped to appreciate that their parents, like all other human beings (including the therapist), are not perfect. We all have our deficits. Helping youngsters become clear regarding which personality traits of their parents are assets and which are liabilities can be very useful. And the therapist is in a unique position to provide such information. This, of course, may require some advance work with the parents; but if the relationship with them is a good one their cooperation can often be relied upon.

The phobic child of a phobic mother can be told: "You know that your mother has many fears that she herself realizes are not real. She knows that there's nothing to be afraid of in elevators or crowded places, but she just can't help herself. She'd prefer not to have these fears and that's why she's seeing a psychiatrist." Ideally, it can be helpful to get the mother herself to verbalize to the child comments such as these. (The reader interested in a detailed account of such parental divulgences in the therapy of a phobic child may wish to refer to Chapter Sixteen of my *Therapeutic Communication with Children*, 1971). The child of divorce can be told: "Your father can be counted upon to give your mother the money she needs to take care of herself and the children. However, as you know, he's not very reliable when it comes to showing up for appointments on visiting days. This doesn't mean that he doesn't love you at all. It does mean that he has less love for you than a father who does show up all the time. This doesn't mean that you are unlovable or that no one else can love you more. You still have many people who like being with you and you can spend time with them when your father doesn't show up." Elsewhere (1976, 1977, 1979a), I have discussed in detail the wide variety of cognitive distortions that the therapist can help correct for children of divorce.

Acquiring a More Accurate View of Oneself   I introduce my next point anecdotally. A number of years ago *Listerine* mouthwash was advertised with the slogan "Your best friend won't tell you." In the typical pitch a young girl cannot understand why dates persistently reject her even though she is bright, pretty, etc. Finally, she realizes that *bad breath* is driving them away! Happily, she chances on *Listerine* , washes her mouth with it, and the boys come flocking. I believe that therapists should be better than one's best friend. They should be able to tell their patients things that even their best friends will hesitate to reveal. And if the therapist's motivation is benevolent and his or her timing judicious, he or she should be able to do so with only occasional dificulty or hesitation.

To put it another way. Robert Burns (1786) once wrote:

'O wad some Pow'r the giftie (small gift) gie (give) us
To see oursels as others see us!
It would from many a burden free us
And foolish notion.

It is the therapist's job to help patients see themselves as others see them. And this is one of the significant benefits that all patients, regardless of age, can derive from treatment. Such increases in self-awareness can indeed free individuals from unnecessary burdens and protect them from the detrimental effects of harboring foolish notions about themselves. Patients should be able to gain, as well, what H.S. Sullivan (1953) called "consensual validation" of their views of the world. For example, a youngster can be told: "You think that the kids really like you when they play with you after you give them money. If you think about it, I think you'll agree that they don't spend time with you *unless* you give them money. I suspect you're doing things that turn them off." And if the patient agrees, the therapist might say, "I wonder what those things might be?"

The boy who feels unpopular may attempt to gain respect and admiration by boasting about various exploits, travels, etc. However, the fear of exposure and possible guilt he may feel ultimately result in his feeling even worse about himself than before. And if (as is often the case) others learn of his duplicity, his social position is further worsened. As part of the therapy of such symptoms the therapist does well to inform the youngster of the injudiciousness of his mode of compensation. For the lonely 13 year-old boy who "clowns" in the classroom, I might say: "I know you think that clowning around in class gets the kids to like you. And I know you think that their laughing at you proves this. However, I believe that although you're good for laughs, they really don't like you in other ways. They still don't seem to invite you to parties nor do they seem to want to see you after school."

Another youngster can be told: "You always seem to want your way when you're here in the office. You always seem to want to do only those things you want. You never seem to care about what your mother or father or I would like to do or talk about. If you act this way with friends, maybe that's why they don't want to be with you." Another example: "You say you're sorry in the hope that a person will no longer be bothered or angry about what you've done. Although people may *say* that they accept your apology and that they're not angry, *deep down inside they really still are.* Even though you've told your father that you're sorry that you broke the television set, I think he's still angry that it's cost him all that money to fix it." I often suggest that youngsters who utilize this common manipulative device (invariably taught by parents) read my story "Say You're Sorry" in my book of psychologically oriented children's stories, *Dr. Gardner's Stories About the Real World* (1972b).

Part of the confrontational process involves helping children gain a more accurate picture of their assets and liabilities (both inborn and acquired). The child with a neurologically based coordination deficit should be discouraged from intensive involvement in competitive sports (although special training and exercises preparing for minmal to moderate involvement may be indicated). In the earliest years children's views of themselves are acquired from what H.S. Sullivan called "reflected appraisals" (P. Mullahy, 1970). In essence, children come to view themselves in accordance with information about them provided by significant figures in their lives, especially their parents. A four-year-old boy runs into the house crying, "Mommy, the kids all call me stupid." Mother replies, "You're not stupid. You're very smart. Although you're four you can write your name, count to 25, and you know nickels, dimes, and quarters. *He's* the one who's stupid, if he calls you stupid." Tears are kissed away and the child leaves the house reassured. The criteria for self-assessment here, however, are externally derived. He *is* what his mother (the final authority on him) says he is. As the boy grows older, he generally gathers information from others (teachers, neighbors, peers, etc) that may modify and expand the information derived from his parents. These facts become his own internal criteria for judging self-worth. It is to be hoped that the accumulated data (derived from parents and others) will be accurate and it is one of the therapist's jobs to help correct any distortions that may have arisen. And this is more easily done in adolescence than in adulthood.

Introducing Alternative Modes of Adaptation   Last, it is part of the therapeutic educational process to introduce to patients alternative modes of adaptation to those pathological and self-defeating ones that they may be utilizing. These options may never have occurred to the patient, nor may he or she ever have been introduced to them. For example, in a boy's family, denial of or flight from awareness of one's deficiencies may have been the only reactions. Such a boy must be helped to appreciate the value of dealing directly with one's deficits and he must be encouraged to try this alternative to see for himself its advantages. Throughout the course of this book I provide many examples of the therapist's introduction of alternative modes of adaptation.

Intimacy and Self-Revelation

When we use the term *intimacy*, we are generally referring to a close personal relationship. I consider a central element in the intimate relationship to be the revelation of personal thoughts and feelings which one would generally not reveal indiscriminately to others. The revelation, however, is made in a situation where one anticipates a benevolent and/or understanding response by the listener. Without the freedom for such self-revelation the term intimacy does not apply. Intimate divulgences tend to bring people closer. The one to whom the information is revealed generally feels flattered by the revelation, especially because he or she has been selected from many possible listeners. Also, intimacy cannot be a one-way arrangement. Both individuals must feel comfortable with such revelations. Unilateral divulgence is not properly called intimate. Accordingly, many, if not most, therapist-patient relationships are not, by the above definition, intimate. They are generally one-way arrangements in which the patient reveals all (the ideal to be achieved) and some therapists believe that it behooves them to reveal nothing (or as close to nothing as is humanly possible). Whatever benefits may be derived from such an arrangement (and I do not deny that there are some), it cannot reasonably be referred to as an intimate relationship.

This situation presents dilemmas for therapists. If they reveal more of themselves, in order to enhance the intimacy of the relationship, they are going to contaminate blank-screen associations. In addition, there is the risk that the patient's time will be used more for the benefit of the therapist than the patient— especially if the revelations focus on problems of the therapist's. This easily becomes exploitive of the patient. In contrast, therapists who strictly hide behind the couch in order to provide their patients with a blank screen, who strictly avoid any self-revelation, may achieve many benefits derived from their patients unadulterated free associations. However, these patients are robbed of the psychotherapeutic benefits to be derived from a close and intimate relationship. I believe there is some point between these two extremes where there is a proper balance of self-revelation by the therapist and self-revelation by the patient. The vast majority of the revelations should be made by the patient, but not every divulgence provided by the therapist need be viewed as unnecessary utilization of the patient's time or exploitation of the patient by the therapist. Such revelations by the therapist—judiciously provided—can be therapeutically beneficial. They bring the two individuals closer, entrench the relationship, and strengthen thereby the foundation upon which therapy rests.

It is difficult to state specifically when the revelations are judicious and when they are not. There are some guidelines however. As mentioned, a revelation made by the therapist—whose primary purpose is to use the patient for assistance in dealing with the therapist's own problems—is clearly contraindicated. Also, if a significant amount of the patient's time is used for such therapist revelations, then this too is exploitive of the patient. One of the best guidelines is that the revelation should have immediate and obvious benefit to the patient's treatment. A personal experience of the therapist's that may help the patient gain insight into his or her problems at that point would be in this category. As mentioned in Chapter Five, metaphorical, anecdotal, and experiential communications often provide a useful vehicle for communicating important therapeutic messages. And the experiences and anecdotal material provided by the therapist can be very much in this category.

Another guideline is that the divulgence of such material should not be contrived or artificial. Rather, it should flow from the natural course of the material provided in the session. Obviously, this guideline is not being followed if the therapist initiates such divulgences at the beginning of the session. My *The Talking, Feeling, and Doing Game* (1973b), to be discussed subsequently, provides therapists with many opportunities to divulge information about themselves in a noncontrived manner. Game cards provide the therapist with the opportunity to make such revelations and, in accordance with the rules of the game, if the therapist doesn't answer the question, he or she does not get a reward chip!

There is another aspect to the therapeutic benefits of the therapist's self-revelations that is particularly applicable to child and adolescent therapy. Children generally enjoy thoroughly hearing details about events that occurred in their parent's lives during their childhood. A child will commonly ask a parent, "Mommy, tell me about how things were with you when you were my age and living with grandma and grandpa." Such information is generally of great interest to children and the divulgence of it strengthens the parent-child bond. Similarly, therapists who judiciously provide such information about their own childhood and adolescence can also strengthen the therapist-patient relationship. What is lost by the resultant contamination of the blank screen is more than counterbalanced by the advantages related to the strengthening of the therapist-patient bond that such divulgences create. Furthermore, when providing such revelations the therapist is serving as a model for the youngster to reveal his or her own feelings and will thereby increase the likelihood that the patient will be freer to provide such revelations. Last, when such revelations involve the therapist's describing shortcomings and deficiencies of his or her own (in a noncontrived way), this too can be therapeutic. It helps reduce the idealization and idolization of the therapist that can be antitherapeutic. It makes the therapist more of a real human being who has both assets and liabilities—just like the rest of the world. Viewing the therapist as perfect will contribute to patients' lowering of feelings of self-worth as they invariably compare themselves unfavorably with their perfect, or nearly perfect, therapist. This too is antitherapeutic. Children and adolescents, especially, already feeling so impotent in their relationships with adults, are therefore likely to benefit significantly from such divulgences.

SEVEN

CONFIDENTIALITY

Adolescent psychopathology, like all forms of psychopathology, is best understood as a manifestation of intrapsychic and interpersonal factors. Although social, cultural, and genetic factors must certainly be considered, most of the therapeutic work focuses on the interpersonal and intrapsychic elements—because there is little if anything that can be directly done by the therapist in the consultation room about the other contributory factors. Outside the office, the therapist may be devoting himself significantly to changing these external factors, but this is not of immediate value to the patient's treatment. In order to address oneself to the interpersonal elements, it is important that the therapist work closely with other individuals who may have contributed to the development of the youngster's difficulties and who may still be playing a role in the perpetuation of the problems. Most often this involves members of the immediate family and, on occasion, other individuals such as grandparents, aunts, and uncles. I cannot discuss the specific ways in which I involve myself with these other individuals without first discussing the issue of confidentiality. Obviously, the guidelines I utilize in

437

deciding whether or not I will reveal what the youngster tells me must be understood before one can discuss meaningfully when and when not to discuss and divulge information. In this section, I will consider the general issue of confidentiality and the principles presented here will be followed in my subsequent discussions of individual treatment, group therapy, and work with parents.

Many therapists believe that the active involvement of a parent in a child's treatment will compromise significantly the youngster's confidentiality, the preservation of which is crucial to meaningful therapy. I believe that such therapists are placing too much weight on confidentiality. The patient is coming primarily for treatment — whether the patient is a child, adolescent, or an adult. The patient is not coming primarily for the preservation of confidentiality. To the degree that the preservation of the confidential relationship serves the ends of treatment, to that degree should it be respected. To the degree that strict adherence to confidentiality will undermine, subvert, or work against the goals of therapy, to that degree should confidentiality be ignored or compromised. One must not lose sight of the primary aim of therapy: to do what is in the best interests of the patient. In order to describe my position more specifically, I will consider the confidentiality issue as it pertains to the treatment of the adult, the adolescent, and the child. Although there are differences with regard to confientiality in these three areas, there are basic similarities that hold for all three categories.

CONFIDENTIALITY IN ADULT THERAPY

If the adult is to have a successful therapeutic experience, he or she must have the feeling that the therapist will not disclose to others what is revealed during the course of treatment. Otherwise, the freedom to reveal will be significantly compromised — to the point where therapy may become meaningless. Most therapists would agree, however, that there are certain situations in which strict adherence to confidentiality may be antitherapeutic. Such is the case when there is a strong suicidal or homicidal risk. Basically, when a human life is at stake, concerns about confidentiality are reduced to the point of being trivial. If the patient is suicidal, it behooves the therapist to enlist the aid of family members and close friends to do everything possible to protect the patient. This usually involves their active participation in hospitalizing the suicidal patient. It would be unconscionable to "respect" such a patient's request that the suicidal danger not be divulged to the nearest of kin. Similarly, when there is a homicidal risk, the therapist should do everything possible to warn the potential victim and to take every reasonable precaution to prevent the murder.

When an adult patient in treatment raises the issue of confidentiality, I will openly state that he or she can feel secure that I will not reveal what is divulged—with the exception of situations in which there is a homicidal or suicidal danger. In most cases, the patient is thereby reassured that confidences will not be divulged because neither of these eventualities seems likely. On occasion, however, a depressed patient will be told that I might divulge the suicidal danger. In such cases I will assure the patient that everything will be done to avoid such disclosure. However, I inform the patient that there might be an occasion in which I might divulge the suicidal risk, if such revelation might prove lifesaving. Interestingly, most patients are not upset by this. Some healthy part of them appreciates that they could conceivably "go crazy," and that at such a time they might impulsively commit a self-destructive act that could cause irreparable damage and even death. My position provides reassurance that should such a situation occur some healthy and stabilizing intervention will take place.

A good example of this phenomenon occurred many years ago when I saw in treatment a 35-year-old man who came to therapy with chief complaints of depression and excessive drinking. Early in the treatment he told me that he suspected that his wife was having an affair. She was coming home at 2:00 to 3:00 am with various excuses regarding why she was so late. None of these were convincing. Finally, he told me that he had hired a private detective to help him determine whether his suspicions were justified. About two weeks later, he telephoned me in a state of agitated rage. The detective had confirmed his suspicions. He had many details about his wife's visit to various hotels and motels with her lover—who turned out to be a "friend" of his. He told me that he planned to go home immediately and kill his wife with a gun that he had in the house. He stated that this was the only way he could "save face." He agreed, however, to come to my office en route home to discuss the matter further.

In our discussion the patient told me that he was terribly humiliated and that the knowledge that his wife was having an affair caused terrible damage to his self-esteen. He reiterated that the only way he could possibly regain a sense of self-worth was to kill his wife. I sympathized with the blow to his ego that the knowledge of his wife's affair caused him; however, I tried to impress upon him my belief that his reactions were definitely exaggerated. I told him that too much of his self-worth was dependent on external events, events that he had no control over. Specifically, if his self-worth were significantly determined by his wife's sex life outside the home, then he was putting himself in a very precarious position because his self-worth was thereby dependent on events over which he had absolutely no control. Furthermore, I told him that I did not agree with him that killing his wife would thereby enhance his feelings of self-worth. Again, it was another example of an external event that was being used in the service of changing an intrapsychic process.

After about two hours of discussion, the patient remained unconvinced and insisted that he was going home to kill his wife. I then confronted him with the various options that were open to me: two of which were to call the police and/or call his wife. He angrily informed me that I had no right to inform his wife because we had a confidential relationship. He went further and threatened that he would sue me for malpractice as well as report me to my psychiatric and medical societies for unethical conduct. The following interchange then ensued:

> *Therapist*: Let me ask you this. Why did you first come here to see me?
> *Patient*: Because I was depressed and had a drinking problem.
> *Therapist*: Yes, that's my recollection also. And what did you ask me to do?
> *Patient*: I asked you to help me with these problems.
> *Therapist*: Yes, that's my recollection. Now, did I ever say to you that I would never, under any circumstances, reveal to others what you told me.

Patient: No, but I didn't think it was necessary. I assumed that I wouldn't even have to raise that question. I assumed that you, as my psychiatrist, would never reveal anything that I said to you. I assumed that we had a confidential relationship.

Therapist: Yes, I agree with you. I never did promise you that I would not reveal what you said to me. I am in agreement with you that if you were to have the feeling that I were to frivolously reveal what you told me, that you would not have the kind of comfort and confidence necessary for good therapy. However, if you had asked me about confidentiality, I would have told you that under certain circumstances I would not respect it—especially in situations where there is a risk of homicide or suicide. And this is one of those situations.

Furthermore, I believe that divulgence in this situation will really serve the ends of your treatment, especially the goals that we set out for ourselves. I believe that if you kill your wife it will not only *not* enhance your self-worth but will result in your going to jail for many years. I believe, as well, that while incarcerated you probably will become even more depressed and your craving for alcohol will probably increase enormously. Accordingly, I believe that I am serving the goals of your treatment by doing everything possible to prevent you from killing your wife.

After further discussion, I told the patient that I thought the best option was to call his wife, invite her to the office, and the three of us would then discuss what we would do. Reluctantly, the patient said nothing while I called his home. Fortunately, his wife was at home and I told her the reasons for my call. She agreed to come to the office. I told her that I thought it would be a good idea for her to drop the gun off at the police station en route to our meeting. The patient suddenly chimed in and asked me to tell his wife that she should drop the gun off at his brother's house. I responded, "No way. The police station." The wife agreed and joined us. After a few hours of further discussion, I felt I could safely let the patient return home with his wife. (By that time I think he was too exhausted from psychotherapy to even lift a gun, if he had one.) Before leaving, arrangements were made for intensive counseling for the two of them.

I believe that this man was basically ambivalent about murdering his wife. Had he been fully resolved to kill her, he would not have called me. In his scheme of things, the only way to preserve his masculinity was to take revenge. However, healthier and more rational forces were operating; otherwise, he would not have called me and, in addition, agreed to discuss the matter with me. It was to these healthy forces that I appealed to when I decided not to respect his confidentiality. What I did, however, was to demonstrate what I considered to have been a greater respect for my patient, namely, I did everything to interrupt an act for which he would probably have suffered regret for the rest of his life.

In recent years there have been a number of cases in which the litigation has centered on this issue. Psychiatrists were sued for malpractice because they preserved patients' confidences, and there was a resultant suicide or homicide that could conceivably have been prevented. The usual defense was that the therapist was respecting the patient's confidentiality and the doctor was acting in the highest ethical traditions of the medical profession. Even in former years, I did not subscribe to this view. It is not in the highest ethical tradition of the medical profession to sit by and do nothing when there might be a suicide or homicide taking place. It is in the highest interests of the medical profession to protect human life. Fortunately, the courts and ethical committees in medical societies are shifting in the direction of supporting divulgences in such cases. This is a good trend.

CONFIDENTIALITY IN ADOLESCENT THERAPY

It is not uncommon for me to have the following conversation with an adolescent:

> *Patient*: Everything I say to you is just between me and you, right? You'll never tell my parents anything I tell you, right?
> *Therapist*: Not right.
> *Patient*: You mean you're going to tell my parents everything I tell you?

Therapist: No, I didn't say that either.

Patient: But my friend goes to a shrink, and his shrink told him that everything they speak about is strictly confidential, and his shrink says that she'll never tell my friend's parents anything about what goes on in a session.

Therapist: Yes, many therapists work that way. But I don't. Let me tell you how I work. As long as you don't do anything dangerous, to either yourself or others, you can be quite sure that what we speak about here will be held strictly confidential. I'm in full appreciation of the fact that it's important that you have the feeling that what we talk about is confidential. However, there are certain exceptions. And these exceptions hold for anyone, regardless of age. My policy is the same for all. It's not just for teenagers. It's the same whether you're 5 years old or 85 years old. The basic policy is this: As long as you're not doing anything dangerous, either to yourself or others, you can be sure that I won't reveal what you tell me. However, if you're doing something that's dangerous, I reserve the right, at my discretion, to reveal to your family whatever I consider important to reveal to help stop you from doing the dangerous thing. I may need their help. What do you think about what I've said?

At that point the patient may ask me to tell him or her what things I would reveal. I will not then provide "food for thought." I do not wish to give the youngster suggestions for various forms of antisocial and/or self-destructive behavior that may not have entered his or her head. Rather, I ask the adolescent to tell me what things he or she might do that might warrant such divulgence. I may then use this as a point of departure for a therapeutic inquiry. However, I do have a "list." It includes: heavy use of drugs (not occasional use of marijuana), heavy use of alcohol, dangerous driving (especially when under the influence of drugs or alcohol), criminal behavior, and for girls, a desire to have an out-of-wedlock child (occasional sexual intercourse is not a reportable item). I also impress upon the adolescent the fact that should one of these dangerous situations be arising, I will not automatically discuss the problem with the parent. Rather, I will exhaust all possibilities of discussion with the patient and the adolescent group before divulging the risk. Usually, such discussions are enough. However, when they are not, the youngster usually knows beforehand that I am going to divulge the information.

There is another aspect of the confidentiality issue in adolescence that warrants comment. The parents have a reasonable right to know whether there is a significant risk of dangerous behavior. When this issue is broached, generally in the initial evaluation, I will tell them that they should know that "no news is good news," i.e., that I *will* divulge dangers to them, and if there are no such divulgences, they can feel assured that no great risks are imminent.

I am fully appreciative of the fact that the adolescent needs a special, separate relationship with the therapist. This is part of his or her developmental need to establish a separate identity from that of the parents. This autonomy is necessary if the adolescent is to grow into an independent, self-sufficient adult. Active participation of the parents in the adolescent's therapy can compromise this goal. However, the goal can still be achieved by some participation on the part of the parents. Occasional joint sessions in which the youngster is seen along with the parents need not interfere with this goal. There can still be a significant percentage of sessions devoted to the adolescent alone, and the confidential relationship can also serve the purpose of enhancing separation and autonomy. The potential divulgence of a dangerous situation need not interfere with this sense of autonomy so important to the adolescent's development.

CONFIDENTIALITY IN CHILD PSYCHOTHERAPY

Although my focus in this book is on adolescent issues, I present here my views on confidentiality in child therapy because many of the principles are applicable to the treatment of adolescents. By child psychotherapy I am referring to the treatment of children between the ages of about four and ten. In my opinion, the confidentiality issue has little if any place in the treatment of most of these children. There are many therapists who will say to such children something along these lines: "Whatever you tell me here in this room is just between you and me. I promise I'll never tell your mother or father what you tell me. You can trust me on that." Many children might wonder exactly what the therapist is referring to. They know of no great secrets that they have from their parents. And this is especially the case for younger children. The parents know quite well that the child is soiling, stealing, lying, truant, etc. They more than the child are aware of these problems, and it is they who initiated the treatment. So the statement must be confusing and even irrelevant to many children.

In addition, the statement sets up a structure in which there are "we" (the therapist and the patient) and "they" (the parents). "We" *and* "they" can easily become "we" *versus* "they." With such an approach the therapist introduces the notion that something undesirable or bad will occur if "they" find out about certain therapist-patient confidences. This cannot but produce or add to the child's hostility toward and/or distrust of the parents. And this concept can introduce new schisms in the family. The family has enough trouble already; it does not need an additional problem brought about by a therapeutic program that adds a new pathological subsystem to the family. The "secret club" that the therapist creates with the patient also impedes open communication. Generally, communication impairments contribute to the development of and perpetuation of psychopathology. The confidential relationship with the child is likely to increase the communication problems of the family. The thrust of the therapy should be to encourage open expression of the issues that are causing people difficulty. A conspiracy of silence usually serves only to reduce communication and defeats thereby an important therapeutic goal.

The therapist should attempt to create an atmosphere in which all things pertinent to the child's treatment are discussed openly with the parents. I do not make any statements about this; I do it as a matter of course. In work with children I generally make no mention of confidentiality. If the child says to me that he or she does not wish me to tell his parents something, I will get very specific about what it is he or she wishes me not to divulge. Almost invariably it is an issue worthy of being discussed with the parents. Usually the child fears repercussions that are unreal or exaggerated. Encouraging the child to express to the parent(s) the forbidden material, either in my presence or at home, is usually therapeutic. It can teach all concerned that the repression (unconscious), and suppression (conscious) of thoughts and feelings is likely to perpetuate problems, whereas civilized discussion is the best way to resolve family problems.

A boy, for example, will say to me that he doesn't want me to tell his parents something. On further inquiry the issue almost invariably is one that should be discussed with the parents, and the child's fears of what will happen if such information is disclosed are unrealistic. Encouraging the child to express the forbidden material to the parents can provide him with the living experience that the hidden thoughts and feelings are not as terrible as he considered them to be and the anticipated consequences are not forthcoming. The therapist can serve as a catalyst for such expression, and his or her presence can make the atmosphere a safer one for the child to first make such revelations.

There is an aspect of S. Freud's famous Little Hans case (1909) that is pertinent to my discussion here. During the one joint session that Freud held with Little Hans and his father, Hans expressed some hostility toward his father that he had not previously revealed. I believe that it is unfortunate that Freud did not direct his attention to this in his report of the case. I would speculate that the reason why Hans had not expressed the hostility previously was that he was afraid to do so because of fears of his father's retaliation. However, in the presence of "Professor Sigmund Freud," a man of whom both the patient and his father were in awe, Hans could safely reveal his anger because of his awareness that his father was not likely to react with severe punitive measures in Freud's presence. I suspect that Hans' having had the living experience that his father would react to his hostility in a civilized manner made it easier for him to express his resentments elsewhere. And this, I believe, was a contributing factor to the alleviation of his symptoms.

Classical psychoanalysts, in particular, are strict adherents to the confidentiality principle. It is they, more than other therapists, who make it a point at the outset to emphasize to the child that they will respect confidences. It is of interest that Freud did not consider confidentiality to be an important issue in his treatment of Little Hans. Hans' father was the therapist and Freud was the supervisor. When reading the transcript of the treatment, one learns that Hans was easily led to discuss bowel movements, urination, masturbation, interest in observing his mother's toilet functioning, sexual fantasies toward his mother, and so forth. If he were indeed hiding material that a child might be ashamed to reveal, I would find it hard to imagine what such material might be. Little Hans knew that his father was revealing their discussions to Freud. In the one joint session that Freud had with Hans and his father, there was open discussion of these intimacies. Classical analysts often point to the case of Little Hans as proof that Freud's theories of infantile sexuality, the Oedipus complex, and castration anxiety are valid. Libraries have been written on these theories—which are supposedly proven by the Little Hans case. However, the structure of Freud's therapeutic program is often ignored by the same psychoanalysts. They do not utilize the parents as assistant therapists (as did Freud), and they enter into a strictly confidential relationship with the child (which Freud did not). In both cases, I believe, they do the child and the family a disservice. Elsewhere (1972a), I have discussed in detail this and other aspects of my understanding of the Little Hans case.

FURTHER COMMENTS ON CONFIDENTIALITY IN ADOLESCENT PSYCHOTHERAPY

Although there are differences in my approaches to the confidentiality issue among adults, adolescents, and children, there are some basic principles applicable to all three age levels. And the most important of these principles is that the patient is coming primarily for therapy. To the degree that respecting the patient's confidences serves the higher goal of the treatment, it should be respected. To the degree that "respect" for the patient's confidentiality is a compromise of the therapeutic goals, it must be ignored. In my discussion of confidentiality in adults and children, there is much that is pertinent to this issue in the treatment of adolescents. For example, an adolescent may say to me: "Don't ever tell my parents what I'm going to tell you now." Here, too, I will not promise in advance that I will respect the confidence. At most, the adolescent will not tell me what it is. Most often, however, with some reassurance that I will lean in the direction of nondisclosure, the youngster will provide me with the divulgence. In most cases I conclude that it will not serve the purposes of treatment for me to reveal the information to the parents and we may go on with our discussion. In extreme cases, in which there is a homicidal or suicidal risk, then there is no problem regarding my providing the revelation. In some situations I will discuss the issue of divulgence, but not belabor the point. Rather, I want to quickly provide the youngster with the *living experience* that such divulgence will not bring about the anticipated repercussions. It is for this reason that I generally advise the parents of my adolescent patients to be available to join in the session by remaining in the waiting room throughout the course of my patient's session. In this way, they are "on call" for quick involvement in our discussions.

There are some older adolescents who come to the session alone. Some of these live close enough to ride to my office on their bicycles. Others are old enough to drive to my office. In such cases, I still advise the parents to frequently (every third or fourth session) come to the sessions because there are usually issues that I wish to discuss with one or both parents. On occasion, youngsters who come alone may miss a session and not tell their parents about it. And they may even try to discourage me from informing their parents that the session has been missed. They recognize that the parents will be billed for the missed session, but hope that my bill will not make a differentiation between missed and attended sessions. I have not yet been in a situation where there is a healthy reason for the request that I not divulge to the parents that a session has been missed and they have therefore wasted their money. Generally, the youngster has a pathological reason for making this request. Usually the session is missed out of hostility and/or self-indulgence. The youngster's request derives from the desire to avoid repercussions from the parents for their having wasted their money. To "respect" confidentiality under these circumstances is to perpetuate psychopathology. It goes against the basic reason for the patient's being in treatment and is a disservice to both the patient and family.

On occasion I will receive a telephone call from a parent who wishes to make an appointment for an adolescent. However, the parent informs me that the youngster has agreed to go for treatment with the proviso that the therapist promise that there will be absolutely no contact at all with the parents, either by direct interview or even by telephone. The parents have reluctantly agreed to such an arrangement because it is the only way that the youngster will go for treatment. I have never agreed to see a patient with such a restriction. I cannot conceive of their being a healthy reason for such a proviso. It generally serves to promulgate some form of psychopathology. The therapist here, in advance, is being used as an ally in the creation of some form of pathological family subsystem. Unfortunately, there are therapists who are willing to see a patient with this restriction. I believe that such therapists are doing both the patient and family a disservice. I generally inform such a parent that I will not agree to such a constraint. I might agree to see the youngster first alone and hear the reasons why family involvement is not desired, but I let the youngster know beforehand (through the parent) that I consider it unlikely that I will be convinced by the arguments and that there is an extremely high probability that I will want to have at least some contact with the parents.

I have never in my experience had a therapeutic situation with an adolescent that justified *total removal* of the parents from the youngster's treatment. I am sure that there are such situations, but I have not yet seen them in my private practice. This is probably related to the fact that if parents are willing to pay for treatment, they are likely to have a degree of involvement that warrants their seeing the therapist—at least sometimes. Generally, I suggest to the mother that she communicate my refusal to the youngster and to tell him or her the reasons why. Sometimes the youngster will then agree to come under the conditions I proposed to the parent and other times he or she will not. I suspect that in the latter case the parents have found a therapist willing to work with this restriction. This is a good example of the principle that patients will always be able to find a therapist who will do their bidding, regardless of how sick the request is and how much the therapist perpetuates psychopathology by complying with it.

EIGHT

INDIVIDUAL
TREATMENT

Three therapeutic modalities can be useful to the adolescent who
warrants psychotherapy. These are individual sessions, adolescent
group therapy, and work with parents. An adolescent who is a
candidate for individual therapy will receive one or more of these in
varying combinations, as warranted. It is rare for a youngster to
receive only one of the three; rather, some combination is generally
utilized. I am not referring here to family therapy. That may also be
useful to the adolescent. In this and the next two chapters, I will
focus on the individual therapy aspect of this treatment program. In
Chapters Eleven and Twelve I will focus on the other two modalities. Although I divide these into three separate sections, it is
important for the reader to appreciate that I am actually referring to
three facets of the patient's therapy. The division is somewhat
artificial because even in an individual session I may ask a parent to
join us. Conversely, a situation in which I am seeing the adolescent
with both parents may be transformed into an individual session,
when warranted. In short, any possible combination of the three

therapeutic modalities is utilized throughout the course of the treatment—or even in the course of a session.

ADOLESCENCE AS A PERIOD OF THERAPEUTIC RECEPTIVITY

As a group, children of four to six may very well be the ones who are most receptive to the therapist's comments. This is a period of rapid superego development when youngsters are very receptive to the comments of authorities (such as a therapist). Teachers will agree that kindergarteners and first graders are typically in awe of their authority, and episodes of nonreceptivity notwithstanding, are generally far more compliant than, for example, fourth graders, eighth graders (they may be the worst), and twelfth graders. Many classical psychoanalysts believe that the rapid superego development that takes place from ages three to five results from the need to repress oedipal fantasies and designs. I am in agreement with Freud that this is indeed a period of rapid superego development, but I do not believe that such growth has anything to do with the Oedipus complex in the vast majority of children. Rather, it relates to the fact that children, during this phase, are expanding their horizons outside the home at a very rapid rate. They are sleeping over at the homes of other children for the first time; they are entering nursery school and kindergarten; and they are doing many more independent things. Accordingly, they are being exposed to a new army of authorities, each of whom has his or her own rules. If they are to adjust in this new, more complex world they have to learn quickly the rules that each of these giants has. And the therapist, coming into the child's life at that time, may also be able to enjoy the benefits of the child's receptivity to rules and regulations. If I say to a five-year-old boy that I'm very sorry but I'm going to have to write down in his chart that he is once again engaged in certain transgressions, he is usually crestfallen and will be quite unhappy that his unacceptable behavior is being so recorded. If I say the same thing to a nine-year-old boy, who exhibits similar behavior, his general reaction would be something along these lines: "I don't give two shits what you write down in my chart." Although he may not use these exact words, every cell in his body is transmitting that message to me.

My statement that adolescence, too, can be a period of therapeutic receptivity may come as a surprise to the reader. Even though it is characteristically one of rebellion, and even though some of the rebellion may be against the therapist, it can be, at the same time, a period of very high receptivity to the therapist's comments. One explanation relates to the quest for identity. As discussed in Chapter One, most adolescents suffer from significant identity confusion and are ever collecting data to provide them with information about what their identity really is. Accordingly, even though quite antagonistic to a therapist, they are likely to be receptive to long discussions on their appearance, hairstyle, attractiveness to others, whether or not a certain defect can be seen from a distance, cosmetics, clothing styles, etc. Fifteen or twenty minutes can easily be consumed on a discussion of whether or not the youngster's ears stick out too much or whether or a girl's eyes are set too far apart. The conversation may include the opinions of peers on these particular subjects and it is not uncommon for a certain amount of controversy to be raging on whether or not a youngster's almost invisible skin blemish is "turning off" the boys. Once the therapist has shown receptivity to discussing these important issues, he or she is more likely to be heard on subjects that may appear initially to be of less importance to the youngster. These discussions, therefore, serve as a good bridge to issues that are uppermost on the therapist's agenda (even though lowermost on the patient's).

With regard to their receptivity to individual sessions, one can divide adolescents into two groups. As a rule, younger adolescents (13–15) are unreceptive to face-to-face confrontations in individual sessions. They are generally made uncomfortable by therapists who ask them to sit alone with them in a room for 45 to 50 minutes, asking them to talk about their problems. Such youngsters, in this regard, are more like pre-adolescent patients. The older adolescents (16 and up) are likely to be more receptive to direct discussion. Actually, this division is somewhat artificial in that there is a continuum between the less talkative and the more talkative youngsters. I will begin this section with a discussion of the more talkative ones and then describe techniques I utilize to engage those less receptive to discussions on a one-to-one basis. For the latter category I will be giving particular emphasis (Chapter Nine) to *The Talking, Feeling, and Doing Game* (1973b) because it has proved to be a valuable instrument for drawing out less talkative adolescents. But even the more loquacious may occasionally find the instrument useful.

Furthermore, the therapist does well to appreciate that many adolescents need to defend themselves against the realization that they have psychological difficulties and may need to have some kind of an excuse to justify their being in the therapist's office. The most common excuse is that the youngster is only there because the parents have forced him or her to attend the sessions. As mentioned previously, the therapist does well to support such a rationalization and provide some sympathy for the youngster's plight. The youngster is voluntarily attending—professions of coercion notwithstanding—and once the "body is in the room" the therapist must do what he or she can to keep the patient there.

BASIC TECHNICAL CONSIDERATIONS

Here I focus on some of the technical and structural aspects of the individual session that may serve as guidelines for these interviews. I generally begin with the youngster alone. This is in contrast to the procedure I use with pre-adolescent children, with whom I generally start the session with the child and parent together. The adolescent needs a sense of autonomy and routinely bringing the parent in with the patient may be therapeutically contraindicated. However, this does not preclude my requesting that the parent stay in the waiting room throughout the course of the session and be "on call."

Beginning the Therapeutic Session

Once seated, I generally begin with the traditional psychoanalytic question "So, what's on your mind?" or "What would you like to talk about today?" Although I have many criticisms of psychoanalytic theory and technique, I still believe that this open-ended question is quite useful (but I don't go too far with it). For example, as mentioned in Chapter Three I don't use this opening with a new patient at the beginning of the first interview. It is much too anxiety provoking at that time. Nor would I use it in a situation where something is obviously going on that demands my attention. For example, if a boy comes in on crutches and his leg is in a cast, I am not going to begin with that question. In such cases I might start with: "I'm sure that I'm not the first person to ask you this question. What happened to your leg?" The reader could argue that I am contaminating the blank screen with such a question. I don't deny it. In my defense, however, I believe that not to ask it has its obvious drawbacks. First, to inquire about the leg is the *human* thing to do. The boy just broke his leg and it is not only reasonable and sensitive of me to inquire about it, but would be somewhat insensitive and even cruel not to ask about the situation that resulted in the trauma. In addition, it is a good principle of therapy not to talk about something while being distracted by something else. Often the distraction may be more important to discuss than the issue under consideration. The leg in a cast would be just such a distraction. In addition, inquiry into the causes might be therapeutically useful in that the injury may have related to psychopathological processes operative in the youngster, e.g., driving when inebriated, show-off antics, or some manifestation of the youngster's delusions of invulnerability. Another example of such a distraction would be the adolescent girl who is being seductive to me. The therapist cannot concentrate on the issues at hand if the patient is being seductive. One does well to discuss the seductivity, get whatever therapeutic mileage one can out of it, and then switch back to the original issue under consideration. But these are exceptions. Most often the situation warrants my beginning with the open-ended question in order not to contaminate the "blank screen."

The Therapist Bringing up a Subject

In the course of the session, as well, I may again depart from traditional psychoanalytic practice by bringing up a subject. If after a significant portion of the session has been used and the youngster hasn't raised up what I consider to be significant material left over from the previous session, I may refer the youngster back to it. If we are moving along in a meaningful way on another subject, I certainly will not rob us of the benefits to be derived from discussing something "hot," i.e., something that is highly emotionally charged. In such cases I will not bring up extraneous material because of my belief that the present material is now taking higher priority. However, if the present material appears to be low priority, and/or even resistance material, I will make some inquiries regarding why the more important issues from the previous session have not been brought up. Generally, I do not specify at the outset what the particular issues are. Rather, I will introduce the subject with a comment such as this: "I don't have the feeling that what you're talking about now is particularly important to you. In addition, we discussed something last time that I think is much more important and you haven't mentioned it yet. Do you know what I'm referring to?" In the formulation of the question, I try to get the patient to recall the issue, rather than my mentioning it myself. To bring up the issue would be "spoon-feeding" and would entrench the patient's dependency on me to do his remembering for him. Also, I want to get some idea as to how deeply repressed and "forgotten" the original issue is. Furthermore, the aspect of the issue that may seem important to me, may be less important to the patient. My making specific reference to it might shift the youngster away from the more psychologically meaningful material. If, after these general introductory questions, the patient still has absolutely no recollection of what I am referring to, I may provide the patient with clues and reminders, but generally will not present the whole issue. Usually one clue will serve to catalyze recollection of the issue. I am generally least prone to bring up past issues in adult therapy, more prone in adolescent therapy, and most prone in the treatment of young children. Young children are not famous for their memories and not to bring up the material (such as is the practice of many child psychoanalysts) is a disservice to the patient.

Dealing with Silences

If the youngster has nothing to talk about and if, in addition, there were no "burning" issues from the previous session, I will allow for a minute or two of silence, but not much more. Many analysts consider this to be a technical error. They would claim that it would be more beneficial for the patient to sit silently, even for many sessions. Many articles have been written in the psychoanalytic literature about the benefits of silences and how much both the patient and the therapist can learn from them. I am dubious. I am not claiming that silence provides no information whatsoever; nor am I claiming that silence is of absolutely no therapeutic benefit. I say only that it soon reaches the point of diminishing returns—after which it becomes a waste of money. Besides which, even if it were highly beneficial therapeutically, and even if it cost the patient nothing, it is quite boring and I like myself too much to subject myself to such masochistic treatment over time—especially 45–60 minutes. Life is short, and I am not the kind of person who comfortably will sit for many hours doing nothing, staring into space, even if some therapeutic benefit might be derived by the patient.

Accordingly, after a few minutes of silence I will generally say something along these lines to the patient: "Well, if you have nothing to talk about why don't we bring in your mother (father) and see if she (he) will have something to tell us." Generally, the parent does have something to contribute and the issue that the parent brings up serves as a point of departure for discussion among the three of us. If, however, the parent has nothing to bring up (rarely the case) then I will generally ask a question about the original complaints and whether or not they still exist. I may even go back to the list of complaints presented by the parents in my questionnaire and described during the first meeting. It may be that things have gotten so much better that therapy is no longer warranted. In such cases we then discuss the question of winding down and even stopping. There are parents (and even youngsters) who continue coming without having any particular clinical problems. They believe that the therapeutic program is designed to go beyond the point where symptoms are no longer present. There are some therapists who also subscribe to this principle. Although it is the more lucrative one, I do not believe that it is the most judicious one from the therapeutic point of view. The clinical symptoms are the "handle" for our treatment. They are the points of departure for our therapeutic interchanges and maneuvers. Without them the therapy becomes sterile, intellectualized, and theoretical. To talk at length, over many sessions, about *why* the patient *had* the symptoms and *why they no longer exist* is a relatively fruitless endeavor. Few if any emotions may be tied to the discussion and it therefore becomes even less therapeutic. This does not preclude spending some time on the subject, especially in the period just after the patient reports significant reduction and even removal of symptoms.

Another reason for avoiding long silences is that one may lose the adolescent patient. Adults, interestingly, are often more naive in this regard and will continue to pay for sessions in which most if not all of the time has been spent in silence. They gullibly believe the analyst that such sessions can be therapeutically useful. Adolescents are not so gullible and will generally not attend more than a few such sessions. They are likely to say that the whole thing is boring and a waste of time and the parents, with justification, are likely to agree with them. Accordingly, engaging in long periods of silence is a good way of losing the patient and depriving him or her of the opportunity to gain some therapeutic benefit.

For patients who do not seem to have much of an agenda, I will often suggest that they make lists between sessions. Again, classical analysts would take issue with this approach, claiming that it is likely to contaminate the blank screen. They claim that they want to know what it is at the forefront of the patient's mind—at that particular point. I cannot deny that the making of lists may result in such contamination. However, if the choice lies between nothing being said and speaking from a list, I would far prefer the list because it is much more likely to be therapeutic. If, however, the therapist suspects that the list is being made as a resistance maneuver, and that the issues being written down are selected because they are likely to provide discussion on issues that are less touchy and anxiety provoking, then the therapist does well to discourage such utilization. This, however, has not been my experience. Most often the youngster who makes lists is one who has a serious commitment to the treatment and genuinely wants to make the best use of the therapeutic time. In addition, I will generally instruct the adolescent to write down his or her dreams. Later in this chapter I will discuss dream analysis for those youngsters who are candidates for such therapeutic inquiry. Usually, these are the older adolescents.

Dealing with Preoccupations
Of Parental Blame

A common topic for adolescents in treatment is blame of their parents. Many youngsters will come in, and when asked what is on his or her mind, will quickly start talking about the various indignities they suffer at the hands of their parents. Even those who profess that they have problems and want to change themselves, are likely to talk at length about the reasons why their difficulties are caused by their parents. This is another time when it is good to have the parents available. Accordingly, I might say to such a youngster: "Well, I've been listening to you for 15 minutes now and all you've been doing is telling me about how terrible your home situation is and how your parents are causing you all these difficulties. It may be that some of your points are valid, but it may be that some aren't. I always find it useful to get the other person's opinion on subjects like this. So let's have your mother come in and get her opinions about what's happened." I do not ask the youngster's permission to have the mother brought in; rather, I rise as I am talking, go to the door, and bring the parent in—before the youngster has a chance to object. This is not to say that I will never listen to, discuss, and try to get therapeutic mileage from such objections; rather I want the pattern established that the parent's participation is crucial if we are to find out exactly what went on at home.

In the course of such a discussion, I may point out what the parent's deficiencies have been, try to get therapeutic mileage out of a discussion of such deficiencies, and make recommendations to the parent about effecting the appropriate changes. In addition, I will point out to the youngster what his or her role has been, try to get the youngster to focus on such defiencies as a point of departure for therapeutic inquiry, and similarly will make suggestions regarding the youngster's changing those contributing factors that have originated within him or her.

In the course of my discussions with patients and their parents—especially discussions in which the patient is particularly insensitive to the parents' affection, willingness to sacrifice, and dedication—I will present what I refer to as the *transplant kidney principle*. This is a typical way in which I present this important concept: "I know you have many criticisms of your parents. I suspect that you believe that you had bad luck when God gave out parents, but I can tell you this: If you were in the hospital and needed a kidney transplant—so much so that your life depended on it—I am positive that of the five billion people on earth your parents would be the first ones on line. Where do you think all the others would be at that time, all those whom you call your friends, all those whom you claim treat you far better than your parents?" Although many youngsters' delusions of invulnerability lessen considerably their appreciation that they will *ever* be in such a position, the message does sometimes have the effect of enhancing some patients' appreciation of their parents. In contrast, parents will generally find it a useful reminder for the youngster who is being particularly callous to them—a common situation when raising an adolescent. Some would be critical of the obvious attempt at guilt evocation when utilizing the *kidney transplant principle*. I have no problem with this. I do not subscribe to the theory that the therapist should never try to enhance guilt. Most adolescents (like most people in this world) need more guilt, not less. And therapy is an ideal situation in which guilt should be engendered when it is sorely lacking.

Asking the Patient to Repeat
What I Have Said

Another useful technical maneuver in the individual therapy of adolescents is to ask the patient to repeat what I have just said, especially if my comments have been somewhat complex. My purpose here, of course, is to ensure that what I have said has been "registered." Patients (regardless of age) are not famous for remembering the details of anxiety-provoking confrontations, no matter how carefully, benevolently, and sympathetically presented. It is only via their reiteration by the patient that we can be sure that we have been "heard." I recognize that the patient may consider such a request demeaning, but I ask the question anyway. I believe that the benefits to be derived from ensuring that my message has been heard far outweigh the possible antitherapeutic elements associated with the patient's feeling of embarrassment associated with the question. And even here, most adolescents do not claim that I am embarrassing or otherwise putting them down by asking them to relate to me their understanding of what I have just said. The question is posed benevolently and the patient appreciates that my request for reiteration is in the service of the goals of the treatment.

Typically, I will use questions such as this: "What I have said may be quite complicated. In order to be sure that you've understood, I'd like you to tell me what I just said." and "Many people find that when I talk about things that relate to their problems it is hard to understand what I'm saying. If you're like most people, there's probably some confusion about what I just said. Any questions?" The patient's questions may enable me to determine whether or not I was understood. If they indicate I was not understood, I might say: "From your questions it's clear to me that some of the points I made might have been a little difficult for you to understand. I'm going to say it again and then I'm going to ask you to tell me what you understood me to have been saying. I'm doing this because we're talking about something that's *very* important." Adolescents who may feel demeaned by this approach may be reassured by the knowledge that I work similarly with adults. Although adults are more likely than adolescents to respond with some indignation to my request for reiteration, most ultimately come to appreciate the judiciousness of the request.

Asking to See My Notes and/or Chart

On occasion a patient will ask what I have just written down or, even further, ask to see my notes in the chart. Only in my residency days would I have considered such a question inappropriate and would have taken great pains not to show the patient his or her chart. My fear then was that the information contained therein might be misinterpreted by the patient and might prove too anxiety provoking for him or her to handle. However, it was during my residency days that I had an experience that taught me something important on this point. Specifically, a borderline patient of a colleague of mine left my colleague's office with his chart and ran out of the hospital. A staff conference was held and various speculations were made regarding the possible detrimental effects of his having read his chart. No one, even the senior supervisor, considered the possibility that good could come from such an act. A few days later, the patient returned with the chart, told his therapist that he had read it completely, and then began to discuss certain points that he disagreed with. It was clear that the points raised were useful and that he had gained much from the experience. I am not claiming that such experiences can be useful for *all* patients; I do believe, however, that reading one's chart can be useful for most.

After the completion of my residency I spent two years in the military service in Germany. I was stationed at a large military hospital in Frankfurt am Main, Germany. The hospital serviced many satellite dispensaries. The soldiers routinely came with their charts in hand because it would have been extremely difficult to arrange for the charts to be sent separately. Furthermore, having each soldier carry his own chart lessened the likelihood of charts being lost, displaced, or sent to the wrong place. This was the practice with all medical services, and psychiatry was no exception. Accordingly, the soldiers routinely sat reading their charts as they waited to see me. In my two years in the service I never found one soldier who suffered from such an opportunity. Rather, most found it useful and their discussions about what they had read provided me with useful data about what was going on with them.

It was from these early experiences (which occurred in the late 1950s and early 1960s) that I developed a much more relaxed attitude about patients seeing their charts. Accordingly, if an adolescent says to me that he wants to see what is in his chart, I will generally respond along these lines: "You know, there is absolutely nothing in that chart that you don't know about. It's all information that you and your parents have told me about yourself. If you'd rather spend your time reading the chart, that's okay with me. However, I think you could make better use of your time. That stuff is all past history, even though some of it was what you said to me during our last session. I think you'd do much better to talk about the things that are on your mind now. But I leave the choice to you." It is rare for the youngster to spend the time looking through his or her chart.

Preventing the patient from seeing the chart promulgates the idea that the therapist has some information about the patient which he or she does not know. This has the effect of giving the patient the notion the therapist has some magic powers, the supernatural ability to know things about the patient that the patient doesn't even know about him- or herself. I believe that promulgating such a view of the therapist is antitherapeutic. My experience has been that once the patient is told that the freedom to look at the chart is his or hers, the whole situation becomes decompressed and the curiosity to see what is contained therein often evaporates immediately. The most predictable way to engender such curiosity is to tell the patient that he or she is strictly prohibited from viewing the material between the chart's covers. Such a position just sets up a morbid situation that generally is going to contaminate the treatment. Last, after the first few sessions, I generally do not take any notes on the vast majority of my patients. I work on the principle that I will remember those things that are important and not remember those that are not important. This is the same principle that exists between friends. Accordingly, no notes are being taken and so no morbid curiosity is being engendered.

The Use of Contracts

There are therapists who draw up "contracts" with their patients. Often these contracts are made along with the parents. A list is made of the various things the youngster will not do, especially antisocial behavior. Sometimes a list of rewards is included in the contract. I have never yet seen a contract which provides meaningful disciplinary and punitive measures if the contract is abrogated. The theory is that the youngster—by sheer dint of will—will adhere to its provisions. The youngster is placed on his or her honor to do so. I have never yet seen a youngster live up to such a contract. I believe that drawing it up is naive on the part of the therapist and is derived, in part, from the hope that the various psychopathological forces that have contributed to the aberrant behavior will somehow be suppressed and repressed in compliance with some vow to subscribe to the provisions of this document. And, the addition of the signatures of all the concerned parties is supposed to add a certain sanctity to it that will increase the likelihood that the vows taken will be subscribed to. This is a naive view of treatment and does not give proper respect to the power of the unconcious forces operative in bringing about the

psychopathology. Unfortunately, the whole experience then becomes antitherapeutic because there are no repercussions for breaking the contract. The youngster then has the living experience that
the failure to live up to one's promises is not going to be followed by
meaningful consequences and so frivolous attitudes towards one's
vows is promulgated.

Soda, Pretzels, and Candy

Some therapists believe that it is crucial for the adolescent
therapist to have a refrigerator of soda pop as well as pretzels,
potato chips, and candy readily available for them. One of the
arguments given for this is that food is a symbol of love and
providing such is likely to entrench the therapist-patient relationship. At best, the therapist can provide the youngster with some
affection in compensation for some of the privations he or she may
have suffered. This, if it is in any way to be meaningful, must evolve
from an ever-deepening relationship. At best, soda, food, and
candy can play an insignificant role in bringing about such a
relationship. The therapist must appreciate that food is a *symbol*; it
is not a replacement for the real thing. There are therapists who are
somewhat deficient in providing that degree of affection optimum in
the therapeutic situation and who may try to compensate for their
deficiencies in this regard by providing food, soda, etc. Such
therapists may be entrenching a common parental problem in which
the parents use food to compensate for their deficiencies in providing genuine affection. Such therapists, therefore, are promulgating
and perpetuating a pathological use of food. Accordingly, I do not
routinely supply food, candy, and soda to my adolescent patients.
This does not preclude my occasionally having such available, but it
is not in any way planned; nor do I feel that I have to stock my
refrigerator and pantry with these items for special distribution for
my adolescent patients.

The Value of Philosophical Discussions

With an adult patient, I generally discourage significant time
spent on such issues as religion, politics, and philosophy. General

ly, such discussions are likely to serve as resistances against focusing on more important personal issues. This is not the case with the adolescent. Normally adolescents are preoccupied with these issues as part of their developmental process. They may spend hours thinking about "the nature of things." They may be deeply absorbed in whether or not they still subscribe to their parents' religious beliefs or whether they should embrace doctrines of another religion, especially one that is quite remote from their parental heritage. In the 1960s and 1970s Zen Buddhism was the most popular alternative religion for adolescents of all ages. Adolescents often preoccupy themselves with some of the traditional questions that have plagued philosophers throughout the ages: questions about God, existence, the purpose of the universe, etc. And they often enjoy talking with anyone at length about these issues. Therapists who refuse to engage in such discussions because of their view that they are thereby sidestepping, circumventing, or avoiding discussions about the more basic pathological issues are making an error.

From the adolescent's point of view, what could be more important than a discussion about the meaning of God and the purpose of the universe? Accordingly, therapists do well to spend time with these youngsters discussing such topics and presenting their own views on them, *after* the youngster has expounded on his or her opinions. I am not suggesting that every minute of every session be spent in such discussion, only that these topics should not be viewed as off limits for the therapist. These discussions bring the therapist on the same wavelength as the patient, especially if the therapist has some views that the adolescent finds of interest and value. They thereby entrench the relationship and provide a foundation for receptivity to the therapist's comments on other subjects. It is as if the adolescent reasons: "He seems to know a lot about the philosophy of religion and the meaning of existence. He's probably worthy of being respected on other topics as well." Although the therapist may not be viewed by experts in these areas to be anything but a novice, from the adolescent's point of view the therapist may be viewed as a *maven*. The groundwork, then, is laid for greater receptivity on issues that are more directly relevant to the patient's problems.

In addition, in the context of such discussions, the issues of values and ethics are likely to arise and this may bring the therapist much closer to the patient's actual problems. In discussing what is right and wrong, good and bad, it is difficult not to touch on aspects of the patient's life relative to these considerations. These need not be discussed directly with the patient as the example. Rather one can discuss these issues theoretically, about third parties, or about people in general, and yet the messages are likely to be received in such a way that the adolescent saves face. The discussion of ethical behavior, again on a theoretical basis, is not likely to be unrelated to the patient's own problems in this area. Ethical considerations in politics will relate to ethical considerations among family members, regarding how they treat one another. And religious ethical doctrines, as well, can easily be related to intrafamilial relationships— again, without necessarily discussing the patient's particular family.

Learning from the Patient

A few years ago, when my three children were then in their adolescence, I was having dinner with a group of colleagues. In the course of our conversation one of them said to me: "Gardner, I want to ask you a question. What do you consider the most important thing a parent can do when raising adolescents?" The colleague was by no means a simple-minded person, recognized that there was no simple answer to his question, and knew that many factors are involved in raising an adolescent. It was a question raised in the course of a dinner conversation and it would not have been proper for me to have started giving a lecture on the multiplicity of factors that would be important to consider. He was basically asking me what factor I would put at the top of the list. He was also asking me to state that which sprung first into my mind, without giving too much thought to the question—in the hope that I might thereby come out with the most important one.

My response was: "Try, if you can, to find something that they can teach you. Try to find an area in which they are genuinely superior to you and avail yourself of the opportunity to learn from them." As discussed in Chapter One, adolescents suffer with significant feelings of inadequacy. Although physically adult and capable of procreation, they are basically still children. They do not have the wherewithal for independent functioning in our complex, industrialized society and are basically quite dependent on their parents for food, clothing, shelter, and even guidance (although they may try to deny their need for the latter). Many of their irritating behaviors are compensatory for these feelings of inadequacy. If the youngster genuinely has an area of expertise, which will enable him or her to serve a useful purpose for the parent, then he or she will not only enjoy an enhanced sense of self-worth but will not have to resort so quickly to injudicious and sometimes pathological forms of compensation for feelings of low self-worth.

A youngster, for example, who is knowledgable about computers, will appreciate that his father is functioning at "the idiot level" in this area. By "educating the poor slob" he not only can lord his superiority over his father but perform a useful service for a "retarded person." Some youngsters may be able to gain these gratifications from having superior knowledge about repairing the family car. Many school subjects allow for the exhibition of such superiority: science, social studies, foreign languages, literature, etc. Parents do well to avail themselves of the "wisdom" of their adolescents and to praise them when it is so imparted. They do well also to express their gratification over having the good fortune for having a youngster who is so knowedgable. The adolescent is likely to consider him- or herself an expert on a particular subject on the basis of the fact that he or she has written a report on it that received an A grade. Although the parent may recognize that the expertise so gained is specious and that the youngster still remains abysmally ignorant about the subject, the parent still does well to learn what he or she can (most often the case) about what the adolescent can teach. I have previously used the word *genuine* when referring to this issue. This is an important point. This is no time for "buttering up" the youngster and professing that one is learning something when one really isn't. The parent does well to find some area in which the adolescent can realistically provide information that the parent is ignorant of. If the adolescent has absolutely nothing that he or she can provide, then that youngster is not going to be able to derive the benefits of this experience.

Therapists are no exception here. They too do well to try to ascertain areas in which the adolescent is indeed superior to them. Here again, school subjects may serve this purpose. If the therapist can make statements such as: "I don't know much about that," "You know much more about that than I do," and "I'd like to hear what you can tell me about that, because I know very little about that subject," he or she may be able to provide a useful therapeutic service for the patient. Again, I am not suggesting that all sessions be devoted to the adolescent's educating the therapist; I am only saying that some time spent on these kinds of conversations can be therapeutically useful. It enhances the patient's self-worth and this cannot but contribute to an alleviation of the wide variety of psychogenic symptoms that derive from feelings of low self-esteem. It entrenches the therapist-patient relationship, the foundation upon which the therapy rests.

Relating One's Own Personal
Experiences to the Patient

Many children enjoy immensely hearing about the events in their parent's lives that occurred in their own childhood: "Tell me Mommy, how were things in your house with Grandma and Grandpa when you were nine, when you were my age." When parents provide their children with details about their early lives they entrench their relationships with them. The divulgences also are a manifestation of the intimacy of the relationship enjoyed by both. Although adolescents are less interested in such conversations (they are people of the present and future, not the past), they still have some interest in and can benefit from them. Therapists, too, can provide such revelations and enjoy thereby the therapeutic benefits to be derived from them. As mentioned previously, such revelations about the therapist—judiciously made—can entrench the therapist-patient relationship because they bring the patient and the therapist closer to one another. However, these revelations should not be made indiscriminately. They should always be made with the purpose of helping the patient in his or her treatment. A divulgence should be selected which has direct relevance to the patient's problems. Otherwise, the therapy may degenerate into a situation where the patient is being used for the therapist's treatment—an exploitation if there ever was one. The therapist's experience may serve as a metaphor for the patient's experience and provide a useful therapeutic communication to the patient without his or her realizing that such is the case.

For example, in the context of a conversation relating to the patient's devastation over being jilted by a girlfriend for another boy, the therapist may relate his own experience in this area when he or she was an adolescent. Obviously, all the details need not be divulged. Rather, the therapist does well to select those aspects that might be of use to the patient. Just knowing that the therapist has had similar experiences can lessen the boy's burden. Knowing that the therapist, whom the youngster may have viewed as being perfect and therefore beyond rejection, has also had this experience makes it easier for him to bear the pains of his rejection. Telling the youngster that his has been a common experience may be helpful. Telling the youngster that the therapist has also had the experience is a little more helpful. But providing some specific details about one or two such rejections can be even more therapeutic in that the concrete example generally has more clout than a theoretical statement. Similarly, if the youngster is dissapointed over not having gained admission to a particular college the therapist might tell about his own experiences in this area. If, however, the therapist has not had that experience then he does well to choose another area of disappointment. (If the therapist had no such disappointments, rejections, etc., he or she would probably not have become a therapist.)

Discouraging Pathological
Use of the Treatment

One of the dangers of psychoanalysis and psychoanalytically oriented therapy is that patients will come to see themseves as helpless victims of their unconscious processes. The notion of conscious control becomes less important in modifying behavior than control by the unconscious. Therapists do well to avoid such a misinterpretation of the psychotherapeutic process. We never know more than a small fraction of the numerous unconscious factors that may be operative in bringing about a particular symptom. We really are not certain how much the insight process brings about therapeutic change. We do know, however, that most patients (even those who are psychotic) have some degree of conscious control over their behavior. Accordingly, I believe that therapists do well to err on the side of assuming that their patients have control over what they are doing. Because of our ignorance of where the line can be drawn between control and noncontrol, we do better for our patients to assume that they have this control and only accept the fact that they haven't when the evidence is overwhelming that this is the case. In short, therapists do well to take a hard line against patients' comments that they are sick and therefore cannot control their behavior. It is important for the reader to appreciate that such an approach is not warranted when the patient is indeed psychotic and really cannot control his or her behavior. But even some psychotic symptoms are controllable. Often, psychotics will not exhibit their symptoms in situations in which they might be put in jail or committed to a hospital. Of course, there are others who are so sick that deterrents do not operate.

When communicating with the nonpsychotic patient's school, either directly or through the parents, school authorities should be told that the patient should not be given any special considerations because he or she is in treatment. If the school is providing such indulgence, it is likely to entrench the pathology by providing secondary gains for its perpetuation. Many teachers will be hesitant to impose traditional disciplinary measures because they "feel sorry" for the youngster who is in therapy. This is a mistake. Some youngsters are given higher grades than they deserve, again because of the misguided belief on the part of school personnel that the patient is less capable of handling the disappointments associated with a low grade. Failing marks become suddenly transformed into Cs and Ds on the day of the last report card. I call such marks "mercy grades" and strongly discourage teachers from giving them. Also, I generally advise parents to request that the patient's teachers give only those grades he or she deserves—nothing higher and nothing lower. And if, at the end of the school year, a course is not passed then the youngster should be required to repeat it over the summer. And if a few courses are not passed, then the youngster should be required to repeat the grade. Promoting on to the next grade is a terrible disservice. The patient is ill-equipped to handle the more demanding material and may then deal with this embarrassment by dropping out of school entirely. Repeating a grade is certainly embarrassing; but more humiliating is the experience of being over one's head in a higher grade and suffering thereby the daily embarrassments of being significantly behind one's peers. The former mortification is generally acute and short-lived; the latter may very well result in lifelong embarrassment. Similarly, at home, disciplinary measures should be imposed in accordance with traditional household practice and the patient should not be given any special dispensation because he or she is in treatment. Providing such indulgence does not prepare the youngster to function in the real world, which will not provide such special considerations. Accordingly, it is a terrible disservice. Again, my comments here are relevant to the nonpsychotic youngster. Patients who are so sick that special considerations are warranted regarding grading and class placements should be in special classes and even special schools. My comments here are relevant to the healthier youngster, the more common adolescent patient one sees in treatment.

"If You're Going to Take Something Away From Someone, You Should Give Him (Her) Something Back in Return."

This is an old saying which has applicability in many situations, but is especially applicable in therapy. In a sense, many of the things that we do in therapy is a taking-away process. We are being asked to "take away" symptoms and we may make the assumption that this can be done without giving something back in return. As mentioned previously, symptoms are not 100 percent destructive and maladaptive. They also have cohesive value and their constructive factors must be appreciated by the therapist. I believe that therapists with a deep commitment to behavior modification as the primary therapeutic process do not give proper attention to this factor when they consider the symptom and the disease to be the same. I am not claiming, as some did in the early stages of psychoanalysis, that removal of a symptom would automatically result in another one popping up unless the underlying problems were completely resolved. Rather, I am saying that we must appreciate that symptoms arise as an attempt to deal with fundamental life conflicts and removing them without giving proper attention to the underlying problems is not likely to work as well as a therapeutic approach that takes unconscious factors into serious consideration. Throughout this book I have been critical of many aspects of psychoanalytic theory and treatment. However, there are many aspects of the psychoanalytic approach that I have deep conviction for and incorporate into my work. My criticism of psychoanalysis notwithstanding, I believe strongly that unconscious factors play an important role in the development of psychogenic psychopathology and that a therapeutic approach that does not give serious consideration to them is far less likely to be effective than one that does.

Adolescents need to rebel. Therapists must differentiate between healthy and unhealthy forms of rebellion. We should not be trying to squelch rebellion entirely. Rather, we should attempt to make a shift, to change pathological forms of rebellion into neutral and even healthy ones. At the same time that the therapist is trying to discourage a youngster from antisocial acting out that is destructive and dangerous, he or she should take a supportive position regarding the utilization of age-appropriate innocuous forms of rebellion such as wearing hair and clothing styles that are "in" for adolescents and viewed as noxious by adults, espousing rebellious philosophies (without acting out), and professing political views that are directly at variance with those of the parents and extended families. A girl with strong sexual urges who is engaging in promiscuous sex is not likely to be helped by the therapist's merely discouraging sexual behavior. One certainly wants to go into the psychodynamic factors operative in the sexual promiscuity and help her work out these problems. No matter how successful the therapist may be toward attaining this goal, the facts are that the girl is still likely to have sexual urges that require release. Dance, sports, and other forms of sublimation may allow for some gratification. But generally these are not enough. Accordingly, the therapist would still do well to encourage selectivity, exclusivity, and masturbation.

Such substitution, unfortunately, cannot always be easily accomplished. For example, a youngster may be drinking heavily. Of the many factors operative in the formation of this symptom an important one might relate to the fact that all of the youngster's friends drink as well. To advise such a patient to stay away from friends who drink is not likely to work in that the patient is being asked to substitute loneliness for camaraderie. The more obvious solution, that the youngster get friends who don't drink, is not likely to be easily accomplished. First, it is probably the case that there are more adolescents who drink than there are those who don't. But there are certainly many adolescents who still do not drink, or do not drink excessively. The problem here, however, is that the nondrinkers may not want to have very much to do with the patient who is deeply involved in the drinking scene. They are different kinds of human beings, have different interests, are on different wave lengths, and are not likely to get along very well. Group therapy can sometimes be helpful to such youngsters in that it helps them acquire some of the social skills necessary for shifting into a healthier group.

The Comparison of the Therapist's Statements with the Parents' Statements

It is common for adolescents in treatment to say to the therapist: "That's exactly what my mother and father say. And that's one of the reasons I don't like you. What are they doing? Sending you letters?" My response to this usually goes along these lines: "Yes, you're right on that point. My view on that issue is identical with that of your parents. However, if you consider me to be their rubber stamp, you're wrong. If you'll think back, I'm sure you'll agree that there were times when I've criticized them and taken your side. I work on the principle that I call the shots as I see them. When I agree with them, I will state so; and when I agree with you, I'll say so as well. I'm nobody's parrot." There are therapists, unfortunately, who take care not to espouse the parents' position to the patient lest they be viewed by the youngster as being the ally of the parents. Such therapists are making an error. There are times when we should be the allies of the parents, and there are times when we should be the ally of the youngster. We should always be the ally of what we consider to be the healthy position. Some therapists believe that if they take the parents' position, under any circumstances, that they will be the target of the same hostility that the parent is receiving. This may very well be the case, but it is not a justifiable reason for lying low and hiding one's true position. There are therapists who believe that they will compromise the child's receptivity to their advice if they take the parents' position on a particular subject. This is an error. The youngster's receptivity is going to be based on the nature of the relationship that has evolved and relates to the multiplicity of factors contributing to the development of that relationship. And there are therapists who believe that strictly siding with the patient is necessary for the establishment of a good therapist-patient relationship and if they were to side with the parents, even once, then the relationship might be compromised, if not destroyed. This too is an error. A relationship is based on many factors. If it is a good one, the youngster will be able to tolerate benevolently motivated criticisms, which may at times be identical to those made by the parents. If it is a poor relationship, it is not going to be helped by strictly protecting the youngster from confrontations with the reality of his or her life.

One of the purposes of treatment is to open the patient's eyes and help the youngster deal more realistically with life's problems. Most adolescents in treatment live in a dream world. They have delusions of invulnerability and fantasies that are often grandiose. They are choosing unrealistic and self-destructive resolutions to their life's problems. Therapy must help them open their eyes and see the world more realistically. This is what the parents have generally been trying to do and, on most issues, it is likely that the therapist will be trying to accomplish the same thing with the patient. The youngster needs all the help he or she can get. The youngster needs input from many sources: parents, teachers, and the therapist. Shutting up because the youngster complains about the reiteration is not a reason for keeping quiet. It works against the principles of therapy. I am not suggesting that the therapist ignore the fact that reiteration may reach a point of diminishing returns. The therapist's droning on, in spite of the fact that the patient is tuning him or her out, is likely to be antitherapeutic. Rather, I am only saying that the therapist should not avoid reiteration because the patient accuses him or her of saying the same things that the parents have stated.

SEXUAL AND DATING PROBLEMS

I will use sexual and dating problems to serve as examples for some of the principles presented above. I have selected this area because it is one of the more common ones dealt with in the treatment of adolescents. As mentioned, it is not the purpose of this book to cover the treatment of the wide variety of adolescent disorders that the therapist may have to deal with. Rather, it is its purpose to present general principles of treatment of such youngsters and to provide clinical examples from the therapy of some of the more common problems. These principles, I believe, will serve the therapist well in the treatment of other disorders not specifically focused on in this book. Furthermore, one therapist can only have experience with a limited segment of the wide variety of psycho-pathological problems that these youngsters can exhibit. Because most psychopathological problems are derived in the attempt to deal with basic life issues, there is much overlap in the treatment of these disorders. Because sexual and dating problems are among the common difficulties that confront adolescents, knowledge of the treatment of these difficulties will often serve therapists well in the treatment of other disorders of youngsters in this age group.

The Therapist's Values Regarding
Adolescent Sexual Activities

One cannot discuss dating and sex among adolescents without dealing with the issue of values. Accordingly, I will present at this point my own values regarding sex among teenagers. Some of this presentation is an elaboration of my discussion of sexual relation-ships in Chapter One. I recognize that my values in this area may not only be different from those of some readers but are different from those of patients I see as well. Youngsters and their parents are entitled to information regarding the therapist's values in this area before involving their youngster in treatment. As mentioned in Chapter Five all therapy involves the imposition of the therapist's values on the patient. Most often, especially in the realm of antisocial behavior, the therapist and the parents share the same values. The subject of sexual values, however, is more often a "touchy subject," especially when the parents are strongly commit-ted to conservative religious beliefs. Furthermore, the reader will be in a better position to appreciate my discussion of the treatment of adolescent sexual problems after a presentation of my own values in this realm.

I believe that it is psychologically healthy (a term that is a substitute for what *my* values are) for a youngster to engage in heterosexual caressing, kissing, and petting, on occasion in the early adolescent period. In the mid-adolescent period, I believe it is healthier for things to "steam up" to the point where the youngster enjoys orgasm. And by 17 or 18 I believe it is healthy for the youngster to have sexual intercourse. However, I believe that parents do well to impress upon their youngsters that the sexual experience is likely to be more gratifying if there is an ongoing intimate relationship with the sexual partner. Transient sex should be discouraged, with the parents' appreciation however that a certain amount of sex might still be engaged in. It is hoped that the youngster will have the *living experience* that sex in the context of an ongoing relationship is ultimately more gratifying. My values here are not that stringent to preclude entirely transient sexual experiences. At the same time, I believe that it is *crucial* that parents impress upon their youngsters the risks of pregnancy and the terrible drawbacks of out-of-wedlock teen pregnancies. In addition, they are grossly negligent if they do not warn their youngsters about the dangers of sexually transmitted diseases, especially AIDS. At the time of this writing (early 1988), the AIDS epidemic is becoming ever more frightening and the warnings for sexual selectivity and the use of condoms ever more compelling. Unfortunately, the oft-mentioned adolescent delusions of invulnerability may work against the youngster's heeding this warning.

Furthermore, parents do well to encourage masturbation as an acceptable release for sexual cravings. They do well to promulgate the notion that no human being need suffer sexual frustration and that when heterosexual opportunities are not available, masturbation is a perfectly acceptable and even desirable outlet. I have often said that the ideal birthday present for a 13-year-old boy would be a five-year subscription to Playboy magazine and a lock on his bedroom door. And the ideal gift for a 13-year-old girl would be a vibrator and a five-year subscription to a teenage romance magazine. (I believe that males are more likely to be "turned on" by stark visual-sexual representations, whereas females are more likely to be turned on by loving and romantic fantasies.)

In my value system I do not consider abortion to be a sin or an inappropriate way of dealing with an unwanted pregnancy. I recognize, however, that there are others who have very strong beliefs that abortion is merely another form of murder and that there is absolutely no situation under which it is justifiable. From the psychological point of view, I believe that the earlier the abortion is done the less the psychological trauma to the mother. Abortions during the first trimester can generally be accomplished through dilatation and curettage (D and C) and are less likely to be traumatic than a second trimester abortion in which labor is induced and an actual fetus comes forth.

In the initial interview the parents have every right to question the therapist about his or her position on these subjects. This does not preclude inquiries into the possible psychological implications of their questions, but they are still entitled to the therapist's direct answers on these subjects. Classical analysts would be unreceptive to such a conversation and would use each of these questions by the parents as a point of departure for psychoanalytic inquiry. I object to this approach in this situation. First, the parents are not analytic patients; they are the parents of the adolescent patient. Second, they are entitled to answers to these questions and the therapist should be willing to provide them. Again, this does not preclude additional discussions regarding the analytic implications of the questions.

I recall a situation in which parents, very religious Catholics, brought their 15-year-old daughter to me. In the first two-hour consultation they very firmly stated that they did not want me to talk about sex with their daughter. I told them that I would make no such promise and that if I am to conduct the therapy properly I must have the right to discuss any issue at all that I consider relevant to a youngster's problems. I told them, as well, that I would not force their daughter to talk about sex if she didn't want to, but that I cannot imagine my conducting a therapeutic program with a 15-year-old girl without the subject coming up at some time or other. I told them that if they felt that this answer was not acceptable to them that it would probably be better for them to seek treatment elsewhere. I informed them as well that I did not believe that any competent therapist would agree to such a restriction on the treatment and that if a therapist did agree to such a restriction they would do well to think about the qualifications of such a person. Although obviously unhappy with my response they agreed to go along with the treatment.

In the next session, the first with the patient alone, she told me that her parents told her that they would let her continue treatment (which she argued strongly for), but made her promise them that she would not talk about sex. I told her that she was free to talk about anything and everything she wanted to and if there was a subject that she did not want to talk about I was not going to coerce her. However, I informed her as well that my experience has been that the most important subjects to talk about in treatment are generally just those very topics that patients don't want to talk about. However, my bottom line statement was that it was her treatment and she was free to talk about anything she wanted to and free not to talk about things she didn't wish to. During the next four or five sessions, she carefully avoided talking about sex. She did get some definite therapeutic mileage out of these discussions of other issues, some of which were not related to sex at all and others only remotely so.

It was at this point that the patient came in with a dream that she herself easily recognized as having obvious sexual implications. She then informed me that her parents had questioned her after each session about whether or not she was discussing sex. Heretofore, she was able to honestly deny that she had and so felt comfortable with the treatment. Now she was faced with a dilemma. If she were to be honest and tell her parents that she discussed sex with me—even though it was she who brought in the dream and that it was she who first recognized its sexual implications—they would pull her out of treatment. If she told them that she did not discuss sex, she would be lying and she would feel guilty about that. In the course of the discussion I pointed out to her that since it was 99.9 percent predictable that her parents would discontinue her treatment if she mentioned the dream, she should consider the possibility that mentioning it might be a way for her to withdraw from the therapy and it would thereby serve as a resistance against the treatment. We discussed also the issue of the resistance not simply being over the discussion of sexual material but other anxiety-provoking issues that had been discussed in previous sessions. The session ended with her not knowing exactly what she would do. The following day I received a telephone call from the father informing me that he was withdrawing his daughter from treatment and that all future sessions were cancelled. He told me that his daughter had informed him that we had talked about sex and that he was going to find a therapist who agreed beforehand not to discuss any sexual issues whatsoever. I wished him luck and, needless to say, I have never heard from these people again.

Since the late 1960s we have experienced what is justifiably called a "sexual revolution." The most dramatic confirmation of this is the ever increasing rate of teenage pregnancies. Prior to the late 1960s, teenage girls generally were quite ashamed to admit that they had sexual intercourse or even sexual experiences. The pendulum has so shifted that many girls are ashamed to admit that they are virgins, especially after a year or two of college. Another reflection of this change is the greater freedom that women have to use profanity. When I was a teenager, in the 1940s, girls who used profanity were generally viewed as crude and even loose. This is no longer the case. A 13-year-old girl was brought by her mother recently at her request. She sought consultation to determine whether or not she had psychological problems because most of her girlfriends had already started to masturbate and she had no urge to engage in the practice at that point. Both the patient and her mother considered this a justifiable reason for seeking a consultation. The girl freely spoke about the subject without any embarrassment. I informed her that I did not consider her to be abnormal and that some people do have strong sexual urges by her age and some do not. From everything else I learned about her I considered it safe to predict that she would be starting to have stronger urges within the next couple of years and that at that time, if she felt the desire, I would consider it perfectly acceptable and normal for her to masturbate. However, I impressed upon her that she should not do it in order to keep up with her friends, but because she herself felt the desire and the need.

Such a consultation would have been unimaginable 20 years ago. And I say this for two reasons. First, the youngster would not have brought it up as a reason for consultation and, even if she did, I can't imagine a mother agreeing that her failure to masturbate at 13 might very well be a manifestation of psychiatric problems. Second, even if she did get to my office for this reason, it would be hard to imagine her speaking in such a relaxed fashion about the subject. In general, my experience has been that pubertal and post-pubertal girls are far less inhibited talking to me about their sexual feelings than they were in the past and therefore I am seeing more females in this age bracket in recent years than I did in past years. I consider this a good trend because many of these girls come from divorced homes in which they have little if any contact with their fathers.

Helping Reluctant Boys Make
Their Initial Dating Overtures

Boys are generally quite fearful of "making the first move"—lest they be rejected. The recent sexual revolution and the modern-day notions of sexual egalitarianism notwithstanding, boys are still the ones who are expected to make the first overtures. (I am not saying that this is either good or bad; I am only stating what is the prevailing practice in our society.) Many boys are filled with various rationalizations for not making the first move. My general approach here is to utilize what I call the *door-to-door salesman principle*. I tell the boy about the experience of the door-to-door salesman who must have the guts (or "balls") to tolerate the frustrations and lowered feelings of self-worth that come with each rejection. They are willing to suffer these discomforts because of their awareness that a certain percentage (often predictable) will ultimately buy their wares. And this happy thought enables them to tolerate their inevitable rejections. Therapists do well to help the adolescent compare himself to such a salesman. They do well to reassure the boy that even if he is rejected by girl number one, and even if he is rejected by girl number two, there is certainly girl number three or four who will be more receptive. This does not preclude my looking into personality qualities of his that might be contributing to his rejection.

Some boys will rationalize their reticence to make overtures with comments such as "All the girls in my school are 'dogs' or 'ugly'." To this I may respond, "From what you describe it appears that sometime around 16 years ago someone put some poison in the town drinking water that brought about severe facial deformities in all the girls that were born at that time." The youngster usually gets my message. I also try to impress upon such boys that I am "100 percent convinced" that there are girls in his very high school who would be overjoyed at the prospect of having a date with him. I also try to impress upon such youngsters the fact that the girls are as "horny" as the boys and that they too are extremely desirous of forming relationships with them.

Next, we reach the point of the initial telephone conversation. Once again, I impress upon such youngsters that anxiety under these circumstances is normal, and that even overwhelming anxiety is normal. However, I inform them that the difference between the brave man and the coward is simply this: whereas both the brave man and the coward are basically afraid, the brave man swallows the lump in his throat and does the thing he's frightened of; the coward flees. I also impress upon the youngster the *nothing ventured nothing gained* principle. Right now he is lonely. If he doesn't make the call he'll remain lonely. If he makes the call there are two possibilities: 1) The girl will be receptive and he is likely to have an enjoyable experience and 2) The girl will reject him and he will once again be lonely. Although such advice may seem obvious, it is not so obvious to the adolescent youngster and he may need repeated proddings of this kind to get him to make the telephone call.

I also try to impress upon the youngster the fact that we cannot be uniformly loved by all people on earth. In fact, only an infinitesimal fraction of people are going to be strongly attracted to us. Accordingly, we cannot take it personally when we are rejected. Although there may be alienating personality qualities (which we certainly must look at in treatment) the rejection may have nothing to do with the rejected individual but simply related to the fact that the boy is not the girl's "type." I also impress upon the youngster that our discussion is actually the *lecture* part of the course and that more important is the *lab* part of the course in which he goes out, makes the call, and then comes back and tells me about what happened. If he doesn't have the gumption to make the call, then his treatment is likely to be sterile, intellectualized, and not go very far. In some cases I will even sternly tell the youngster that his making the call is a "homework assignment" and that I will be very disappointed in him if he comes back next time not having done his assignment.

I have found it useful to engage the youngster in a "practice" telephone call in which I play the role of the girl he is calling and he plays himself. We then enact various scenarios which involve both acceptance and rejection. Usually, I get significant input from him regarding what I should be saying and inform the youngster that because he knows the girl far better than I he is more likely to speculate what responses she might make. In the course of such a scenario I educate the youngster regarding the significance of the girl's responses. For example, I help him differentiate between the response "Sorry I'm busy" with nothing stated thereafter from "Sorry I'm busy" and an invitation to discuss alternative arrangements. If the youngster is placing himself in a humiliating position I will often point this out to him as a step toward helping him protect himself from future such embarrassment. For example, if the youngster reports to me that he had offered six different alternatives after the first telephone rejection, and was rejected on each, I will inform him that that was far too many. Two, or at most three, should be the upper limit—unless the girl provides convincing reasons why she cannot accept the invitation and suggests on her own an alternative time and place. I help the patient appreciate that such a response indicates that she is quite receptive to going out with him and her refusal to accept the first invitation is not a manifestation of disinterest. As will be discussed in Chapter Eleven, the section on adolescent group therapy, such conversations may be particularly useful when the girls in the group provide their input. And the role-playing of such conversations may also be useful.

Sometimes a boy will complain to me that the girl's situation is the preferable one in dating because she doesn't have to suffer the fear of being rejected. She knows that once an overture is made the boy has singled her out from others and is demonstrating interest and attraction. I try to point out to such boys that they are taking a narrow view of the situation and that each sex has its advantages and disadvantages in the dating situation. Furthermore, it is difficult to say which one's position is the preferable one at that stage of life. Although the boy is correct here that, with regard to this aspect of dating, the girl does not have to suffer the fear of being rejected, she suffers the anxiety of not being chosen. Present mores strongly dictate that the boy be the assertive one and make the initial approach. The girls experience thereby a certain sense of impotency in that they may have little if any control over whether or not they will be selected. Of course, a certain amount of flirting and expression of interest in the boys may result in their "coming on," but such maneuvers may very well fail.

I try to engender in each sex a sense of sensitivity to the other. For example, a girl who is pretty, vivacious, and sought after by many boys may become insensitive in the way she rejects them or even taunt and tantalize them in a sadistic way. She has to be helped to appreciate how hostile her mechanisms for self-aggrandizement are and has to be helped to place herself in the position of the boys and appreciate how she would feel in their situation. Similarly, there are attractive boys who will be cruel in their rejection of girls who have demonstrated their interest.

I present now a clinical vignette that demonstrates well the approach to initiate dating I used with a sexually inhibited 14-year-old boy. Harry entered treatment because of poor school performance, in spite of extremely high intelligence, and profound shyness. Both his parents were professional scientists and highly unemotional and intellectualized. Their pressures on Harry to perform well in the academic area were formidable. Harry's poor school performance was, in part, a rebellion against his parents' coercions. In addition, they had a condescending attitude toward practically everyone and little meaningful involvement with anyone outside their family. Harry's shyness and uninvolvement with others was a reflection of his parents' attitudes about people. The family was Catholic, very religious, and puritanical in their attitudes about profanity, sex, and pleasurable activities.

After about a year of therapy, Harry joined his parochial school's computer club, where he immediately became recognized as the most knowledgeable and enthusiastic member. The activity suited him well because of his very high intelligence and his interest in activities that did not involve emotional expression. A few months after joining he began to report in session his club's new project: computerized matching of boys in his school with the girls of a nearby Catholic school. All students in both schools were to fill out a questionnaire describing various basic physical characteristics, interests, personality preferences in members of the opposite sex, etc. All these data were to be fed into a computer and every boy and girl would be matched to three others. A large dance was to be held, everyone was to be assigned a number, and at prescribed times each student would dance with the partner assigned by the computer.

For weeks Harry spoke excitedly of the details of this project. I was most pleased about it, not only because of his enthusiasm (a rare quality for Harry to exhibit) but because it would provide Harry with the opportunity to involve himself with girls in a way that would produce less anxiety than some of the more traditional methods of boy-girl meeting. When the week came for the students to fill out their questionnaires, Harry spoke animatedly about the large numbers of questionnaires being received and how happy he was that everything pointed to the program's being a success. In the context of this discussion I casually asked Harry what answers he had written on his questionnaire. Harry replied, "Oh, I'm not putting in any questionnaire. My job is to organize the whole thing and make sure that everything works well with the computer." I was astonished. For weeks we had spoken about this activity and not once did I ever consider the possibility that Harry himself would not enter. The session took place the day before the deadline for the submission of the questionnaires. There was little time to work things out, to help Harry assuage his anxieties, and to help him appreciate what he was doing.

Speaking more as a frustrated father than as a therapist, I told Harry that I was astonished that he wasn't submitting his own questionnaire. I told him he was making a grave error, that everybody gets nervous in such situations, and that he has to push through his fears if he is to enjoy the rewards of a new situation. I spoke quickly and somewhat heatedly—ending with the the warning that if he came back to the next session without having submitted his questionnaire I would not only be very disappointed in him but very irritated with him as well.

One could argue that my approach was extremely antitherapeutic. I was coercing this boy; I was pushing him into an anxiety-provoking situation; I would be producing unnecessary guilt and self-loathing if he did not comply with my request; and I was jeapordizing the therapeutic relationship by such coercive and antitherapeutic tactics. I agree completely with these criticisms and I was completely aware of these dangers as I spoke to Harry. My hope was that this risk would be more than counterbalanced by Harry's appreciation, at some level, that my frustration, anger, and coercion came from a deep sense of concern; that only an uninvolved therapist could sit calmly by and allow him to pass up this wonderful opportunity. (I am reminded at this point of a psychiatric ward nurse who once reported to me overhearing a conversation among three children. The first said, "My mother's a bitch." The second, "My father's always hitting me." And the third, "My father never even hits me!" Obviously the third's situation was the worst.

Having a father who never even bothers to discipline and even punish is a severe deprivation indeed.) I hoped also that the general strength of our relationship was such that he not only would comply, but that he would appreciate that I was being basically benevolent.

Harry did submit his questionnaire. On the night of the dance he "could not find" one of the girls with whom he was matched and the second "didn't show up." However, he did spend some time with the third. But because he didn't know how to dance (and forgot my suggestion that he ask her to teach him a few steps), they talked awhile and then went their separate ways. I was not surprised that no great romance developed from this first encounter with a female. One cannot expect a patient to overcome lifelong inhibitions in one evening. However, the ice was broken. Had I not reacted as I had, I believe that Harry would not have taken this step and I would have therefore been somewhat remiss in my obligation to him. I saw no evidence that Harry's relationship with me had in any way suffered because of my coercion; in fact, I believe that it was strengthened. However, this improvement could not have taken place if the coercion had not occurred at a time after a good relationship had already formed. To have used such an approach very early in treatment might very well have destroyed, or seriously compromised, our relationship.

Helping Sexually Inhibited Boys

Sometimes a sexually inhibited boy can be made to feel less guilty about his sexual desires by my demonstrating sexual interest of my own. For example, when a boy tells me that he feels somewhat guilty about the fact that he is interested in and turned on by girlie magazines such as *Playboy* I might say, somewhat sarcastically, "I think the best way I can help you with those feelings is to take a look at that magazine myself, especially the centerfold. It's only when we discuss this with an actual picture in hand that we will be in a good position to talk about your feelings. Of course, I'm doing this purely from a *clinical* point of view. (I may then start smiling.) It's not that I have any *personal* interest in seeing those pictures. It's purely for *your* therapy. If you think for one minute that I myself would be titillated by such pictures you would be entirely wrong." Almost invariably the patient gets my message which, I believe, helps assuage his guilt. Basically I am saying that I too find those pictures titillating and this helps the patient feel less loathsome for his own interest. I believe that this is one of the situations in treatment where sarcasm is warranted in that it enhances the efficacy of the therapeutic message. If a boy feels inhibited about masturbating over such pictures, I try to assuage his guilt and impress upon him that this is an extremely widespread phenomenon and that most boys, if they were to be honest, would admit that they engage in the practice. If he claims that most of his friends deny that they do so, I try to convince him of the fact that they are most likely lying. I may tell him, "There are two kinds of boys: those who jerk off over these pictures and *admit* that they do and those who jerk off over such pictures and *deny* that they do." If the youngster has any misguided or erroneous notions about the dangers of masturbation, I will try to correct these distortions. He may believe that masturbation causes sexually transmitted diseases, sterility, rings under the eyes, or other telltale signs. All these distortions must be corrected.

A 16-year-old boy once told me that he had read in the newspapers that some women in Washington D.C. were going to protest the city's law that women are not permitted to appear in public with their chests bare, whereas men can. They were going to protest en masse by appearing publicly, completely bare from the waist up. This was told to me by a boy who was quite inhibited in telling me about his own interests in girls. In response to his information about the Washingon demonstration I took my pen and pad and said, "That's very interesting. Where did you say that demonstration was going to be held? What city did you say? When did you say it was going to take place? I'm very interested in the exact day and the exact time. And I'd like to know *exactly* where they're going to be demonstrating. These are the kinds of demonstrations that *really* interest me." The patient quickly got my message. I too was telling him that I thought it was a turn-on. Of course, the patient appreciated that I was not actually going to make a trip to Washington, but my intense interest (exaggerated somewhat) transmitted to him the message that I found the prospect titillating. I continued then: "I'm fully sympathetic with what these women are doing. The law is inegalitarian and I'm 100 percent against it. I'm convinced the world would be a better place if women were free to walk around topless. These women have a definite *point* to make, or should I say *points*." By this time the patient was chuckling along with me. I was not only providing here a guilt-assuaging message in an enjoyable vehicle but, possibly more important, was adding a note of levity to the therapy—counterbalancing thereby what can often be a morbid and grim experience. This is likely to entrench our relationship and strengthen thereby the foundation of the therapeutic process.

It has been my purpose in this section to discuss primarily the approaches I utilize when helping youngsters become more comfortable in the dating situation. I will, however, present here one of the most important bits of advice I provide all men (adolescent or adult) when counseling them regarding their sexual involvement with women. I generally refer to this as the *"ladies first" principle.* All young men should be introduced to this principle in their adolescence and it is unfortunate (for both men and women) that too few adolescent boys are given this important advice. Once the youngster starts becoming engaged in sexual activities I tell him about some important biological differences between men and women regarding orgastic capacity. I advise him of the fact that there is great variation among women regarding the speed with which they become aroused—varying from those who take an extremely long time to those who may be aroused almost instantaneously. Accordingly, I advise patience and tenderness with those women who are slow to become aroused. I then move into the subject of orgasm and apprise the youngster of the fact that women are generally more capable of achieving multiple orgasms, often in rapid succession, than are men. Even women who are extremely slow to be aroused, once they reach orgasm, may be capable of achieving one after another. Men, in contrast, have varying degrees of what is known as a "refractory period." This is the time of loss of arousal that immediately follows ejaculation. Some men have a relatively short refractory period (a few minutes), but most men have longer refractory periods (as long as a few hours). The older the man the greater the likelihood of a longer refractory period. Also, during the refractory period the man is less likely to be able to maintain an erection and thereby satisfy the woman intravaginally.

Accordingly, if the man reaches his orgasm first he may not be in the mood to continue sexual involvement with the woman, whether with an erect penis or in any other way. This can leave the woman frustrated and resentful. If the man holds back, however, until the woman reaches her orgasm (or a few orgasms) and then has his discharge, his refractory period will not generally be a source of significant frustration and/or resentment to the woman. I tell him that the *method* by which the woman reaches orgasm is not crucial; it doesn't matter whether the stimulation be penile, oral, or manual (by the lover or the woman herself). Nor is it important whether the site of primary stimulation is clitoral or vaginal. What is important is that the the man be patient and sympathetic so that the woman can reach her orgasm first.

I inform the patient that one of the most common complaints that women have about their male lovers is their lack of appreciation of these facts and their insensitivity to the woman's frustration after the men have enjoyed sexual release and not considered the woman's needs. I go further and inform the youngster that there are many lesbians who state that one of the important reasons they have turned to women for sex is because women are more sensitive to them and are appreciative of these important facts. So important is this principle that I believe even the most staunch feminists will generally agree that men who subscribe to this type of "ladies first" behavior are not sexist and are not "male chauvinist pigs." So vital is this principle that it may be the most important advice I give my adolescent boy patients in the course of their treatment. If they get nothing else out of the therapy, they will at least have obtained some help in becoming better lovers—and this cannot but be therapeutic.

Helping Girls Who Feel Unattractive

A girl feels unattractive. In the course of her therapy I help her appreciate that there are a wide range of facial and body types and that no one can be uniformly attractive to everyone. Although her particular appearance may not be attractive to some boys, there is no question that her appearance is attractive to others. And I point out that this is the case for everyone, including myself. The fact that her therapist has had his share of rejections makes it easier for her to accept hers. However, I don't stop there. I try to look into anything she might be doing that might be detracting from good grooming and attractive appearance. If this is the case, I *benevolently* point out these oversights to her and do what I can to help her rectify the situation. Sometimes, as a man, I recognize that my ability to provide such information may be compromised and I thereby advise her to speak with her mother, other adolescent girls, a beautician, and those who are more knowledgeable than I in this area. This does not preclude my going into the question of *why* she has not done what other girls her age are routinely doing. The adolescent girl may be more receptive to a discussion of *what* she can do for herself and improve her appearance than the issue of *why* she is not concerned with her grooming. Both areas are important even though the youngster may be more receptive to information about grooming than analytic inquiry.

If the youngster then shows efforts to improve her appearance I make it a point to mention my awareness of the changes. But I do not do this simply at the intellectual level. When the changes are made, I don't wait (as many classical analysts would) until the youngster says something. And, when I do speak up it's not simply at the intellectual level, for example, "I see you've changed your hairstyle" or "I see you're more careful now with the clothes you are choosing to wear." Rather, I will say, "I want you to know that I noticed the change as soon as you came into the room. It's striking how pretty you look now. I'm sure the boys' heads turn when you walk into the room." My hope here is to get across the message that I find the girl attractive and *somewhat* titillating. Some classical analysts would say that my comments here are seductive and therefore a terrible therapeutic contaminant. I am in disagreement. I am not communicating to the youngster specific sexual fantasies that she might now be engendering. Rather, I am merely communicating a mild level of titillation that most men would have in her presence. D.J. Holmes (1964) discusses this point in his vignette about an adolescent girl who was making efforts to make herself more attractive. With regard to the issue of what comments, if any, the therapist should make Holmes states (p.277): "If she has put much honest labor into restyling her hair or making an attractive dress for herself, it would probably be more damaging to withhold comment. She might secretly wonder if her therapist has gone blind, but would be even more likely to marvel at the magnitude of his inhibitedness....This open expression of appreciation on the part of the doctor naturally carries a hint of sexual interest. As such feelings are inevitable anyway, any effort to write them off entirely as 'countertransference' will be correctly interpreted by the patient as an act of emotional cowardice—an uneasy withdrawal from the very kinds of feelings which she finds so difficult to tolerate in herself."

Helping Promiscuous Girls

As mentioned, I consider a girl's having sexual intercourse in late adolescence to be normal and healthy. The ideal that I try to promulgate is the one that sex is most enjoyable in the context of an ongoing relationship, but an occasional experience outside of such a relationship can also be a source of pleasure. I emphasize also that such experiences outside of the relationship are likely to be a cause of pain and grief to one's special partner and that this must be taken into consideration before embarking on such additional experiences. I point out, as well, that in a marriage they are most often so devastating that they can contribute to the breakup of the marital relationship. I want to lay the groundwork here for dealing here with a future situation and/or conflict that the adolescent may very well ultimately have.

If a girl is promiscuous, i.e., she indiscriminately engages in sex with a large number of boys, there is generally a pathological problem operative. Often it relates to feelings of low self-worth, and the feeling that she could not attract boys without providing them with sex. I try to help such girls appreciate that they are humiliating themselves and that the lack of respect the boys have for them for their promiscuity is likely to lower even further their feelings of low self-worth. Some of these girls are so naive and gullible that they do not see the obvious fact that they are being exploited, so deep seated are their cravings for any manifestation of affection. I also look into other problems that may be contributing to the promiscuity. These may relate to family difficulties, deprivation of affection from mother and/or father, and various psychological traumas that may contribute to her looking for sexual gratification as an antidote to her grief, tensions, and frustrations. To the degree that one can help her work these out, to that degree will the therapist help her with her promiscuity problem.

CLINICAL EXAMPLE
OF A THERAPEUTIC REPORT

Recently, with increasing frequency, I have found it useful to provide adolescents I see in consultation with clinical reports in the form of a letter written directly to the patient. Reproduced here verbatim (with minor changes to hide his identity) is an example of such a letter to a 21-year-old boy (psychologically still very much a mid-adolescent) who came to me for consultation from a distant city. He manifested mild symptoms of schizophrenia, abused drugs and alcohol, yet was functioning well in many areas.

February 28, 1988

Dear Robert:

This is the report I promised to send you regarding my consultation conducted on February 23, 1988. As you know, my opinions regarding your situation are based on the three hours of interviews I conducted with you, your mother, and father as well as my review of your records—especially those from the T. Hospital. I want you to know that I consider your decision to get a report a judicious one in that many people do not remember all the things I say during consultations such as yours. Having this letter will enable you to refresh your memory should you wish to in the future.

I think you do well to consider yourself to have a disorder that affects the proper functioning of the nerve cells and pathways in your brain. On the basis of the tests that were performed and my own evaluation of you, I think it is reasonable to conclude that only certain small sections of your brain are involved. The rest appears to be working quite normally. No one knows with certainty exactly what kinds of impairment are involved in your disorder. The disorder is probably related to chemical and/or electrical impairments in nerve cell functioning. It is not only the nerve cells and their fibers that are involved but probably the places where the nerve cells connect with one another. Considering the fact that a number of people in both of your parents' families, especially your father's, suffered with what sound like psychiatric disturbances, it may be that you too have inherited some genetic predisposition to psychiatric disturbance. It would be a serious error, however, for you to consider yourself incapable of doing anything about this situation. We are not dealing here with something like hair color or eye color, which is also genetically determined. In the course of this letter I will make reference to the things you can do to help yourself.

One way of looking at your condition is to consider yourself to have a disorder that is very similar to seizures. Seizures result from firing off or discharing of nerve cell fibers at times when they shouldn't be, and in ways which they should not be. At times some of your nerve cells work in improper ways and so you start having thoughts and feelings which you recognize are strange, unusual, and probably not accurate. Your thoughts about your knee accident somehow being planned by others and your thoughts about women's vaginal bleeding are in this category.

I mentioned to you at our meeting that I suffer with a similar phenomenon related to a disorder of internal brain functioning. Specifically, I have mild hearing loss associated with ringing in the ears (called tinnitus). However, the tinnitus does not arise in the ears primarily but in the brain stem. When I pay attention to it it sounds like crickets or buzzing sounds. When I do not pay attention to it, it is as if it were not there. I have had it for about 10 years now and I have learned to live with it. When it gets louder I don't pay attention to it, and just do other things.

You do well to treat your strange thoughts as I treat my tinnitus: something not to take too seriously. Many people with your condition will refer to these strange ideas as the "crazy thoughts" and try not to take them seriously and do not act out on them. It is to your credit that most often you do not. People with more severe cases of your condition take them seriously and then get into difficulty because they may even act out on their thoughts and feelings because of their belief that they are true. It is fortunate, as well, that your thoughts do not take malevolent forms, that is, cause you to believe that people wish you harm or want to hurt you. People with more severe cases of your condition commonly have such kinds of thinking.

Just as people with seizure disorders can obtain relief from anticonvulsant medication, which suppress the nerve cell activity that produces seizures, the Haldol you are taking can suppress some of these "crazy thoughts." Your doctors have tried a number of different medications, and I have good reason to believe that the medications you are presently taking are proper. These are powerful medicines and, like all powerful medicines, there are strong side effects. From what I can see the Cogentin is suppressing the abnormal involuntary movements often produced by the Haldol. You describe yourself as somewhat fatigued by the Haldol, and I myself observed this during our interview. You mentioned that Dr. R.S. spoke of raising your Haldol from 5 mg. to 10 mg., but that you were reluctant to do so because of the lethargic side effect. I suspect that you are right on this point.

Because you are depressed your doctors have put you on the antidepressant amitriptyline. Although your depression may also be related to impairments in nerve cell functioning, I am convinced that other things that have gone on in your life have contributed to the depression. To the degree that you can improve these (to be discussed below), to that degree can you hope to discontinue the antidepressant medication. It may be, however, that you will have to be on the Haldol (or similar drug) for a long time.

Unfortunately, your lifestyle has been one in which you have worsened the condition of your brain cells. This is especially the case for the LSD, which is not only a very powerful stimulant of nerve cells but also damages them. It will very quickly produce a state of toxic psychosis, a severe form of the kind of disorder with which you are suffering. One could say that it was just about the worst possible substance you could take.

Furthermore, the marijuana you have smoked, unlike

alcohol, gets stored in the protective covering (insulation) of nerve cell fibers and just sits there interfering with nerve cell functioning. The body has to work to pump out marijuana. It can take a long time for this to happen. I understand also that you have been smoking hashish, a more powerful form of marijuana. I hope you appreciate that hashish's capacity to damage the nerve cells in your brain is even more powerful than that of standard pot.

I understand, also, that you have used cocaine and opium. I hope you appreciate that when a person becomes addicted to these substances they become incorporated into the body chemistry. The intense craving that the addict has for these drugs relates to the biological need for them created by the addiction. These substances lock into places on nerve cells that are supposed to be occupied by normal body substances. Obviously, they do not help normal nerve cell functioning; rather they compromise the functioning of the nerve cells and this cannot but do you harm.

All the drugs you have been abusing not only interfere with nerve cell functioning but can *destroy* nerve cells as well. As I mentioned to you during our meeting, once a nerve cell is destroyed it never grows back. It is replaced by what is called connective tissue, which fills up the space where the disintegrated nerve cell was but does not function as a nerve cell. People who are alcoholics also do damage to the nerve cells of their brain. A small amount of alcohol, taken once or twice a week, would probably not do you any harm. Even alcohol, however, impairs judgment—even one drink. What happens, then, is that the individual who promises him- or herself to stop after one drink then loses good judgment and continues drinking—sometimes to toxic levels. The owners of the gambling casinos in Las Vegas and Atlantic City know this phenomenon well. They give free drinks to all people who sit at the gambling tables. They know quite well that once a person has one or two drinks, the individual is more likely to lose good judgment and gamble away his or her money. One could argue that the gambling houses should *pay* the gamblers to drink, because the owners ultimately earn so much more from customers who are inebriated. I hope you will think about the potential of alcohol to impair your judgment when you do decide to have one drink only and promise yourself that you will not drink more. Furthermore, the women who serve drinks at gambling casinos are often scantily dressed, exposing much of their breasts. This too distracts the men who are gambling, causes them to stay longer at the gambling tables, interferes with their sober judgment, and causes them to lose more money.

You have gone beyond judicious levels of alcohol consumption. It is clear, as well, that one factor involved in this is your excessive dependence on your peers and your strong need to "keep up with the others." It is unfortunate that you feel embarrassed telling your friends that you don't wish to drink. If you cannot overcome this problem, then you should make a promise to yourself that you will drink only one drink in the evening, and then "nurse it" as long as you can. It is no crime, either, to say you like ice cubes in your beer. This will keep it cool longer and also water it down so you'll get more mileage out of the drink. I hope you will promise to limit yourself to no more than one or two drinks a week. You may not be able to improve the functioning of the impaired nerve cells you were born with, but you certainly have full control over whether or not you will make them worse. You have been damaging your nerve cells voluntarily and you have thereby worsened your condition.

Now to your habit of smoking 1-1/2 packages of cigarettes a day. I will not dwell upon the fact that smoking is a terrible irritant to your lungs, so much so that it can produce lung cancer, emphysema (a disease of the lungs which results in severe interference with breathing and even death), and other lung disorders. Nor will I talk about the effects of smoking on your circulatory system and its contribution to strokes and heart attacks. Nor will I focus on the fact that nicotine is an addicting substance. Rather, I want to focus on the effects of smoking on your brain cells and not in some distant, remote time but each time you smoke a cigarette *now*. The hemoglobin molecules in your blood stream pick up oxygen from the alveoli, little air sacks in your lungs. There is a place on the hemoglobin molecule in your red blood cells where the oxygen gets attached. The smoke you inhale is very rich in carbon monoxide. The carbon monoxide molecule fits perfectly into that spot on the hemoglobin molecule where the oxygen should be. Once the carbon monoxide molecule is there the oxygen cannot attach. Accordingly, you are carrying large amounts of carbon monoxide to your brain when you smoke. The brain cannot use carbon monoxide and so you are voluntarily depriving your brain cells of oxygen. This has to impair your thinking. You should think about that when you smoke.

Psychological and environmental stresses can also worsen your condition. The more you get your life in order, the more you handle yourself in a mature, adult way, the better will your nerve cells function. The happier and more secure you are, the less attention you will pay to your "crazy thoughts." With regard to these environmental influences, I believe you were quite lucky with regard to your parents. As you know, I know your parents well from my previous evaluation of your family a few years ago. I consider your parents to be loyal, dedicated, and most loving of you and your brother. Their dedication during your formative years helped protect you from the kind of worsening of the problem that many people with your genetic predisposition suffer. In addition, although there were some problems in their relationship with one another, from what I can see, they have been dedicated to you and have not exposed you to any significant detrimental environmental influences. Your genetic predisposition makes you more susceptible to developing severe psychiatric illness than those who do not have such genetic programming.

I did not get to know you well enough during our consultation to explore in depth the various psychological problems that you have. Your parents consider you to be functioning at the 17-year level. I am in agreement with them on this point. I do not think you have come to the realization that you are now almost 22, an adult by most people's standards. You have yet to buckle down and take life seriously. Although your involvement with peers is a good sign, your involvements are too much at the teenage level. My hope is that when you go to college in September you will take your education very seriously and work toward your career goal. I believe that your decision to major in business is a reasonable one for you and I wish you luck in it. You also have a problem in being accident prone and this is clearly related to many difficulties, both physical and psychological. The stresses associated with your accidents can only worsen your brain cell condition.

As you know, the name of the disorder that you have is schizophrenia. Like all disorders, there is a range from those with very mild cases, to those who have very severe cases. I consider you to have a very mild case, but a case of it nevertheless. Your main symptoms are the "crazy thoughts" that we have spoken about. I consider your case mild for a number of reasons. First, you are most often able to look at your inappropriate thoughts and recognize them as improper. As mentioned, many people with your disorder are not able to do this and they not only believe their thoughts, but act out on them. In addition, many people with schizophrenia have severe impairments in their relationships with others. This is not your situation. From what I can see, you have very good relationships with your brother and friends outside the home. Many people with schizophrenia are immediately labeled as odd by those who come in contact with them. Fortunately for you, this is not your situation. Many people with schizophrenia withdraw from life; it is as if they have given up. You are out there plugging and involving yourself. Many people with schizophrenia have significant sexual problems. From what I understand, you have functioned fairly well in this area and are in the normal range. A sexual relationship—with someone with whom you have a close, tender relationship—can be one of the greatest pleasures in life. So enjoy it.

It is to your credit that when you broke up with your old girlfriend you started to look for a new one. That is a sign of health. Some people would just bemoan their fate and wallow in self-pity. I believe that a healthy, loving relationship with a girl can be one of the most potent antidepressants. And when you have established such a relationship it might even work to the point where it might lessen your need for antidepressant medication. Although your depressive states may have biological factors involved, there is no question that environmental and psychological factors operate as well. The more you do to make your life happier, the less you will need to rely upon antidepressant medication. Many people with schizophrenia draw very bizarre pictures of other people when asked to do so. Your drawings are in the normal range, although somewhat on the immature side. This is consistent with what I said earlier about your functioning more on the 17-year level than on the 22-yer level.

At this point I would like to comment on your feelings that there are "bugs" crawling through your hair and flying around your face. The dermatologists have found no evidence for any disease of your scalp. This symptom is called for*mic*ation. Do not confuse it with "for*nic*ation." (They are very different things.) It may be that this is a symptom of your nerve cell impairment. It may be a result of the irritation and destruction of nerve cells that was brought about by your taking drugs, especially LSD. Perhaps it is purely psychological, although I do believe it has some kind of a physical basis in nerve cell functioning. I think you do well to view it as one of your "crazy symptoms" and try to go about your business like I suggested you do with the other "crazy thoughts." The more you get your life in order the less you will think about these things.

You mention that you have been working with Dr. R.S. for about two years and that you recently decided to drop from a frequency of once a week down to a frequency of once every other week. From what you tell me you appear to have a good therapeutic relationship with him. It sounds like you are talking to him about the things that are important for you to discuss. I believe it would be an error for you to cut down to less than once a week at this point. When you are on drugs, you get less out of psychotherapy. When a person is stoned, he is not going to accomplish much in a therapeutic session. When a person's brain has residua of drugs taken previously, that individual is also going to be compromised in what can be accomplished in a psychotherapeutic session. I hope this will serve as another motivation for you to *stop taking drugs.*

I hope you find this letter useful. I am also sending a copy to your parents and an extra copy for you to give to your doctor. Last, I have one request of you. And that is that you either drop me a note or give me a ring in about six months. I would like to find out how you are doing.

Sincerely,
Richard A. Gardner, M.D.

I believe the letter speaks for itself. The patient and his parents considered the letter to be quite useful and he frequently made reference to it in his treatment. Although I had verbally presented him with just about all of the information and advice contained in the letter, writing it down provided a permanence to my comments that enhanced the likelihood that my advice would be remembered and reviewed. Furthermore, the written word has a power that the spoken word does not. Although it is probably not justified, most people show greater respect for that which is written than that which is spoken. Letters such as these take advantage of this phenomenon. The letter has also been reproduced because it incorporates some of the therapeutic messages I impart to adolescents in the course of my individual work with them.

NINE

THE TALKING, FEELING, AND DOING GAME

I have mentioned in passing *The Talking, Feeling, and Doing Game* as an instrument that may be useful in the treatment of adolescents. Here I will present the game in detail and discuss its utilization in adolescent therapy. As mentioned, it is likely to prove more useful with younger adolescents (ages 13–15) than those who are 16 and older. However, one can use it occasionally with these older youngsters as well. Because younger adolescents are often uncomfortable in the direct face-to-face therapeutic situation, the game may be valuable in providing them with issues for conversation. In fact, many adolescents in this age group will state openly that the game gives them ideas to talk about.

THE BASIC FORMAT OF THE TALKING, FEELING, AND DOING GAME

The game is similar in appearance to the typical board games with which most children are familiar (Figure 9-1). It includes a playing

501

board, dice, playing pawns, a spinner, a path along which the pawns are moved, reward chips, and cards that are drawn from the center of the game board. This familiarity, as well as the fact that it is a *game*, reduces initial anxieties and attracts the patient to the therapeutic instrument.

To begin the game both therapist and patient place their colored pawns at the START position. Alternately, they throw the dice and move their pawns along a curved path of squares which lead to the FINISH position. A pawn can land on one of a number of squares: white, red, yellow, SPIN, GO FORWARD (a specific number of squares), and GO BACKWARD (again, a specific number of squares). If the pawn lands on a white square, the player takes a Talking Card; on a yellow square, a Feeling Card; and on a red square, a Doing Card. If the pawn lands on SPIN, the player spins the spinner and follows the directions. Generally, these provide gain and loss of chips, or forward and backward movement of the playing pawn. Similarly, landing on GO FORWARD or GO BACK-WARD squares results in movement of the pawn. The spinner and movement squares are of little, if any, psychological significance. They are included to ensure the youngster's fun and relieve some of the pressure associated with a high frequency of drawing only the aforementioned three types of cards.

Of course the core of the game is in the directions and questions on each of the cards. As their titles imply, the Talking Cards instruct the player to make comments that are primarily in the cognitive area. The Feeling Cards focus primarily on affective issues. The Doing Cards usually involve play acting and/or some kind of physical activity. The child is given a reward chip for responding to each of the cards. Although a token reinforcement is provided, the game is by no means a form of behavior modification. Positive reinforcement is not being given for behavioral change at the manifest level. Rather, the patient is being reinforced for providing psychodynamically meaningful material for psychotherapeutic utilization. The patient's and the therapist's responses are used as points of departure for therapeutic interchanges.

There is no actual time limit for the game. Both the therapist and the patient play similarly, and each responds to the cards. The first player to reach the FINISH position receives five extra reward chips. The other player continues until he or she also reaches

FIGURE 9-1

FINISH. If the game is interrupted prior to one player's reaching the FINISH position, the one who is closest to that position receives three extra reward chips. The therapist should discourage active competition on the patient's part for the acquisition of chips. The game should be played at a slow pace, and each response should serve as a point of departure for psychotherapeutic interchange.

There are 104 cards in each stack. I always randomize them and have never "stacked the deck" with specific cards that I hope the child will draw. The cards are so designed that any card will be relevant to any player. About five percent of the cards in each stack are so simple and nonthreatening that just about any patient will respond. Basically these are placed there for the extremely fragile patient who would be threatened by the cards that might touch on basic problems of living. These simpler cards ensure that the patient will get chips and thereby remain motivated to participate in the game. The most liberal criteria are used when deciding whether or not the patient should be given a chip for responding. Again, the therapist wants to do everything possible to draw the youngster in and maintain his or her interest. Some typical low-anxiety cards: "How old is your father?"; "What's your lucky number? Why?"; "What is your telephone number?"; "What is your address?"; "What's your favorite flavor ice cream?"; "What present would you like to get for your next birthday?"; "What's your favorite smell?"; "Make believe you're blowing out the candles on your birthday cake."; and "Make a funny sound with your mouth. If you spit, you don't get a chip."

The remaining questions and directions are far richer psychologically and are at the "heart" of the game. These are not as anxiety provoking as a request to make up a story that will reveal free fantasies; however, they provide highly meaningful therapeutic material. Some typical cards: "All the girls in the class were invited to a birthday party except one. How did she feel? Why wasn't she invited?"; "Everybody in the class was laughing at a girl. What had happened?"; "A boy has something on his mind that he's afraid to tell his father. What is it that he's scared about?"; "What's the worst thing a boy can say to his mother?"; "Suppose two people were talking about you, and they didn't know you were listening. What do you think you would hear them saying?"; "What things come into your mind when you can't fall asleep?"; "If the walls of your house could talk, what would they say about your family?"; "Tell about something you did that made you proud."; and "What's the worst thing that ever happened to you in your whole life?".

The patient's responses are usually revealing of the psychological issues most relevant to him or her at that point. The questions and instructions cover the wide range of human experiences. The material elicited is likely to be relevant to the underlying causes of the patient's disturbance. The questions are designed to direct the patient's attention to the basic life conflicts which are being resolved in inappropriate and maladaptive ways by the symptomatology. They direct the patient's attention to the issues that I referred to previously, that is, the basic life conflicts that are at the foundation of psychopathological processes. As mentioned, each response serves as a point of departure for therapeutic interchanges. The therapist does not merely provide the patient with a chip and then race on with the game to see who can reach FINISH first. Rather, the therapist tries to get "as much mileage" as possible from each response, using his or her discretion in deciding how much discussion is warranted for each patient. Highly defensive and resistant youngsters will not be able to tolerate the kind of in-depth discussion in which the healthier child can readily participate.

The therapist answers the same questions as the patient. The greater the therapist's knowledge of the youngster's problems, the more judicious will be his or her responses. Obviously, it is not the therapist's role to provide answers relevant to his or her *own* life problems. Rather the responses should be designed to provide therapeutic messages pertinent to the patient's difficulties. I always respond honestly. Often I will provide a response that will relate to an experience of mine in childhood that is relevant to the patient's problems. Children generally enjoy hearing about the events of their parent's lives that occurred at that time in the parent's childhood that corresponds to the age of the child at the time of the conversation. Such discussions draw children closer to their parents. The same principle holds in therapy. Such revelations, then, can contribute to a deepening of the therapist-patient relationship. As mentioned, a good relationship is crucial if therapy is to be successful. Without it, there will be little receptivity to the therapist's messages and practically no identification with him or her.

Many therapists, especially those with a classical psychoanalytic orientation, may take issue with the freedom with which I reveal myself. They would argue that I am contaminating terribly the therapeutic field and making the patient's free associations practically useless. I am in full agreement that such revelations contaminate the patient's free associations. However, the classical approach is not without its drawbacks. It does indeed provide the so-called "blank screen" for the purest projections. However, the acquisition of such information is done in a setting which, I believe, is antitherapeutic. It creates a distance between the therapist and the patient that compromises the development of a good therapist-patient relationship. The patient's thoughts and feelings about the therapist become distorted and divorced from reality. The situation increases the likelihood that the patient will develop delusions about the therapist and will idealize him or her. It will widen the gap between them as the patient comes to view the therapist as perfect. We can love most those whom we know nothing about—but such love is more delusional than real, based as it is on a paucity of information. What is gained in the way of pure free associations is more than counterbalanced, I believe, by a compromise of the therapist-patient relationship and the antitherapeutic experience of the patient's comparing him- or herself unfavorably with the therapist. *The Talking, Feeling, and Doing Game* provides the therapist with the opportunity to reveal defects in a noncontrived and nonartificial setting. He or she thereby becomes more human to the patient, and this is generally salutary for their relationship. In addition, my revelations are not those that would compromise my own privacy and that of my family. Even with these restrictions, there is enough that has gone on in my life to provide me with a wealth of potential revelations.

I answer all questions. Some highly defensive patients, however, may find it difficult to do so. Sometimes, I will inform such youngsters that failure to answer the question will result in their not getting a reward chip, and this will lessen the likelihood that they will win the game. Some patients are motivated by this "threat" and try to respond to the card. On occasion, a patient will refrain from answering most cards but still involve him- or herself in the game. Many of these children listen attentively to my responses and, I believe, gain thereby from the game. Although I am working here in a partial vacuum, because I am not getting as much information from the patient as is desirable, my knowledge of the youngster's history and background provides me with enough information to give responses to the cards that are meaningful to the patient and pertinent to his or her problems.

The question is sometimes raised about winning and losing when playing therapeutic games with children. *The Talking, Feeling, and Doing Game* obviates this problem. It may not be immediately apparent to the reader that the main determinant of who wins the game is *luck*. If each player answers each card, the determinant of who wins the game is the dice. If a player obtains many high throws, then he or she will reach FINISH earlier and thereby acquire fewer chips. If a player obtains a larger number of low throws, more chips will be acquired when going from START to FINISH. Because low and high throws average out for each player, the number of wins and losses also average out over the course of treatment.

Although *The Talking, Feeling, and Doing Game* was originally devised to engage resistant children in therapy, it has proved useful for less defended children as well. In fact, it has proved to be the favorite therapeutic activity of the children in my practice. Many other therapists have informed me that this has been their experience as well. This therapeutic boon is not without its drawbacks, however. One danger of the game is that it will lure the patient (and, unfortunately, the therapist) away from utilizing techniques that are more likely to elicit "deeper" psychodynamic material. Dealing with this material is also important in therapy. Accordingly, the therapist should not injudiciously "respect" the patient's wishes to devote the entire therapeutic experience to this technique.

EXAMPLES OF CARD RESPONSES

Talking Cards

Human behavior lends itself well to being divided into thoughts, feelings, and actions. It was from this observation that I decided to name this game *The Talking, Feeling, and Doing Game*. Furthermore, the sequence here is also important. Thoughts generally precede feelings, and feelings precede actions. Certainly, the sequence is applicable for fight-flight reactions. One sees a danger. A possible emotional reaction is fear. In response to the fear one flees. The fear emotion enhances one's efficiency in fleeing. One runs faster when one is afraid. Another possible emotional reaction is anger. When one fights, the anger enhances one's efficiency in protecting oneself from the attacker. For emotions such as sexual arousal and hunger, feelings may precede thoughts. One feels hungry, then one experiences thoughts related to food acquisition. Then one takes action and attempts to obtain food. Because therapy is more likely to deal more with fight-flight emotions than those related to eating and sexual arousal (not that these aren't involved in treatment at all), I decided to place *Talking* before *Feeling* in the name of the game.

The Talking Cards encourage the patient to speak about his or her opinions on a wide variety of subjects. The questions are designed to elicit information related to the fundamental problems of life which confront all children. As discussed in Chapter Five the solutions to these problems can either be adaptive or maladapttive. We refer to a maladaptive solution as *symptomatic*. The game is designed to elicit discussion of these issues in the hope that the patient will learn how to deal better with these problems of life and thereby not have to resort as frequently to the pathological adaptations.

It is vital for the therapist to appreciate that *there are no standard answers for the therapist to provide*. Rather, each response must be tailored to the particular youngster with whom the therapist is playing the game. Accordingly, it would be an error to use the responses I provide here as models for the therapist's answers. Rather, they should be viewed as selected examples of the *kinds* of responses that I might provide and as guidelines for the therapist's own responses. The therapist's answers in this game should be designed to fit the patient's needs. Now to examples of Talking Card questions and the types of responses I provide.

Question: What sport are you worst at?
Response: I never really was very good at sports. So there are a lots of sports I am pretty bad at. Of the sports that were commonly played in my neighborhood when I was a kid, I would say that the one that I was worst at was basketball. I

guess that I didn't try hard enough. It's not that I was born a klutz; I just think that I didn't work at it enough. I used to feel pretty bad when kids would choose up sides and I was the last one to be chosen. Had I worked harder at it, it probably wouldn't have felt bad when others played better.

The card "What sport are you worst at?" essentially forces the therapist to reveal an area of weakness. Even if the therapist were an olympic decathalon champion, he or she would still be provided with the opportunity to talk about a sport in which there is weakness. Besides providing the aforementioned benefits of such revelation, I use the response to put in a plug for the work ethic. The response also provides the patient with the knowledge that I too had my rejections and that I too was not chosen for involvement in various activities when I was a child. This is a universal phenomenon, and it is helpful for the patient to know that the therapist too suffered such rejections. It contributes to a sense of communion with the therapist and this cannot but be therapeutic.

Question: What things come into your mind when you can't fall asleep?

Response: If I had let someone take advantage of me during the day and didn't do anything about it, it would tend to linger on my mind. I would keep thinking of the thing over and over again—especially how I might have said something or done something, but I didn't say or do anything at the time. I'm sorry then that I didn't speak up or do something. But later, it was too late. And there may be nothing that I can then do about it. So I have trouble falling asleep because I keep thinking about what I should have done. Sometimes, however, there is something I can do about it, and then I do it at the time. Then I get it off my chest. Then I feel better. Then I can fall asleep more easily. I did the thing that I was supposed to do.

For example, something happened when I was a kid that caused me to lose a lot of sleep for a few nights. I was in junior high school at the time. I was walking out of a classroom. Some kids in the class made some kind of a smoke bomb and threw it into one of the desks. The teacher wasn't there and as they left the room the smoke started to pour out of the desk. I was scared that the desk would catch on fire. I wanted to run over and pull everything out of the desk because I was so scared that the whole school might burn down, but I was afraid that the other kids would call me "chicken." So I walked out of the classroom with the others. About five minutes later, I heard a fire alarm bell and I wasn't surprised. It was a big school with almost 1000 kids. And we all quickly left the building. As we got outside I could see the smoke coming out of the classroom. The fire engines came and put out the fire. Fortunately, it was caught in time and no one was hurt. Also, the fire didn't spread too far. The kids who lit the smoke bomb were kicked out of school.

I was really sorry that I hadn't had the guts to pull the stuff out of that desk and stomp on it. I think there were other kids in the classroom who wanted to do the same thing, but none of us had the guts. For the next three nights I kept thinking about how much trouble I would have saved everybody—especially those boys—if only I had done what I knew was the right thing. I know some kids probably would have laughed at me, but I would have known I was doing the right thing. It was a big mistake. And I still remember it after all these years, even though I only lost some sleep for a few nights.

Although my response at the beginning is designed to be general, the example I give makes particular reference to self-assertion. In particular, I focus on the importance of doing what one considers to be "right," even though it may be the unpopular thing. This message is especially important for adolescents who typically are slavishly dependent on peers, even when antisocial. I try thereby to encourage self-assertion, independent thinking, and action. Otherwise the pent-up resentments that such patients cause themselves can distract them from learning in school. It also contributes to their becoming targets for bullies and scapegoaters.

Question: What's the best story you ever heard or read? Why?

Response: Of all the books that I ever read when I was young, the one that I remember to have been the best was the one describing the life of Thomas A. Edison. As you probably know, Thomas A. Edison was one of the greatest inventors who ever lived. Although he wasn't the only man to work on these things, his inventions were important—giving us the electric light bulb, the phonograph, and the moving picture camera. He was a poor boy who grew up in Ohio. He was a very hard worker and was an extremely curious person. He was immensely interested in how things work.

He had a laboratory near his home in New Jersey and it is said that he would sometimes work most of the night on his inventions. He loved learning about how things work, and he loved trying to figure out better ways of doing things. To this day, people all over the world use his inventions. To this day, he is remembered as having given mankind some of its greatest inventions. He must have really felt great about himself because of all the good he did for mankind. It was mainly his curiosity and hard work that did these things both for himself and for others. It was Thomas A. Edison who said: "Genius is 1 percent inspiration and 99 percent perspiration." Do you know what that means?

Edison epitomized the gratification and fame that can come to someone who is strongly committed to the work ethic. I emphasize here the great benefit that can come to others from the efforts of a strongly motivated person. My aim is to engender some desire on the youngster's part to view Edison as an admirable figure worthy of emulation and inspiration. Obviously, one such message is not going to achieve this goal. However, the seed is planted and with reiteration over time it is quite possible that Edison will become incorporated into the youngster's psychic structure and join with other introjects to serve as a model for identification and emulation.

Question: Suppose two people you knew were talking about you and they didn't know you were listening. What do you think you would hear them saying?

Response: I might hear the people saying that I'm the kind of a person who is direct and honest. Although people might disagree at times with what I've said, they would agree that I am direct about what my opinions are and don't pussyfoot about them. They know that when they ask me a question, they'll get an honest and direct answer with no hedging, beating-around-the-bush, or saying things that I don't believe to be true. I am not saying that they would say that I never lied in my whole life and that I never will, only that they are pretty confident that I'll be honest with them.

You see, I believe that there is truth and wisdom to the old saying that "honesty is the best policy." If you tell a lie, you have to go around worrying that people will find out that you've lied. Also, lots of people feel bad about themselves when they lie. They feel guilty about it. And when people find out that you've lied, then they don't trust you even when you've told the truth. So these are the main reaons why I find it better to tell the truth rather than to lie. What's your opinion on this subject?

Identification with the therapist and modeling oneself after him or her is an important part of the therapeutic process. This is very similar to the educational model in which the child learns, in part, because of identification with the teacher and the desire to gain the same gratifications that the teacher enjoys from learning. The therapist not only serves as a model for learning, but should be serving as a model for other desirable attributes as well, e.g., healthy self-assertion, sensitivity to the feelings of others, feelings of benevolence toward those who are in pain, and handling oneself with dignity and honesty. This card enables the therapist to provide examples of such traits. However, the therapist should select traits that are particularly relevant to the patient's problems. Furthermore, the therapist must avoid presenting these with a flaunting or holier-than-thou attitude.

Question: Tell about something you did that you are ashamed about?

Response: I had an experience many years ago when I was a medical intern, that was very embarrassing. It was so embarrassing that I still remember it clearly to this day. An intern is a young doctor just out of medical school. Well, one Friday morning the resident, the doctor who was my boss, told me that I should prepare a speech about one of the patients that I was treating. He told me that I was to give it the first thing the following Monday morning. He told me to look over the patient's present and past charts as well as to study all the old X-rays. The patient had been sick for many years, and there was a lot of material to cover. He told me that if was important that I do a good job because this was the biggest conference of the month and that all the doctors in the hospital would be there. The hospital had over 200 doctors and it was a very important conference.

Anyway, Monday morning I got to the hospital and started to work with my patients. I noticed that none of the other doctors were there and wondered where everyone was. Suddenly, the telephone rang and I answered. It was the resident. He was very upset and he asked me why I wasn't at the conference. I was so surprised and shocked that I almost fainted. I realized that I had totally forgotten about the conference. I had prepared nothing! I was sick to my stomach. I immediately grabbed the patient's chart, the two X-rays that I could find, and rushed to the conference room.

What I should have done was to publicly announce that I was unprepared and to express my apologies. However, I tried to get away with it. I tried to go through the chart and give a speech about the patient, when I had very little information. I didn't lie or anything like that. I just tried to take a little information from one place and a little from the next but it didn't hang together. Finally, one of the older doctors who organized the conference interrupted me and suggested that we discontinue the conference. I was humiliated. But I was also relieved. I certainly learned an important lesson that day. And I have never again forgotten to prepare a speech. That event took place many years ago, and although it was painful and embarrassing, I learned an important lesson.

The request to "Tell about something you did that you are ashamed about" again requires the therapist to reveal an area of deficiency. In the vignette that I selected, I also provide a message about preparing things in advance, thinking ahead, and thereby protecting oneself from humiliation. This message is likely to be of some relevance to most youngsters in treatment.

Question: If you became mayor of your city, what would you do to change things?

Response: If I became mayor of my city, I would do everything in my power to bring about the passage of two laws. One would prohibit smoking in public places and the other would fine people large amounts of money for letting their dogs crap in the streets. Let me tell you my reasons for saying this.

I, personally, find cigarette smoking disgusting. I'm not saying this because smoking causes cancer of the lungs. I'd say this even if smoking *cured* cancer of the lungs. I'm just saying it because I find smoking nauseating. I think that if anyone is stupid enough to smoke, that person should be required to do it privately, in his or her own home. Many people who smoke don't care about other people's feelings. As far as they're concerned, other people can choke or even croak on their smoke. They don't think about the feelings of the people who are suffering because of their smoking. Unfortunately, a lot of people don't speak up and say how the smoke bothers them. But more and more people are doing this.

The other law, about there being big fines for people who let their dogs crap on the streets, would be for the same purposes. People who let their dogs do this don't think about how disgusted others feel when they step in the dog shit. It's really a disgusting thing to have to wipe dog shit off your shoes. It's too bad there are so many people in this world who don't think about other people's feelings.

What do *you* think about people who smoke and people who let their dogs crap on the streets?

The major thrust of my responses here is to help an insensitive patient appreciate how one's acts can affect others and that those who don't think about how they are affecting others are generally scorned.

Question: If a fly followed you around for a day and could then talk about you, what would it say?
Response: I followed Dr. Gardner around all day and I noticed that the people he's with hardly ever have any doubt in their minds about what he thinks. He's not afraid to tell people what's on his mind and to express his thoughts and feelings. He avoids a lot of trouble this way. If people had to wonder

what he thought, there would be a lot of confusion and trouble. He also gets many things accomplished that he wouldn't have if he didn't speak up.

For example, during his lunch break one day, he went to a restaurant with a friend. He asked to be seated in the *No Smoking* section. After they were there awhile, a man sat down at the next table and started to smoke. Dr. Gardner immediately complained to the waiter and the man was asked to either put out the cigarette or sit in the *Smoking* section. The man quickly apologized and put out the cigarette. Some people probably would have sat there and said nothing. However, Dr. Gardner didn't. By speaking up, he stopped a person from doing something that was making him uncomfortable.

During the evening he went to the movies with his wife. The sound was on much too loud and lots of people were bothered. However, no one was doing anything about it. Dr. Gardner got up, went out to the lobby, and asked for the manager. He asked the manager to lower the volume of the sound. At first, the manager didn't believe him, so he asked the manager to go into the theater and hear for himself. The manager did so and realized that Dr. Gardner was right. He then lowered the volume and everyone was more comfortable. Again, he saved himself and other people a lot of trouble by politely and firmly expressing his thoughts and feelings. Of course, every once in a while, he may not express his thoughts and feelings and this usually causes some trouble. This helps him remember that the best thing, most often, is to tell people about things that bother you—but to do so in a polite way.

This is another example of my view that it is useful for therapy to help the patient learn important principles in living, which can be applied to specific situations as they arise. Clearly, my hope here is that this description will impress upon the patient the value of self-assertion. My hope also is that my own ways of dealing with these problems will served as a model for the youngster.

Feeling Cards

The Feeling Cards, as their name indicates, encourage primarily the expression of feelings. Many therapists view such expression to be the primary goal of the therapeutic process. These therapists will frequently ask such questions as: "How did you feel about that?" and "That must have made you feel very angry (sad, happy, etc.)." Others speak of therapy primarily as a place where the child can let out or get in touch with his or her feelings. Some pride themselves on their skill when, for example, they get a boy to express the anger he feels toward his father by hitting the head of the father doll with a toy hammer. I believe that this view of therapy is naive. I consider the expression of feelings to be a first step toward the alleviation of difficulties. Feelings serve in part to enhance one's efficiency toward reaching a goal. When frightened, we run faster; when angry, we fight harder and more effectively. When sexually excited we make love more ardently. When hungry we eat, sometimes voraciously. And when tired we sleep more deeply.

The therapist's goal should be that of helping patients express their thoughts and feelings at the earliest possible time that is reasonable and appropriate. At such times, the feelings are generally at a low level and can be used most effectively. When feelings build up to high levels they are likely to interfere with their effective utilization. When we are irritated we can use our irritation to attempt to remove the noxious stimulus that is evoking our frustration. If, however, we do not express outselves early, the angry feelings build up to levels of rage and even fury. When expressed under these circumstances the anger is not likely to be focused on the particular source of frustration. When it is expressed in a wild and even chaotic fashion, we are not likely to remove expediently the source of irritation. Furthermore, when feelings reach an extremely high level their gratification may become an end in itself, with little further purpose. A murderer, for example, will generally accomplish his of her goal with one or two stabs in the chest. The murderer who continues to stab the victim is no longer using the anger in the service of killing the victim. The same phenomenon applies to sexual gratification, eating, sleeping, and drinking.

As is true of the other cards, the patient's reactions should serve as a point of departure for therapeutic interchanges. The examples given here do not present such discussions. Again, there are no "right" answers to the questions and instructions on the Feeling Cards. Rather, my responses presented here may serve as guidelines for the therapist's responses when playing the game.

Question: What do you think happens to people after they die?

Response: No one knows for sure. Some people think that there is some kind of life or existence after death. Some believe that there is a soul or ghost that remains after we die. Some people believe that we actually come back to life in another form. And some people believe that there is absolutely nothing that happens after you're dead. They believe that your body just rots away in the ground and that there is no such thing as a soul or ghost or spirit or anything else. They believe that that's just the end of it all forever. That's my personal opinion as well. I don't believe that there is any kind of life or existence after you die. I'm not 100 percent sure, but it's the theory that seems most reasonable to me.

Therefore, because I believe that I only have one life, I try to make it the best life possible. I try not to do things that will foul me up. I work hard so that I'll be able to get the things I want in life. This doesn't mean that I don't take out time to have fun. I do that as well. I try to balance them out and spend time both at work and at fun. However, some of my work is also fun. And some of my fun is also work. The two tend to get mixed up at times. For example, writing books is work, but it's also fun for me. Hiking is fun for me, but it also involves some effort and work.

I think one of the worst things that can happen to a person is to reach the end of his or her life and look back and realize that most of it has been wasted. To avoid this, it is important for people to do those things each day that make life as good as possible. No matter what people believe about what happens after death, most of them agree that it's important to make the one life they have the best possible one. Do you think you're doing this for yourself?

Like many of the questions, the brighter the patient, the greater the likelihood the post-response discussion will be rich and meaningful. Although we may enter into a somewhat philosophical discussion, my main purpose here is to help the youngster gain a sense of the sanctity of life and the importance of doing the best one can for oneself at any point along the way. I believe that people who have a greater appreciation of this unhappy fact are more likely to be motivated to make the most of the relatively short time we have here.

> *Question*: What's the happiest thing that ever happened to you?
> *Response*: I've had many happy days in my life. Three of the happiest were the three days on which each of my children were born. Of course, that happened many years ago, but I still remember each of the days clearly. I was so happy on each of those days that I cried. They were tears of joy. I still have those warm feelings when I see little babies. It's hard for me not to touch them and sometimes I'll even ask the mother to let me hold the baby so I can cuddle and kiss the child. Although my children, like all children, may give me trouble at times, they also give me great pleasures. And the pleasures are certainly greater than the pains.

We speak often of the importance of the therapist-patient relationship in therapy. However, the factors that contribute to the development of a good relationship in this area have not been well delineated. This question can be used to help foster a good patient-therapist relationship. My hope here is that the patient's relationship with me might improve (admittedly in a small way) by the recognition that children produce warm responses in me. The response conveys the notion that I have the capacity for such pleasure with children in general and this response is not simply confined to my own children.

> *Question*: What's something you could say that could make a person feel good?
> *Response*: One thing you could say that could make a person feel good is to compliment the person on an accomplishment, that is, on something he or she did very well. For example, if a boy worked very hard making a model airplane, and it turned out very well and looked very good, then I'd say to him, "That's a beautiful job you did!" That would make him feel very good about himself. Or, for example, if a girl started the school year as a very poor student and then improved

significantly, she would also feel very good if someone complimented her on her accomplishment. If, for example, she was spending a lot of time in the early part of the year goofing off and fooling around, then she wouldn't feel very good about herself. Let's say that she then begins to study much harder. After a lot of work over a period of time, the teacher might say on her report card: "Congratulations, Sarah, you have really improved. Whereas you were once a pain in the neck because you never tried hard or did your homework, now it's a pleasure to have you in the classroom. It's a pleasure to be your teacher. You've really come a long way. Keep up the good work." Now that's the kind of thing that would make the girl feel good about herself. What do you think about what I've said?

When I congratulate a patient on an accomplishment, I generally focus my attention primarily on the deed or the act and direct the youngster's attention to the good feeling he or she must experience over the accomplishment. I secondarily mention other people who may be pleased over the patient's accomplishment and/or external rewards such as high grades, certificates, awards, etc. Also included here is the notion that hard work is necessary if one is to enjoy these benefits.

Question: What is the best kind of job a person can have? Why? Make believe you're doing that job.

Response: I think the best job a person can have is one in which that person earns money doing something that he or she finds enjoyable. Normally, the more education a person has, the greater the likelihood he or she will be able to get such a job. People who don't have much education, or who drop out of school early, are not likely to have such jobs. It's more likely that they'll have a miserable or lousy job that they hate.

Less important than the fact that they'll earn less money than the more educated person, is the fact that they hate what they're doing. And this is a bad way to spend one's life. It's much better to get education and training. Then, it's more likely that the person will be able to earn money doing something that he or she enjoys. Therefore, my answer to this question is that there is no one best job. My answer then is that it's any job that the person enjoys doing. And there are hundreds of different kinds of jobs different people can enjoy doing. What kind of job do you want to have when you grow up?

My hope is that my response will contribute to the patient's appreciation that what he or she is doing now is going to play an important role in his or her future life. In addition, my hope is that the response will contribute (admittedly in a small way) to the youngster's motivation to think about the future and to expend some effort toward gaining greater knowledge and skill.

Question: What do you think is the most beautiful thing in the whole world?
Response: Watching a beautiful sunset, whether it be from the top of a mountain or at the seashore, is to me one of the most beautiful things in the world. It makes me feel relaxed and happy to be alive. Sometimes I read poetry while watching such a scene. And the poems also make me think of beautiful things that help me appreciate how beautiful the world can be if one is willing to stop and enjoy them. Sometimes I will bring along a tape recorder and play a tape of some calm, beautiful music while watching such a scene. This is indeed one of the great pleasures of life.

Healthy pleasure is well viewed to be a general antidote for just about all forms of psychogenic psychopathology. When one is enjoying oneself in a healthy way, one is at that time not suffering the psychological pain attendant to psychiatric disorder. In addition, the pleasurable feelings are esteem enhancing. Because feelings of low self-worth are often involved in bringing about psychopathological reactions, any experience that can enhance self-worth can be salutary. And aesthetic pleasures are in this category. Accordingly, anything a therapist can do to enhance a patient's appreciation of beauty is likely to be therapeutic.

Question: What do you think about a boy who sometimes plays with his penis when he's alone?

Response: I think that it's perfectly normal—as long as he does it when he's alone. Of course, there would be something wrong with him if he did that in the open, in public; but as a private thing I think it's normal. In fact most teenage boys do it a lot, and many kids play with their penises when they're younger as well. There are some kids, however, who think that playing with their penises is a terrible thing. They think it's sinful, or wrong, or dirty. I completely disagree. Those kids are the ones that have a problem, and not the ones who play with their penises once in a while in private. What's your opinion on what I've just said?

Question: What do you think about a girl who sometimes plays with or rubs her vagina when she's alone?

Response: I think it's perfectly normal for her to do that when she's alone. Of course, that's not the kind of thing that one would generally do in front of other people. It's a private matter. What do you think?

For the sexually inhibited youngster these responses enable the examiner to approach a forbidden subject in a noncontrived way. Discussing the subject in itself is therapeutic as it provides the child with the living experience that such discussions do not result in dire consequences. That which is unmentionable is far more anxiety- and guilt-provoking than that which is spoken about. The child whose parents never speak about sex will generally become far more inhibited than the child whose parents preach often about the sins and evils of sex. Of course, the latter approach is likely to produce guilt as well, but probably not so much as the guilt produced by the situation in which the subject is unmentionable. For the child who is excessively guilty, I might add:

There are some children who think that touching them- selves is a terrible sin or crime. They think it's the worst thing a person can do. This is a strange idea because touching oneself is perfectly natural and normal. It only becomes a problem if the person does it most of the time and then doesn't do other things, or if the person feels very bad or guilty about it. Feeling that it's a terrible sin or crime is then the problem, not doing it. What are your opinions on this subject?

Question: Make believe you're reading a magazine showing pictures of nude ladies. What do you think about such magazines?

Response: Boy, there really are some exciting looking women in some of those magazines. I think they're great to look at once in a while. They have some of the most beautiful and luscious women in those magazines. Some people are ashamed to admit that they're interested in looking at those women. I don't think it is wrong, bad, or sinful to look at those pictures. I don't agree with those people. I think it's natural and healthy. It's only a problem if the person doesn't want to have anything to do with real people and wants to spend a lot of time looking at those pictures. What is your opinion on this subject?

This response is the one I provide for boys who are uncomfortable expressing sexual interest. Obviously, I attempt here to convey some of the excitement that most boys and men have when looking at pictures of nude women. I also attempt to lessen any guilt the patient may have over such interest. My hope is that the youngster will be receptive to my opinions on the subject and will identify with my attitude.

Question: A boy was laughing. What was he laughing about?

Response: This boy was not only laughing, but he was cheering. He was just jumping up and down with joy. He had just gotten his eighth grade report card and learned that he had gotten into three honors classes in the ninth grade. He was very happy. He had worked very hard in order to make the honors classes and had hoped that he might make one or two of them. But he didn't think that he would get into *all three*. He was very proud of himself and couldn't wait to get home and tell his parents. His teacher had written a note on the report card that said: "Robert, I am very proud of you. Good luck in high school." He was also very happy that he knew that, when he applied to college, having been in three honors classes would look very good on his record and this would help him get into the college of his choice. And so he ran home from school laughing and singing all the way. It was really a happy day for him. What do you think about what I said about that boy?

This is the kind of response I provide for youngsters with low academic motivation. My purpose here is to enhance their school interest by demonstrating the joys and ego-enhancement that are the potential benefits of such commitment to the educational process.

Question: Tell about an act of kindness.

Response: A good example of an act of kindness would be visiting someone who is sick in the hospital and giving up a fun thing that you'd prefer to do. Let's say that a boy was in an automobile accident, injured his leg, and had to be in the hospital for six weeks. Even though his mother and father visited him often, he was still very lonely. His really good friends were those who were willing to give up fun things like playing baseball, watching their favorite television programs, or just hanging around and relaxing. Instead they went to visit him in the hospital. He was very grateful when they came to see him. And they felt good about themselves for their sacrifices. Visiting the friend was an act of kindness. Do you know what the word sacrifice means?

This is the type of response I provide self-centered patients, those who have difficulty putting themselves in the positions of others. In the ensuing discussion, I try to help the egocentric patient appreciate the feelings of loneliness suffered by the hospitalized child. I also try to engender in the patient the feelings of self-satisfaction and enhanced self-worth that come from benevolent acts.

Question: Was there ever a person whom you wished to be dead? If so, who was that person? Why did you wish that person to be dead?

Response: During my childhood and early teens there lived a man in Germany named Adolph Hitler. He was a madman. He was insane. He was the leader of Germany during World War II and was personally responsible for the deaths of millions of people. He was one of the greatest criminals in the history of the world. He used to murder people whose opinions, skin color, or religion differed from his. He not only had them shot but he gassed them to death and burned their bodies in ovens. Millions of people died this way.

When I was a boy, I used to wish that he would die. I wished that someone would kill him. I hoped then that maybe all this crazy murdering would stop. To this day, I and many other people in the world feel sorry for the millions of people he killed and all the millions of friends and relatives who also suffered because of his murders. Even though the war ended in 1945, there are still millions of people who are suffering because of the terrible things Adolph Hitler did. These are the people who were put in his prisons and concentration camps and escaped, or were fortunate enough not to have been killed. And these are also the people who are the friends, relatives, children, and grandchildren of those who died there. He was a very cruel man. I really hated him, and I often wished he would die or be killed. Finally, in 1945 he committed suicide. If he hadn't killed himself, he would have been captured and executed for his terrible crimes.

This question can be particularly useful for children with antisocial behavior disorders who have little sensitivity to the pains they inflict on others. My hope here, by elaborating on Hitler's atrocities, is to engender in the antisocial patient a feeling for the pain that criminal behavior causes others. It is important for the reader to appreciate that when responding to Feeling Cards the therapist does well to try to dramatize as much as possible his or her responses in order to bring about a kind of resonating emotional response in the patient. To engender these feelings in the patient who is out of touch with them or who has not experienced them to a significant degree is one of the goals of treatment.

Question: Say something funny.

Response: Okay, I heard a funny riddle. "What's invisible and smells like worms?" (Generally, the patient does not know the answer. In such cases, I will give it.) "A bird's fart!"

This joke generally goes over quite well, except among the most inhibited. Incidentally, it is a statement of the low levels to which the child and adolescent therapist may have to stoop in the service of his or her calling. The joke, however, may be useful as an icebreaker for the patient with sexual-inhibition problems. Sexual and scatological issues often get fused and inhibitions in the sexual area often extend to this area as well. By telling the joke the therapist serves as a model for what I consider to be healthy, normal sublimation. It may contribute to a lessening of sexual inhibitions. The child may reason: "If it's okay for him to talk this way, it's okay for me." In addition, the introduction of some levity into the therapeutic experience is also useful. It lightens the session, makes the therapist more human, and increases the likelihood that the child will become involved. It is part of the seductive process, so important in child and adolescent therapy.

Doing Cards

The Doing Cards involve physical activity in association with the child's responses. These cards, more than the Talking Cards and Feeling Cards, involve a fun element, and this serves to make the session more enjoyable. My purpose here is to counterbalance some of the less pleasurable aspects of therapy that are likely to reduce the motivation for treatment of even the most highly involved patient. Some of the Doing Cards involve modeling and this can also be therapeutic. There are some therapists who consider role modeling and physical activity to be a central part of therapeutic process. I am not in agreement. Often, there is an artificial quality to role modeling, and this makes it less therapeutic than actual experiences or imitations that are spontaneously derived from a situation that arises naturally in the course of the therapeutic session. Accordingly, I most often use the Doing Cards as a point of departure for direct discussion. My hope is that in the course of such discussions the patient will have emotional reactions and experiences that will contribute directly to therapeutic change.

Question: What is the most selfish thing you ever did? Make believe you're doing that thing now.

Response: Well, the most selfish thing I ever did was a long time ago—it was right after the Second World War—it was in 1946 or 1947. I was looking for a way to earn money to pay for my education in college. It was very hard to get jobs after the Second World War. All the war factories were closing down, and people were fired from their jobs. They didn't need so many people anymore to make tanks and guns and things like that. And all the soldiers were getting out of the Army. And everybody was also getting out of the Navy and Air Force. There were millions of people trying to get jobs. Well, I finally got a job selling magazines to the wives and mothers of soldiers who had been in the war. I told the people how important it was to buy the magazine because it would help the veterans, the people who fought in the war. After working a few days I found out that this magazine was kind of phony. A lot of people weren't getting the subscriptions they were paying for, and I felt very guilty about what I was doing.

I was preying on people's sympathy. I was saying that this was very important for the parents and the wives of the soldiers who were killed or who had fought in the war, and it was a kind of phony organization. I didn't realize it when I got the job, but after I started working I realized it, and I soon quit. But I felt very guilty, and I think I worked a day or two too much because I needed the money so badly that I stuck with it awhile, but then my guilt overcame me and I quit the job. It had been a selfish thing to do. Sometimes when people are hungry, when they need money a lot, then they do things that they would never want to do. I was ashamed of myself when I did that. Do you want to say anything about that?

As mentioned, *The Talking, Feeling, and Doing Game* provides therapists with the opportunity to reveal their own deficiencies in a noncontrived and natural way. This lessens the likelihood that the patient will idealize the therapist. It makes the therapist a more real human being. It lessens the likelihood of the development of the unfavorable comparison in which the patient views the therapist as perfect, and views him or herself as a bundle of psychopathology. The particular incident was chosen because it demonstrates how guilt can be useful in preventing a person from engaging in antisocial behavior. This is the kind of response I provide for patients who do not have enough guilt over their antisocial behavior. My hope is that the vignette will contribute to the development of a slightly stronger superego.

Question: You're standing in line to buy something and a child pushes in front of you. Show what you would do.

Response: Let's say I'm a kid and I'm standing here in line and some kid pushes himself in front of me. A part of me might want to push him away and even hit him. But another part of me knows that that wouldn't be such a good idea. I might get into trouble or he might hit me back and then I might get hurt. So the first thing I would do would be to say something to him like, "Hey, I was here first. Why don't you go back to the end of the line and wait your turn like everybody else." If that didn't work I might threaten to call some person like a parent, teacher, or someone else around who is in charge. But sometimes there are no other people around to call, so I might just say that it's not worth all the trouble and that all it's causing me is the loss of another minute or two. If, however, the person starts to push me, then I might fight back. But that would be the last thing I would try. Some people might think that I'm "chicken" for not hitting him in the first place. I don't agree with them. I think that hitting should be the last thing you should do, not the first. I don't think that people who hit first are particularly wise or brave; rather, I think they're kind of stupid. So in this sitation I'd talk first and try to solve the problem. If that didn't work, I'd drop the whole thing. It's not worth fighting about.

This is the type of response I am likely to provide the antisocial patient. As is obvious here, I am trying to educate the antisocial youngster to the more civilized option that individuals have learned to use in order to bring about a more relaxed and less threatening society. These options may not have been part of the antisocial patient's repertoire. Whatever the underlying factors are in such a patient's antisocial behavior (and these, of course, must be dealt with in the treatment), such education is also a part of the therapy.

Question: Make believe you're smoking a cigarette. What do you think about people who smoke?

Response: First of all, I want to say that I have not once in my whole life ever smoked a single cigarette. I remember when I was about 14 years old I went to a party. Some of the kids there were smoking. One kid gave me a cigarette. I really didn't want to smoke it, but I felt that if I didn't take it, all the kids would think that I was "chicken." So I took the cigarette, and I lit it, and I took one puff. I then gasped and started to choke. It really make me sick to my stomach. I then put out the cigarette and said to the guy that had given it to me, "I can't really believe that anybody can like this shit. The only reason that you guys are smoking is because you want to look like big shots. It must take a long time to get used to smoking this filthy weed." And that was the first and last time I smoked a cigarette in my whole life.

Now, if I'm to get a chip, I've got to make believe that I'm smoking a cigarette. Okay, here I go! (I imitate cigarette smoking.) Ugh, is this terrible. (I start coughing heavily.) This is disgusting. This is nauseating (more heavy coughing). Ugh, I can't stand this any longer. I hope I've done enough of this to get my chip. It's a heavy price to pay for a chip. People who smoke cigarettes must be crazy. Not only is it a disgusting habit but it can give you all kinds of terrible diseases like lung cancer, heart disease, and diseases of your blood vessels.

I think kids start to smoke because they want to act like big shots. It makes them feel like adults. Then they get hooked on cigarettes and they can't stop. When they get older, and begin to appreciate how really terrible it is, they still can't stop. It's a heavy price to pay for looking like a big shot. Also, it's no great stunt to smoke. If you really want to feel big you have to do things, over a period, that make you feel good about yourself. Thinking that you're going to feel good about yourself by putting a cigarette in your mouth is simple minded. It just doesn't work that way. What do you think about what I've just said?

The response, of course, touches on the most common patho-logical mechanisms that contribute to adolescents' beginning to smoke. It is quite likely that the antisocial patient subscribes strongly and somewhat blindly to these sick values. Not having basic competence in meaningful areas, he or she is likely to embrace quick and superficial methods for enhancing self-esteem. Of course, the utilization of smoking in this regard is strongly promulgated by the advertising of the cigarette industry. Cigarette manufacturers know well that they will increase sales if they associate cigarette smoking with sexual attractiveness and adult "maturity." My response also directs itself to the peer-pressure element in the initiation of cigarette smoking. As mentioned, I do not create stories when responding to the cards in *The Talking, Feeling, and Doing Game*. The experiences I relate in my response actually occurred and my reasons for not smoking are those that I genuinely hold.

> *Question*: Make believe someone grabbed something of yours. Show what you would do.
> *Response*: I would first try to use talk before using action. I'd tell the child to give it back and threaten to grab it back if he or she doesn't return it. If the child was my size or a little taller, I'd try to grab it back, providing it wasn't something that could break. If it was something that could break and/or the person was bigger, I would threaten to call the teacher or my parent(s) if it wasn't given back immediately. I might ask a friend or two to help me get it back. But I wouldn't just stand there, say nothing, and let the person get away with it.

This response is designed for youngsters with self-assertion problems. My response provides advice regarding the sequence of steps one does well to follow when one's rights are being infringed upon.

> *Question*: Make believe you're playing a dirty trick on someone.
> *Response*: I don't think I'm going to get a chip on this one. I don't like playing dirty tricks on people. I remember when I was a kid how badly I felt if someone played a dirty trick on me. And I used to feel sorry for those kids who had dirty tricks played on them. I remember once a kid in my class used to like stealing other children's books and hiding them. He thought it

was very funny. Actually, it was cruel. Then the kid whose book was stolen would go home and not have a book to do his or her homework. He or she would have to go to a lot of trouble to borrow someone else's book or go over to someone else's house. Sometimes the kid wouldn't even find the book and then the person whose book was stolen would have to pay for it. Sometimes dirty tricks can be dangerous. I remember once a boy in my class thought it was funny to trip another kid in the classroom. Well the boy that was tripped fell down and banged his head against the desk. He hit his head right above his eye and his eye almost got knocked out. He got a big cut over his eye and it was bleeding terribly. I really felt sorry for him and everybody was angry at the kid who tripped him. That kid, of course, got into a lot of trouble. The kid who got hurt had to go to the hospital for stitches and for treatment of his eye. His parents threatened to sue the other parents. However, the parents of the boy who tripped the kid agreed to pay for all the medical expenses. So at least they both didn't have to pay for lawyers. These are just some of the reasons why I don't like playing dirty tricks on anyone. How do you feel about playing dirty tricks on people?

In an attempt to strengthen the antisocial patient's superego I elaborate upon the pains that can be caused by those who hurt others. Youngsters with superego deficiencies, who act out their hostility, generally do not think about the discomforts and pains they cause others.

CONCLUDING COMMENTS

The popularity of *The Talking, Feeling, and Doing Game* has been a great source of gratification. It has become standard equipment for the child and adolescent psychotherapist, and many therapists consider it vital in their work with youngsters. Over the years I have received many letters in which the therapist has expressed gratitude for my introduction of the game. I have even had the dubious compliment on a few occasions of plagiarized versions being introduced. These, to the best of my knowledge, have never enjoyed similar popularity. (One such plagiarizer lost motivation to continue marketing the game after a letter from my attorney "reminding him" of the consequences if he did not cease and desist.)

Although the game was originally devised in an attempt to engage children who were not free enough to provide self-created stories when utilizing the mutual storytelling technique and its derivative games, it has proven useful for more cooperative and insightful children as well. In fact, I would say that it is a rare child who will not get involved in the game.

The game can also be useful in selected family therapy situations. Generally, unsophisticated and/or uneducated parents may welcome the game as a catalyst for family discussion; more sophisticated and/or educated parents will generally not need such assistance in their family therapy work.

The Talking, Feeling, and Doing Game is not without its disadvantages. All good drugs have their side effects. In fact, it is often the case that the more powerful the drug the greater the side effects. One of the main drawbacks of *The Talking, Feeling, and Doing Game* is that it may be *too* enticing to both the patient and the therapist. It is seemingly an easy therapeutic modality. Many therapists, I am certain, play it without fully appreciating its complexities and how difficult it can often be to utilize it properly for therapeutic purposes. The patient, too, may find it attractive because it seemingly protects him or her from talking about more painful subjects directly. It should not be used as the only therapeutic modality because it will deprive the therapist of some of the deeper unconscious material that can more readily be obtained from dreams and discussions. In short, therapists should not be tempted into using the game throughout every session; they should do their utmost to balance the therapeutic activities with other modalities.

TEN

PSYCHOANALYTIC INQUIRY AND DREAM PSYCHOANALYSIS

The younger the child, the less the youngster is cognitively capable of psychoanalytic inquiry. In the early adolescent period there are occasional youngsters interested in this kind of endeavor; my experience has been that most are not. For younger adolescents, those who generally will play *The Talking, Feeling, and Doing Game*, there are certain questions that may be useful in increasing the likelihood of the youngster's involving him or herself in more introspective discussions. In the first section of this chapter I present some vignettes that demonstrate the utilization of these game cards for this purpose. In the next section I will present my views on dreams and their analysis. Finally I will present a clinical example that demonstrates psychoanalytic inquiry via the analysis of a dream. Dream analyses serve as excellent vehicles for demonstrating psychoanalytic theory and technique. Although I am often quite critical of many aspects of psychoanalysis, it would be an error for the reader to conclude that I disagree entirely with all aspects of the theory and its utilization. I consider myself to be judiciously selective, taking those aspects of the theory and its implementation that appear reasonable and useful and rejecting those that do not.

THE USE OF THE TALKING, FEELING, AND DOING GAME IN FACILITATING PSYCHOANALYTIC INQUIRY

As mentioned, there are rare children who can make use of analytic inquiry. I am not against children's doing so. I am only against the attempt to apply the technique to the vast majority of children and adolescents. *The Talking, Feeling, and Doing Game* often has value in facilitating inquiry in youngsters who are possible candidates for such an introspective approach to the alleviation of their problems.

> *Question*: Of all the things you own, what do you enjoy the most? Make believe you're doing something with that thing.
>
> *Response*: Of all the things I own, one of the things I enjoy the most is my video cassette recorder and camera. I like making television programs of myself and the people whom I treat. It's even better now since I bought a color TV system, because now we can see it in color rather than black and white. It not only helps me learn things about the people who come to see me, but it helps me learn things about myself. The TV system gives people a chance to see themselves the way others see them. It's very hard for most people to look at themselves clearly. The TV system helps people do this. Even though some of the things that people learn from it may not be pleasant, the information can be useful. I'm very interested in understanding why people do the things they do, and the television system helps me learn these things. I'm very curious about how the human mind works. I find it an interesting and fascinating subject to learn about. And that information can help me be of help to other people, and the television set helps me to learn these things.

My hope here is that some of my own enthusiasm for psychological inquiry will engender a similar interest in the patient.

Question: What is one of the stupidest things a person can do? Show someone doing that thing.

Response: One of the stupidest things a person can do is to make believe there is no problem when there really is. The person who does that is not going to do anything to solve the problem. So it's going to continue to exist and may even get worse.

At this point I might ask the patient if he or she can think of an example of someone who does this, that is, someone who has a problem and makes believe that there is no problem. My hope is that the patient will provide an example that relates to his or her own situation. If not, I might provide the following example of the youngster who is unmotivated in school and denies the problem.

Response: Well, one example would be a girl who is doing very poorly in school and is making believe that she has no problem. She just thinks about other things. When others try to tell her that she's having a problem in school, she doesn't want to listen. Then she doesn't do anything to correct the problem or to solve it. Then things will probably just get worse and at the end of the year she may find that she'll have to repeat the grade. Or, even if she gets promoted, she may find that she gets very embarrassed in school because most of the others know the answers and she doesn't.

I might at this point discuss with the patient my story "Oliver and the Ostrich" from *Dr. Gardner's Stories About the Real World* (1972b). The story deals with the issue of the denial mechanism in the context of a discussion of the ostrich. In the story it becomes apparent that the ostrich does not hide its head in the sand in times of danger ("The ostrich wouldn't do such a foolish thing"). It focuses on the adaptive mechanisms (primarily involved in flight or fight) that ostriches actually do utilize in dangerous situations. (They do not differ from the rest of the animal kingdom in this regard.) This story has proven popular among my patients, and it can contribute, I believe, to a reduction in the utilization of denial mechanisms.

Question: What is the worst problem a person can have?
Response: I think one of the worst problems a person can

have is to make believe that there are no problems when there really are. Such people don't do anything about the problems they have. By making believe there are no problems, they continue to ignore them; but problems don't just go away. Because these people make believe there are no troubles, they don't do anything to solve their problems.

A boy, for example, might be doing very poorly in school, but might not wish to think about it. When his parents try to tell him about the trouble, he might stick his fingers in his ears so that he can't hear them, or he might close his eyes so that he can't see them waving his poor report card at him. This may make him feel better at the time because he then doesn't have to think about his terrible report card. However, he might end up with having to repeat the grade. By then, it would have been too late to do anything about the problem. Perhaps then he'll learn his lesson. Perhaps then he'll start thinking about *why* he has this problem. That's why I say that making believe there's no problem when there really is can be one of the worst problems a person can have.

Question: Who was the best teacher you ever had? Why?

Response: The best teacher I ever had was a man named Dr. Geoffrey Osler. He was a neurologist. A neurologist is a kind of doctor who specializes in diseases of the nerves. He really loved being a teacher. He was very excited about what he taught. When he taught, everybody in the class got excited about the subject matter as well. Enthusiasm spread throughout the whole class. In his class, learning was fun. In addition, he had a tremendous amount of knowledge and everyone respected him for it. Although it's been over twenty years since I took his course, I still remember many of the things he said. In addition, he started me thinking about a lot of things I hadn't thought about before and I still find myself trying to learn more about those things. He increased my curiosity. He increased my desire to find out the answers to interesting questions. I feel very lucky to have had such a teacher.

Dr. Osler was also interested in understanding how the human mind worked. He was also a psychiatrist, but he was primarily a neurologist. He liked to understand why people did the things they did. I, of course, am a psychiatrist, and I want to learn even more about the reasons why people do the things they do. And I try to get my patients to be curious about that as well. It's sometimes amazing to find out the reasons why a person does what he or she does. Often, people don't understand why they do something and, when they come to understand why they do things, they are really amazed. Also, when they do understand these things, it can often help them prevent or avoid trouble.

My aim here, clearly, is to sweep the child up in the same enthusiasm that I had, and still have, about Dr. Geoffrey Osler. My hope here also is that the child may develop some curiosity about finding out about the inner workings of his or her own mind.

Question: What turns you on, that is, what excites you?
Response: One of the things that excites me is puzzles and games in which you have to try to figure out answers. I remember when I was a kid I used to love playing checkers and chess. I also used to like doing puzzles in children's books. Later on I used to like doing crossword puzzles in newspapers. When I was in junior high school, and started to learn algebra, I used to love to figure out mathematical problems, especially those that were very hard to figure out the answer. I remember when I was a teenager there was a program on the radio called *The Quiz Kids*. They used to take the best students from the various high schools and ask them very hard questions. I wasn't smart enough to be a quiz kid, but I used to love listening to that program. I used to love trying to figure out the answers to the questions and once or twice I even got an answer when none of the quiz kids did. I really felt good about myself then. But more important I found it a lot of fun to try to figure out the answers to difficult questions. That's the kind of thing that really turns me on. It also turns me on to understand why people do the things they do. That can help people stop doing those things.

Here I attempt to engender in the patient the same kind of excitement I have about learning. My hope is that the reponse will enhance the patient's curiosity and motivation to learn, both about things in general and about his or her own mental processes.

Question: Make believe you've just opened a letter you've received from someone. What does this letter say?

Response: Let's say it's a letter from a former patient. I'll read the letter:

Dear Dr. Gardner:

I am writing to you from college. I appreciate very much your therapy. Before I came to treatment, I was not doing very well in school. In treatment I learned some of the reasons why I was having trouble in school, and I solved some of these problems so that I now have been able to go to college. When I first came to you, I didn't want to think about the reasons why I was doing certain things. But after I started thinking about them, I realized that I could learn some important things about myself. And that helped me get better. Thank you for all your help.

Your friend,
Bob

Anything you want to say about that?

My hope here is that the patient might be motivated for self-inquiry in order to enjoy the benefits derived by Bob.

DREAM PSYCHOANALYSIS

The best way to demonstrate psychoanalytic technique is via the analysis of dreams. I am in full agreement with Freud who held that the dream is the "royal road to the unconscious." Because the same principles are applicable to the analysis of other material as well, I will use dream analysis to present my view on this treatment modality. The same principles that I utilize with adults are applicable to adolescents; however, as will be seen, I must modify these when working with younger patients.

The Purposes of Dreams

It is reasonable to speculate that human beings have wondered about the meaning of dreams as far back as there were people dreaming. Wise men and seers have often been viewed as particularly astute in ascertaining the meaning of dreams. Joseph's dreams in the Bible are well known. I have many criticisms of psychoanalytic theory and technique, but I still consider certain elements in psychoanalysis to be extremely useful. One of these is its contribution to dream analysis. Although I am not in agreement with the reflex way in which many analysts see oral, anal, and oedipal themes in them, I am in agreement with some of the basic theories of Sigmund Freud regarding the meaning of dreams. Particularly I believe that the emergence of unconscious material is more likely to take place at night. During the day the necessary involvements and distractions of real living do not allow us much time to attend to potentially emerging unconscious material. At night, when external stimuli are reduced significantly, unconscious material becomes freer to enter into conscious awareness. However, because of guilt and/or anxiety attendant to the emergence of such material, the individual disguises it. The dream is a product of such disguised emerged material. I consider it to be one of the richest (if not the most rich) source of information about unconscious processes. It is also a testimony to the creativity of the human being (even that of a child and adolescent) because of the ingenuity that is sometimes utilized in its formation. I present here what I consider to be some of the most reasonable theories regarding the meaning of dreams. I do not claim that this is an exhaustive statement, only that these theories appear most reasonable to me. Our paucity of knowledge about the meaning of dreams also compromises our ability to provide a comprehensive statement about their meaning at this point.

The Dream as a Vehicle for Wish Fulfillment   The theory that the dream serves the purpose of wish fulfillment is ancient. Many dreams are obvious examples of this mechanism. The hungry person dreams of food. The thirsty individual dreams of drink. The sexually frustrated person dreams of sexual gratification. And the angry person dreams of wreaking vengeance. Freud too considered wish fulfillment to be one of the dream's primary purposes. Freud went further, however, in describing dreams to have a *latent* and a *manifest* content. The latent material resides within the unconscious because its emergence into conscious awareness produces guilt and/or anxiety. However, so strong are the forces pressing for release of unconscious material that its emergence into conscious awareness cannot be long prevented. Accordingly, an internal psychological compromise is devised in which the repressed material is permitted access to conscious awareness, but in a disguised form. By using such disguise mechanisms as *symbolization* and *condensation*, the individual essentially fools him or herself into not recognizing the true nature of the material that has now entered conscious awareness. It is as if the right hand has fooled the left hand. In addition, the individual utilizes the mechanism of *secondary elaboration* in which the dream is given an organization that it does not intrinsically possess. Such organization enables the individual to feel more comfortable with the dream because it now follows some traditional sequence. Secondary elaboration also serves the purposes of self-deception in that the reorganization process disguises the dream even more.

Associated with the dream's wish-fulfillment function Freud also believed that one of the dream's purposes was to preserve sleep. For example, a hungry person might be awakened by hunger pangs that threaten to interrupt the vital sleep process. By dreaming of eating, the individual again "fools" the hunger pangs, fantasizes satiety, and thereby preserves sleep. Another example provided by Freud of the dream's sleep-preserving function is that of the person who, while dreaming, hears loud environmental noises. In order to prevent the noise from awakening the dreamer, the fracas is incorporated into the dream. In this way, the dream satisfies its sleep-preservation function. However, Freud had difficulty fitting the nightmare into this theory in that this kind of dream usually ends with the person's awakening. This exception did not cause him to abandon the general theory of sleep preservation; rather, he concluded that the nightmare was an exception to this principle and when an individual had a nightmare the dream process was considered to have broken down and failed in its primary function of sleep preservation. Although I am in agreement with Freud that one of the purposes of the dream is to provide wish fulfillment, I believe Freud put too much emphasis on this dream function, to the neglect of others. I consider the wish-fulfillment function to apply only to one possible category of dream. As I will discuss, I consider there to be other functions unrelated to wish fulfillment. And the nightmare, which I will discuss below, is an example of one of these functions.

Freud ascribed many sexual meanings to dreams, interpretations that I would be less prone to consider sexual. In particular, many of the symbols found in dreams were considered by him to be phallic or vaginal. However, Freud also emphasized the importance of utilizing the patient's own free associations in order to ascertain what the symbols meant for that particular patient. He presents, thereby, a somewhat contradictory theory about the symbols. He considered certain symbols to be universal, especially in the phallic/vaginal realm. Yet he viewed other symbols to be idiosyncratic and devised by the patient. I have little conviction for the notion of universal symbols that are somehow inherited from the unconscious minds of one's parents and ancestors. (Carl Jung was especially committed to this notion.) Rather, I believe that environmental influences (familial, social, and cultural) are the most important (if not exclusive) determinants of what a symbol (dream or otherwise) will mean. In addition, I am far less likely to ascribe sexual meanings to many of the symbols that Freud and his followers so quickly assumed to have such significance. These criticisms notwithstanding, I consider Freud's *The Interpretation of Dreams* (1900) to be a monumental contribution and recommend it to all those who are interested in learning about the classical psychoanalytic theory of dreams.

There are some dreams in which there is simple release of pent-up thoughts and feelings which might also be considered a kind of wish-fulfillment dream. I am referring here to sexual dreams in which the individual gains sexual gratification as a way of providing release for pent-up and frustrated sexual feelings. The adolescent boy's "wet dream" would be an example. As the youngster grows older and has greater opportunities for sexual fulfillment, he experiences a diminution in the frequency of such dreams. The association of the dream with ejaculation raises some interesting questions. Does the dream fantasy precede the sexual excitation and resultant ejaculation, or does the hormonally induced genital arousal stimulate the production of the dream fantasy? Another type of simple release dream would be one in which an individual fantasizes harm befalling some individual toward whom intense angry feelings are felt. In these simple release types of wish-fulfillment dreams, there is little, if any, disguise. The individual is generally quite clear about the basic function of the dream. However, if there is guilt and/or anxiety over the release of these feelings, then some disguise elements may be introduced, such as substituting the identity of the object of the sexual or hostile feelings.

The Dream as a Vehicle for Alerting the Individual to Danger This is an extremely important function of the dream, which I believe was not given proper attention by Freud. In fact, I believe that the dream may more commonly serve the alerting role than the role of simple wish-fulfillment. Most dangers are not repressed. The individual looks at them squarely and then reacts appropriately, generally either by fight or flight. However, there are certain situations in which an individual may wish to ignore the fact that a danger exists because to appreciate it might result in guilt, anxiety, or other untoward reactions. Under such circumstances the information about the danger is relegated to unconscious awareness. An internal psychological conflict then arises. On the one hand, thoughts of the danger press for release into conscious awareness in order to alert the individual to its existence. On the other hand, such appreciation may result in a variety of unpleasant and even painful psychological reactions. Again, the dream compromise is brought into play. The danger emerges into conscious awareness in disguised form, satisfying thereby both arms of the conflict.

Let us take a theoretical example of this kind of dream: a situation in which a personnel manager in a large corporation has an appointment with a prospective employee. About an hour prior to the interview with the job candidate, he receives a call from a senior official in his organization telling him that the interviewee is a relative of his wife's and that he should be given special consideration. During the interview the personnel manager scans briefly the man's application, but does not give it the detailed perusal that he normally does. Following the interview the personnel manager decides that he is going to recommend the applicant for a position and hopes that this decision will place him in a favorable position with the senior official who recommended that he give the man every opportunity. That night the personnel manager has a dream in which the applicant that he saw that day, now an employee in the company, stealthily enters the company vault and successfully absconds with a huge sum of money. Then, after the theft is discovered, the personnel manager finds himself under serious criticism—even to the point where his job is in jeopardy—because he has hired the man. He wakes up, horrified over the prospect of losing his job.

Let us carry the example further and place this man in psychoanalytic treatment. The analyst encourages the patient to think about any possible clues he was given that the man might have had criminal tendencies, or even a record. The patient states that he had absolutely no awareness of such. However, when reviewing carefully the details of the interview, the analyst learns that the patient rapidly looked over the application. Recognizing this as atypical behavior, the analyst suggests that the patient review again—but this time very carefully—the application. The patient then returns to his office, reviews the material very carefully, and notes that there was a two-year period which appears to be completely unaccounted for. This occurred when the interviewee was between 19 and 21 years of age. Immediately, he calls back the applicant and, in the course of the interview, asks him about the gap in his school and work history. At this point, the applicant, somewhat apologetically, states that he was in jail during that period, but dismisses it as the result of a series of "adolescent indiscretions" that were not even worth mentioning. He goes on to reassure the personnel manager that these incidents are "water under the bridge," that he has learned his lesson, "paid his debt to society," and can be relied upon to be a "solid citizen." The personnel manager returns to his next analytic session and, in the discussion of what has transpired, comes to the realization that the applicant is *still* somewhat psychopathic, in that he initially withheld the information rather than disclose it, and that such deceptive tendencies not only existed in the past but exist at the present time as well.

He now finds himself presented with a new problem. Does he hire the man in order to keep himself in favor with the senior company official or does he reject the applicant and risk thereby the disfavor of his superior? As a result of further analytic work he decides that this dilemma is not a burden he need assume himself; rather, he can present all the information (pro and con) to the senior official and let *him* decide what to do. This is not an option that he had previously considered, but it emerged from the analytic interchange. It is an example of the way in which therapy opens up new options, options that may not have been considered previously by the patient, options that are often preferable to those already operating in the patient's repertoire. If he follows this course, he need not feel responsible for any untoward consequences of hiring this individual. Now it becomes the senior official's responsibility if the applicant does not prove trustworthy.

This example has been presented because it demonstrates well how the dream can serve to alert an individual to a danger that he or she might not previously have been aware of. In this case, the man had to repress from conscious awareness his recognition of the gap in the application to avoid risking the displeasure of a senior official. There was a danger, however, and it pressed for release into conscious awareness. A dream compromise was made, one that satisfied both unconscious and conscious processes. Had the man not been in treatment he might not have appreciated the significance of the dream and might thereby have suffered significant untoward repercussions for his oversight. Furthermore, and unrelated to this discussion of dreams, the vignette demonstrates how therapy, by opening up new options, can help individuals deal better with the fundamental problems of life in ways that they might not have previously considered.

At this point, I will present a dream that I myself had about a patient. It serves as an excellent example of the dream's value as an alerting mechanism. Many years ago a man of 25 requested treatment for homosexual difficulties. He considered his homosexuality to be psychogenic and hoped that therapy would help him achieve a heterosexual life pattern. The patient was born and raised in New England and had attended a prestigious boarding school and Ivy League college. His father had died when he was three and he had absolutely no recollection of him. He was raised with his mother and three older sisters, all of whom doted over him. His mother often undressed in front of him, even into the teen period. He first began having homosexual experiences in boarding school, but did describe some successful heterosexual experiences as well. However, his homosexual experiences were much more gratifying to him. In his early twenties he married in the hope that this might bring about a heterosexual orientation. He had not told his wife about his homosexuality at the time of his marriage. After about a year she became aware of his activities and at first hoped that she might be able to salvage the marriage. When I saw him, she had decided upon divorce and he went into therapy, hoping that he could avoid future similar consequences of his homosexuality. At the time he entered treatment, he was also in difficulty in the firm where he worked. He was employed by an investment banking firm, and it was becoming increasingly clear to him that he was being passed over for promotions because of suspicions of his homosexual lifestyle.

During the first two months of treatment, the patient appeared to be involving himself well in the therapy. He was a mild-mannered man who was quite polite and formal. His relationships, however, were invariably tempestuous, especially his homosexual relationships, in which there was significant jealous rivalry. In association with the stresses of these relationships, he would often drink heavily and sometimes become quite depressed.

Consciously, I did not consider the patient to be significantly different from other patients I was seeing with regard to any particular thoughts and/or emotional reactions that I might be having about them. One night, however, after about two months of treatment, I had a dream in which the patient was pursuing me with a knife in an attempt to murder me. Although I fled in terror, he was gaining on me and I awakened just at the point where he was about to stab me. The pursuit seemed endless. When I awakened, it was with a sigh of relief when I appreciated that it was only a dream. I was in analytic training at the time and so I began to think seriously about what the possible meaning of the dream could be. I had to consider the most obvious explanation, namely, that my dream was a reflection of unconscious homosexual desires toward my patient (his putting a knife = penis into me). Because I have never had any particular inclinations in this direction, I found it difficult to accept this as a possible explanation. However, I also had to accept reluctantly the latent homosexual explanation because of the way unconscious processes operate. I was also taught in analytic training that when a therapist has a dream about a patient, it invariably indicates inappropriate countertransferential reactions. I was not too comfortable with this unflattering explanation either. I could not recall having had any dreams previously about my patients (nor have I had any since), but I did, on occasion, exhibit what I had to accept were inappropriate countertransferential reactions. Accordingly, I was left with the feeling that the dream was important but without any particular explanation for its meaning. (At that time, I was not appreciative of the alerting value of dreams.)

About two weeks after the dream, the patient entered the session in an agitated state. Although I do not have verbatim notes on the interchange that ensued during that session, the following is essentially what took place:

Patient (quite tense): I'm very upset. I can't take it any longer. I can't continue this way.

Therapist: Tell me.

Patient: This is very difficult to talk about.

Therapist: I suspect that it will be, but I know you appreciate that it's important for you to discuss those things here that you are hesitant to speak about.

Patient: Yes, I know I have to tell you but it's difficult.

Therapist: I'm listening.

Patient: I can't stand it any longer. I've got to tell you. I'm in love with you. And I've been in love with you since the first session. I can't stand it any longer. While I'm talking to you about my problems, I keep thinking about how much I love you.

Therapist: You know, the word *love* can mean many things. It would be helpful to us if you could tell me the *exact* kinds of thoughts and feelings you've been having when you say that you love me.

Patient: That's even harder.

Therapist: I can appreciate that; however, if we're to fully understand what's happening, it's important that you try to tell me.

Patient: If you really want to know, I want to have sex with you.

Therapist: Even there, having sex with someone is a statement that covers a lot of ground. I'd like you to try to be more specific about the particular kinds of thoughts and feelings you're having when you say that you want to have sex with me.

Patient (hesitantly): Well, I just wouldn't want to start having sex right away. I'd want there to be some overtures on your part, some advances by you.

Therapist: I'm starting to get the picture. Now what specifically would you want me to say and do.

Patient: Well, I just wouldn't want you to simply ask me. I'd want you to plead.

Therapist: What would you want me to say specifically?

Patient: I'd want you to beg me. I'd want you to get down on your knees and beg me to have sex with you. (Patient now becoming agitated.) I'd want you to be extremely frustrated, to be very horny. I'd want you to be on the floor kissing my feet, begging me over and over again to have sex with you.

Therapist: What then?

Patient: Well, I wouldn't just have sex with you then. I'd want you to beg more. I'd want you to kiss my feet. I'd want you to promise to do anything at all to get me to have sex with you. You'd be on the floor crying and pleading. But I still wouldn't gratify you. I'd let you squirm. I'd let you plead. (Patient now becoming enraged.)

Therapist: What then?

Patient: Finally, when I felt you had enough punishment, I'd make you get undressed and then I'd make you lie down on the ground on your belly. Then I'd fuck you in the asshole and reduce you to my level. I'd humiliate you and gratify you at the same time.

Therapist: Is that the end of the fantasy or is there more?

Patient: Oh, there's more; I just wouldn't stop at that. First, I'd call your wife. I know you're married; you have that ring on your finger. And I saw those pictures on your desk; I assume those are your kids. Anyway, what I'd do then would be to call your wife. I'd tell her that you're a fag. And I'd tell her that you have sex with your patients.

Therapist: What do you think would happen then?

Patient: Then she'd divorce you. What woman would want to live with a fag?

Therapist: Anything else?

Patient: Yeah, I wouldn't stop there. I'd call the people who are in charge at the Columbia Medical School, the dean or whoever it is. I'd tell him that they have someone on the faculty there who fucks his patients. I'd also tell them you're gay. And I'd tell them that you had sex with me. Then they'd kick you off the faculty.

Therapist: Anything else?

Patient: Yeah, one more thing. I'd call the medical society and tell them what you really are, a fag, a gay doctor who fucks with patients. And they'd take away your license.

Therapist: Anything else?

Patient: No, that's it.

Therapist: You know, you started this session by telling me that you "love" me. Is this your concept of love?

Patient: Well, maybe it's not love, but it's the way I feel. Maybe it's the way I feel because I know that you don't love me the way I love you.

Therapist: Here you tell me you love me and then you tell me how you want to humiliate me, expose me as a doctor who has sex with patients. Then you tell me that you would like to have my wife divorce me and then I'd be kicked off the faculty at the medical school and then lose my medical license. It sounds to me like you want to destroy me. It doesn't sound very much like love to me. It sounds to me like the opposite, like hate.

In the ensuing discussion, the patient was too upset to be able to gain any insight into what was going on. His treatment did not last much longer. He left about two weeks later, claiming that I really did not have very much affection for him. If I genuinely wanted to show my affection, I would have sex with him.

Although the vignette demonstrates well an important psychodynamic mechanism operative in some patients with male homosexuality, namely, the use of love as a reaction formation to hate, it is not presented here for that purpose. Rather, it is presented as an example of an alerting dream. It is reasonable to speculate that at the time of the dream I was already receiving subtle signals of the patient's hostility. I was not aware of these consciously and may have been threatened by them. However, the awareness of the hostility built up in my unconscious and finally erupted into conscious awareness via the alerting dream. Had the man continued in therapy I would have used the dream to help me make decisions regarding hospitalization. The dream suggested that this was indeed a dangerous man. Of course, one would not and should not use one's own dream as an important criterion for deciding whether or not to hospitalize a patient. The clinical behavior must be paramount; however, the dream should not be ignored either. As I hope the reader agrees, the dream can be a powerful source of information about dimly sensed but not overtly recognized dangers.

The Dream as a Method of Desensitization to a Trauma   This is another function of the dream that has nothing to do with wish fulfillment. Here the individual has been exposed to a severe psychological trauma and the dream serves the process of desensitization. Following the trauma the individual is not only consciously preoccupied with thoughts and feelings associated with the trauma but is so overwhelmed by it that many of the psychological reactions associated with it become relegated to the unconscious awareness as well. This is not specifically related to the fact that the individual feels guilt and/or anxiety over thinking about the trauma; rather, the trauma is so overwhelming that sleep time must also be utilized if one is to effectively accomplish the purposes of desensitization. The principle of desensitization is basically this: Each time the individual reexperiences the trauma it becomes a little more bearable. And, over time, with repeated reliving of the trauma, even though only in fantasy, the individual adjusts to it.

A situation in which desensitization dreams are common is the one in which a soldier has been exposed to uninterrupted battlefield condtions over an extended period. He may have been injured and observed friends to have been injured and even killed. Under these circumstances he may have suffered a severe enough stress reaction to the combat that hospitalization may prove necessary because he has become ineffective in his capacity to function adequately on the battlefield. In the hospital the soldier has repetitious dreams in which the battlefield conditions are being reexperienced. In the dream he may hear shells blasting around him and even may respond with the same fright reaction that was present during combat. So powerful may be the need to relive the experience that the dreams themselves may not appear to be enough and he may actually hallucinate the same experiences, again in the service of densensitization. Whereas the dreams occur at night, the hallucinations take place in the waking state. The dreams and hallucinations may not be the only vehicles for sensitization. The soldier becomes obsessed as well with thoughts of the battlefield conditions. And each time they are relived mentally, some adjustment takes place. Last, he is likely to be talking about his experiences frequently and such discussions serve as a desensitization mechanism as well.

The Nightmare   In the typical nightmare the child is fearful that some malevolent figure will cause him or her terrible harm. Typically, the figure is a monster, other frightening creature, or sometimes even a nebulous blob or point that is approaching the child menacingly. Usually, the figure comes into the child's room from a window, or out of a closet, or out from under the child's bed. The closer the malevolent fantasy gets to the child, the more frightened the child becomes. And the child generally awakens just at the point when the malevolent creature is about to touch or envelop the child. At the point of awakening, the child is generally quite frightened, is often crying, and is usually consoled by parents who reassure the child that there are no such things as monsters, creatures, etc. The creatures in nightmares have a way of evaporating completely when lights are turned on and do not appear in broad daylight. Like vampires, they abhor the rays of the sun.

In my residency days I was taught that the malevolent figures in a child's nightmare represent one or both parents. In order to ascertain whether the creature is symbolic of mother or father, the examiner was advised to question the child in order to elicit information about the sex of the interloper. If male, then father was viewed to be the hostile parent; if female, then mother got accused. The child who dreamed of witches was to be viewed as one whose mother was inordinately hostile to him or her, and the child who dreamed of monsters (usually identified as male) had the misfortune of being brought up in a home where father was hostile. Even then, I was uncomfortable with this explanation and suspected that I was falsely accusing parents of being hostile when there was no signficant evidence for more than the normal amount of irritation and impatience that any parent will exhibit from time to time in the child-rearing process.

It was with these considerations that I began to formulate

another concept of the meaning of the nightmare. Specifically, I came to believe that the interloper is better understood as the incarnation of the child's own unacceptable angry impulses that have been relegated to the unconscious. Nightmares begin when children are about two to three years of age. This is a time when they are continually being frustrated by parents who must—if they are worthy of the name *parents*—inhibit and restrict the child continually throughout the course of the day: "Don't go into that cabinet," "Don't stick your hand up on top of the stove," "Stay away from the baby," "Big boys don't wet their pants," "Don't run out in the street," etc. There is hardly a five-minute period when children of this age are not restrained, constricted, and warned about some catastrophe that will befall them if they're allowed to go their merry way. The resentments engendered by such frustrations are enormous, yet they cannot be expressed overtly because of the fear the children have that they may lose the affection of significant figures who are vital for their well-being and even survival. Also, there are many other stimuli impinging upon the child during the day that distract him or her from the pent-up anger. At night, when these other distracting stimuli are removed, the pent-up hostilities of the day, which are continually pressing for expression, are allowed release. Daytime activities such as sports, sibling fights, and television—which have provided some release of hostility—are no longer available. At night, residual hostility from unresolved daytime frustrations is then freer to press for release.

In the nightmare, the symbolic derivatives of the child's anger (the robber, monster, terrible creature, etc.) press for expression into the child's conscious awareness (symbolized, I believe, by the child's room). The child disowns the angry feelings that are his or her own by projecting them outward. They are viewed as coming from outside the house, the closet, or from under the bed. Accordingly, the child utilizes two mechanisms for reducing guilt and/or anxiety over the expression of anger: symbolization and projection. Via symbolization, the anger is not viewed as anger; rather, it is viewed as some malevolent creature. And via projection, the anger is not viewed as the child's own; rather, it is projected outward in the form of a creature that comes toward the child from without. The child wakes when the anger is about to enter the child's own space, at the point where there is the risk that it will be recognized as coming from within. The malevolent figure may (as I was taught in residency) symbolize hostile elements within significant figures (such as parents). I believe, however, that this explanation should not be given first priority. It is the child's *own* anger that is basically feared. When the frightening figures threaten to abduct or kidnap the child, then the dream may reflect separation anxieties.

In my theory of the meaning of a child's nightmares, I generally do not consider them to be an abnormal phenomenon between the ages of two and seven or eight, unless they occur with a frequency greater than three or four times a week. I consider them to be a normal way of dealing with the inevitable frustrations and resentments that arise during the course of the child's life in this phase of development. Accordingly, I do not consider them pathological, nor do I consider them worthy of psychoanalytic inquiry. If they are occurring more frequently than a few times a week, then one must look for some problems in the child's life that may be contributing to their intensification. Generally, this would involve looking for abnormal degrees of anger-engendering experiences, such as harsh treatment by parents, neglect, and rigid, and/or punitive teachers.

Last, it is important that the examiner differentiate the nightmare from the *sleep terror disorder*. I generally view the former as a psychological phenomenon which may reach pathological proportions. Most psychiatrists today agree that the latter is a physiological disorder associated with very specific EEG changes. Phenomenologically the sleep terror disorder is quite different from the nightmare in that during the nightmare the child is lying in bed with eyes closed and some restlessness may be observed. In the sleep terror disorder the child's eyes are open and the child may even be running around the house—even though in an altered state of consciousness. In addition, when the nightmare is over the child generally remembers most, if not all, of what he or she has dreamt. When the child is awakened or wakes up spontaneously from the sleep terror disorder, there is generally amnesia for the event. Viewing as I do sleep terror disorders to be of neurophysiological origin, I do not consider them worthy of psychoanalytic inquiry.

The Panic Dream   On occasion I have seen patients who have dreams in which there is no recollection at all of any cognitive material. They wake up panicky and, as hard as they try, they cannot think of any associated fantasies. Many psychoanalysts hold that such dreams are a manifestation of the threatened eruption into conscious awareness of unconscious thoughts and feelings over which the individual feels formidable guilt and/or anxiety. Whereas some individuals are able to allow themselves release of such material via symbolization, condensation, projection, and a variety of other disguise mechanisms, these individuals are so fearful of release of these thoughts and feelings that even the disguised representations are not permitted eruption into conscious awareness.

A number of years ago I had such a patient, a young woman of about 21. She was clearly a very tense and inhibited individual, who not only did not allow herself to enjoy sexual experiences, but even denied having sexual urges. I suspected that her panic dreams related to the threatened eruption into conscious awareness of sexual feelings over which she was so guilty that she could not even allow their expression through dreams at night. I theorized that her dreams produced awakening just at the point where some kind of symbolic release might materialize. A friend and colleague of mine at the time was actively involved in sleep research and we both agreed that she might be a good candidate for study. Specifically, the plan was that we would monitor her sleep in the sleep lab, awaken her immediately after she had dreamt, and then learn the nature of her dream fantasies.

Although this occurred about 25 years ago, I still remember the night quite clearly. The patient went to sleep in one room and was wired up to my friend's equipment in the adjacent room, where we could observe her and review the recordings of her sleep patterns. Because of his sleep research, my friend had already adjusted well to being a night person. Because I was very much a traditional day person, it was decided that I would sleep as much as possible, only to be awakened when my patient showed evidence of dreaming. There being no bed in the monitoring room, I had to sleep on the floor. On five or six occasions throughout the course of the night my friend awakened me and whispered excitedly that my patient was now dreaming. However, after a few seconds, she would spontaneously awaken—at which point she denied any recall of any dreams. This was not surprising because there were only a few seconds of dream activity recorded. Finally, around six in the morning, my colleague informed me that she was now having what appared to be a lengthy dream. At the end of this dream we awakened her to have her record her dream verbally on an audio tape recorder. Her response: "I dreamed that I was with these two men. I don't know who they were. They were strangers. They kept asking me to go on a picnic with them, but I wouldn't. They kept asking me to go on the picnic and I kept telling them no. That's all I can remember, but I know that I never went to a picnic with them." The only conclusion that one can definitely draw from this experience is that a patient's resistances can be so formidable that they can prevent the revelation of anything the patient really doesn't want to reveal—no matter how intrusive the examiner's tools of investigation. I cannot say whether the "picnic" the patient envisioned my friend and I to be taking her to involved sexual activities. I could only say that whatever its purpose, she was going to have no part of it.

In recent years, most psychiatrists would consider this kind of dream to be the nighttime equivalent of the panic attack. It would be interpreted simply as some kind of cerebral discharge, analogous to a seizure. I believe that this explanation has some merit. I believe that there are some people with very low threshholds for flight reactions, with the result that these reactions may be triggered by inconsequential stimuli. The panic attack, then, may be a manifestation of such a reaction. I would not, however, completely discount the psychoanalytic explanation as being totally inapplicable to all patients. I still hold that the aforementioned patient's attacks were more likely related to the threatened eruption into conscious awareness of unconscious material (in this case sexual) over which she felt guilty. She never had any similar attacks during the day. This, of course, does not disprove my explanation but it certainly may lend some support to it. At night, without the distracting stimuli of the day, the repressed sexual urges were more likely to pressure for release and attention and produce the panic (anxiety) attack (dream).

The Dream as a Mechanism for Providing Brain Cell Stimulation   I do not believe that the aforementioned categories cover all the different types of dreams. They cover the main kinds of dreams that I have had experience with in my work with patients. There are many dreams that I do not understand. Even after eliciting the patient's associations, I am still left without the faintest idea about the dream's meaning. I suspect that for some of these dreams, there may not be a meaning and that they may simply be a manifestation of nocturnal cerebral activity. Just as muscle cells need to be constantly stimulated to remain strong and viable, so do nerve cells. Tonic contractions of muscle cells keep them "in shape"; perhaps nerve cells in the brain need cognitive stimulation to keep them in shape. Such nerve cell stimulation may be provided in the daytime by cognitive rambling and daydreams, and during the nighttime by dreams that may have no additional meaning other than to provide such stimulation. This notion, of course, is one that many psychoanalysts would have difficulty with in that they would argue that the contents of a dream are selected from a universe of possible combinations of thoughts, feelings, and imagery, and that it must be highly meaningful. Although I approach dream work with the goal of analyzing and with the belief that most are analyzable, I am still left with the lingering feeling that my failure to analyze some (but not all) of them has less to do with inadequacies on my part (certainly possible) and more to do with the fact that the dream may not be analyzable. And the reason is that there is nothing to analyze. The dream is merely a manifestation of some kind of cognitive brain activity taking place throughout the course of the night. Last, I recognize that there may be other categories of dreams that I am not appreciative of, and so I do not consider these additional possible explanations when attempting to understand a patient's dream.

Teaching Adolescents How to Psychoanalyze Dreams

Adolescents Who Are Candidates for Dream Analysis The older the youngster the greater the likelihood he or she will be able to profit from a psychoanalytic inquiry into a dream's meaning. Also, the more intelligent the patient the more receptive will he or she be to the therapist's suggestion to try to understand the meaning of the dream. Introspective patients are more likely to be receptive to such endeavors than those who tend to act out their thoughts and feelings. Youngsters whose parents are introspective, especially if they have had psychoanalytic experiences themselves, are more likely to involve themselves in the endeavor of analyzing a dream. Another factor is intellectual curiosity. Youngsters who are good students are more likely to be good dream analyzers. They are interested in expanding their horizons and learning new things. They enjoy learning for learning's sake. And learning about the meaning of a dream is just another example of an opportunity to satisfy one's intellectual curiosity.

If the therapist has had a successful dream experience with the patient, then the likelihood of the youngster's involving him or herself meaningfully and enthusiastically in further dream analysis is enhanced. Such a successful analytic experience would be one in which the patient and the therapist together have successfully analyzed a dream with the result that the youngster has had the *experience* that such inquiries provide interesting and useful information. This experience is hard to define. It is one in which the patient essentially says "Ah ha, now it all fits together," or "That's right," or "What do you know?". There is a kind of "eureka" response. Not only is there an intellectual understanding, in which everything seems to fall into place, but an associated emotional reaction of having made a wonderful discovery. This is an important goal to be worked toward. If this aim is realized, then one is more likely to have a patient who will be receptive to dream analysis (regardless of age); and if one does not reach this goal, then one is not likely to have a patient who will commit him- or herself in a meaningful way to dream analysis. Obviously, the older the patient, the greater the possibility that the therapist will be successful in reaching this goal.

If, during my initial two-hour consultation, I consider the patient to be a possible candidate for dream analysis, I will recommend that the youngster place a paper and pencil at the bedside and jot down any dreams that occurred during the previous night. I suggest that the youngster make a deliberate and conscious attempt to try to recall *any* dreams that occurred during the night. I emphasize that there is no dream that is so short, silly, or embarrassing that it doesn't warrant my attention. I try to impress upon the patient the fact that dreams have a way of evaporating and that even the most brilliant person with the most prodigious memory is likely to forget just about all of his or her dreams within a short period. I also impress upon the patient that merely writing the dream down does not suffice; rather, it is important that the dream be brought to me so that I can peruse it while we are analyzing the dream. I believe that it is reasonable to state that 95 percent of all the patients I see (including the most seemingly motivated adults) do not recall this whole message. Any part of it is generally forgotten, whether it be to write down the dream or, if written down, to bring it to the office. Most commonly, people will state: "It's so vivid I didn't think I had to write it down" or "I wrote it down, but I didn't think it was necessary to bring it to the office." Such failure to recall my statement is clearly in the service of the disguising mechanisms of the dream and is a true testimony to their power. Whereas some adults will obstruct the dream analytic process by "forgetting" to write them down, adolescents are more likely to flatly refuse to go to the trouble and will state so.

Fundamental Principles of Dream Analysis As a foundation for my discussion on teaching adolescents how to understand the formation of dreams and techniques for analyzing them, I present here what I consider to be the basic theory of dream formation by unconscious processes. This is not intended to be a comprehensive theory of dream formation. As the reader can already appreciate, my discussion above of the various types of dreams can only lead one to the conclusion that they are quite complex and that there is still much that we have to learn. These qualifications notwithstanding, I believe that the principles outlined here can serve well to help adolescents analyze their dreams. Their repertoire of knowledge is smaller than adults' and the information they can draw upon to form dreams is less comprehensive. In addition, the processes of symbolization, condensation, and projection tend to be less complex and sophisticated than those utilized by adults. The dreams of adolescents are generally more complex than those of younger children but less sophisticated than those of adults.

One does well to view the dream setting as a theatrical production. The dreamer not only writes the script, but is also the choreographer and dictates the movements, gestures, and behavior of all the protagonists. The dreamer also sets the stage and decides what props shall be brought in, where they shall be placed on the stage, and when they shall be utilized. The individuals who appear in the dream may be drawn from the whole gamut of humanity: real and fictional, past and present, well known and unknown. The props can be selected from the infinite variety of things, scenes, and objects. Animals may be used and even composites of a wide variety of animate and inanimate objects. Traditional rules of logic, movement, and sequence need not be respected.

The protagonists of the dream generally represent the dreamer and/or individuals who are of significance to the dreamer at the time. An individual may divide him- or herself into two or more parts, with each part representing one or more aspects of the dreamer's personality. For example, a very religious adolescent girl, who is guilty over her emerging sexual feelings, may have a dream in which she is observing the Virgin Mary reprimanding a prostitute. It is reasonable to conclude that the girl is symbolizing herself here in three separate forms: 1) the Virgin Mary, a symbol of her desire to be pure, 2) the prostitute, who symbolizes her emerging sexual inclinations, and 3) the observer, the girl herself who is witness to her conflict. The dream is also a demonstration of her guilt over sex and her view that people who do not engage in such activities are pure and innocent and those who do are no better than whores.

Another rule that is useful to follow in understanding dreams is that the individuals who appear in the dream who are ostensibly of trivial or inconsequential significance are generally not so. If, for example, an adult woman of 50 has a dream in which she is walking with another woman whom she has not seen since childhood, then one does well to conclude that the friend is being brought into the dream as a symbol of some quality that exists in the dreamer herself. They were both childhood friends and therefore the two lend themselves well to serving as alter egos of one another. The examiner does well to ask the woman what thoughts come to mind regarding the old friend whom she has not seen for many years. With rare exception, the qualities that she recalls the friend to have had during childhood are likely to be qualities of her own that are of some concern to her (the dreamer) at the time of the dream. The old friend is not being brought in for the friend's benefit. Rather, she is being brought in for the dreamer's benefit. Our dreams are very egotistical, and we do not waste our valuable time for the benefit of others, especially people we haven't seen in 40 years. Although adolescents obviously have less past time into which they can dip, the same principle holds.

It is also reasonable to assume that the dream is dealing with issues related to events that occurred within the day or two prior to the dream's occurrence. Each night, the dream deals with the "unfinished business" of the day. Most people's lives are so filled with various kinds of recent "unfinished business" that we do not dip back in time to weeks or months before the dream to work through older problems that may not have been resolved. Generally, the unresolved problems of the day are dealt with the same night or the next night. Then, even though older business may be "unfinished," there are newer events that take priority over older unresolved issues. The "old stuff" appears to pass into oblivion and is superseded by material that now commands our attention. We cannot go around endlessly nursing old wounds or continually trying to resolve every problem that confronts us.

Our minds tend to work on the same principle as that used by the administrator who files away reports of problems without the need to resolve them. The difference, however, is that the administrator may never deal with any problem and file them all away. We may try to deal with each problem each day and try to deal, as well, with problems that may have taken place the day before. However, the attempt to do so is complicated by the fact that we continually have to deal with new problems that confront us and command our more immediate attention. It is hoped that the dreams will at least solve some of these problems so that our minds do not end up like the filing cabinets of the administrator. It would be an error for the reader to conclude that the older material *never* is dealt with in dreams. If the older material relates to severe psychological traumas, especially those that have persisted over time, then the dream may be utilized in the service of dealing with these. An example of this would be the desensitization kind of dream that is used to deal with the psychological traumas attendant to prolonged exposure to military combat. Under these circumstances, the older material takes priority over newer; however, it does so because it has remained a present-day concern as well.

Consistent with this notion of the higher priority that dreams give recent material, the props that have been brought in are more likely to be related to recent events, especially the previous days' experiences. Whatever the object that the patient selects to put on the stage—and these are selected from a universe of possible objects—it generally has some relevance to events that were taking place during the day or two prior to the dream's occurrence. Also, one must consider the general ambiance of the dream. Does it take place in the frozen snow or the hot jungle? Are there grey clouds or bright sunshine and a clear sky? Is it underground in a cave or above ground on top of a mountain? All these aspects of the environment are of meaning in the dream because they have been selected from the infinite variety of possible milieus.

As mentioned, I do not believe that a particular symbol necessarily has the same meaning for everyone. Freud was especially prone to ascribe sexual meaning to many dream symbols. A snake, for example, may very well symbolize a penis. But it can also symbolize feelings of low self-worth and surreptitiousness. Snakes crawl on the ground and are quite "sneaky" in the way they approach us. However, snakes are also poisonous and they may, therefore, symbolize hostility and murderous wishes. One cannot know what the snake means to any particular person unless one elicits that individual's free associations to it. There are individuals for whom a snake may have some special significance, unrelated to the aforementioned more common possible meanings. The examiner who approaches dream analysis with the assumption that the snake has some particular meaning is likely to lead the patient into incorrect interpretations of the dream. Furthermore, even traditional sexual symbols may stand for other things. A phallic symbol may not simply stand for a penis but for power and strength—traditional associations to the penis in our society. A vaginal symbol may not simply stand for the vagina but for femininity, passivity, and child rearing. These, too, are traditional associations to the female in our society. (I am making no statements here as to whether or not these associations are "good" or "bad." I am merely stating that they are common associations in our society at this time, although things may be changing somewhat.) A common dream experience is one in which the individual feels like he or she is being overwhelmed by bugs, insects, or other noxious vermin. These often represent threatened eruption into conscious awareness of a variety of unacceptable thoughts, feelings, and impulses. One must try to ascertain from the dreamer's associations what these noxious intruders might symbolize.

Explaining the Theory of Dream Formation and Analysis to an Adolescent With the aforementioned principles as background, the examiner is in a better position to explain the principles of dream formation and interpretation to the patient who is a potential candidate for dream analysis. I generally begin in the following way: "Did you know that the mind has two parts, a conscious part and an unconscious part?" (The reader may wonder here whether I have forgotten about the superego. Of course, I have not. I simply use this oversimplified dichotomy for the purposes of helping a patient learn the basic principles of dream analysis.) I then try to get the patient to appreciate that in the *conscious mind* are facts that people are generally aware of, for example, age, address, name of school, name of teacher, favorite flavor ice cream, etc. I will then discuss the kinds of things to be found in the *unconscious mind*. Here are thoughts and feelings which the youngster may feel guilty about and may think are wrong. For example, a youngster may think that it is very bad to have an occasional wish that a brother or sister might get hit by a car. To such a patient I might say, "That boy (girl) doesn't realize that to have a thought like that *once in a while* is *normal* and that it doesn't really mean that the person wishes the brother or sister *really* to be hit by a car. It only means that the person is angry at that brother or sister at that point. Anyway, if the person feels very bad about such a thought and thinks that only the worst kinds of people have such a thought, then that person is going to push that thought out of his or her mind and push it into the unconscious part of the mind so that he or she doesn't have to think about it at all."

I then engage the youngster in a discussion of the kinds of thoughts and feelings that might be relegated to the unconscious and those that a person might comfortably accept as conscious. When the patient provides examples of thoughts and feelings that might be relegated to the unconscious, I may learn something about the things that that particular youngster is guilty about.

Once the concept of conscious/unconscious has been understood, I proceed to a discussion of the process of dream symbolism. One technique that I have found useful in helping adolescents understand this concept is that of the "secret code." I ask the patient if he or she has ever seen a James Bond movie. I generally receive an answer in the affirmative. I try to help the youngster recall some secret agent therein who used a secret code. We then discuss the formation of secret codes, for example a code in which the number 1 stands for A, 2 for B, 3 for C, etc. When one "cracks" the code, one merely tries to figure out which letter stands for which number. In this way the code is "decoded." I will generally use the terms "crack the code" or "decode the code" to refer to the process of analyzing the symbol. Once this concept is understood, I explain to the patient that dreams also make up their own codes. I explain that the unconscious mind changes information into code form before the information is released into the conscious mind. In this way the person may not feel so bad or ashamed about the thoughts and feelings involved.

I will then ask the patient to see if he or she can decode or crack the code of a dream that I will now present. I have found this example to be useful:

> A little girl is walking down the street. She sees a boy her own age making wee-wee. In her home she was taught that it's naughty to look at a little boy doing that. She wanted to look at the boy, but she felt very bad and guilty because she wanted to look at him. So she turned away and didn't look. But she was still very curious to see what his penis looked like. That night she had a dream. In that dream she saw that *very same* little boy watering the grass with a hose. He was holding the hose in his hands and a stream of water was coming out of the hose. The water curved out from the hose down to the grass. What do you think the hose stands for? What do you think the water stands for? Do you think that dream had anything to do with what happened that afternoon when she saw the boy making wee-wee and wished that she could see his penis?

The overwhelming majority of youngsters will generally "figure out" the meaning of this dream. When they do, I try to emphasize the point that the dream satisfies a wish: "The little girl wished that she could see the boy make wee-wee, but felt that it was wrong or bad and so could not satisfy her wish. At night, she gratified the wish to see his penis. However, because she felt this was the wrong thing to do she had to put it into a code form."

To emphasize further the wish-fulfillment function of the dream, I will generally provide questions to the youngster that provide practice with the use of the dream for this purpose. For example, I might give this question:

> A boy's father comes home one day and tells him that he has tickets for a football game that weekend. He's very happy. He's very excited about the fact that he'll be going to a football game in a few days. In fact, he tells all his friends about the fact that that Saturday he's going to a football game. Unfortunately, on Friday the boy gets sick. He's so sick that he has to stay in bed and he can't go to school. He has a high fever and a headache and he's nauseated and he vomits. The doctor says that he'll have to stay home and will have to remain in bed for at least three days. The boy is very sad. He wishes that he could go to the football game. What do you think he dreams of that night?

Again, it is a rare patient who does not get the correct answer to this question. I then take the wish fulfillment issue further. I may discuss the kinds of dreams a poor boy may have, a boy who has no money. Or the kinds of dreams a very hungry girl might have, a girl who hasn't eaten or drunk anything for many days. I will then follow these relatively simple dreams with dreams in which there is a combination of both wish fulfillment and symbol formation. For example:

> A boy named Tom started a fight with his younger brother Bill, and Bill went crying to their father and told him what Tom had done. The father got very angry and punished Tom. He told him that he could not watch his favorite television program that night. Tom was *very sad* that he couldn't watch his television program. He was also *very angry*, so angry that he felt like doing something very mean and cruel to his father. But he quickly put that thought out of his mind because he realized that if he were to do something mean or cruel to his father that he might even get a worse punishment. That night Tom had a

dream about his father in which the angry feelings came out. Can you make up a dream showing how the angry feelings came out?

If the patient tells a dream in which the anger is acted out overtly, I may accept that as an answer. However, I may also say, "Well, that's one possible dream. However, this particular boy felt very bad about such angry thoughts. He felt so bad and guilty about having such thoughts that he could not let them into his conscious mind. He had to make up a code. He had to disguise the angry thoughts before he could let them come into his conscious mind." I will then ask the youngster to make up a dream in which the anger is released in coded form. If the patient cannot do so, I may suggest a dream in which the boy's *friend* hits the father with a baseball bat. Or, the boy might have a dream in which he is hitting a policeman. Or the father, while driving his car, has an accident. In this way I help the patient appreciate the concept of wish fulfillment by symbolic processes.

With this introduction into the theory of dream formation and analysis, I may then turn to the patient's dream and ask him or her to try to figure out what it means. A good principle to follow is that the element that is most likely to produce useful information is the most idiosyncratic or atypical one. These are the more highly individualized symbols and are more likely to provide useful leads regarding the dream's meaning. The therapist must keep in mind the fact that his or her suggestions regarding the meaning of a particular element in the dream are always speculations. The therapist should do everything to get the patient to present his or her own guesses and hunches regarding a symbol's meaning before the therapist offers any speculations. Even the patient's "wild guesses" may be more on point than the therapist's carefully considered explanations. The patient's guesses are more likely to be related to the unconscious issues that have brought about the dream's formation.

One device that I have found useful in getting youngsters to free associate to a dream entity is to utilize what I call the "foreign boy" question. Let us say, for example, a patient has a dream in which a shoe appears. One could simply ask the youngster what comes to mind in association with the word *shoe*. If the patient appears to have difficulty providing associations I might ask this question: "Suppose a foreign boy moved into your neighborhood and he didn't know very much English. Suppose he asked you what the word *shoe* means. What would you say?" I have found this question to provide a much higher percentage of useful associations than the more general question, "What comes to mind about the word *shoe?*"

It is only after the patient has exhausted all possible associations and explanations that the therapist should offer his or her interpretations or hunches for the patient's consideration. The hope here is that the patient will latch on to the explanation and have the aforementioned feeling that "It fits," "You're right," or "That's it." When the therapist observes this response, then he or she knows that the interpretation is likely to be valid. But if the patient just merely says, "Yes, that sounds right," without the feeling that the explanation "clicks" or is on target, then one cannot be sure that the interpretation was indeed valid. Last, one does not merely analyze dreams as an intellectual game. The purpose is to utilize what is learned in the service of the therapeutic goals.

CLINICAL EXAMPLE OF DREAM PSYCHOANALYSIS

George entered treatment at the age of 15 because of difficulties in forming relationships with friends. Clearly of superior intelligence, in terms of academic abilities, he had a brain like a sponge and sopped up knowledge from a wide variety of sources. It appeared that he never forgot any fact that related to expansion of useful knowledge. But he did not absorb information indiscriminately; rather, he had a keen interest in what was going on in the world and did not concern himself with frivolous and useless bits of information. However, from kindergarten days he was different from the others, primarily because of his intellectual precocity. Although some youngsters with George's genetic endowment might still relate well to others, George did not. It was not that he flaunted his knowledge; rather, he seemed to engender jealousy from his peers. Over the years of his elementary education he became increasingly isolated from others, mainly because he withdrew from taunts rather than deal with them more directly.

When the patient was about 12 years old and began to exhibit his pubertal growth spurt, the parents noted a slight limp. On neurological examination it was found that there was asymmetry between his left and right side. The consulting neurologist considered this to be a residuum of slight cerebral palsy, related to mild trauma to the brain incurred during birth. Apparently, the damage was extremely slight, affected only certain motor pathway functioning and obviously did not in any way interfere with intellectual functioning. The asymmetry was accentuated by his pubertal growth spurt but gradually reduced itself spontaneously. George's psychological reactions to the disorder were greater than the physical impairments engendered by it. In fact, it did not interfere with his going into track as his favorite sport during the junior-high- and senior-high-school periods.

By the junior-high-school level George was involving himself to a significant degree in his own fantasies. However, I did not consider him to be schizophrenic. Instead, I considered him to have a somewhat schizoid personality disorder. During that period he began involving himself with boys who spent hours playing *Dungeons and Dragons*. For the reader not familiar with this game, it is primarily a fantasy game in which the players weave stories around a wide variety of medieval figures. The game generally goes on for a few hours and sometimes all-night marathon sessions. There are rare instances in which youngsters have been so swept up in the game that a wide variety of pathological acts have ensued, including murder. On the one hand, I considered the game to be psychologically detrimental to George and advised him of my opinion in this regard. On the other hand, it did serve as a vehicle for his involving himself with peers. I presented George with both arguments and told him that he must make the final decision about his involvement. Not surprisingly, George decided to continue playing the game although he would not let himself get swept up into all-night marathons.

George's mother was a somewhat cold and restrictive woman, but a good mother nevertheless. His father was a more outgoing person. Both parents dedicated themselves to bringing up George and his sister in as healthy a way as possible. There were no significant marital difficulties. George's sister was a more outgoing person and had no significant psychiatric difficulties. At 13 she was starting to become interested in boys. In contrast, George at 15 still showed absolutely no interest in involving himself with girls. In fact, he even denied any feelings of sexual excitation. I suspected that powerful psychological forces had suppressed significantly his normal sexual urges.

During his first session I told George that I would like him to place a pencil and pad at his bedside and, each morning, think about any dreams he had. I told him that I would like him to write down his dreams and that he should not assume in advance that a dream was too short, simple, obvious, or inconsequential to be so recorded. I emphasized that even the most miniscule dream, even one word, may be a rich source of information for our work. I impressed upon him that there should be absolutely no excuse for not writing down a dream and that if he found himself giving himself excuses he should recognize that he was rationalizing. I also impressed upon him that it was important that he bring the written dream to me so that I could read it and that merely writing it down and leaving it elsewhere would compromise significantly our utilization of it. Furthermore, I emphasized that it was important to write the dream down *immediately* because they have a way of evaporating and no one, no matter how brilliant and no matter how good his or her memory, is going to remember a dream for long. Last, I also advised him that if he didn't write it down, I would have to waste time in the session writing it down and the later rendition might not be as accurate as the original.

It may be of interest to the reader that I have been presenting this spiel to patients for over 30 years. It is a rare patient who will then bring in a dream in accordance with the aforementioned instructions. In fact, I cannot recall a patient who has done so. Every possible excuse is provided, e.g., "It was so obvious and clear in my memory that I knew I would remember it," "I wrote it down but I didn't know that you wanted me to bring in the paper," "It was very short, only a sentence, so I didn't write it down," and "I know what it means so I didn't write it down." So common are the rationalizations and so frequent is the forgetfulness regarding these instructions that I can safely say that I cannot remember one patient who has ever come in the session after my initial instructions and followed every single one of them. Rather, for most it may take weeks and even months to get them to do so. And there are some who do not follow through with these instructions throughout the full course of their treatment. The consistency with which patients do not "remember" these instructions is a strong statement about the power of psychological defense mechanisms and the threat that dream analysis poses to patients. As will soon be seen in the transcript below George was no exception and he too provided a rationalization for not recording his dreams.

In the session during which I discussed with George the writing down of his dreams, we also discussed our making a video cassette tape of each of our sessions. In recent years I have been encouraging all my patients to make video cassette tapes of their complete sessions, from the beginning to the end. They then watch the tape at home between sessions. I have found this an extremely helpful therapeutic modality and cannot recommend it highly enough. Elsewhere (1989a) I have described in detail this valuable utilization of the video cassette tape in treatment. The clinical vignette presented below was being videotaped and the dream George discussed incorporated the video equipment into it. Presented below, verbatim, is a transcript from George's tenth session. The discussion of the dream is presented in toto, but I will periodically interrupt with descriptive and analytic commentary.

> *Therapist*: So what's doing?
> *Patient*: Really, nothing much has been happening in the past two days. No exceptional dreams or anything, I haven't written down...
> *Therapist*: No dreams at all?
> *Patient*: There was this one dream. I don't remember the end of it when I woke up.
> *Therapist*: Okay. What did I tell you about dreams?
> *Patient*: Write them down.
> *Therapist*: Did I tell you no matter how short, no matter how fragmented, no matter how silly? No matter how inconsequential they may appear?
> *Patient*: Yes.
> *Therapist*: Very important. No matter how simple and

obvious it is, write it down and don't trust to memory, okay? So when did you have this dream?

Patient: Last night.

Therapist: Let's hear what you remember of it. We may not be able to make anything of it, but we may. But if you don't bring it in...

Patient: It was simply that we were taking my dog Charlie to some show or something...

Therapist: To a show. What kind of a show? Like a dog show?

Patient: A talk show.

Therapist: Like a TV talk show?

Patient: Yeah.

Therapist: Okay. And what was his participation?

Patient: He was basically there on a talk show...for some reason I can never understand.

Therapist: But he was going on a show?

Patient: No, I was taking him on a show.

Therapist: And he was going to be the guest?

Patient: I guess so, yeah.

Therapist: He was going to be the guest. Anything more in the dream?

Patient: No...I woke up...

Therapist: Okay, tell me about your dog Charlie. What can you tell me about him?

Patient: He's a golden retriever. He's an adult. We got him from my uncle when they had to move to Sweden. He sometimes runs away but he always comes back. He likes to be petted. He likes attention. He's really not mean to anything, except our cat. He's terrified ...

Therapist: He's scared of the cat?

Patient: No, the cat is scared of him.

Therapist: What does he do to the cat?

Patient: Chases him.

Therapist: Does he ever harm her?

Patient: I don't know if he means to harm her. The cat just runs up a tree. Then the cat comes down and looks one way and looks the other way...

Therapist: So he kind of bullies the cat, huh?

Patient: Yeah. Also, he likes to get his cookie at night—a dog biscuit. After we let him out for the night we give him his cookie and we give him his worm pill. He doesn't do tricks or anything like that. He just likes a lot of attention, and if you're mad at him he knows he's done something wrong. He sleeps in the house. He eats about anything.

Therapist: He eats anything?

Patient: Anything edible.

Therapist: If you were asked the question—I'm asking the question—are there any similar traits that you and Charlie have in common? It's a difficult question to ask, but sometimes people can answer quite easily. Would you say there are any traits you and Charlie have in common?

Patient: I guess I like attention now and he likes it too. I like to be petted a lot like Charlie. A lot of time I seem to understand a little bit what he wants or what my cat wants ...

Therapist: Let's look at the question of similar traits. They like attention. They like to be petted. Any other similar qualities you and Charlie share?

Patient: We like the family. I think that's about it. I usually don't get hyper over a cookie or anything like that.

Therapist: Let's go back to the dream now. Do you have any idea what the dream means?

Patient: No.

Therapist: What could the talk show stand for?

Patient: I don't know.

Therapist: Okay, look. How does this sound? The talk show might have something to do with your therapy. How is this like a talk show?

Patient: You've got microphones. You turn on a VCR. You've got the George/Dr. Gardner show ...

Therapist: We've got a camera there. We've got a television camera, right? We've got microphones and what do we do?

Patient: We talk.

Therapist: Right. And it's kind of a show because we use the tape. We can show it and look at it later.

Patient: Of course, we don't nationally televise.

Therapist (humorously): Well, if you want to do that, we'll see what we can arrange. We've got some very interesting sessions ...Okay, so we think it's reasonable to think the talk show might represent therapy?

Patient: Yeah, it might.

Therapist: And we're having a chat like you would in a talk show. I'm the host, you're the guest. Right?

Patient: Yeah.

Therapist: Okay. So let's say that the talk show in your dreams represents what we're doing here. So what else?

Patient: Why does Charlie represent me? I don't know. Charlie is someone I really like. I really like Charlie.

Therapist: Okay. How does this fit in? He was to be the guest on the talk show. There's a special switcheroo here. So what about Charlie?

Patient: Charlie is something very special to me, for one thing. I don't know exactly what Charlie represents. He's not an exceptional dog in any way.

Therapist: So why do you have *him* coming to be the guest?

Patient: And me just bringing him? That's another one that I can't understand.

Therapist: What's your guess?

Patient: Not to play a mean trick on you. Would it?

Therapist: A trick? Okay, let's follow that up.

Patient: But you were not expecting a dog though. Not you. But the talk show was expecting Charlie though.

Therapist: Okay, it's a trick on me. You want to play a trick on me.

Patient: The uncomfortableness, with the psychiatry thing.

Therapist: Okay, uncomfortable with psychiatry. So how did the trick of Charlie work?

Patient: To give you a hyper dog to talk with!

Therapist: Is he a hyper dog?

Patient: Half the time he's not, half the time he's asleep.

Therapist: So you've given me a hyper dog to talk with. What would happen?

Patient: He'd jump around all over the place.

Therapist: Yeah. And what would happen then? You said

something about discomfort with psychiatry? A little while ago? So how does the dog fit in there with discomfort with psychiatry?

Patient: Like dog-day afternoons or something?

Therrapist: What does that have to do with discomfort with psychiatry? You said discomfort with psychiatry didn't you?

Patient: Yeah, as a possible subconscious discomfort.

Therapist: Okay, how would having Charlie come here as the guest relate to discomfort with psychiatry?

Patient: He would replace me. And I would be safe?

Therapist: You would be safe. Why?

Patient: You would be filming my dog instead.

Therapist: How do you feel about that in terms of your treatment? How much would I learn from him? In terms of going to a talk show, how much is he going to talk?

Patient: Not too much. I got him there, and I got him on stage and stuff.

Therapist: Okay. So what is the dream saying then?

Patient: I still like to elude you every now and then.

Therapist: Uh huh. So by substituting your dog you are protecting yourself from revealing certain things, right?

Patient: Yeah.

At that point I believed that George and I had basically analyzed the dream. However, an important determinant regarding whether or not a dream interpretation "sinks in" is the patient's reaction to it. Ideally, the therapist wants the patient to reach the point where there is a deep sense of appreciation that the interpretation "fits." More valuable is the patient's having the experience that can be best stated with the words "Eureka! That's it, of course!" Most patients are dubious about the value of dream analysis, especially early in treatment. If the therapist can bring about a situation in which the patient, after analyzing a dream, has the aforementioned eureka experience, then it is more likely that more dreams will be forthcoming because the patient will have had the living experience that dreams can be useful. This conviction for dream analysis can then spread into the conviction for other kinds of analytic inquiry.

Therapist: Okay. I'm going to ask you this question. Do you think that our interpretation that we have derived is a valid one? Does it grab you?

Patient: It does sort of grab me, yeah.

Therapist: Does it add to your conviction that dreams, even fragmented ones, even the little seemingly silly, ...

Patient: As a reflection of the subconscious to the conscious ...

Therapist: Does this analysis add to your conviction as to the use of these dreams in understanding what's going on here?

Patient: Yeah, I think it does.

Therapist: Because I hoped that it would, in the hope that it might motivate you to write them down. Now I don't think we're finished with this, I'm just saying this to you now in the hope that it will spur you on to see what else we can derive from this dream. The big question is what are the things that you are hiding from me that you are using Charlie to help you hide? That's the question.

The transcript cannot convey the degree of conviction associated with the patient's words. The tonal quality of his voice and his gestures led me to the conclusion that George indeed did have a mild kind of eureka experience. But George was not the kind of boy who exuded enthusiasm about anything. His relating more dreams in the future was the best evidence that the dream analysis had "grabbed him." I then began an inquiry that would enable us to get more mileage out of the dream. These derivative discussions are an important part of dream analysis. The therapist should not simply be content with a simple analysis of the dream. One wants to take the material revealed and extract from it as much therapeutic mileage as possible. Therefore, I asked George what things he might be hiding from me, things not alluded to, except indirectly, in the dream.

Patient: That too is in my subconscious.

Therapist: Just guess, whatever comes into your mind.

Patient: Like how we never really talk about the cerebral palsy and stuff, maybe.

Therapist: Okay. Let's talk about that. What things about that do you want to say?

Patient: Well, I didn't really tell anybody about it, not that I think about it half the time, if not three-quarters of it. Because I feel that it is irrelevant, or has very little relevance, or very little impact on my life, it really doesn't affect it.

Therapist: So you don't think there's much to talk about that?

Patient: No. I never felt it was a *strong* hamper on my life.

Therapist: Have you ever felt it was a *weak* hamper on your life?

Patient: The one time it really affected me was when I had the little vein problem, or tendon problem, or whatever it was. Where I really grew too fast for myself.

Therapist: Okay. Is there anything else you want to say about that?

Patient: Well I do work here on the mental dysfunction and stuff, right?

Therapist: Yes.

Patient: Yeah, and the effect on the brain. You said in the first meeting that it might have some effect on my friendship relationships.

Therapist: Okay, and how did I say it might have some effect?

Patient: Certain processes of my brain are weakened like putting myself in other people's fears and stuff.

The patient is referring here to remarks I made near the end of our first two-hour consultation. I was commenting on his impairments in putting himself in other people's positions. I mentioned that this might have a neurological substrate, especially considering that there was some brain dysfunction associated with brain trauma. However, I also pointed out that environmental and psychological factors played a more important role and related to his withdrawal from involvement with others.

Therapist: Okay. What are some of your thoughts on that now? Is there anything about that issue of putting yourself in other's people's position you are afraid to talk about or hesitant to talk about?

Patient: No, not usually, I just don't really talk about it.

Therapist: So that isn't something that you're hesitant to discuss with me? I would be more interested in things that have gone on, thoughts and feelings you've had which you have said to yourself, "Oh, I wouldn't want to talk to him about that" or "That makes me very shy, I prefer not to discuss that." By the way, you are free to reveal, or not to reveal, any parts of these tapes. In terms of watching them, you can say to your parents, "I prefer not to have you see this," or you can even say,"I prefer not to have anybody view any part of that tape." That tape is yours, and you can show or not show it. You can obliterate it all by going over it with some other material. So, getting back to the question: is there anything that's happened to you where you would say, "Oh, I'd rather not discuss that"?

Patient: Yeah, sometimes some of my dreams and hopes and stuff like that. Like I usually used to daydream and I didn't like to tell people.

Therapist: What are the things done in your daydreams?

Patient: I find myself daydreaming less and less now, but...like I said, the daydreaming has to do partially with my retreats from myself that we talked about Monday.

Therapist: Monday—to do with what?

Patient: The retreats from reality, and being George.

Therapist: Okay, where are you at, at this point, with these daydreams?

Patient: Like I said I'm doing it less.

Therapist: Why do you think you're doing it less?

Patient: Because I'm trying to do it less.

Therapist: And why are you trying to do it less?

Patient: Because you and my parents and everybody has pretty much shown that the less I do it the more receptive to real people and the better I become.

Therapist: What are you substituting for it? What are you doing instead?

Patient: What I'm planning to do partially is, trying to write some stuff. I've been thinking about it. A lot of my retreats are stuff that I think could be good for maybe writing down one day and make into stories and stuff.

It certainly would have been nice if the patient had said that he was substituting human involvements for his daydreams. However, that would have been too much to ask at that point. Such a great leap forward in therapy would not likely have taken place and, if he professed such interest, I would be a little dubious. His substitution of writing for fantasizing is certainly desirable, but it is only a small step forward in that it is too solitary an experience.

> *Therapist*: Okay, so you're writing material for stories?
> *Patient*: Yeah.
> *Therapist*: What kind of stories. Let's hear about those.
> *Patient*: I usually write down how people would react to exceptionally crazy stuff, to an exceptionally crazy situation.

As mentioned so many times in this book, abstractions and generalizations are of little therapeutic value. The therapist does well to get specific examples of the issues patients are talking about. These concrete examples are the therapist's handle for grabbing on to an issue that can be discussed meaningfully. Maintaining the discussion at the abstract level is likely to be a complete waste of time from the therapeutic point of view.

> *Therapist*: For example?
> *Patient*: How do aliens come down, pick up TV waves, and send clones of The Three Stooges down for observation?
> *Therapist*: Go ahead. What else, what other kind of stuff?
> *Patient*: And from there I pick up like how the Defense Department would react after they got these pictures of three big fat guys. And what the generals would do. And like tanks coming out against The Three Stooges and they think like they're very evil. Strange aliens with sonic weapons and it just goes on like that...
> *Therapist*: So the main thing is that evil, strange, aliens...
> *Patient*: Not evil or strange...
> *Therapist*: Did you say *evil* before?

Patient: Now, you've got these aliens, right? From outer space, and they are observing things here on Earth. And they pick up TV waves, right? Because they're sent here from outer space. Okay. An Earth spaceship picks it up and sees The Three Stooges. The aliens figure Earth is very violent, but they want to send down observers. The aliens see only three people around to do the observing. The three people they've got on their video tape. So they clone them, in order to be inconspicuous. The only people the aliens saw were The Three Stooges. So they cloned them. So they sent these clones down and they're discovered. Word was sent to the army about the three clones.

This general, now he's playing Battleship for the admiral on the big computer board. He picks this up: "We're being invaded." First thing he says, "by Russians or some others?" Then he goes, "not by Russians." Then he goes, "by the Chinese," and he's going down all this list. He's not letting his subordinate really break in. And then his subordinate says "aliens." And the general says, "You mean from Mexico?" And he just says, "No, from outer space." And there is very little description, what do the aliens look like? Green-eyed, tentacled, no, there are The Three Stooges. And he says like, "Oh well, we better just stay quiet about it." And he's asking, "Who knows what, does the KGB know about it?" "No." "Does the FBI know about it?" "No." "Okay, fine. Worst thing: Does the press know about it?" "Yes." "Yeah...watch the press... watch the press." And they're just running from the army and the press and everybody and it's really crazy after a while.

Therapist: So everybody's kind of persecuting them?

Patient: Uh, yeah.

Therapist: Why are they persecuting them?

Patient: Why, because they're aliens. It's not persecution. The press just wants to talk to them, but the army doesn't want to get shown up by three aliens who look like Larry, Curly and Mo. I guess some people help them every now and then. The army is chasing them because they're aliens.

Therapist: So the army doesn't want to get shown up? I'm not clear about that.

Patient: What happens is that the army doesn't really want to be looked on as a fool. We have to stop and catch these three aliens. You know Larry, Curly, and Mo look really stupid. The army couldn't do that.

Therapist: The army would be fools if they couldn't capture them, but they are trying to capture them and everybody else views them as kind of atypical and oddballs and crazy.

Patient: They're aliens.

Therapist: And what is the main goal once caught? What will they do with them?

Patient: Well I guess a view would be to really capture or kill, because they're figuring armies of real mean green men could follow afterwards ...

Therapist: Okay, so that's the kind of fantasy you're putting down into a story?

Patient: Yeah.

Therapist: How does it end?

Patient: Eventually they're taken back up into the space-ship.

Therapist: And then what happens?

Patient: And then they're replaced with two different replacement aliens that may be a little more inconspicuous.

Therapist: Okay, what do they look like?

Patient: Normal people. And then he closed the curtains.

Therapist: Okay, this is a self-created story? You didn't get this from anything did you?

Patient: No, this is my own story. It does have some definite references to other stories. This is one of a kind by itself, though.

Therapist: You know, a story is like a dream, in a way. It tells something about the personality of the person who makes it up, and it can be analyzed like a dream. Do you understand that, do you appreciate that?

Patient: Yeah.

Therapist: How would you analyze this "dream"?

Patient: Maybe The Three Stooges represent my own alienation?

Therapist: Okay, how? The stooges represent how you feel about yourself, as an alien?

Patient: Yeah, I guess so.

Therapist: And who are the army people?

Patient: They are the people who want to ostracize me from the community or something.

Therapist: Yeah. Does that grab you?

Patient: Yeah, I thought of it more as a good story. I really like it. I was telling it to one or two of my friends some of the stuff I was going to put in and he really liked it so I think I'm going to eventually write it down.

Therapist: Okay, let's talk about it from the analytic point of view, okay? So here we have a story in which you see yourself as an alien, as being different and as being persecuted, pursued, and they want to get rid of you. Does this say something about how you see yourself?

Patient: Yes.

Therapist: The important question is what are you doing that is contributing toward this alienation from others?

Patient: Well the stooges are running because the army has tanks, and guns, and stuff like that. And they're running and hiding.

Therapist: Okay, I understand that, that is part of the persecution. The question I'm asking you is with regard to yourself as contributing to your own alienation. What are you doing in reality to contribute to your own alienation from others?

Patient: Like you know, not being assertive or anything.

Therapist: Yes, that's certainly true. Okay, what else?

Patient: The retreats, and withdrawal, and stuff.

Therapist: What else?

Patient: My passivity, my sometimes...with regard to the helping complex and stuff. My doing things for people that I really don't want to.

Therapist: Say that again?

Patient: The helping complex sometimes hurts when I go overboard or something? It's basically like you said, a lot of it is self-esteem. Like you said loss of self-esteem, self-confidence,

Therapist: Okay. Any recent examples of lack of self-assertion?

Patient: Not really too much.

Therapist: Any experiences recently where you asserted

yourself in situations in which you wouldn't have done so in the past?

Patient: Like basically the lack of assertiveness is a passiveness like my mother is. Like with Larry and the refrigerator.

The patient is making reference here to a problem he was having with a friend, Larry. Specifically, Larry was quite insensitive to the patient's feelings and acted in George's house as if he were in his own. For example he would repeatedly go to the refrigerator in George's home and eat enormous quantities of food without asking permission. At first, the patient was squelching his resentment over Larry's behavior in his home. As a result of my conversations with him, George asserted himself with Larry and confronted him with his insensitive behavior. In response, Larry "laid a guilt trip" on the patient. His essential message was that he (Larry) was a very depressed and disturbed boy and that if George were to restrict him from going to the refrigerator that Larry might become more depressed and even commit suicide. He even got the patient to believe that if he did commit suicide it would be George's responsibility. And this resulted in George's pulling back and suppressing all self-assertion lest he be responsible for Larry's death. Here again, I impressed upon George that he was being manipulated and there was absolutely nothing about Larry's behavior that suggested to me that he was significantly depressed or that suicide was a genuine risk.

Therapist: Where do things stand on that? That was the friend who you didn't want to go into your refrigerator.

Patient: Yeah.

Therapist: Okay. And he was making you feel responsible for his depression and suicidal thoughts.

Patient: As I said last Monday, for some reason, he plays upon my feeling of responsibility for him.

Therapist: In what particular area, for example.

Patient: Like if he says, "I'm going to commit suicide" or "I'm going to write a suicidal letter," I feel responsible for it even though I shouldn't.

Therapist: Where do things stand on that right now?

Patient: Like I said we haven't seen each other any more since Monday because Mom doesn't let him over.

Therapist: Has anything happened since then? Have you heard about anything?

Patient: No.

Therapist: Okay, so how do you feel about that whole thing at this point?

Patient: I used to feel okay about it, because I did assert myself, didn't let Larry play on my guilt or anything.

Therapist: Any other examples of self-assertiveness?

Patient: Not recently.

Therapist: Because if you are passive and submissive and you let people take advantage of you, then you contribute to that view of yourself as an oddball. Well, look, we have to close. I think that we have to talk more about this view of yourself as an oddball, as an alien. I think that you have to realize that these stories you write may give us useful information in therapy. But they could, at the same time, be a substitute for fantasizing and another form of withdrawal. You have to recognize this.

Patient: I do think a lot about the stories.

Therapist: But there's a certain danger to them.

Patient: Yes, when you get into the stories, but they can help also, because I can write a story down and maybe it serves my creative juices by writing down...

Therapist: Yes, there's a positive element in it. I'm not denying it, but then again too much time with them takes you away from reality.

At the time of this writing, about 20 months later, George is in his last year in high school. He is still in therapy. He has become much more assertive and outgoing but still is (and probably always will be) a somewhat uptight and intellectualized person. His knowledge of the world is sometimes astounding. He is a good example of the kind of patient who can definitely teach me things from time to time and I sometimes have to stop our discussions because I recognize there is the danger I might be exploiting him by tapping his knowledge to a significant degree. All (yes, all) his SAT scores and achievement tests were in the high 700 range. He was immediately accepted to his first-choice college. Unfortunately, I was not able to make much headway with his fear of girls. At the time I write this he has still not had his first date. Nor has group therapy helped him very much in this area. I just can't seem to get his sexual hormones secreted into his bloodstream. George has come to recognize, however, that he does have a problem in this area. My hope is that in the more sexually stimulating atmosphere of a college co-ed dorm, his juices will finally start to flow. There is no question that he would make a fascinating boyfriend for a highly intelligent, intellectually curious girl.

ELEVEN

GROUP THERAPY

There are some who would consider group therapy to be "adjunctive" to individual work. I consider group work to be as important as and, in some situations, even more important than individual work and so I do not use the word adjunctive when referring to group therapy, whether it be for the adolescent or the adult. Rather, I prefer to use the term "combined therapeutic approach" in which I include individual, group, and family work.

TYPES OF GROUP THERAPY

Some therapists make a sharp differentiation among a variety of different types of group therapy. The most common types described in the literature are psychoanalytic group therapy, behavior group therapy, cognitive group therapy, transactional analysis group therapy, and Gestalt group therapy. Each of these focuses on a particular therapeutic aspect. I do not apply any of these labels to the kind of group therapy I provide. Rather, I see myself as genuinely eclectic and feel free to use any element from these various types (and others) that I consider warranted. My group therapy is certainly psychoanalytic in that I am committed to the belief that unconscious processes operate in bringing about many forms of psychogenic psychopathology and that gaining insight into such processes can play a role (with other factors) in bringing about therapeutic change. Such an orientation does not preclude my utilizing behavior modification techniques as I encourage desensitization and provide various forms of reinforcement (most often of a psychological nature). I am very committed to the notion that cognitive distortions play an important role in bringing about psychopathology and that the correction of these can contribute to the alleviation of problems that result from such distortions. I believe, as well, that many of the "games" that the transactional analyst describes are useful in understanding certain forms of interpersonal psychopathology. Although I believe that transactional analysts do not give proper attention to the unconscious processes operative in bringing about the development of these games, this still does not lessen my enthusiasm for their utilization in treatment. Last, although less committed to Gestalt therapy than other forms, I still use play acting and role modeling to a limited degree (as will be discussed below).

The reader may note that I have made no mention of encounter groups. These came into vogue in the late 1960s and early 1970s and residua of the philosophy still prevail in some circles. Manifestations of these remnants are to be seen in the "let it all hang out" philosophy and the notion that merely releasing thoughts and feelings, often indiscriminately, is in itself therapeutic. One of the aims of such emotional displays was to engender similar emotional reactions in other group participants. The theory here was that this in itself would be therapeutic for the others. I have serious reservations about this approach. Although I am very much in favor of a certain amount of emotional release, the release must be tempered with cognition if it is to be properly channeled into healthy directions. Children typically rant and rave when something bothers them; mature, healthy adults have learned that there are better ways to deal with one's emotions, ways that involve judicious combinations of cognition and emotion.

PRIMARY BENEFITS OF
GROUP THERAPY

Of the three age levels—childhood, adolescence, and adulthood—group therapy is probably most useful for the adolescent, next for the adult, and least for children. Adolescents appear to be natural "groupies." They gravitate toward groups in order to compensate for feelings of inadequacy. They recognize, at some level, that the group has far greater strength than the sum of the individuals within it. They learn from the group what are the "in" styles, customs, lingo, etc. of the day. They are slavishly dependent on their peers and this dependency can be utilized in group therapy. The therapist, who like the parents is a member of the adult generation, is likely to be distrusted and such distrust may compromise the treatment. In contrast, the adolescent's peers "know where it's all at" and are viewed as having opinions that are more worthy of respect.

Adolescents, especially younger ones, do not generally relish the notion of sitting in a room alone with a therapist for 45 to 50 minutes while his or her "beady eyes" are staring at the patient asking him or her to "say what's on your mind." In the group the youngster can talk when he or she wishes and sink into the woodwork when silence is desired. Whereas in individual sessions the therapist must rely upon the youngster's renditions of what goes on with peers, in the group therapy session the therapist has the opportunity to observe directly such interactions. And this may be one of the greatest benefits of group psychotherapy. Furthermore, in the group the youngster can directly have therapeutic social experiences. Thus, those youngsters with a paucity of friends can be provided greater opportunity for social experiences as part of the therapeutic program.

There are a wide variety of ways in which the group experience can be useful for adolescents. The group helps adolescents improve their peer relationships, something that cannot but be therapeutic. It enables the examiner to observe firsthand the youngsters' interactions with others, providing the therapist thereby with more accurate data about the patient's problems—especially those that are interpersonal. The group helps adolescents learn better ways of dealing with the fundamental problems of life which, as mentioned so many times previously, are at the foundation of most forms of psychogenic psychopathology. The group provides new models for identification, both the therapist and other group participants. It is hoped that the identifications are healthier ones than those that the youngster has utilized previously when dealing with life's inevitable difficulties. The group forces an introspective stance, which can be useful in working out both intrapsychic and interpersonal problems. However, the group focuses more on interpersonal than intrapsychic problems, in that it is not a place where one conducts individual psychotherapy with six or seven observers. Of course, the issues brought up in the group can serve as points of departure for such inquiries in individual sessions. Accordingly, the analysis of a dream would rarely be conducted in group therapy. The group fosters open expression of pent-up thoughts and feelings with an aim toward their healthier utilization (not just blind expression).

GROUP STRUCTURE AND TECHNICAL CONSIDERATIONS

The treatment of an adolescent may involve individual sessions, group therapy, and sessions in which the youngster is present with one or both parents and other family members, as warranted. Nor does one have to have a fixed program regarding the alternation of these various treatment modalities. If any one of the three is likely to be fixed, it is the group therapy sessions in that the group is generally an ongoing, open-ended arrangement in which youngsters may enter and leave at various times, but the group maintains its continuity. Individual and family sessions, however, may be scheduled on a periodic or aperiodic basis as indicated for the particular child. The main criterion by which the therapist should determine the therapeutic structure is this: Are the sessions being used productively? If there are long silences and/or people have little if anything to say, then it is not likely that such therapeutic sessions are useful. The arrangement most likely to be sterile is the individual session in which the patient is alone with the therapist.

Family sessions and group sessions are much more likely to be productive because with more people in the room, there is much more likely to be an agenda and therapeutic activity.

The Question of
Optimum Group Size

The ideal situation in which a group can be formed is the one in which there is a large pool of adolescent patients. Furthermore, I believe that it is preferable to have two groups: one of junior-high-school age and one of senior-high-school age. When one pools youngsters together who span ages 12 through 18, there is the risk that some of the younger ones will have antitherapeutic experiences. The younger ones are not as likely to be as sophisticated as the older and may therefore suffer from the embarrassment of their opinions' not being respected. Also, the younger ones may be prematurely exposed to "heavier" psychopathology involved with sex, antisocial behavior, and drugs.

I believe that the ideal number of youngsters to have registered as group members is eight or nine. However, this is not the ideal number to actually have at any specific session. By having eight or nine registered as ongoing members, it is likely that in any week six or seven will be present and this, I believe, is the optimum number. I know of situations in which people have had 15 or 20 patients in a group at the same time. This is unconscionable. Generally, it is not the therapeutic indications that have warranted this number. In private practice, it generally represents greed on the part of the therapist in that 20 people can provide a sizable income. In clinic settings it often represents an attempt at "efficiency" in a situation where a large number of people are being serviced because the facility is clearly not adequate to handle all the referrals in an effective way. The group therapy then becomes an administrative maneuver to satisfy those who are paying for the treatment and possibly dupe all concerned into believing that adequate treatment is being provided.

Obviously, if one needs about 18 teenagers to form two adolescent groups, it is not likely that one is going to be able to form such groups in most private practices. Only in clinic settings is there generally a large enough pool of patients available to form two groups of this kind. Therapists in private practice, however, may still be able to form adolescent groups if they pool their resources. Specifically, one therapist could run the junior-high-school level group and another the senior-high-school level group, with therapists in the consortium referring patients to the groups. This arrangement is not as effective as one in which the same therapist is seeing patients in both individual and group therapy; however, it is preferable to one in which no group therapy is available at all.

Homogeneous vs. Heterogeneous Groups

I generally prefer that the group be mixed boys and girls. Adolescent youngsters have to learn how to relate to members of the opposite sex and a group therapy experience can provide such opportunities. I also prefer heterogeneous over homogeneous groups. Some prefer homogeneous groups such as those for drug addicts, obese patients, alcoholics, etc. Although there are certainly some good arguments for such homogeneity, I believe that the arguments for heterogeneity are stronger. As mentioned so often throughout this book, all patients, regardless of their psychogenic symptoms, are basically utilizing their symptoms to deal with the fundamental problems of life with which we are all confronted. Because therapy focuses on better ways to deal with these underlying problems, it is not crucial that the other members of the group utilize the same symptomatic solutions to these problems. In fact, when they do, the focus often becomes too great on the external symptoms and this takes the group away from focusing on the more important underlying issues. For example, in a group for adolescent youngsters suffering with anorexia/bulimia, it is likely that an inordinate amount of time will be spent on weight, diet, and exercise. In fact, there are some groups of youngsters with this disorder in which each of the meetings is started with a "weighing in" ceremony. Although the prospect of embarrassment may play a role in bringing about therapeutic change, I believe such focus on symptoms robs the patient of the opportunity to delve into the underlying problems from which the symptoms emerge and the understanding of which is important in the psychotherapeutic process. Similarly, a group consisting of youngsters on drugs is likely to focus significantly on what particular drugs they ingested since the last meeting, what dosage, what reactions they had, etc. Here again, although some therapeutic benefit may be derived from such discussions, I believe a heavy price is paid, namely, the opportunity to discuss in depth the underlying problems at the foundation of the substance-abuse.

Although I consider it preferable to have patients with a variety of problems present in the group, I do not indiscriminately place every single adolescent in a group. Youngsters with severe learning disabilities and/or borderline intelligence will not do well in a group of youngsters with normal and above average intelligence. They are likely to be humiliated, merely tolerated, and not taken seriously. And this must be antitherapeutic. It is preferable for such young- sters to be in groups with others who are of the same intellectual level. Although one could argue that I am now recommending a homogeneous group, there can still be heterogeneity among the youngsters in this intellectual bracket. I also would not put severely sick youngsters in a group of adolescents whose problems are mild. The psychotic and/or autistic youngster is also likely to be humili- ated, tolerated, or ignored in such a group and this will definitely be antitherapeutic. It is also important that the antisocial youngsters be outnumbered by those who are not antisocial. If the former are in the majority, then there is the possibility that those who do not have problems in this area may begin to develop such. This becomes a situation of the "bad apples spoiling the whole barrel."

The Optimum Duration of the Group Meeting

I have found meetings of 90 minutes to be optimum. If the group becomes smaller, down to four of five youngsters, then 60 minutes may work well. I usually have only one group meeting a week, but believe that in a residential treatment setting, where the youngsters are obviously more readily available, two and even three group meetings a week of even longer duration could probably be useful.

After-Group Meetings
Without the Therapist

In my group work with adults I have generally found it useful for them to meet together alone, without me, in an after-group meeting. Ideally, this takes place in their homes and, if the situation warrants it, they can alternate homes each week. If this is not practical, then they can meet in a restaurant. The purpose here is not socialization but further group work at no additional cost. Although this arrangement serves well for adults, it is generally a bad idea for adolescents. One is setting up a situation for freedom to act out and it can thereby become antitherapeutic. Providing the group members the opportunity to meet alone, without the therapist's supervision, increases the likelihood that youngsters who do not act out may be drawn into such behavior. Accordingly, my adolescents in group therapy are usually dropped off by their parents and picked up after the meeting. I have no objection, however, if the parents set up car pools. In fact, this can often be useful in that it provides more contact among the youngsters, but still under supervision.

A Comparison of the Three Levels of Child
and Adolescent Group Therapy

Group Therapy for Latency-Aged Children   When discussing adolescent group therapy, it is useful to consider the progression from group therapy with latency-aged children, to the junior-high-school level, to the senior-high-school level. Any therapist who has attempted to conduct group therapy with latency-aged children will agree that formidable obstacles are likely to impede the smooth flow of the group sessions. Children in this age bracket are traditionally poor candidates for group therapy because of their age-appropriate rambunctiousness. Horseplay is the rule rather than the exception. Children at this age level are not famous for their desire to sit around in a circle discussing their problems. Giggling, poking, wrestling, and teasing are much more likely to take place than serious discussion. Passing gas is a common prank in such situations—with each member accusing the other of having performed the despicable act: "You did it!" "You're a liar." "You did it.! "No I didn't, it smells like yours." Of course, the therapist might use this issue as a point of departure for group discussion and thereby transform the prank into a therapeutic experience for all concerned. The disadvantage of this, however, is that it may encourage more farting because of the attention it provokes.

I have sometimes found myself in the position of informing a latency group troublemaker that if the antics don't cease instantly, he or she will be sent out of the room. Although there may be some therapeutic value to such a maneuver, it is hard to justify charging parents money under these circumstances. Accordingly, the therapist often finds him- or herself serving more as a disciplinarian than a therapist. Other disruptive antics involve arguing about where each person should sit and then bickering throughout the course of the "therapy" regarding the desire to change one's seat. Another common maneuver is imitation. While one youngster speaks, the other mouths his or her words and tries to engage a third party in similar antics. One youngster coughs and all the rest then start coughing. If the therapy is interrupted by a telephone call, pandemonium is likely to break out.

The Talking, Feeling, and Doing Game (Gardner, 1973b) provides an organization and a structure that is often so powerful that children in this age group may be diverted from their horseplay. One can use it for this purpose in a number of ways. One way I have found useful is to have the first child respond to a card and then get input from each of the other players on the first player's response. Each of the other participants, of course, receives a chip for his or her contribution. The second child may now answer the same question or choose another. In this way I go around the board, engaging each child in the responses of the other. When utilizing the game in this manner, the therapist can choose whether to participate as a player or merely as the one who keeps the game structured and calls on the various participants to wait their turn, respond at a given point, etc. I generally prefer to play as one who takes the cards him- or herself for the sake of "egalitarianism" as well as the desire to provide the patients with the therapeutic benefits to be derived from my revelations about myself. Although *The Talking, Feeling, and Doing Game* may provide some structure in latency group therapy, it is not always successful in this regard. The main determinant is the percentage of children who are going to engage in horseplay. When the group members' disruptive antics are formidable, such therapy may be a "lost cause"—the utilization of *The Talking, Feeling, and Doing Game* notwithstanding.

Group Therapy at the Junior-High-School Level   It is useful to view group therapy at the junior-high-school level to be at a mid-point between group therapy with latency-aged children and those at the senior-high-school level. At the junior-high-school level, the youngsters are more likely to sit around and talk directly about their difficulties. However, their capacity to do this is less than that of older adolescents. It is at this middle level, especially, that *The Talking, Feeling, and Doing Game* may be particularly useful. As is true of the situation when one works with these children individually, they often have difficulty initiating and perpetuating a discussion of their problems. Many have directly told me that they enjoy utilizing the game because it gives them ideas and hints about things to talk about. At the junior-high-school level one must be much more structured regarding the group therapy than when treating older youngsters. Also, at this age level I am more likely to bring in parents on occasion than I am at the senior- high-school level. Their participation can be particularly useful. A youngster may complain bitterly about various indignities he or she has suffered at the hands of the parents. Most often the child's view is a distortion and an exaggeration. By bringing in a parent for "his or her opinion" regarding what had happened, it can often provide useful corrections of these distortions and a more meaningful group discussion. Parents sometimes feel uncomfortable being brought in under these circumstances in that they see themselves as being witnesses in a court of children, but they recognize the value of their participation.

Group Therapy at the Senior-High-School Level   Work with the senior-high-school students approaches much more closely that of the traditional adult group. At this level I generally do not have an agenda and I let the youngsters begin the discussion with any issue that might come to mind. I generally do not need *The Talking, Feeling, and Doing Game* to provide ideas and suggestions regarding what to talk about. This is in contrast to the younger groups in which I am much more prone to bring up issues. However, there are still certain differences between the structure of the senior-high-school level group and that of my adult group. For example, if a particular youngster is typically reticent to involve him- or herself in discussions, I feel no hesitation actively drawing that youngster in. I might say, "You know, Jane, we've heard from everyone else on this subject but not you. Let's hear what you have to say." If the child is still hesitant, I might say, "I know that your brain has been working throughout the course of this discussion and that you have thoughts on what has been said. We both know that you need *practice* expressing yourself and the group provides you an opportunity to do so in a way that will not result in any problems for you. This is not the case outside of this office where, on occasion, what you say might get you into trouble. But, as we have said many times before, it generally won't." I ordinarily would not take such an approach in adult treatment in that the patient would thereby be infantalized and I would be involving myself in an antitherapeutic maneuver. One could argue that the adolescent is being infantalized by such overtures. I agree that this might be the case, but I believe that the disadvantages are more than compensated for by the experiences the youngster has after being brought out and involving him- or herself in the group discussions. As in all therapeutic maneuvers, there are advantages and disadvantages. It behooves the therapist to identify what these are and then make decisions regarding whether or not to utilize the particular technique.

Sibling Involvement

On occasion, I have invited a sibling of one of the patients to join us in a group session. This usually comes about after the patient has been complaining bitterly about the sibling and I suspect that the situation might be somewhat different from the way the patient has described it. Just as parental participation in this way can be useful, so can sibling involvement. On a few occasions I have actually had two siblings in the group at the same time. I recognize that some therapists would consider this antitherapeutic because it would deprive each of the patients of the privacy and confidentiality necessary for meaningful therapy. I recognize this risk, but I do not believe that it invariably is the case for all adolescent siblings.

There are strong arguments for considering this option. One relates to my view that the optimum therapeutic arrangement is one in which the therapist is seen as the "family therapist." I am not using the term here to refer to the situation in which the therapist does family therapy (although this is one possible option). Rather, I am using the term here in the sense that each of the family members views the therapist as the person to go to when he or she has psychiatric difficulties. And the therapist will see one or more of the family members, as warranted for each particular situation. This does not preclude "farming out" specific individuals in certain situations. Rather, the basic philosophy is that the best approach is one in which all family members see the same therapist and consider this arrangement to be the preferable option. It is only when there are compelling reasons that warrant a split off of one or more people to another therapist that this alternative should be considered. This approach is the antithesis of the one in which it is automatically assumed that each family member shall have his or her own separate therapist and that any comingling of patients with one another's therapist must be a contaminant to the treatment. Psychiatric problems have both intrapsychic and interpersonal contributing factors, and the therapist does well to be familiar with as many factors as possible in both categories. The best way to accomplish this goal is for the therapist to have contacts with all family members. This does not mean that all family members must be in treatment; rather, it only means that intermittent contacts and familiarization with all family members is important for optimum therapeutic progress.

Seeing both siblings together in the same group is consistent with this general philosophy. Accordingly, when sibling number two is being considered for entrance into the group in which sibling number one is already a member, I approach the issue in a matter of fact manner and operate from the general assumption that there will be no problems. This does not preclude my exploring with each youngster his or her thoughts and feelings about being in the group together. Most often there are no problems. When there is hesitation, I will generally explore the reasons for the reluctance. Sometimes the reluctance is justifiable, and then the second sibling will not be brought into the group. Sometimes the reluctance is a manifestation of pathological processes. In such cases I make every attempt to work these out before the second youngster enters. However, I have had one or two occasions when the pathological attitude has not been resolved. In these circumstances I have still brought in the second sibling, the reluctance of the first notwithstanding. Not to do so would be a manifestation of my complying with a patient's pathological demand and such compliance is generally antitherapeutic. My experience has been that the psychological problems that contributed to the reluctance have then been resolved and the two benefit from the therapy. I am not claiming that this will always prove to be the case; I am only recommending that the second youngster be brought in in spite of the first's protestations. There is an important principle of child rearing that is also applicable to therapy: just as parents do well to do what is in the child's best interests, not merely what the child wants, the therapist does well to do what is in the patient's best interests, not necessarily what the patient wants. What people *want* and what is in their *best interests* are not necessarily one and the same.

THE GROUP THERAPY EXPERIENCE

Preparing Newcomers For the Group

Before a youngster joins the group, I generally spend time in individual sessions providing general background information about the group. I will usually tell the youngster how many are presently in the group and what the sexual breakdown is. I give no specific information regarding the nature of the problems that the youngsters have and will not answer questions to that effect. To do so is asking for trouble. The patient will then enter the group wondering which of the youngsters has X problem and which has Y problem and this inevitably compromises free associations, blank screen fantasies, and projections. I assure the newcomers that they are free to speak when they wish to and free not to do so when disinclined to talk. I impress upon them that group therapy is a unique experience in life because one can be completely honest about one's thoughts and feelings about another person and yet there is no need to fear repercussions or other consequences. It differs, thereby, from all other interpersonal experiences in life in which we generally do not reveal certain thoughts and feelings that we have about another person because of the recognition that a certain amount of such withholding is necessary for civilized interaction and effective living with one another.

I impress upon the youngsters the importance of confidentiality and inform them that they have the same obligations for secrecy that I have. It sometimes happens that the youngsters in the group may learn about friends they have in common. At such times I reenforce the importance of their not revealing to third parties (nongroup members) the fact that a particular person is in the group. I impress upon them that even the divulgence of the *name* of a person in the group is a breach of the confidentiality because the person has the right not to reveal to others that he or she is in therapy. I try to separate this respect for privacy from the notion that there is something to be ashamed of about being in treatment. One can respect privacy without feeling ashamed of the fact that one has problems that warrant therapy.

I advise the newcomers that the more they reveal about themselves the more others will benefit from their presence in the group and the greater the likelihood they will get useful feedback. Conversely, those that say nothing learn nothing about themselves and give nothing to the others. As mentioned, adolescents crave information about themselves and this statement generally enhances their motivation to join the group and participate in it. I then explore with newcomers their thoughts and feelings about the group and what anticipations they have. Often such projections can be useful points of departure for therapeutic interchanges. Having no actual reality experiences on which to base these anticipations, they become more useful therapeutically because they are pure projections. Similarly, I do not provide the group members with any information about people who will soon be joining the group. Rather, I only make a simple statement like, "Next week there'll be a new boy (girl) coming into the group." The group might discuss something about the newcomer and I will try to derive as much therapeutic benefit as I can from the interchanges. However, I will strictly refrain from providing any information about the new-comer—lest the blank screen be contaminated.

The First Meeting

When a youngster comes to the group for the first time, I generally begin by introducing him or her to the other members. Very quickly the other patients will ask the newcomer why he or she is there. If the youngster is tense and anxious and prefers not to answer the question at that point, I do not press the issue—in accordance with my previous promise to the patient that I will not force or pressure anyone to talk. Sometimes the youngster will make a comment along these lines: "There's nothing wrong with me, I'm only here because my parents have made me come. They've told me they'll ground me if I don't keep coming here." The other patients may try to puncture the newcomer's defense with comments such as, "Dr. Gardner doesn't take normal, healthy people in here. There must be something wrong with you if you're here." On other occasions the oldtimers will leave the newcomer alone, recognizing that this is a defense and will not push him or her at that point. As mentioned earlier in this book, many adolescents have great difficulty admitting that they have problems that require treatment and may need the rationalization that they are only in treatment because they are submitting to overwhelming parental pressures. As mentioned also, one does well to leave this defense alone as long as the patient is talking about therapeutic issues anyway.

Most often, however, the youngster will say something about the presenting problems. The other patients then generally introduce themselves and say a few things about their problems. After that, there is no particular sequence of events that usually ensues. If at any point an oldtimer is pushing the newcomer hard to discuss certain things, and it is apparent that the newcomer is reluctant, I will generally protect the new person and advise all of his or her "rights" not to discuss a particular issue. However, I am quick to add that my hope is that the time will come soon that the newcomer will feel more comfortable discussing that particular topic. My hope is that after observing others discussing touchy subjects, the newcomer will be more comfortable to reveal him- or herself. And this is most often the case. Often a youngster will ask where the newcomer lives. When the newcomer answers the question, he or she may be asked about third parties (nongroup members) whom they both may know. At this point I will invariably warn all group members about the importance of the confidentiality, even to the point of divulging that a person is in treatment.

Corrective Emotional
Experiences

F. Alexander and T. French (1946) and F. Alexander (1950) introduced the term "corrective emotional experience" to refer to an extremely important aspect of therapy. Specifically, therapy provides the patient with a special kind of *experience*, which may or may not be associated with intellectual insight regarding what is occurring. This experience is associated with emotions (often strong) that increase the likelihood that the patient will remember it. It may or may not be associated with insight. In either case, most important is the fact that the experience brings about behavioral change and is thereby of therapeutic value. By placing the adolescent in an environment with other youngsters— and with proper monitoring by the therapist—there is a great likelihood that youngsters in the group will enjoy the benefits to be derived from corrective emotional experiences.

For example, a newcomer enters the group because of a problem with drug abuse. Consistent with my policy of not providing any up-front disclosure, the youngster enters without any knowledge of the nature of the problems of the patients already in the group. Within about ten minutes, he learns that one of the other members has a similar problem. (It often doesn't take longer than this for two drug users to spot one another.) The two immediately embark on a discussion of the various drugs they have used, the "trips" they have taken, and engage in a wide variety of drug-related interchanges. Subsequently, each time they talk they quickly become enmeshed in a discussion of drugs and nothing else. Finally, after a few sessions of this, it is likely that one or more of the other members will point out to them how limited is their repertoire of topics to talk about and how boring they are becoming to the others. Because they have heretofore surrounded themselves with other drug users, they may not be aware of how limited their lives and conversations have become. Being provided these facts by a therapist in an individual session is not so likely to sink in as having the *living experience* of rejection from peers who are bored, irritated, and otherwise alienated by the narrowness of their obsession. It is hoped that this will play a role in their expanding their horizons into other areas and thereby lessen (admittedly in a small way) their need for drugs.

A 19-year-old boy, Jim, entered treatment because of long-standing problems with academic motivation. Basically, he floated through high school and learned very little. Because of his high intelligence he did manage to get through, but attended a school in which the policy was to promote just about anybody who was willing to attend classes for 12 years. He lived in a dream world that he was getting an education but showed no evidence for genuine academic motivation or intellectual curiosity. He then went to "college." I place the term in quotes because the school he was attending was just another one of those institutions in the business to accommodate parents who believe that it is important that their children go to college, but do not concern themselves with whether or not they are receiving an education. Jim had an "eye opener" during his first meeting. Two group members were highly intellec-tualized boys who were deeply committed to their educations. They were seniors in high school and then in the throes of applying to colleges. Although they were both somewhat pedantic and exhibi-tionistic with regard to their knowledge, they provided Jim wiith a new experience. He had never been involved to any significant degree with boys who were turned on by academic learning. Intellectually, he knew of such types, but generally referred to them as "nerds." However, he had never had personal experiences of this kind and had never appreciated that such discussions could be a source of gratification. He felt inadequate as he compared himself to these intellectuals; he felt envious of their knowledge; and he felt that he wanted to be like them as well. A new world had been opened to him by the group and the experience played a role in his ultimately becoming more committed to his academic program.

Mark, a 16-year-old boy, entered treatment because of severe rage outbursts. He was an extremely angry boy, but did not engage in antisocial behavior. Rather, the outbursts occurred over minor frustrations and disappointments. In one group session he was confronted by the others with his lack of sensitivity to their feelings, his frequent and discourteous interruptions, and his bombastic ways in general. The patient became quite angry and then turned to me for my opinion on the criticisms. I agreed that he did exhibit these qualities and advised him to consider the possibility that the criticisms were valid. I suggested also that he then try to do something about them. As I was talking to the patient, it became quite clear that he was becoming increasingly enraged. He suddenly got up from his seat and came toward me menacingly. While waving his fist, he screamed, "You God damned fucking liar!" Mark was a big boy, bigger than I, and quite strong. Furthermore, I have twice been hospitalized because of herniated cervical disks and cervical osteoarthritis. A blow in the head or the neck could literally cause me lifelong disability and even paralysis. As Mark approached me, I pointed toward three buttons protruding from the wall near my seat. Putting my finger close to the police button I said, "If you move one step closer I will press the police button. Believe me, these aren't decorations." Fortunately, the patient stopped, was temporarily immobilized, and then returned to his seat.

I then told Mark that therapy was for people who had enough self-control to talk about their thoughts and feelings, rather than act them out against me or other members of the group. I informed him that people who could not do this were not candidates for office treatment and might be considered for hospital or residential treatment—where there would be more external controls for their behavior. I informed him that there were three buttons on that panel, one for medical emergencies, one for fire, and one for police. I spoke determinedly but calmly. I informed him that I was definitely frightened because of my neck condition and was not going to place myself in any position where I would jeopardize my health.

I then used the experience as a point of departure for group discussion. Some considered my response an "act of cowardice" in that I was too "chicken" to handle the situation myself and was so weak that I had to bring in more powerful forces. In the ensuing discussion, they ultimately came to see that there are situations in which it is more judicious to ask for help than to fight alone, especially when the likelihood is that you will lose and even suffer terribly. The flight reaction and/or calling for help are not options that many adolescents consider seriously because of their need to maintain a "macho" image of themselves. We then discussed in detail fight/flight reactions and I expressed my opinion that in our society (especially among men), the flight reaction is not given the respect it deserves. I told them: "When a wolf chases a rabbit, the other animals in the forest who are observing don't call the fleeing rabbit 'chicken shit.' " I tried to help them respect more the flight reaction in certain situations and explained how it is part of our biological repertoire and can be life-saving. I then spoke about situations in which it is perfectly respectable to ask for the help of those who are more powerful and how that too is not necessarily demeaning. Last, I believe that all group members had the experience that their therapist is not omnipotent, that he too has his weaknesses. This too is therapeutic in that it contributes to a lessening of the idealization of the therapist that I consider to be a common antitherapeutic experience.

Peer Influences

Mention has already been made of the slavish dependence of adolescents on their peers. I.D. Yalom (1975) considers the member to member comments to be the most important in the exchanges that adolescents experience in group therapy. The therapist, as an adult, is viewed to be of the parents' generation and is thereby to be distrusted. Adolescent peers, in contrast, are viewed to be the final authorities on what is the "latest" and what is "in," and are thereby viewed as more trusted authorities. This phenomenon is compounded by the fact that many adolescents in group therapy do not "practice what they preach." For example, youngsters who are antisocial must know what is "social" in order to know how to be "antisocial." Interestingly, such youngsters may sermonize to others about being "good" and define very specifically the guidelines for their more desirable behavior. Although not engaging in such behavior themselves, their wisdom is still respected and contributes to therapeutic change. Of course, one must discuss with the preacher the fact that he or she is not subscribing to the guidelines of his or her sermons.

Cigarette companies capitalize significantly on the adolescent's dependence on peer pressure and delusions of invulnerability. More than any others, these two factors contribute to the widespread addiction to tobacco that we have been experiencing for many years. The companies know that an adolescent can be made to believe that he or she will never develop any of the dreaded diseases that the world knows are caused by cigarette smoking. They can also rely upon the adolescent's gullibility, in that he or she can be easily made to believe that smoking makes one more sexually attractive and helps one appear more mature. They also know that the best people to market their weeds are other adolescents in that the nonsmokers are likely to follow the smokers via their slavish need to go along with the group.

Group therapy can be an effective vehicle for counterbalancing these nefarious influences. The same process can be used to help smokers "kick the habit." They can be helped to appreciate that they can indeed die of the terrible diseases that cigarette smoking causes. They can be helped to appreciate that smoking does not necessarily make one look sexy or mature. Many youngsters can be brought to the point of admitting that they initially hated smoking but overcame their disgust because of their strong need for acceptance by their peers. And they can be helped to stop smoking by taking the advice of their nonsmoking peers in the group. Sometimes, in a discussion about dependency, I will sarcastically make comments such as: "That's the kind of person I am. I respect those people who live by the principle: If it's good enough for them, it's good enough for me. I'm a rubber stamp. I'm the kind of person who goes along with the crowd. If the crowd says it's all right, then I'll say it's all right." Generally, the youngsters get my message. This is another example of how the selective use of sarcasm can be used therapeutically. I believe that when my messages are provided in this vehicle, they have more clout than when stated directly.

Frank entered treatment at the age of 14 because of obsessive-compulsive rituals. These involved his having to perform acts twice that would generally be performed only once by others. If he closed the door behind him, he would have to return and open it, and then close it once again. When he turned off the television set, he would have to go back, put it on, and then turn it off again. The compulsion extended to a wide variety of everyday activities — resulting in severe tension, discomfort, and even depression. The symptoms were of six-months duration when he came for therapy.

After the first month of treatment I had absolutely no idea why Frank was having these symptoms. During the fifth week of treatment, his mother mentioned that when he was seven years old he had had sexual encounters with two girls, ages eight and nine. The girls initiated the game and involved him in an activity that closely approximated sexual intercourse. It wasn't until one year prior to the onset of treatment that Frank's mother learned about these two encounters (each time with the two girls) and they had been a source of guilt and embarrassment for him during the intervening years. Unfortunately, the mother's responses did not assuage his guilt. Rather, she made comments such as, "I'm really sorry you did such a thing," "I hope you won't do that again until you're married," and "If you'd only told me then, I would have told their mothers." I then concluded that an important element in Frank's compulsion was his attempt to assuage the guilt he felt over his sexual encounters. The onset of the symptoms at the time of puberty related to the enhanced sexual urges he was experiencing as well as the intensified guilt that he now felt after disclosing the experiences to his mother. He had hoped that she would help ease his guilt; unfortunately, she did the opposite.

Part of the therapeutic program involved helping Frank become more comfortable with his sexual urges. In one group meeting, Frank mentioned how "disgusting" girlie magazines were and, fortunately, the other members of the group disagreed with him. With some encouragement on my part, the group members admitted that they experienced sexual urges when looking at the pictures in such magazines and even masturbated while looking at them. The discussions with the group, as well as my own lengthy discussions with him (alone and/or with his parents), resulted in a diminution of Frank's guilt over his sexual urges and a concomitant diminution of his symptoms. His therapy ended after four months, at which time he was free of his compulsions.

Self-Esteem Enhancement

I have described elsewhere (Gardner, 1973a) the multiplicity of factors that contribute to the development of a high sense of self-worth. Low self-esteem is at the base of many (if not most) forms of psychogenic psychopathology and symptoms are well understood to serve in part to provide compensation for feelings of low self-worth. Accordingly, anything the therapist can do to bring about a genuine enhancement of self-esteem is likely to be therapeutic. The reader should note that I use the word genuine because artificial esteem-enhancing maneuvers, such as gratuitous praises, platitudes, etc., are likely to work in the opposite way. And there are certain elements in the group therapy process that are likely to enhance self-esteem and thereby serve the goals of therapy. Most patients who enter treatment, regardless of age, generally consider themselves to be unique with regard to their symptoms. They often anticipate that the therapist will be revolted when he or she hears about their problems. Simply reassuring a patient that his or her problems are common may be useful. However, when a group of one's peers provide such reassurances, they are likely to be accepted with greater conviction. Helping other youngsters with their problems is also likely to be esteem-enhancing. Similarly, gaining the respect of one's peers for one's advice regarding *their* problems is likely to contribute to the enhancement of a youngster's feeling of self-worth.

As discussed in detail in Chapter Five, one of the purposes of treatment is to help patients deal better with the fundamental problems and conflicts of life with which we are all confronted. Getting information that enhances one's repertoire for dealing with these problems is esteem-enhancing. Knowledge is power and knowledge also enhances one's feelings of self-worth. After all, one is then more worthy because one is more capable of dealing with life's problems.

One area in which many patients can have useful, esteem-enhancing therapeutic experiences is in the realm of self-assertion. Such patients may avoid or remove themselves from a frustrating situation in which they are being taken advantage of rather than speak up and demand their rights. In the group, such avoidance is less possible. Others may make comments such as "Why do you sit there and let him talk that way to you?" and "How come you're not saying anything when she does that to you?" The therapist, as well, can encourage self-assertion with comments such as "You're saying nothing while he's screaming at you. Come on, tell me what thoughts are on your mind. What feelings are you having?" The patient is encouraged to talk about what he or she anticipates would happen if these thoughts and feelings are expressed. Although an intellectual discussion on how the anticipated repercussions will not be forthcoming might be useful, it is far more useful for the youngster to have the living experience that such expression does not result in these reactions. Of course, one must then go beyond the group and discuss the possibilities of such anticipated responses in the world outside the consultation room. The similarities and differences are delineated. The likelihood is that after a series of self-assertive experiences in the group, the youngster will be more comfortable expressing him- or herself beyond it.

One situation in which group role playing of this kind can be useful is the one in which a boy is hesitant to call up a girl for a date. He feels awkward regarding his knowledge of what to do and say and is quite fearful of rejection because of his ineptitude. A make-believe telephone call to one of the girls in the group can be particularly useful here. The boy is invited to make his initial statement. One girl is asked to respond. This interchange then serves as a point of departure for group discussion. In the course of such discussions the youngster learns the various ways to initiate the conversation and the various responses that the girl may make. These are roughly divided into those that indicate receptivity and those that indicate the opposite. Although such information can generally be provided in individual sessions, it is much more effective if the provider is an adolescent girl. She is generally viewed as a far greater expert on such matters than an adult therapist, even a female therapist.

Many youngsters in group therapy are shy about entering the dating scene. Here advice, pressure, and urging to desensitize can be useful for such youngsters. I recall one group's focusing on a forthcoming senior prom. At that time three boys in the group were quite inhibited regarding asking girls to the prom. Reassurances to them that there were certainly girls in their schools who would be most desirous of attending the prom did not help them overcome their reluctance and fears. During the same meeting there was a discussion of SAT scores. This group was particularly bright and many were applying to excellent schools. They were well versed with the format of examinations such as the SAT. In the ensuing discussion I told the group members that I was going to give them a multiple choice question, such as the kind one sees on the SATs. It was presented as a question to see how smart they were. The question:

> Which of the following courses of action would be the preferable one for a senior-high-school boy regarding attendance at his forthcoming prom?:
>
> a) Push through his fears. Ask a girl to go with him. Take her to the prom and have a good time dancing, feeling the closeness of her warm body against his, and possibly having a great time—both in and out of bed;
>
> b) Sitting at home alone, depressed, envying all the others at the prom because of the good time they're having and then ending up the evening by jerking off and going to sleep;
>
> c) Spending the evening with some other lonely, horny guys, all making believe that they're having a good time and trying to forget the fact that the others at the prom are probably enjoying themselves immensely;
>
> d) Going to the dance with another guy, one of you dressed as a girl;
>
> e) If you do not consider any of the above to be an appropriate answer, then state what you would consider to be a preferable way to spend the night—when all the others in your class are enjoying themselves immensely at the prom.

Last, as the group evolves into a cohesive unit (its openendedness notwithstanding, there are still some ongoing members at any given point) they develop a sense of camaraderie which can also be ego-enhancing. One develops an attachment to the group and a sense of loyalty to it and this makes one feel better about oneself by being a member of such a unit.

Encouraging Desensitization

Behavior modification can be viewed as nature's natural form of treatment. Long before psychiatry came on the scene, people were alleviating their untoward reactions to various traumas and stresses by reiteration and the associated desensitization that accompanies it. My main complaint about those who are deeply committed to behavior modification as the primary treatment modality is that they do not give proper attention to unconscious psychodynamic factors that are operative in bringing about symptoms. There are some behavior therapists who recognize that unconscious factors are operative but pay little if any attention to them in their therapeutic approach. And there are others who deny their existence entirely.

I believe that an optimum psychotherpeutic program gives serious attention to behavior modification as a therapeutic modality. However, it incorporates such techniques into the natural course of the treatment, without artificiality and without contrivance. In such a program one attempts to provide the patient with a desensitization process that goes naturally with the course of the treatment and the therapeutic experiences. It does not involve clip boards, score keeping, artificial and childlike rewards, or magic reinforcements. There is a place for conscious control and forcing oneself into anxiety-provoking situations in treatment. Whatever understanding one may have of underlying processes that are operative in bringing about one's symptoms, there is no question that the therapeutic approach must involve, as well, forcing oneself to tolerate painful and stressful situations and providing oneself with living experiences that work against the perpetuation of the pathological processes.

There is an overlap between behavior modification and role play. The overlap exists at the point where the role playing attempts to help desensitize an individual to an anxiety-provoking experience. My primary criticism of role play is its artificiality. There are therapists who will ask patients in a group to sit in different chairs as they make believe they are performing the part of various individuals. I find such play-acting contrived. I believe that one does better by merely asking questions like: "Imagine now that you are in your mother's position. What would she say to you if you just said that to her?" "I would like you now to imagine yourself in conversation with your father and he has just said to you what you told me. I'd like you to get some practice now and tell me what would be a good response to him under these circumstances." No body movements are requested; no artificial movements are advised; only a natural and somewhat spontaneous entry into the imagined conversation.

Dealing With a Breach of Confidentiality

As mentioned earlier, I generally make every attempt to respect the patient's confidentiality. In life and death matters and other serious situations, breach of confidentiality may be warranted. However, in such situations I generally follow a fixed sequence. First, I discuss with the patient alone the potential breach, which generally involves reporting selected information to the parents. I do everything possible to get the patient to discuss these issues directly with them. When that fails, we then turn to the group. Here, again, I try to enlist their aid in getting the patient to discuss the problem with his or her parents. If this fails, I then decide what information to provide the parents and what information not to.

I recall one situation in which a teenage girl became pregnant and was not going to tell her parents. She refused to discuss what she planned to do and I suspected she just wanted to deny the pregnancy entirely and hold off worrying about it until some future point. She was already two-months pregnant when I learned of her condition. I knew that the parents' religious beliefs would not have precluded an abortion. It was obvious, also, that the longer she held off telling them, the less the likelihood that this option would be available to her. After two weeks of group discussion, she still refused to tell her parents. At that point, I informed her that I would be telling them. Although she reacted with rage, I suspected that at some level she wanted me to divulge the pregnancy. I invited the parents into a session and gave the patient the choice of joining us or not. Whereas initially she said that she would not participate, she subsequently changed her mind and joined with them in the session. I knew the parents well enough to know that, although distressed by the news, they would not react with inappropriate or punitive measures. The girl was convinced that the "shit would hit the fan" (which it did) and that "they would flip out" (which they partially did) and that "horrendous things" would happen to her. Only the latter prediction did not prove true. Although the abortion was a psychologically stressful experience, her parents were sympathetic and understanding and did not add to her burdens (which is exactly what I had anticipated). By breach of the confidence I not only helped this girl deal with the pregnancy in a more judicious way but provided her with the living experience that her parents would not be so punitive as she had anticipated. In addition, the whole experience brought the family closer together, the nature of it notwithstanding. The girl did continue in treatment with me. Had she really not wanted her parents to know and had she genuinely felt that my divulging her pregnancy was a breach of her confidentiality, she probably would have discontinued treatment. This vignette provides another example of my view stated many times previously that adolescents often want to be coerced.

The reader who is interested in further information about group therapy in adolescents does well to refer to the articles by I.H. Berkovitz (1972), The American Psychiatric Association Task Force Report (1973), I.H. Berkovitz and M. Sugar (1975), I.D. Yalom (1975), I.A. Kraft (1979), and M.A. Riddle and L.A. Vitulano (1986).

TWELVE
WORK WITH PARENTS

As mentioned frequently throughout the course of this book, I work closely with the parents of my adolescent patients. On the one hand, adolescents do need individual work—especially because of their need for independence, autonomy, and relationships outside the home. On the other hand, therapists need ongoing contact with the patient's parents if they are to provide adolescents with a proper therapeutic program. In this chapter I elaborate on the ways in which the parental contribution enhances one's therapeutic efficiency. Therapists who allow adolescents to prohibit parental involvement in their therapeutic work are seriously compromising their treatment. Such involvement with the parents does not have to inhibit the adolescent's opportunity to develop autonomy within the stucture of the therapeutic program. Individual and group work with the adolescent is still certainly possible as the primary therapeutic modalities and these can contribute to the development of the youngster's growth toward independence.

THE VALUE OF THE THERAPIST-
PARENT BOND IN ENHANCING AN
ADOLESCENT'S TREATMENT

Parental participation can strengthen the therapist's relationship with the parents in many ways. And the stronger the parent's relationship with the therapist, the stronger is the patient's bond with the therapist likely to be. Seeing the therapist "in action" enables the parents to know firsthand exactly what is going on in the sessions. They are not left in the dark about the therapeutic procedure. In the traditional approach to treatment, in which parents are excluded from the therapy to a significant degree, parents are ignorant of what is going on, and this can be a source of irritation and alienation. This is especially the case when the parents are communicated with only to pay for the treatment. When they know exactly what they are spending their money for, they are less likely to harbor negative distortions and criticisms.

The effects of parental participation on the treatment are important and may be even more important than the specific way in which a parent can be useful to treatment. Whereas originally I was taught that such participation would compromise my relationship with the patient, my experience has been just the opposite. It is difficult to have a good relationship with someone who is a stranger, and whose only or primary contact is the monthly bill. Not only is such a situation likely to produce some alienation, but the paucity of contact increases the likelihood that negative distortions and misinterpretations about the therapist will not be corrected. Direct work with the parents provides them with opportunities to air their grievances, express their resentments and disappointments, ask questions, etc. This is the best way to prevent or resolve such problems. Both parents' feelings toward the therapist are extremely important in determining what the patient's feelings will be. A parent's animosity toward the therapist frequently, if not invariably, will be picked up by the patient. A dispute between the therapist and the parents will produce a loyalty conflict in the patient. Most often he or she will side with the parent. After all, the parents are providing the food, clothing, and shelter; they are the ones who are with the youngster the remaining hours of the week. The patient knows where his or her "bread is buttered," and it is extremely unlikely that the patient will, over time, basically support the therapist's position when it is in conflict with the parents'. Accordingly, anything that can improve the relationship between the therapist and the parents is likely to strengthen the tie between the therapist and the patient.

Most parents feel some guilt that their children require treatment. In fact, I would go further and say that parents who do not feel guilt about bringing their youngster to therapy probably have some deficiency in parenting capacity. Traditionally, therapists will try to assuage such guilt by reassuring the parents that they did their best at all points and that, in spite of their benevolent intentions, things went wrong. Such efforts of guilt mollification are not likely to prove useful, especially if the therapist then goes on to ask questions about child-rearing practices. These usually evoke even more guilt as the parents' deficiencies become exposed. When, however, the parent becomes involved directly in the therapeutic process, the guilt associated with the child's involvement in treatment is likely to be lessened. After all, the parents are now working actively in turning around and reducing the problems over which they feel guilty. Therapists who deprive parents of this opportunity deprive them, as well, of a mechanism for reducing their guilt.

PARENTAL COUNSELING
REGARDING THE PATIENT

The work with parents that I will be describing in this chapter is most appropriately called *parental counseling*. Such counseling is offered at the outset as part of "the therapeutic package." Most often this is done at the same time that the youngster is present. In this way the patients are given the opportunity for active input into the parental decisions being made about them. If such counseling is done without the patient's participation, there is the risk that the treatment will be seriously compromised. The adolescent's awareness that meetings are taking place behind his or her back— meetings which are secret from the patient—inevitably produces distrust of both therapist and parents and this will compromise treatment. The vast majority of parents welcome such counseling because they invariably have questions regarding how they should deal with their adolescents. Parents who come to me from other therapists, who have excluded them to a significant degree from the therapeutic process, are even more pleased with the opportunity to meet with me regarding their youngster. Although I believe that many therapists exclude the parents because of their firm belief that their involvement will compromise the adolescent's autonomy and thereby be antitherapeutic, I believe that there are therapists who exclude parents because of their own ineptitude and fear of being observed in their work.

Counseling Parents of the Adolescent Who Tries to Preclude Their Involvement in Treatment

There are adolescents who will tell their parents that a proviso of their entering into treatment is that the parents will have absolutely no contact at all with the therapist. I will have no part of such an arrangement. I cannot think of a healthy reason for such a restriction. Invariably it represents an attempt on the youngster's part to prevent the parents' input into the treatment, input that might "smoke out" the adolescent's fabrications or otherwise expose schemes which the adolescent would like to perpetrate with the therapist. On one occasion, many years ago, when I was young and naive in these things, I did agree to see a 15-year-old girl who I was told by the referring physician would see me with the understanding that I would have no contacts at all with the parents. Earlier in this book I described what occurred during this girl's "therapy." In short, she was completely silent and I discontinued the treatment after a few sessions. I subsequently learned that, after refusing to go to treatment, her father had stupidly bribed her with $15 for every session she attended. I only learned this from the referring doctor after I had discontinued treatment because of my conclusion that it was a total waste of time and her father's money.

On occasion, I have received telephone calls from parents who recognize that their youngster needs therapy and state that the adolescent absolutely refuses to come, even for a consultation. After hearing something about the problem, I will generally make one of two recommendations. Sometimes I will tell the parents that they should insist upon the youngster's coming for the consultation with the threat that if he or she does not, certain restrictions and disciplinary measures will be imposed. I make this recommendation in those situations in which I think that the youngster needs some kind of coercion as a face-saving device for coming to the session. At other times I may decide that such a threat is unwarranted or it has proven not to work. In those cases I will advise the parents to set up the appointment and advise the youngster that they themselves will attend and he or she is invited to do so as well. In addition, I advise them to inform the youngster that decisions will be made that will affect him or her and it therefore behooves the youngster to attend if he or she is to have any input into those decisions. When even this doesn't work, I will see the parents alone and give them advice. I provide whatever advice I can and set up another session at which the adolescent is again invited to attend. Sometimes the parental feedback motivates the youngster to participate and thereby protect his or her rights. Generally, after two or three such sessions, if the adolescent still does not attend, we reach a point of diminishing returns and then I may see them again only on a request basis.

Parental Ambivalence About the Adolescent's Treatment

Parental involvement in a child's treatment is, at best, tenuous. Although parents may profess commitment to the therapeutic process, they are generally quite ambivalent and their mixed feelings about the treatment may interfere significantly with its progress and even result in their prematurely terminating therapy. In this section I discuss some of the more common reasons for impaired parental commitment to the therapeutic process. An understanding of these factors can be useful in increasing the likelihood that the therapist will be able to engage the parents more successfully and thereby increase the likelihood of the youngster's involvement in treatment. Some of the more common ways in which parental resistance exhibits itself: lateness to the sessions, canceling sessions for frivolous or weak reasons, forgetting to follow through with the therapist's recommendations, complaining to the patient about treatment (its cost, time consumption, etc.), and withholding payment (ultimately one of the most predictable ways to bring about a cessation of therapy).

The Cost of Treatment   Compromised parental commitment to therapy is often caused by the financial privation that it may involve. This is especially the case when the youngster is in private treatment. Whereas initially the parents may agree to commit themselves to the cost involved, when the bills start coming they often have a change of heart and remove the child prematurely from therapy or support the patient's resistances, which are inevitably present. Because the services the therapist provides are not tangible, the parents are likely to consider it a waste of money much earlier than they would after receiving other medical services.

The Expenditure of Time   The parent who brings the patient (more often the mother) can generally think of better ways of spending her time. If she has other children and cannot afford housekeepers, then bringing the patient to treatment may become an additional burden. Here again, these extra pressures compromise her commitment to the therapeutic process. I have had a number of parents who were initially enthusiastic about treatment, even though travel to my office involved a significant expenditure of time. Initial enthusiasm, however, waned when they actually experienced the drainage on their time and energy that such trips involved. Accordingly, I will generally see people who come from great distances for consultation only and discourage strongly their committing themselves to an extended therapeutic program. The patient also is likely to be drained of energy by a long trip and will thereby not be a good candidate for therapeutic sessions.

Parental Guilt   Most parents experience guilt when the therapist advises them that their child needs treatment. They consider it proof that they somehow failed in the child's upbringing (H.S. Lippman, 1962). A common way that parents assuage such guilt is to rationalize withdrawal of the child from treatment. This is done either overtly or covertly. After all, if they can justify removing the youngster from treatment, especially if they can believe that he or she does not need it, they thereby absolve and even obviate their guilt. Therapists should tell such parents that they appreciate that at every point in the child's development the parents did what they considered to be in the child's best interests (usually the case) and that through misguidance and/or unfortunate circumstances, and/or the unavoidable effects of their own difficulties, their child developed psychiatric problems. Furthermore, the therapist does well to advise such parents that, at the present state of our knowledge, we do not understand all the factors that contribute to a child's psychiatric difficulties. Thus, even if they themselves had no psychiatric problems, and even if there had been no detrimental circumstances, and even if they had assiduously followed the best available advice, their child might still have developed difficulties (J.W. Kessler, 1966). Moreover, they must be helped to appreciate that innate temperamental factors may be contributing significantly to the patient's problems (A. Thomas, S. Chess et al., 1963). My experience has been that a discussion of these factors can often be useful in reducing parental guilt and thereby increasing the likelihood that they will support the patient's therapy.

One of the most effective ways of reducing parental guilt and the resistances that emerge from it is to have the parents participate actively in the patient's treatment. They are thereby helping "undo" what they have "done." By working closely with the parents, the therapist is more likely to develop a good relationship with them. The patient will sense the parents' feelings about the therapist and will then be more likely to develop such involvement him or herself. When parents have a good relationship with the therapist, they are more comfortable expressing resentments and disagreements. The failure to express such differences and complaints is one of the most common sources of parental resistance to the youngster's treatment and removal of the patient from it.

The Therapist's Alienation of the Parent as a Contribution to Parental Ambivalence   Therapists who believe that it is their role to protect adolescent patients from the indignities suffered at the hands of their parents are likely to alienate parents. The preferable position should be one of impartiality. The therapist should be viewed by all family members as someone who criticizes the parents when such criticism is warranted and, similarly, criticizes the

youngster, again when warranted. The therapist's criticisms, however, should be benevolent and he or she should not "keep score"
regarding who is getting more or less. The therapist neither takes
the side of parent or child; rather, he or she supports the side of
healthy behavior regardless of who exhibits it. Therapists who
distance themselves from the parents, who view the parents'
involvement as a compromise of the youngster's treatment, and
whose only contact with the parents is the monthly bill are also
likely to alienate them. Such distance-making operations deprive
them of the opportunity for asking questions, expressing disappointments, and voicing resentments. Problems between the parents and the therapist then become unresolved and this can
ultimately result in their removing the child from treatment.

**Therapy as a Potential Disruption of a Pathological Parent-
Child Bond**   Another common source of parental resistance to
treatment derives from the situation in which the parent may not
genuinely want the patient to be relieved of his or her presenting
symptoms, despite claims to the contrary. The patient's problems
may play an important role in the family equilibrium. For example,
the overprotective mother may want her child with separation
anxiety disorder to stay at home and may undermine the therapist's
efforts to get the child back to school (R.A. Gardner, 1984). Parents
of delinquent youngsters often gain vicarious gratification from their
adolescents's antisocial acting out (A.M. Johnson, 1949, 1959; R.L.
Stubblefield, 1967). Ostensibly parents may want their youngster to
do better academically but, unconsciously, may undermine the
treatment because they fear that the child will surpass them
educationally and socioeconomically. I once had a patient, the child
of such parents, who came into treatment because of a severe block
in achieving academic success. He had a recurrent dream in which
he was walking up a mountain on a treadmill. He kept trying to
move ahead but got nowhere. The dream was a symbolic statement
of a neurotic compromise, both for himself and his parents. On the
one hand, he could tell his parents that he was trying harder
(something they allegedly wanted him to do). On the other hand,
he could point out that he was getting nowhere (in compliance with
their unconscious wishes).

Parental Jealousy of the Therapist   Many parents become jealous of the patient's intimate relationship with the therapist and may act out such feelings by undermining the treatment. They may consider themselves to have been the ones to have done all the "dirty work": changed the diapers, taken the child to the pediatrician at all hours of the night, and made the hundreds of other sacrifices necesssary for successful child rearing. Yet the therapist is "the good guy" who is viewed by the youngster as benevolent, kind, and sympathetic. Often the parents are threatened by the anxiety-provoking revelations about themselves that inevitably emerge in the patient's treatment, and the desire to avoid these can contribute to their impaired commitment to the process.

It behooves therapists to appreciate these and the multiplicity of other factors that may contribute to the parental undercommitment to the therapeutic process and even removal of a youngster from treatment. The therapist should try to detect these compromising factors during the initial evaluation and deal with them at the outset. Otherwise, they may cause a compromise and even a cessation of the therapy.

COMMON ADVICE GIVEN PARENTS OF ADOLESCENT PATIENTS

Differentiating Between the Controllable and the Uncontrollable

I, like most psychiatrists, have at times had the thought of putting on my walls some important proverbs, maxims, and old sayings that are likely to prove useful to my patients. Most of us recognize that it is unwise to do this because such statements might serve as contaminants to the therapeutic process, especially to free associations in psychoanalytic therapy. There is, however, one quotation on my wall. I place it there because it is probably the most common advice I give to my adult patients and the parents of my adolescent patients. Rather than merely repeat it each time, I take the plaque off the wall and show it to the parents. Most often they are familiar with it. The advice is in the form of a little prayer attributed to the theologian, Reinhold Niebuhr:

> Give me the serenity
> to accept the things I cannot change,
> the courage to change the things I can;
> and the wisdom to know the difference.

Actually, this is an ancient wisdom and its antecedents are to be found in the Bible. The parents of adolescents, especially, have to become strong adherents to this dictum. Otherwise, they are doomed to lead very frustrating lives. The implementation of this philosophy is expressed well in the statement a parent might make to a daughter with antisocial problems after being counseled by me on a number of occasions:

> Dr. Gardner's right. One of my problems has been that I haven't differentiated between the things that I can control and the things that I can't control. And I've got them straight now. And you'd better get them straight also. I can control what happens in this house, but I can't control what happens outside it. First, *I decide* who comes into this house. Those new friends of yours are *bad news*. I refuse to let them in my house. You state often that this is your house, but it's not. It's my house and we permit you to live here. I decide who comes into this house and those low-life characters are not entering this home. What you do with them outside I can't control. But I can tell you this: they spell *trouble*. The more you hang around with them, the more difficulty you're going to have in your life.
>
> Next, with regard to your hiding illegal substances in this house, you have no privacy. As long as I think that you're hiding drugs here, I have every right to search through your drawers and do whatever I want with any illegal substances I find. Your claims for privacy are merely a way of hiding the drugs you've been using. And when I find them, I'll flush them down the toilet. I don't care how expensive they are. When I no longer think you're hiding drugs, then I'll respect your privacy. Respecting your privacy now is just contributing to your drug problem.

Your father and I have been making idiots of ourselves by trying to find out where you go at night. You told us last week that you were staying over Joan's house. We called Joan and she told us that she hadn't seen you in a week. Once again, you lied to us. Then, like idiots, we started calling other homes and even woke up people at one and two in the morning. They have every right to be furious with us and we're not going to do that any more. We are also not going to run around town like crazy people looking for you in parks and parking lots. That was insane. We're cutting that out. We know that you're screwing around and we're petrified that you're going to get some disease or get pregnant. Know this, though, if you do get a disease you're the one who's going to suffer much more than we. And if you do get pregnant, you too will have a much greater burden than we. If you get an abortion, you'll have to live with the knowledge that you scraped out your own kid. And if you keep the baby, then you're going to screw up your life with your new dependent. And if you give it away, you'll live with the knowledge that somewhere, someplace, there's a child of yours—a child you gave away to a stranger. You'll have to live with your guilt. What way do you win on that one?

We don't know what you're so angry about. We know that what you've been doing the last couple of years relates to anger at us, more than anyone else. Sure we've made mistakes; but we certainly don't deserve this. Let's say that you get the extreme vengeance you want. You'll have your father and I rolling around on the floor, tearing our hair out, crying out eyes out, and beating ourselves. So what, then, will you have accomplished? Yes, you will have gotten vengeance, but what you are *not* considering is what you have to do to yourself in order to get it. What you are blind to is the fact that you're fouling up your own life in order to hurt us. All you see is the vengeful gratification, and you don't see the *self*-destructive aspect of what you're doing.

And there's one more thing for you to think about, and that is Dr. Gardner's *kidney transplant principle*. Of the five billion people on earth, who do you think will be on line at the hospital if you ever needed a kidney transplant? Give that some thought when you shit on us!

Of course, a parent is not going to make this speech after the first counseling session. However, a number have been able to make it following a series of sessions that prove that they have conviction for what was said therein. Not only does it contain the message of differentiation between what can be controlled and not controlled by a parent but it provides a youngster with some important insights about what he or she is doing as well.

Differentiating Between
Normal and Abnormal Behavior and
Dealing with Noxious
Normal Behavior

A common problem for parents of adolescent patients, especially for the first youngster to achieve that status, is that of differentiating between normal and abnormal behavior. Although many parents may have read books on the subject and heard about the fact that adolescents often become rebellious during this phase of their life, they often forget what they have learned when it comes to their own youngsters. Accordingly, parents have to be helped to appreciate that a certain amount of rebellious behavior is normal (and even desirable) and they must not take too seriously many of their youngster's criticisms and denigratory comments. I often tell parents that "you've got to thicken your skin." Furthermore, I may also say, "Every parent expects to have to change diapers for a new baby. This is an expected part of the child-rearing process. Similarly, you have to accept the fact that your adolescent is going to shit on you and that too is an expected part of the child-rearing process." Many of the problems that the parents have to deal with result form their difficulties in making these differentiations.

An example is the parents' attitude toward the adolescent's room. Typically, these youngsters are comfortable living in pigsties. I generally advise parents to accept that it is normal for adolescents to be comfortable living as pigs. They should allow the youngster to assume this lifestyle *in his or her own room only*. This does not, however, mean that adolescents should be allowed to create health hazards. They can leave their books, clothing, etc. on the floor or wherever else in their room they decide to leave their "droppings." However, they cannot allow food to decay in their rooms because of the obvious attraction to vermin and the creation of other health hazards. Under those circumstances there must be certain restrictions imposed as well as disciplinary measures utilized (see below).

With regard to leaving clothing in other parts of the house, I advise parents that it is normal for adolescent youngsters to leave a trail of garments as they race through the house. The best solution to this problem is for the parent to pick these up in a bundle and dump them on the floor of the adolescent's room. Of course, clothing on the floor of the room is not then picked up and cleaned by the parents. Rather, the rule of the house is that the only clothing that is cleaned by the parents is that which is placed in the hamper or other designated spot. At some point the youngster will run out of clothes and then have the choice of wearing dirty ones, going out naked, or placing all clothing in the proper receptacle.

It is also normal for adolescents in our society to want to play their stereos at ear-splitting levels. Most communities have ordinances prohibiting such noise (I have no hesitation using that term to refer to much of their so-called "music") after 11:00 p.m. However, this may not be enforced. But even if it is, this does not protect the family throughout the earlier evening from the devastating effects of the cacophony. Telling adolescents that listening to music at such levels is likely to bring about hearing loss and ultimately (in many cases) tinnitus (ringing in the ears) is not likely to prove useful. Because of their delusions of invulnerability, they are not likely to believe that this will happen to them. Telling them that those who play in rock bands already have hearing loss and they keep playing the music louder because they cannot hear it at lower levels, also does not help. One partial solution is to have the youngster listen only with earphones. Although this may provide the family with some peace, it increases markedly the likelihood that the youngster will damage his or her own ears. Warnings that this is likely to occur will generally not be "heard." Some youngsters, however, who insist that earphones compromise their musical enjoyment, will insist nevertheless on blasting their music. A simple solution to this problem is for the parents to take the stereo player and lock it in the trunk of his or her car. After two or three weeks of such privation, the youngster is likely to "remember" to play the music lower.

Discipline and Punishment

The word discipline is derived from the Latin *discipulus*, which means a disciple or a student. The word emphasizes the educative value of the disciplinary measure to the wrongdoer. The word punishment is derived from the Latin word *punire* which means to punish, but which has the connotation of the infliction of pain on the wrongdoer. The emphasis is on penalty and retribution. D.J. Holmes, in his excellent book on adolescent psychotherapy (1964) states: "Discipline, though aggressively energized, denotes a complex of attitudes and actions which is consciously intended to help people live more effectively and, in the long run, more happily. Punishment, in contrast with discipline, denotes a type of action which is primarily motivated by the wish to hurt, cause pain, retaliate in the spirit of vengeance. It is much closer to the acting out of primitive, infantile wishes to destroy and cause pain....No reliable decision can be made about whether a given act is disciplinary or punitive by knowing only the nature of the action. This decision turns instead upon knowing something of the individual's predominant motives for behaving as he does....This distinction between discipline and punishment in no way diminishes the ease with which one may rationalize flagrantly sadistic, destructive actions as being for the victim's 'own good.' "

Obviously, it is preferable that the parents use disciplinary measures when dealing with their adolescents. However, we are all human and the provocations of the adolescent are such that, at times, it is reasonable to expect that parents will be implementing measures that can more appropriately be called punishments. One of the important differentiating criteria between these two is the degree of anger and rage exhibited by the parent when implementing the restriction. The more the rage, the more likely the term punishment is applicable.

It is important for parents to appreciate that all children and adolescents need limits. They are not born with some inner knowledge as to what is right, wrong, good, or bad. (The reader will note that I have no hesitation using such words, even though they are considered to be injudicious by many people in our field. I generally do not like euphemisms. Those who abhor the word *bad* believe that its use lowers the child's self-esteem and may easily be interpreted to indicate that the child is intrinsically and perenially defective. I do not believe this. A loving person who uses the word and who does not basically feel that it has the aforementioned implications will not produce the kinds of ego-debasing responses that are anticipated by those who strictly avoid the word's utilization.) One way of learning what the limits are is to do something bad and then see what the parental reaction will be. In this way the child "learns" what he or she can get away with. It is the far more common procedure than that of asking the simple question of whether or not a certain thing can be done. It appears that the child knows him- or herself that experience teaches much better than an intellectual statement. Not only do children need limits but they generally need strong limits. I often say: "Benevolent despotism is the best system of government for children and other primitive peoples." (Please give me credit for this.) Parents must be somewhat despotic with their children, they must be hardnosed at times, and they must be firm. Parents who "respect" their children to the degree that they do not learn the rules of society are not creating a healthy atmosphere for them. More important, they are not helping them adjust to a world that will not be indulgent and tolerant of their alienating behavior.

It is extremely important that parents avoid using empty threats. If a parent is going to use a statement such as "I won't tolerate that," the parent does well to have some backup action behind it. Otherwise, the threat is meaningless, and the youngster soon learns that it is not to be taken seriously. A related phenomenon is threatening punishments that are so Draconian that they will never be implemented in their entirety. For example, the parent may threaten a youngster with no television for a month for a certain transgression. The youngster knows that there is no way the parent is going to be monitoring the television for a month, especially because there are three sets in the house. Knowing that it cannot or will not be implemented makes the threat empty and contributes to the youngster's ignoring it. Of course, if there is one television set in the house, this can be conveniently locked in the trunk of the car (with the aforementioned stereo set). Even then the parent does well to keep it there for a month or else make more reasonable threats. But, if this threat deprives the parent him- or herself of television viewing, then the parent must suffer along with the youngster (unless the parent has a way of watching television inside the trunk of the car).

I am a very strong proponent of the demerit system as a

disciplinary measure. The system allows one to get significant mileage from the disciplinary plan. Specifically, a particular desired activity is set up as a goal. An example might be a boy's attending a special football game on Sunday. On the evening of the previous Sunday the youngster can be told that he will not be permitted to attend the game if he gets three demerits a day, or 21 demerits over the course of the week. If the youngster gets more than three on Monday, then the parent starts working on Tuesday. And, once 21 demerits are received, the child will be told that he will definitely not be attending the game on the weekend. The ticket may then be either sold or given to another party. It is best that such demerits be non-negotiable, i.e., one should not be able to work them off by good behavior. Otherwise the parent gets into a game of manipulations that may make the whole system inoperative. One of the beauties of the system is that it enables the parent to get a lot of mileage out of it and utilize it for a whole series of transgressions. If one simply deprives the child of the football game after one transgression, then one may have to come up with 20 more deprivations to get the same effect.

There are many youngsters, especially those with severe anti-social behavior, for whom "nothing works." In Chapter Thirteen I will discuss in detail the approaches to such youngsters.

The College Disease

Earlier in this book I have commented on what I refer to as the *college disease* that many parents suffer from and the plethora of so-called educational institutions that have sprung up in order to provide an educational product for these purchasers. The "students" who attend these so-called educational institutions generally view their sojourns there as just a winter camp experience which alternates with summer recreational programs. What they most often learn there are some new sexual techniques, what their tolerance for alcohol is, and perhaps some new drugs that they haven't tried before. They also learn how easy it is to get a college diploma.

Some parents in this category bring their adolescents for treatment because of poor academic motivation. These youngsters often attend schools where the educational standards are quite low and they are automatically moved ahead every year and then dropped off the edge of the system when they complete the twelfth grade. Some, however, are in more demanding high schools, but they still have little commitment to the educational process. Sometimes the youngster's lack of motivation is indeed related to intrafamilial and intrapsychic problems. At other times, the youngster is merely one of a stream of hundreds of thousands who are moving along an educational system track that demands little and provides even less. Their teachers are uncommitted and unmotivated, watch the clock, do not give homework (homework for the student is homework for the teacher), and so do not provide models for their students — models of people who are "turned on" by learning.

Whatever the cause of the youngster's impaired academic motivation, I often tell such parents that my treatment is not likely to work as long as the youngster knows that, whatever happens, he or she will still go on to college. I ask them if they have the guts to make a bona fide threat, a threat that will under no circumstances be withdrawn. I ask them if they will say to the youngster that if he or she does not show significant improvement in academic motivation that under no circumstances will he or she go to college for four years of nonlearning and self-indulgence. I advise them to warn the youngster that grades themselves will not be the only criterion to ascertain whether or not the youngster is deserving of college. This is important because of the grade inflation that exists in our school systems as well as the capacity of youngsters to manipulate their teachers into giving them higher grades. Rather, the criteria that will be used will be SAT scores and the parents' own observations of the youngster's commitment to learning and the educational process. It is best to leave this vague. To use as a criterion a certain number of hours of homework per night is not useful because the youngster may easily satisfy this requirement with feigned commitment to homework. I warn the parents that they should not make this threat unless they intend to follow it through. I generally advise them to think about it for a week of two and discuss it in detail before making it. I tell them also that they do well to have a plan of operation if the youngster does not indeed go to college.

My experience has been that most parents do not make this threat. They just don't have the "balls" to do it. The notion that their youngster should not go to college is one that is painful, if not impossible, for them to behold. They would consider it humiliating if their child did not have a so-called "higher education." They don't know how they could face their friends. They point out other youngsters who entered college with the same lack of motivation and then turned around at some point along the program. I agree that such youngsters exist, but my experience has been that they are a relative minority.

Some parents of unmotivated adolescents believe that the problem lies in the school and the solution is to transfer to another school. This rarely works. I try to emphasize to such parents that the problem lies in the youngster's head and not in the building in which the learning is taking place. Although stories about people such as Abraham Lincoln and others who learned significantly under conditions of privation may seem cliché, they should still be told. Again, many parents do not follow my advice, spend a lot of money in a special private school, and still find that the youngster is not particularly motivated. When I see an adolescent who is already in the first year of one of these "colleges," is getting low marks (even with grade inflation and limited standards), I generally advise the parents to tell the youngster they are no longer going to "piss away" their money on him or her. I advise them to remove the youngster from school and have him or her go out into the workplace for six months or a year and then rethink the whole college decision. Out in the "real world" the youngster is in a better position to make decisions regarding education vs. other options. In addition, if the youngster is really motivated to go to school, then he or she should be willing to work to contribute toward tuition. Regardless of the affluence of the parents, such youngsters do well to contribute a reasonable fraction of their educational expenses. Such requirement helps separate the truly motivated from the jokers. Unfortunately, most parents with the college disease do not accept this advice.

On occasion, I will see a youngster who is a high school or even college dropout who stays at home and does nothing. The parents are not complaining so much about the fact that the youngster is not getting an education (they are long past that point); they are now complaining about the fact that they have a "parasite" on their hands. And indeed, they do. The kid sits around the house all day, watches television, listens to music, and bullshits with friends. Although in his or her late teens, the youngster is functioning at the three-year-old level. Most often (but not always) there has been a longstanding past history of significant indulgence. And this indulgence must be dealt with at the present time. The parents have to be advised to make life tough for such youngsters. No services should be provided. Such youngsters should be required to cook their own meals, purchase their food, do their own laundry, and be made uncomfortable in many other ways. If possible, television sets should be removed and certainly stereo players. Rather the youngster should be provided, as much as possible, with an atmosphere of sensory deprivation. Even telephone services should be restricted and cut off when possible. Otherwise, the youngster is going to sink into a chronic state of morbid dependency on the parents. Again, many of these parents are not capable of following through with these recommendations, so deeply entrenched is their overprotectiveness.

WAYS IN WHICH PARENTS (USUALLY THE MOTHER) CAN BE USEFUL IN AN ADOLESCENT'S INDIVIDUAL SESSIONS

I generally advise the parent who brings the patient (usually the mother) to sit in the waiting room during the course of the session. I discourage her from leaving, taking a walk, or shopping because I may want her at a moment's notice to participate in the session. Although fathers are most often not available to join the sessions, I invite them to feel free to attend, without prior notification, any session that they might be available. My experience has been that this occurs from five to ten percent of the time. As I do with children, I generally refer to the parents as my "therapeutic assistants."

When an adolescent is talkative, I generally start the session with him or her alone. If the adolescent is not likely to "start the ball rolling" so quickly, I will often bring the mother in at the beginning of the session. I still start with the open-ended question to the youngster to say what's on his or her mind. However, if nothing is forthcoming, I then turn to the mother and invite her to bring up some issue. Most often, she has something to tell me. If she also has nothing to say, I then ask the two of them to try to refresh their memories regarding why the youngster was brought to treatment in the first place. Generally, this question will result in useful material on which the patient, mother, and I can focus. However, if even then both have nothing to say I will suggest that we review the presenting symptoms and discuss the youngster's progress at that point. Usually, residual symptoms are present and we then use their manifestations as a point of departure for discussion.

On occasion there will have been signficant alleviation of the presenting symptoms. In such cases, the question of reducing the frequency of sessions and even discontinuing treatment is discussed. The therapist must appreciate that there are some parents who continue to bring their youngster to treatment even after the patient is asymptomatic or almost so. Bringing the youngster to therapy becomes routinized and the parents may believe that, even though symptom free, the therapist is seeing things that they don't which warrant further treatment. There are therapists, of course, who believe that one should continue seeing asymptomatic patients. This is especially true of classical psychoanalysts who will treat on the basis of their decision that underlying psychodynamic factors, even though unconcscious, warrant treatment until they too become normal. The fact that such human beings do not exist does not deter these individuals from recommending ongoing treatment. In some cases the therapists have genuine conviction for what they are doing; in other cases they are simply exploiting gullible people. I am not claiming that I immediately discontinue treatment as soon as the patient is relatively free of symptoms. I will still recommend some ongoing contact in order to be sure that the changes brought about by the treatment are becoming entrenched into the psychic structure. But even then I will generally cut down on the frequency of sessions.

The presence of the mother in the room enables the therapist to observe mother-child interactions that would not have otherwise been seen. The modes of interaction that we utilize in our relationships with other people are derived from the types of involvements we have established with our parents in earliest childhood. The reproduction of these in psychoanalytic treatment is often referred to as *the development of the transference neurosis*. By bringing in a parent one can observe firsthand the original modes of interaction of which the transference neurosis is a derivative. Observing it in its "pure form" puts the therapist in a better position to understand it. In addition, one can learn directly from the parent—the individual who initiated the particular mode of interaction—exactly what factors were operative in bringing about the particular pattern.

The presence of the parent in the room increases the likelihood that more experiences will take place that will be therapeutically useful. For example, a youngster may fear that a parent's reaction to a particular divulgence will be extremely punitive. The therapist may believe that the adolescent's anticipation of dire consequences is an exaggeration and unnecessarily pessimistic. Verbal reassurances are not likely to work very well. Encouraging the youngster to provide the divulgences between sessions is certainly a better idea, but if the youngster's resistances are strong, he or she will "forget" or claim that he or she was "too busy" to follow up on the homework assignment. By bringing the parent in immediately, after minimal discussion, the youngster can have a firsthand experience regarding the anticipation of formidable parental retaliation. Although we may discuss the pros and cons of the parent's joining us for a few minutes, I generally do not prolong the discussion. My experience has been that the longer one talks about it the more difficult it may be for the youngster to avail him- or herself of the experience. Rather, I discuss it briefly and then, unless the adolescent argues vehemently against the parent's participation, I bring the parent in and proceed quickly with the issues at hand. Before the youngster knows what has happened to him or her, an experience is provided which proves, better than anything I could say, that the anticipated repercussions were not forthcoming. But this is only one example. Any possible type of interpersonal interaction can be useful in the treatment, provide grist for the therapeutic mill, and, when properly monitored, provide corrective emotional experiences.

The mother's observations of the ways in which I handle the youngster, especially when the patient is being difficult, can be useful to her because it provides a model for dealing with these situations herself. (I am not claiming that I always handle every situation in the most judicious fashion. However, I believe that I do so more frequently than most of my patients' parents.)

Sometimes, a mother can be useful in helping analyze a patient's dream. This is more often true with prepubertal patients, but she can also be useful in the analysis of an adolescent's dream, especially a younger adolescent. The therapist should certainly obtain as many associations as possible from the patient. This, of course, is the best way of determining exactly what a dream figure symbolizes for the youngster. However, when the patient provides only a paucity of associations to the dream symbols, the mother's input may be valuable. She can ask the youngster questions about the figure and she can often be a better interrogator than the therapist because she may have some hunches about what is important. And, when this fails, her specific and direct comments about the dream figure(s) can often provide the therapist with useful information for understanding the dream.

One of the important roles of a parent in an adolescent's session relates to keeping the youngster honest. The main reason why adolescents are reluctant to have their parents participate in their sessions is that they fear that the parent will confront them with their fabrications and bring them to the attention of their therapist. Adolescents would much prefer to "sell their therapists a bill of goods" in which the therapist is duped into believing every one of the youngster's distortions and complaints about the parents. The therapist is generally not witness to the events the youngster describes; the parent often is. Accordingly, the parent is in a far better position to "smoke out" the youngster's lies. I wish to emphasize again that the presence and participation of the parents does not usually compromise the therapist-patient relationshp with the youngster—although this is what I had been taught, and this is what many still believe. The basic determinant of the relationship between the therapist and the child is their own personalities. A healthy mother does not believe that her relationship with her first child will be significantly compromised by the appearance of the second or third. No competent therapist would advise a parent to have only one child, lest the relationship with the first be compromised by the appearance of a second. No healthy mother strictly excludes the father's presence on those occasions when she is with her child, with the argument that it will compromise her relationship with her son or daughter. It is not the presence of one or a few others in the room that is the primary determinant of the relationship between two people. The relationship depends more on qualities that exist within and between the two of them. Therapists who strictly adhere to the traditional view—wherein third party participation in the adolescent session is viewed as therapeutically detrimental—may be providing the patient with an antitherapeutic experience. This view expresses, both explicitly and implicitly, the notion that exclusivity is crucial for a good relationship. This can only engender possessiveness, egocentricity, intolerance for sharing, excessive dependency, and other untoward reactions.

SITUATIONS IN WHICH THE PARENT'S INVOLVEMENT IN THE TREATMENT IS CONTRAINDICATED

Excessively Punitive and Sadistic Parents

There are certain situations in which parental involvement in the adolescent's treatment may be contraindicated. These are relatively uncommon but still worthy of mention. Most parents can be relied upon not to punish the youngster for revelations made during the joint session with them. However, some parents are so disturbed that they will use such revelations as an excuse for sadistic and brutal retaliation. It is preferable that such parents not be involved in the therapy, except possibly at the most superficial level. There are also parents who will react with Draconian measures to an adolescent's sexual involvement, no matter how superficial. They are so fanatic in their reactions that it is probably best not to involve them in any discussions directly or even indirectly related to the youngster's sexual activities.

Psychologically Fragile Parents

Some parents are so psychologically fragile that they cannot tolerate the criticisms and other forms of negative feedback that would come their way during the joint therapeutic sessions. This is especially the case for parents who are psychotic or borderline. Such a parent may be so defensive that he or she would not be able to handle many of the therapeutic revelations, even though expressed symbolically. Were the parent to sense the underlying meaning of a hostile symbol, it could be ego-debasing and precipitate psychological deterioration. Involvement of such a parent in the youngster's therapy could be considered cruel and would be likely to alienate significantly both the parent and the patient. Any benefits that the youngster might derive from the parent's presence might be more than offset by the possible compromise of the therapist-patient relationship caused by such exposure. In addition, such benefits might also be obviated by the parental psychiatric deterioration and its resultant compromise of parenting capacity. This is not a common situation, but I mention it because it does occur.

Parents Who Exhibit Formidable Hostility Toward the Therapist

There are parents who are extremely hostile, and such hostility might be exhibited toward the therapist. All therapists must accept the fact that they must tolerate a certain amount of parental hostility. I am discussing here those who exhibit more than the usual amount of hostility that is often directed toward therapists. No matter how hard the therapist tries, such parents never seem to be satisfied. No amount of explanation or discussion seems to reduce their hostility. Yet, such parents may bring their children for therapy. When they are invited to participate actively in the youngster's treatment, they may use the opportunity for the collection of ammunition, for example, "Is this what I'm spending all my money on?—to have you tell him exactly what I tell him?" "How is answering questions about whether or not he gets along with other kids going to help him obey me at home?" and "My husband is right: psychiatry is just a lot of bullshit!" Such parents tend to "cramp my style" when I am working under their observation and scrutiny. I have the feeling that everything I say is going to be used as ammunition against me. Attempts to discuss their negative attitudes often prove futile. Accordingly, I have found it in the patient's best interests to have such parents sit in the waiting room or go out shopping. Although I am deprived of their input, such loss is more than counterbalanced by the enhanced efficiency of the individual therapeutic process with the patient. It is the lesser of the two detrimental alternatives. Therapy, like life, often boils down to such a choice. If there were a better option, I would utilize it. So I work under these compromsied circumstances.

Overbearing, Intrusive Parents

One might ask the question: "What about the overbearing mother who is always intruding in the youngster's therapy? Shouldn't she be kept out of the room?" My answer to this question is: "Not so quickly." Let us take, for example, the following situation. I am in session with Jimmy and his mother. I ask Jimmy a question; his mother answers. At that point I consider myself to have a golden opportunity for a meaningful therapeutic inter-change — an opportunity that would not have been possible had the mother been out of the room. At that point I will say to Jimmy, "What just happened?" Jimmy may respond, "You asked me a question." And I will respond, "And what happened then?" My hope is that he will respond, "My mother answered you." To which I will respond, "Right! And what did you do?" Jimmy may answer, "I didn't do anything." To this I will respond, "Yes, Jimmy, that's right. You didn't do anything. But I believe that you had certain thoughts and feelings when your mother answered my question and didn't give you a chance to answer it yourself. What exactly did you think at the very moment she answered? Exactly what were your feelings at that time?"

Here, of course, I will try to get the patient to express the thoughts and feelings that he probably had about his mother's intrusiveness. It is generally easier for the youngster to do this in the therapist's presence. The patient may recognize that the therapeutic situation reduces the likelihood that the mother will react with severe punitive measures while the therapist is there. The youngster may fear, however, that there will be "hell to pay" when he or she gets home, but the patient also knows that there will be at least some protection in the consultation room. This is exactly what happened to Little Hans, Sigmund Freud's famous patient (1909). As I have discussed elsewhere (1972a), I believe that Little Hans was comfortable expressing hostility toward his father in Freud's presence that he was not comfortable expressing elsewhere. I suspect that he felt that his father would not retaliate for such hostile expression in Freud's presence. Unfortunately, Freud did not direct his attention to this important experience that Little Hans had in his consultation. If the therapist is successful in bringing about such expression during the session, and use it as a point of departure for a therapeutic approach to the mother's intrusiveness, it will have served a very useful purpose in the child's treatment.

As mentioned, the richest therapy is that which provides experiences. When the parent is in the room, there is a much greater likelihood that significant experiences will take place. The therapist should view such experiences as golden opportunities, to be grabbed onto and milked to their utmost. They are the most meaningful aspects of the therapeutic process and they should be cherished. Accordingly, I do not quickly remove intrusive parents from the room. I can conceive of the possibility of a parent being so compulsively intrusive that I would not have the opportunity for such interchanges, and that no living space would be provided the patient. However, this has not yet occurred, and I have been successful in utilizing the situations in which intrusiveness was exhibited as a step toward a reduction of the problem.

The Parent with an Incurable Illness

A rarer, but nevertheless very important situation in which the parent's presence is generally contraindicated, is the one in which the parent is suffering with an incurable disease. If the parent is openly discussing the disease, then the parental involvement can be salutary for both the patient and the parent. However, if the parent is using denial and other related defense mechanisms as a way of dealing with his or her reactions to the illness, then parental participation in the youngster's therapy can be detrimental to the parent. One would not want to have such a parent exposed to the patient's working through his or her reactions to the inevitable death of the parent. Such exposure can be cruel and inhumane. Having the parent present would probably lessen the likelihood that the patient will reveal his or her true feelings because of the appreciation (depending upon the patient's age, sophistication, and intelligence) that his or her revelations may be painful and psychologically detrimental to the parent.

CLINICAL EXAMPLE OF PARENTAL AND STEPPARENTAL INVOLVEMENT IN AN ADOLESCENT'S TREATMENT

Bob and Sally were five and three years old respectively when their parents separated. The family lived in a large Eastern city. Their mother remained in the apartment with the children, and the father took an apartment in a nearby neighborhood. He was reliable, attentive, and provided the children with meaningful parental input. About a year later the father met another woman and a year after that moved to a suburban community. He still remained loyal and dutiful to the children and would take them to his suburban home during his weekend visitations. One day, when the children were about eight and six, the mother appeared at the father's doorstep with the children and announced that she had met a man who lived 200 miles away, was going to live with him, and he could now have permanent and complete custody of the children. The mother explained that the father now had a full family with a suburban home and that he could provide the children with a much better life than she. She said she thought it would be in the children's best interests that she have limited if any contact with them again. And so the children moved in with their father and stepmother. The father's new wife had not previously been married, had married the children's father during her mid-thirties, and welcomed the opportunity to have a "whole family" at this relatively late period in her life.

During the next five years the children did not see their mother at all, but did occasionally receive a Christmas present. Then, she suddenly appeared at the father's home and announced that she wished to visit with the children once again on an ongoing basis.

The father's response was to permit the mother to visit the children, but he absolutely refused to finance their air transportation (which he could well afford) or even involve himself in any transportation to airports if the mother were to pay for flights (which he knew she was ill-equipped to do). Rather, he insisted that if the mother wished to see the children she would have to pick them up herself and return them to his home. Accordingly, for each weekend visitation she would have to leave her home early Saturday morning, drive four to five hours, pick the children up, and then drive home with them. Because she no longer had any friends or relatives in the area where the father lived, most often she returned back to her own home 200 miles away. The stepmother had settled in with this tailor-made family and had absolutely no desire for the natural mother to disrupt her now deeply entrenched lifestyle. She basically saw no place for the natural mother in her or the children's lives and viewed her as a noxious intruder. She had no appreciation that the natural mother could still provide valuable input to the children, her abandonment notwithstanding. If the mother was lucky with regard to the traffic, the trip took all day. She would spend Saturday evening and Sunday morning with the children. Then, on Sunday afternoon, she would drive them back (usually hitting Sunday evening traffic), and then drive back to her home. Thus, a weekend of visitation would generally involve 16 to 18 hours of driving. The father was so intent on punishing his former wife for abandoning their children for five years that he had blinded himself to the discomforts of such unnecessary travel that he was causing his children to suffer.

There had never been anything but an extremely strained relationship between the mother and stepmother. When the mother would call the home to arrange for visitations, the stepmother would not even engage in innocuous amenities, but would immediately turn the phone over to her husband, cooly saying, "It's her." When the mother would arrive to pick up the children, she was not permitted in the home; rather, she was required to honk the horn outside and the children would be sent out. And this situation prevailed during the seven-year period of *rapprochement* at the end of which my services were enlisted. At that point the mother was planning to litigate for more money in order to get some relief from this oppressive visitation program. However, all had decided to try to avoid litigation and seek a consultation outside of the legal process.

During my initial evaluation it became apparent that the children were contributing significantly to the polarization of the mother from her former husband and his wife. Although now in their teens, they were still saying to each parent what they believed that parent wanted to hear. They were exhibiting thereby an extremely common maneuver used by children of divorce. I cannot emphasize this point strongly enough. The vast majority (if not all) children of divorce have a loyalty conflict and utilize this maneuver in order to ingratiate themselves to each of their parents. Examiners do well to make the assumption that it is always taking place, because of the rare situation in which it is absent. And the process does not stop in childhood; it generally extends well into the teens and even beyond.

As a result of these maneuvers by Bob and Sally, each parent was brought to believe that the other was the incarnation of all the evil that existed on earth. After a visit with their mother, the children would tell their stepmother and father what a terrible time they had and how many indignities they suffered at her hands. Similarly, when with their mother they would describe the terrible conditions under which they lived in their father's home. Having no direct communication with one another, the parents were in no position to appreciate that they were being "buttered up" in order to gain affection. This is one of the important ways in which the litigious process enhances and perpetuates alienation. Without having the opportunity for direct contact with the other side, the worst distortions became entrenched and delusions of malevolence are likely to persist. And this is especially the case when the children, from the fear of rejection, feed into the process by their fabrications.

After seeing the suburban family in varying combinations, and after seeing the mother alone (she traveled the 200 miles to my office for the purpose of the interview), I recommended an interview in which the three adults, the two children, and myself would be present. The father and stepmother were horrified at this suggestion and initially refused to discuss it further. The mother, although reluctant, was more receptive. Finally, I was able to prevail upon the father and stepmother to try one such interview and to use experience rather than speculation to make their decision regarding whether or not they wished to participate further. Accordingly, an open-ended interview was set up.

When the interview began it was clear that all the parties were quite tense. I believe that the parents were tense because they anticipated the worst kinds of treatment from each other. And the children were tense, I suspected, because they realized that their lying would be disclosed. My experience has been that the best way to "smoke out" these polarizing maneuvers by the children is to conduct a family interview. In fact, it is extremely difficult to get the parents to see how they are being manipulated without such a meeting. Within about a half hour everyone became more relaxed and the adults began to appreciate that they were not indeed the ogres that they had viewed one another to be. In the ten years that the stepmother and mother knew one another, they had never really had one civil conversation. The actual experience for each one of being in the same room and seeing that the other was a human being, without horns, without fire or poison spitting from her mouth, was successful in correcting their distortions. Years of separate psychotherapy would not have accomplished this. I would go further and state that each of these parties could have been in psychoanalysis five times a week and not have accomplished as much on this particular problem as they did in the first hour of this meeting. Next they came to appreciate that they had been "buttered up" by the children. Interestingly, as is often the case, the children showed little regret over the troubles their fabrications had caused.

In the ensuing discussion the father came to understand that he was so enraged at his former wife that he had blinded himself to the distress he was causing his children by insisting that the mother assume all the travel obligations of visitation. Accordingly, he agreed to drop the children off at the airport close to his home and to pick them up there on their return and the mother would pick the children up at the airport on their arrival to her home and drop them off at the airport in order for them to return back to their father. The father decided as well to contribute to the financing of the air travel. As the meeting drew to a close the father stated that he thought it had been quite useful and invited his former wife to join him, his wife, and the children at his home for further discussion. All agreed that this could prove useful, but the stepmother (as was expected) was somewhat reluctant for this meeting in her home. The result was a resolution of the primary problems without resorting to adversary litigation. I am convinced that had this family not chosen this more judicious course, they would have involved themselves in extremely expensive and psychologically draining litigation—which would have been far less likely to have solved their difficulties.

There is another important principle demonstrated here. It relates to a phenomenon that may initially appear to the reader to be totally unrelated to the issue of parental involvement in an adolescent's treatment, but is very much applicable. I am referring to the appreciation by airport officials that when hijackers have seized a plane and threaten destruction of the passengers if their demands are not complied with, it behooves the airport officials to stall the hijackers as much as possible. They recognize that the longer they are successful in keeping the hijackers on the ground, the less the likelihood they will murder the hostages. They know that, at the time that the plane is seized, the passengers are generally viewed as subhuman creatures—as people of a different race, religion, or creed—whose lives are not worth very much. If the hijackers and the passengers are required to remain together for long periods, it is likely that they will get to speak with one another—language barriers notwithstanding.

Gradually the hijackers will recognize similarities between the hostages and their loved ones at home. They are likely to compare the passengers with relatives and friends at home. One woman reminds the hijacker of his sister, another of his grandmother. Some children remind him or his nieces and nephews. And another gentleman reminds him of his grandfather. Ultimately, the hijackers may come to appreciate that all human beings, all over the world—regardless of race, religion, or creed—basically want very similar things for themselves and their families. Specifically, they want their children to grow up physically healthy, reasonably educated, with the opportunity to become self-sufficient, independent human beings capable of supporting themselves and their families with a reasonable degree of comfort and freedom from fear and disease. They come to appreciate that everyone has aspirations and disappointments, hopes realized and hopes dashed. Once such familiarity has been experienced, the hostages are no longer viewed as vile and worthless creatures, and it becomes far less probable that they will be slaughtered. The same phenomenon was operative in the group family session described above and is one of the ways in which joint interviews with a youngster's family can achieve results that may be difficult—if not impossible—to obtain in individual treatment.

DIRECT TREATMENT
OF PARENTS

On occasion, parents ask me about marital counseling and even individual therapy for one or both of them. When I was in training, I was taught that such an arrangement *must* compromise the adolescent's treatment. The theory was that it was only via an *exclusive* relationship with the patient, one in which other parties had no significant involvement with the therapist, that therapy could possibly hope to succeed. I consider this position to be one of the great myths of psychotherapy. I believe that just the opposite is true. Therapeutic work with the parents entrenches more deeply the therapist's relationship with them and enables him or her to be in better touch with factors going on in the home that are contributing to and perpetuating the patient's illness. In addition, therapeutic work with the parents is a statement of their commitment to the therapist and this will increase the likelihood that they will be genuinely supportive of their youngster's work in treatment. The ideal relationship that the therapist should have with the family is that he or she be viewed as the "family therapist." I am not using the term here to refer to the situation in which the therapist only does traditional family therapy in which the whole family is seen together on an ongoing basis. Rather, I can use the term to refer to a situation in which the therapist sees one or more of the family members, in any combination whatsoever, as long as treatment is warranted. When an individual no longer considers therapy to be warranted, the person can discontinue the treatment. However, this does not preclude reinvolvement in treatment if warranted. Life is such that new stresses will inevitably occur, stresses that might warrant reentrance into therapy. Last, working directly with parents provides the therapist with even more information about the adolescent's environment than the therapist would have without such intensive involvement. And this cannot but be immensely beneficial to the adolescent patient's therapy.

THIRTEEN

SPECIAL CONSIDERATIONS FOR THE TREATMENT OF ANTISOCIAL BEHAVIOR

Throughout the course of this book I have made comments about adolescents' antisocial behavior. In fact, it is reasonable to state that more of this book is devoted to adolescents' antisocial behavior than to any other symptom. The primary reason for this is that antisocial behavior is the most common problem for which parents seek treatment. In this chapter I will provide elaborations of some of the points made previously. It is important to appreciate that what we refer to as antisocial behavior is very much determined by what is the norm in a particular society or cultural subgroup. For example, when I was a child attending the public schools in New York City all boys were required to wear ties. On assembly day we had to wear white shirts and red ties. A boy who refused to wear ties was considered to be "bad" and would be viewed as exhibiting antisocial behavior. High school girls at that time uniformly wore bras. If a girl refused to wear a bra during that period she might find herself expelled from school. This was not the case in the 60s and 70s and, even to a certain extent, today. A girl today, however, would be considered antisocial if she went to school wearing nothing above the waist. She might even get arrested. There are certainly cultures in which females walk around exposed in this way and are not considered atypical or antisocial. When I went to high school, if a girl were pregnant she would be expelled. There are high schools now where teen-age pregnancy is so ubiquitous that youngsters may even bring their babies to school in order to provide care for them. Last, it is important to appreciate that all children and adolescents, at times, exhibit what could be considered antisocial behavior. It is only when the antisocial acts become repetitious and consistently cause trouble that the youngster should justifiably be considered to have a psychiatric problem in this area.

FURTHER COMMENTS ON THE
CAUSES OF ANTISOCIAL BEHAVIOR

At various places in this book I have discussed some of the causes of antisocial behavior. Specifically, in Chapter One I presented a theory on the development of the capacity to experience guilt. I discussed there: 1) operative genetic-neurological factors, 2) the phenomenon of imprinting and its relationship to the development of antisocial behavior, and 3) the three stages in guilt development that relate to parental responses to good and bad behavior, namely, the pleasure-pain stage, the shame stage, and the guilt stage. Also in Chapter One I discussed rebellion and strivings toward independence as normal adolescent phenomena from which symptomatic antisocial behavior may emerge. In Chapter Two, in my discussion of situations conducive to the development of psychopathology in adolescence, I focused on social, cultural, and educational factors that could contribute to adolescent antisocial behavior. Specifically, I focused on day-care centers, socioeconomic deprivation, school systems, television and movies, and the legal system. I also discussed the relationship between antisocial behavior and parental deprivation of affection, identification with pathological parental traits, and parental sanction of antisocial behavior. Readers who have not read this material would do well to do so if they are to understand fully the material I present in this chapter. This material is best viewed as an extension and elaboration of that which has been presented previously, with specific focus on the previous material's relevance to the treatment of adolescents with antisocial behavior disorders.

Anger

Anger is the basic emotion with which antisocial youngsters are dealing. Fight and flight reactions are necessary for survival. When an animal is confronted with a threat to its life it generally does one of two things: it either fights or flees. Anger is the emotion attendant to the fight reaction; fear is the emotion attendant to the flight reaction. Anger has survival value in that it enhances our capacity to deal with irritations and dangers. We fight harder and more effectively when we are angry. Anger builds up when there is frustration and helplessness, and it is reduced when the irritants are removed. However, when the noxious stimulus remains, the anger persists and may even increase—resulting in even stronger emotional reactions. When there is a prolonged sense of impotence over the failure to remove a noxious stimulus, *rage* results. The difference between rage and anger is that anger is generally rational, but in the state of rage behavior becomes irrational in the service of removing the noxious stimulus. In mild irritation and anger one can still focus on the irritant and make reasonable attempts to remove it. However, with prolonged frustration and the rage that results, the anger reaction will neither be coordinated nor directed toward a specific goal. Rather, the reaction will be chaotic and therefore less likely to be effective. Even when rage is effective in removing the irritant, there are untoward side effects after its utilization. There are still "pieces to be picked up."

The term *fury* is sometimes used to describe a degree of rage that is so great that the inappropriate reactions reach insane proportions. In rage, the reaction, although inappropriate, would still not generally be considered crazy. In the state of fury, one may even commit murder—so deranging is the rage. In the state of fury the anger has reached a point where acts of violence may be repeated without reason, as if they have a life of their own. A murderer stabs the victim once or twice, but does not stop there. He or she may continue stabbing 20, 30, or 40 times. Obviously, after the first few stabs, it is likely that the victim is dead and subsequent thrusts of the knife into the body serve no further purpose. The anger has "gotten out of control" and almost has a life of its own. This is just one of the kinds of derangement that one sees in the fury reaction. Youngsters with antisocial behavior are generally suffering with frustration—frustration that has not been dealt with properly in its early phases. Accordingly, the resultant anger escalates into the phases of rage and fury and the patient thereby exhibits a wide variety of inappropriate, injudicious, and unhealthy ways of dealing with irritations and frustrations.

TYPES OF ANTISOCIAL BEHAVIOR

I divide antisocial behavior into five categories: social or gang, neurotic, psychopathic, borderline or psychotic, and antisocial behavior in the learning disabled. This is an elaboration of R.J. Marshall's four categories (1979). Although the reader may be able to identify youngsters with antisocial behavior who do not fall into one of these five categories, I consider such exceptions to be rare.

Social or Gang Delinquency

Youngsters in this category often (but certainly not always) come from homes in which they have grown up in an atmosphere of socioeconomic deprivation. As described in Chapter One, these youngsters live in constant frustration over the disparity between their own lives and those of others who are more economically sufficient or affluent. Their watching TV only intensifies their pain as they compare that which they have with that which others have (or seemingly have). The frustration and resentment they suffer build up into rage and even fury and contribute to their acting out their anger against those who they may consider to be much more fortunate than themselves. They gain support from gangs and others in the same situation. The mob has a strength greater than that of each of its individuals and this gives each member much greater power than he or she would have alone. In addition, there may be parental sanction for the gang's antisocial behavior. The parents recognize that if they themselves act out their anger against those who they consider to be more fortunate in society, they may suffer significant repercussions. Their adolescent youngsters, however, have poorer judgment and usually suffer with delusions of invulnerability. They thereby become willing candidates to act out their parental hostility because they do not really believe that they themselves will suffer. The group enhances the delusions of invulnerability in that each individual can feel even more protected by the belief that if there are to be any dangerous repercussions those around them are more likely to be affected.

I made reference in Chapter One to studies that indicate that antisocial behavior is much more likely to be present in children who have grown up without fathers. In our society the father figure, much more than the mother, appears to be the model for a strong superego as well as the work ethic. I believe that one of the important reasons for the high delinquency rate among inner-city black ghetto children is the absence of a significant father figure in the home. There is hardly a day that passes that we do not see on television or read in the newspapers the plight of the blacks in our society and the various indignities they have suffered over the years. Although much attention has been given to a wide variety of social, cultural, economic, and psychological remedies, I do not believe that enough attention has been given to the absentee father. In the last ten years we have seen the influx of many ethnic groups into this country, a massive wave of immigration from countries all over the earth. This has been especially the case for Chinese, Japanese, Indians, Vietnamese, and Koreans. It is reasonable to state that these groups have done quite well for themselves, both educationally and economically. There is no question that they are moving into many niches in our society that could have been filled by blacks. However, the blacks have not filled these niches, even though programs have been developed to ease their entry and progress.

I believe *one* of the important factors that explains this unfortunate phenomenon relates to the absence of an adult male role model. In all of these other groups there is generally a very tight family structure with father, mother, siblings and extended family involved deeply in the children's upbringing. The fathers not only serve as models for socially acceptable behavior, but for the work ethic, educational commitment, and (in many cases) business acumen. This is not the experience for the vast majority of black children. In New York City, during the 1960s, many of the stores in Harlem were owned by white people (especially Jews). The blacks considered themselves to have been exploited by these entrepreneurs and sometimes literally burned down their stores and drove them out. Thereafter, the U.S. government provided generous and ample small-business loans to encourage blacks to enter into their own businesses. Yet, more than 20 years later, in these same areas, one finds that most of the stores are not owned by blacks. Rather they are owned by Vietnamese, Indians, Koreans, Chinese, some Jews, and an assortment of other ethnic groups. I believe that the main reason for this relates to the aforementioned absence of a father figure to provide for the children a model for the kinds of qualities necessary to run a small business, namely, reasonable education, commitment, punctuality (not "black man's time" but "white man's time"), and adherence to the work ethic. Blacks are not oblivious to this problem. One black comedian gave the following advice to his people (words are not accurate, the message is): "My suggestion is that you get up in the morning, take a pencil and a piece of paper, follow around an Oriental, and make notes of exactly what he does every single minute throughout the course of the day. Then you start doing the same thing."

There are certainly vicious cycles going on here. This is especially the case in the educational system. Black children, having few models for educational commitment at home, could have such models in their schools. Unfortunately, the public schools they attend only rarely provide such models. Their black teachers may have grown up in homes with a similar lack of educational and work commitment. The white teachers that such schools attract are often so disillusioned with the poor quality of the educational program, or so uncommitted to it, that they only "go through the motions" of teaching and thereby do not serve as good models. The teachers may merely put in their time while spending most of that time vigilant to the dangers they are exposed to in the schools. The few who are committed are so rare that they do not have a significant effect on the total system. Furthermore, many of the teachers are products of a psychopathic society in which there is a psychopathic educational system, and so they have little meaningful involvement in the educational process.

For many youngsters, both in and out of the ghettos, antisocial behavior can serve to fill up the emptiness of their lives. Hanging around on street corners can be quite boring. Antisocial behavior provides excitement. It also gets attention, even if from the police. For most youngsters, if the choice is between being ignored and getting negative or painful attention, the latter is generally preferable. There is adventure in trying to escape from the police. It is well known that drug abuse is epidemic in inner-city ghettos. Drugs serve to desensitize these youngsters to the hopelessness of their plight and provide them with some pleasure in compensation for the pains and privations they suffer daily. Having developed few if any skills by the time they reach their teens, either in the educational or extra-educational realm, they gravitate toward drugs as a narcotic to deaden their psychological pain. Drugs also serve as a tranquilizer to reduce the tensions and anxieties they feel, and as an euphoriant to compensate for their depressed feelings. Drugs, of course, can be used in group situations or in isolation. When used with others, drugs can lessen the sense of alienation and self-loathing that the drug abuser may feel. But drugs cost money, and the average adolescent is not in a position to independently afford to pay for them. Delinquency and crime provide the quickest route to supporting the drug habit.

Adolescents in the group-delinquent category are not likely to be good candidates for psychotherapy. Their problems are far more broad and extensive than can reasonably be dealt with in individual therapy, family therapy, or even group therapy (in many cases). Rather, the social and economic problems that have contributed to the development of their difficulties must be dealt with. However, even if these were dealt with at the present time, in some magic way, it probably will not do the present-day adolescents very much good. They have already been too scarred (even though only in their teens) to hope for significant cure or even amelioration of their problems. They have already been deprived of a father figure for 15 years or so. Accordingly, their chance of rectifying such a formidable defect is small. In addition, the scarring they have suffered in association with prejudice and their other privations may be so deep-seated that it is lifelong. We therapists do well not to exhibit manifestations of what I have referred to elsewhere in this book as *The Statue of Liberty syndrome*. We would also do well to heed the aforementioned ancient advice to differentiate between the things we can control and those we cannot and not try to change that which is uncontrollable. We certainly cannot control the socioeconomic factors that contribute to group delinquency while sitting in our offices doing individual therapy. Any efforts we may wish to make toward changing the situation must go far beyond that venue.

Neurotic Delinquency

I use the term neurotic delinquency to refer to neurotic behavior which is the result of maladaptive ways of dealing with intrapsychic conflicts. Here I am utilizing psychoanalytic concepts. For example, the youngster may be very angry at his parents because of the frustrations he suffers in association with their continual fighting. He recognizes, either consciously or unconsciously, that were he to express his resentment directly toward them he might suffer formidable painful punishments and even further rejection. He thereby displaces his anger onto teachers and school administrators—safer targets. The utilization of the displacement mechanism is the hallmark of the neurotic adaptation. Adolescents with severe dependency problems are not likely to express overtly their infantile needs and dependency cravings, lest they suffer significant rejection from their peers. After all, adolescents are supposed to be big and strong. Acting-out behavior, especially if exhibited over a long period, may ultimately result in one's being placed in a residential treatment center or even a jail. Although this may appear to be an undesirable placement from the point of view of the outsider, the youngster may secretly enjoy the incarceration because he can gratify therein his dependency cravings in a socially acceptable way. In such places one is insured food, clothing, and shelter without having to worry about a job. This can be accomplished in a socially acceptable way because, after all, everybody knows that only "tough guys" go to jail, not the jelly-fish types. And because everybody knows that prisoners hate jail the youngster can publicly profess that the experience is detestable, restricting, etc.—while enjoying dependency gratifications.

Occasionally, one will see an adolescent with a hypertrophied superego. This youngster has problems that are just the opposite of those described by A. M. Johnson (1949) in which "superego lacunae" result in deficiencies in conscience mechanisms. These youngsters have consciences that are too strong. Accordingly, they feel guilty over their unconscious impulses, especially those in the sexual and anger realms. When these impulses press for expression into conscious awareness the youngster feels guilty. By engaging in behavior that results in punishment, the adolescent can assuage his or her guilt. For such youngsters antisocial behavior may be attractive because it promises punitive repercussions. Although this mechanism is described frequently in the classical psychoanalytic literature, my experience has been that this is not a common phenomenon. I believe that the problem for most of my patients— as is the case for most people in western society today—is that they have too little guilt, not too much. Also this category of youngsters with hypertrophied superegos includes those who project their own superego dictates onto society and their parents and view them as persecutors. This may also result in their acting out anger against external authorities. Again, I have not seen this mechanism to be operative in more than a very small fraction of all delinquents that I have seen.

Psychopathic Delinquents

In this group are those delinquents who have superego deficiencies that result in impairment in their ability to feel guilt when they have caused others pain and suffering. The main deterrent to their antisocial behavior is the appreciation that they may be "caught in the act" and thereby punished. They are best understood to have suffered during infancy the kinds of deprivations described in Chapter One. Specifically, there were impairments in the formation of their initial attachment bonds resulting in compromises in the development of their internal guilt-evoking mechanisms. As stated in Chapter One, I believe that both genetic predispositions and deprivation of parental affection have generally played a role in bringing about these deficiencies in the development of conscience. It is important to appreciate that there is a continuum among individuals with regard to the presence of internalized guilt-evoking mechanisms. On the one extreme are those who exhibit practically no evidence for the presence of such mechanisms. These individuals can indeed be referred to as psychopaths. At the other end are those with extremely powerful guilt-evoking mechanisms. Such individuals might be considered to have hypertrophied superegos. Going down the continuum again toward the extreme psychopathic end are individuals with varying degrees of psychopathic traits. The greater the absence of the factors (described in Chapter One) that contribute to the development of conscience, the greater the likelihood that the individual will exhibit psychopathic tendencies. In Chapter Two I have also described other factors—such as identification with psychopathic parents and parental sanctioning of antisocial behavior—that might contribute to the development of psychopathic delinquency in adolescents.

Last, there may be some overlap between individuals who would be classified as social or gang delinquents and those who would be classified as psychopathic delinquents. In both cases the deficiency in superego development may be the same. However, in the social delinquent the likelihood is greater that the individual comes from a socioeconomically deprived group and has learned or been taught (by direct instruction or modeling) the delinquent behavior by peers in the neighborhood. Although psychopathic delinquents may very well come from such neighborhoods, they also can come from other strata of society. However, those who do come from middle- and upper-class homes do not often have their psychopathy supported and promulgated by gangs. Rather, the home and family influences have been important in the development of the psychopathy. This factor is also related to the phenomenon that youngsters who grow up in inner-city ghettos—whose families are intact—are far less likely to develop delinquent behavior. These youngsters are more likely to have caring parents, especially father figures, who serve as models for healthy development of internalized guilt-evoking mechanisms. In short, the family influences, far more than the neighborhood, are the important determinants as to whether psychopathic behavior will arise.

Borderline or Psychotic Delinquents

Youngsters in this group suffer with severe psychiatric disturbances. Sometimes a genetic loading factor may be operative in producing the psychotic behavior. Here too there may be some overlap with the social delinquent, but the category is still useful to consider as a separate item. Like most other forms of psychopathology, it is more highly represented in the socioeconomically deprived. However, one sees delinquents in this category from middle- and upper-class homes as well. In extreme cases the youngster exhibits paranoid delusions, which may be intimately related to antisocial acting out. Believing that they are persecuted, these delinquents may act out against those whom they believe are out to harm them. Their hallucinations may dictate antisocial behavior. The voices they hear may continually urge and even demand them to harm and even kill their fantasized persecutors. These individuals will show extremely poor reality testing and other manifestations of psychosis such as looseness of associations, concrete thinking, flight of ideas, deteriorated behavior, suicidal attempts, and long-standing impairment in the ability to form meaningful relationships with others. These individuals are not likely to be members of groups because of their severe interpersonal problems. Rather, they are very much loners.

Learning-Disabled Delinquents

Many of these youngsters are quite angry because they are required to suffer daily humiliation in school where they appreciate the painful disparity between their own intellectual levels and those of their peers. When they reach the teen period they often find themselves having little if any competence in major areas. They cannot feel good about themselves regarding academic achievement because of their learning disabilities. Nor have they gained a sense of accomplishment in sports and other recreational activities because of their coordination and cognitive deficits. And they have few friends because of their neurologically based social deficits as well as their gradual removal from the mainstream of life.

Accordingly, they are excellent candidates for gravitating toward antisocial groups. They are willing to pay any price for admission to such groups, even if the price be drug addiction, alcoholism, or delinquent behavior. Because of their naiveté and gullibility they make perfect followers for leaders of delinquent

groups. Because they are more likely to have delusions of invulnerability than the average youngster they are more likely to involve
themselves in dangerous behavior. This is the group that explains
the common finding that the IQs of delinquents are lower than
nondelinquents. Elsewhere (1987b) I discuss my belief that many
learning-disabled children do not have a disorder per se, but are
merely unlucky enough to have cognitive weaknesses that ill equip
them to succeed in the educational system designed to qualify
people for functioning in our higher level, industrialized, sophisticated society. These same individuals would have done quite well
had they been born into an agrarian society, where their cognitive
weaknesses would not be apparent and they would not thereby be
exposed to ridicule and humiliation.

TREATMENT OF ANTISOCIAL ADOLESCENTS

Many of the comments made in Chapter Eight are applicable to
antisocial youngsters as well. However, here I focus on further
techniques that may be particularly useful in the treatment of these
youngsters. The treatment of delinquents is particularly difficult
because of their antagonism toward the therapist. They are typically
self-centered and narcissistic. They consider themselves superior to
the therapist as well as other adults in the older generation. Their
attitude is generally one of scornful condescension. They cannot
allow themselves to accept the fact that they have psychiatric
difficulties.

It is most important that the therapist determine which of the
five categories of delinquent he or she is dealing with. It is especially
important to differentiate those patients whom we can help from
those whom we cannot. Adolescents in the psychopathic delinquency group are not often candidates for meaningful therapy. One
should try to ascertain whether the youngster has ever related to
any significant figure in his or her life. If there is no such history
then it is not likely that the patient will now relate—for the first
time—to the examiner. Under these circumstances, the therapist
does well to save everyone significant time and trouble at the outset
by not embarking on a treatment program. In Chapter One I

described those youngsters with psychopathic traits which render them poor candidates for therapy. Their impairments in the ability to form relationships with others are so severe that they are not going to have the kind of foundation crucial to successful psychotherapy. With no past experience in forming psychological bonds with any other human being, it is not likely that the therapist is going to be the first exception to this pattern.

The Contributions of August Aichorn

August Aichorn was a Viennese schoolmaster who attempted to apply Freudian psychoanalytic techniques to the treatment of delinquent boys. In his classic *Wayward Youth* (1925) he described the difficulties that arose in such boys' psychiatric treatment because they were very defiant of authority and tended to see him as just another authority against whom to rebel. Aichorn was quite "street smart" and could readily identify with delinquent youngsters. He could easily talk their language and this capacity served as a catalyst for the development of a relationship with them. His basic respect for delinquents and his ability to empathize and sympathize with them played an important role in his capacity to form relationships with them. In the early phase of treatment, he would often gain their confidence by demonstrating that he was even more knowledgeable than they about crime. This resulted in their admiring and respecting him and entrenched thereby the therapeutic relationship. He even joined them in their criticism of society and its flaws. Once such a relationship was established, however, Aichorn gradually shifted his position and then attempted to foster stronger superegos in these youngsters. His hope was that their desire to maintain their relationship with him would motivate them to follow along as he encouraged and became a model for socially sanctioned behavior. His hope was that he would thereby create a neurotic, intrapsychic conflict in these youngsters, which would then be amenable to psychoanalytic treatment.

As an obvious duplicity is involved in such an approach, I would not be comfortable utilizing it. I also would have difficulty with this method because I do not consider myself particularly "street smart." However, I utilize a somewhat modified aspect of

Aichorn's method. Specifically, I do try to gain delinquents' respect by not allowing them to manipulate or deceive me. For example, if such a youngster were to start flattering me, obviously in the service of gaining some particular personal advantage, I might say: "What do you hope to gain by such flattery? It's obvious to me, and anyone who could hear you now, that you have absolutely no conviction for these compliments." By not allowing myself to be exploited I might thereby gain the respect of the psychopathic youngster. Like Aichorn, I can certainly use profanity quite freely, and I am generally far superior to these youngsters with regard to my repertoire of low-level jokes. In this way, I might also instill some admiration in the delinquent teenager.

Another complication of Aichorn's approach—and one that he does not describe in his book—relates to the fact that youngsters continually were admitted to and discharged from his facility. Under these circumstances it is easy to imagine how an "old-timer" might say to a "newcomer": "You're new here so you're probably impressed with his facade of being one of the guys. You just wait awhile, you'll see he'll change his tactics. He'll soon go into phase two in which he'll try to get you to feel guilty about what you've done." Although the old-timer may not be as articulate as the theoretical youngster just quoted, I believe that the basic appreciation of what was going on must have been known to the delinquents and have been communicated to each other. This, I suspect, must have compromised the efficacy of Aichorn's work. The approach, if one were to utilize it, is probably "safer" in a private practice setting where the patients have less opportunity to clue each other in on what is going on. J. S. Schimel (1974) and R. J. Marshall (1983) discuss Aichorn's work in greater detail.

Catharsis

Catharsis played an important role in Freud's earlier work. He believed that many of the young women he saw who suffered with hysterical paralysis were sexually inhibited. It was his theory that the paralyzed parts of the body were "cathected" with sexual libidinal energy that was not permitted free expression because of the patient's rigid superego dictates against sexual expression. It was the analyst's job to help such women become more comfortable with their sexual feelings. Such release was then supposed to alleviate and even cure their symptoms. So "liberated" these women no longer needed to utilize such symptoms as hysterical paraplegia to protect themselves from sexual overtures.

A more direct cathartic treatment related to the expression of pent-up feelings from earlier psychological traumas. In this aspect of the theory the individual's symptoms were derived from his or her failure to deal properly with earlier traumas. Especially needed was the opportunity to express the thoughts and feelings attendant to the trauma. Even years later, these suppressed and repressed complexes could contribute to the development and perpetuation of symptoms. The patient was encouraged to re-experience the early trauma (referred to as abreaction) and to release the bottled-up thoughts and feelings that were associated with it (catharsis). The analogy to an abscess is relevant here. The psychiatric disorder was viewed to be the result of the containment of the pathological process into a separate compartment of the psychic structure similar to the encapsulation of an abscess. The psychotherapeutic process of abreaction and catharsis was considered to be analogous to the surgeon's procedure of incision and drainage of the abscess. Although Freud subsequently came to appreciate that things were far more complex, some of his followers continued (and still continue) to view psychopathology in this somewhat simplistic manner. These practitioners are strong proponents of the view that patients should be encouraged to "let out their feelings." Like broken records they are constantly saying to their patients "What are your feelings about that?" and "Tell me your feelings."

The encounter groups of the 1960s and 1970s were very much in the spirit of this philosophy. Patients were encouraged to rant and rave about anything that bothered them, to "let it all hang out." The notion here was that such orgies of ventilation were therapeutic. I believe that such spectacles do not warrant the term therapy. What we want to do in therapy is help people get in touch with their thoughts and feelings—at the very earliest moments—and to direct them in civilized ways toward the sources of their frustration and difficulty. This should be done *before* the anger builds up to the level of rage and fury when the actions taken in association with such violent feelings are not likely to be judicious. In addition, the "let-it-all-hang-out" principle was sometimes used in the service of sadism. Such indiscriminate expression often ill equipped patients in these groups to deal more effectively with others in real life who were not committed to the same philosophy. Still there are physicians who naively subscribe to this belief and will refer patients with the message "He needs someone to talk to" or "He needs someone to let his feelings out on."

With regard to the proper therapeutic use of anger, I like to use the analogy of the tea kettle on a stove. The flames under the kettle cause the water to boil and the steam to be emitted from the spout. If a person has an anger-inhibition problem, one could symbolize it with a cork in the spout, obstructing the release of the anger (boiling water). Under such circumstances one could consider the therapist's job to be that of helping the patient remove the cork to allow the anger to be released. However, I believe this to be a somewhat oversimplified view of the therapeutic process. Removing the cork is only the first step. One still has to deal with a reduction or removal of the frustrations that are generating the anger in the first place (as symbolized by the flames). By connecting a tube from the spout to the flames under the kettle one can extinguish them. Then, there is no frustration, no noxious stimuli, and no anger generated. This is clearly a preferable therapeutic goal.

On occasion I will have an adolescent who uses the session to bombard me with a barrage of vilifications without cessation. Although there is much *Sturm und Drang,* and although it can become tiring to listen to the harangues, there is no question that I am serving, in part, as a safe target for the ventilation of the youngster's anger. I have often wondered in such situations what other functions I am serving, because the youngster voluntarily comes and voluntarily uses the session for this purpose. It is clear that I am a safe target and will not retaliate in ways that teachers, principals, and even parents might consider. At times, I suspect that such youngsters are trying to determine whether I still accept and tolerate them as human beings, in spite of the primitive barrage being directed at me. My "hanging in there" provides reassurance that they are not as vile as they may believe themselves to be. Also, my failure to react punitively may reassure them that their thoughts or feelings are not as dangerous as they might have considered them to be. Although I do not understand completely what has gone on,

I do know that therapists who work with antisocial adolescents have to have "thick skins" and a formidable degree of tolerance for such displays. However, this should not preclude the therapist's making every attempt to understand the sources of the anger and doing everything possible to help the youngster direct the irritation toward the initial source of provocation and to deal with it effectively.

Setting Limits

Children and adolescents most often want to learn what the limits are and most may need limits imposed upon them. Most try to get away with as much as they can and the therapist who does not impose limits may be contributing to the perpetuation of an adolescent's antisocial behavior. A therapist who is of the persuasion that one of the functions of treatment is to allow patients to express themselves fully, without significant interference by the therapist, has a misguided notion of his or her work. One of the purposes of therapy is to help people function better in the real world. The real world is not going to indulge antisocial patients. Rather, the real world may very well reject and even incarcerate antisocial individuals. Learning self-restriction should take place in the therapeutic atmosphere.

When I have a patient who acts out physically and from whom I may fear bodily harm, I inform the youngster at the outset that office treatment is for those who have enough control to inhibit themselves and not act out on their impulses. I let the patient know that if there is such threat to my person or property then I will seriously consider discontinuing office treatment and consider hospitalization. I do not make this statement as an empty threat. It comes from the conviction that a therapist cannot work in a setting where he or she is fearful of bodily harm. In a hospital setting there are certain protections that enable the therapist to work in a more relaxed fashion. One may say that I am threatening the patient here. I am in full agreement that I am. But life is filled with threats. If one doesn't pay one's electric bills, the electric company turns off the electricity. If one doesn't pay the telephone bill, the telephone company turns off the telephone. If one misuses one's drivers license it may be taken away. And a threat of discontinuation of treatment and consideration for hospitalization is in the same category. Although parents may have indulged antisocial behavior and not provided proper and reasonable consequences, this does not mean that the therapist is going to make the same mistake. I have mentioned previously the three-button panel that I have near my seat (fire, police, and medical emergency). I have on a couple of occasions pointed to the buttons, informed the patient that they are functional and have found it useful. Fortunately I have not had to use these buttons to date.

Important Themes to Focus On

It is crucial that the therapist ascertain the main sources of the youngster's anger. The primary purpose of the extended evaluation (Chapter Four) is to ascertain what these factors are and were. The therapist does well to differentiate between contributory factors from outside the home and those from within the home. Such a distinction is important because the therapist is not likely to get very far with the patient if there is extensive focus on the extra-familial factors. Some insight into these contributions is certainly warranted; however, there is little if anything that the therapist can do about these factors from the office setting. I am not suggesting that therapists remove themselves entirely from these extra-familial issues. In fact, they may even wish to devote themselves to changing these environmental factors, and this is certainly a noble and lofty endeavor. I am only stating that such changes involve what may be lifelong efforts and there may be little immediate change brought about by such endeavors. In the office we have to direct our efforts toward changing those things that we *can* (or hope to) change within the patient and family. Because each situation is different, I will present here some of the common themes that come up in individual sessions with antisocial adolescents.

Vengeance   Often the antisocial acting out is a way for such youngsters to wreak vengeance on parents for indignities (real or fantasized) that they may have suffered at their hands. Such youngsters have to be helped to appreciate that no matter how successful they may be in causing their parents pain and retaliation for what they themselves have suffered, they do so at their own expense. They have to be helped to appreciate that they are so blinded by their rage that they do not consider what price they themselves are paying in the service of hurting their parents. We live in a world where "getting even" is considered the macho thing to do. In contrast, standing by and allowing oneself to be subjected to occasional discomforts is often considered to be weak. The youngster has to be helped to appreciate that both sides lose in a war and most victories are Pyrrhic. For youngsters who are not familiar with the origins of the term *Pyrrhic victory* I will tell them about King Pyrrhus who lived in Greece over 2000 years ago. King Pyrrhus was obsessed with battle and drained his country's treasuries in his various conflicts. Once he fought a particularly horrible battle against the Romans at Asculum. Although he won the battle, he lost his most important officers and most of his men. At the end of the battle Pyrrhus is said to have declared, "One more such victory and I am lost." After telling this story I will try to get the youngster to relate it to his or her own situation. This is just another example of how much I prefer to rely on metaphor, allegory, parable, etc. (Chapter Five) in order to get across my points in the treatment of my patients.

Slavish Dependence on Peers   Another area I find useful to focus on in individual work with antisocial adolescents is that of refusing to go along with the crowd. Adolescents, their professions of independence notwithstanding, are basically sheep. The notion of being different from others will horrify most of them. They will often allow themselves to be swept up into dangerous situations rather than stand up and refuse to go along with the crowd. They have to be helped to have the courage to be truly independent, buck the tide, and not do that which, they know in their hearts, is wrong or dangerous. They have to be helped to appreciate that the person who does this is far braver than the one who blindly goes along with the crowd. Many youngsters involve themselves in smoking, drinking alcohol, and taking drugs in these kinds of situations. At the outset they basically do not particularly like these substances and may even detest them. However, in order not to be singled out as different they tolerate the discomforts attendant to their use during the initial phases. Once they have desensitized themselves to the noxious aspects of their utilization they feel good about themselves because they are now accepted by the "in" group. The next step, of course, is addiction. Then—and this may take many years—when they realize that they have been injudicious it may be too late, so addicted have they become.

I have literature which I will frequently give to adolescents describing the dangers of alcohol, marijuana and other drugs, as well as cigarette smoking. Unfortunately, these have not proved too useful. Delusions of invulnerability are generally so strong that these youngsters do not believe that they themselves can suffer the consequences of the utilization of these substances. Sometimes they are introduced into using them by a dare from some group leader and his or her followers. Such youngsters have to be helped to appreciate that it is braver to defy a dare than to submit to an injudicious one. At first the therapist may have great difficulty convincing the youngster of this obvious fact, but this should not discourage the effort.

Fight vs. Flight. Macho vs. Chickenshit Antisocial adolescents are generally unappreciative of the judiciousness of the flight reaction. They are most often products of a society that views flight to be a sign of cowardice and fight the only proper reaction to danger. I try to help such youngsters appreciate that the flight reaction is also part of natural survival mechanisms and that all animals in the world utilize each, depending upon the situation. Both serve to preserve life. I try to impress upon the youngster that we human beings somehow have not given proper respect to the flight reaction. I believe that women in our society are much more respectful of it than men. In demonstrating the point I will often say: "When a rabbit runs away from a wolf the other animals who observe the rabbit fleeing do not generally call him 'chicken.' " I may describe the appeasement gestures found in certain lower animals. One of the best examples is the one utilized by wolves. When two wolves are fighting, they generally try to bite each other in vulnerable places—especially the neck. In the course of the fighting, at a point when it becomes apparent to both which one is going to be the victor, the animal who is on the brink of being killed will turn its neck to such a position that the area of the jugular vein and carotid artery is directly exposed to the jaws of the victorious one. This is generally referred to as an *appeasement gesture*. One would think that the victorious animal would now seize this opportunity to bite the subdued animal in the neck and end the fight instantly. However, he does no such thing. He pulls back and allows the subdued animal to escape. In fact, he cannot do otherwise. His withdrawal is locked into his genetic programming. It is a lifesaving maneuver for the subdued animal and he too has no choice but to utilize the appeasement gesture when he is on the brink of victory. I try to help the patient appreciate the importance of this maneuver, especially with regard to its lifesaving function. I emphasize that appeasement sometimes enables an individual to avoid a conflict that might result in loss of limb and even life.

In the course of my discussion I might relate to the youngster an experience I had with my son Andrew when he was about seven or eight years old. I had taken him to an amusement park. At lunch time the restaurant was quite crowded. Andrew sat down to reserve a table and I went to the counter to buy our hotdogs. There was no particular line and people were crowded about, calling out their orders to the people behind the counter. As I was standing there, it became quite clear that the young man serving hotdogs was playing a sadistic game with the customers. He was purposely avoiding giving any recognition to those who came earlier and was randomly accepting orders from the crowd. I, and a number of the other people who were trying to order, became increasingly frustrated and resentful. At one point a newcomer, who was at least three or four inches taller than I, younger, more muscular and certainly stronger, was immediately offered service by the young sadist behind the counter. The chosen one was there long enough to realize what game was being played and snickered joyfully when his request was elicited.

At that point, the anger already building up in me to a high level suddenly boiled over and I yelled to the employee: "You sadistic bastard, you know damn well that that son-of-a-bitch over there just came here...." Before I could say anything else I was confronted by the big man, red with rage, ready to lunge at me, and screaming out: "Who the hell do you think you are calling me a son-of-a-bitch? You take that back. If you don't apologize I'll beat the shit out of you." The man was ready to lunge at my neck. I had already had two hospitalizations for herniated cervical discs and I immediately recognized that the man could easily injure me for life, and possibly make me a paraplegic. But even if that were not the case, I would have responded in the same way. In a voice loud enough to make a scene that would attract as much attention as possible I responded, "Sir, you are correct! I insulted you and I had no business doing so. My apology and these people around here are all witnesses to it." At that point, the man's hands dropped to his side. There was about a 10-second silence, and he walked off and asked for his hotdogs.

I then returned to my seat and said this to Andrew: "Andrew, I want you to always remember what just happened. I hope you'll never forget what you just saw. Most fathers would not have done what I just did. Most fathers would have thought that it would be "chicken" of them to apologize to that man, especially when their sons were around. They would think that only cowards would apologize in such a situation and that they would be a poor example for their sons. I believe that I set a good example for you by what I just did. There are times when it's smart to fight, and there are other times when it's smart to run away. There are times when it's smart to apologize, and there are times when it's stupid to apologize. This was a time when it was smart to apologize. That man was wrong and he knew he was wrong. I made a mistake too. I shouldn't have called him that name. I could have thought of it all I wanted to, but it was a big mistake to say it. There are lots of crazy people in this world, and you have to be careful, or terrible things could happen to you. You know about all the trouble I've had with my neck. If that man had tried to choke me he might have broken my neck, and he might have even killed me. When I apologized I saved myself a lot of trouble, and possibly my life."

I believe that my son found this a useful experience. It may be of interest to the reader to know that I, too, found it a useful experience in that I have never again called a stranger a sadist or a son-of-a-bitch. I believe, also, that describing the experience to a patient has therapeutic benefits. It not only communicates the message of the wisdom of flight in certain situations but does so in a way that is more likely to have clout than a simple statement of the principle. Moreover, it provides an opportunity for communicating to the patient that I, too, am not perfect, I "lost my cool," and that I at times act irrationally. I thereby hope to counteract the risk that

the patient will idealize me and suffer the antitherapeutic consequences of this view.

In the context of my discussions on fight and flight I will focus
on the macho image that boys and men in our society are encouraged to assume. I will try to help the youngster appreciate that the
macho stance—especially when it has become a deep-seated personality pattern—is generally an attempt to compensate for feelings of
inadequacy. I try to help the youngster appreciate that true strength
does not have to be advertised. Of course, I am working against the
powerful influences of society, the military, the advertising industry, women who believe that macho men are more sexually potent,
and a variety of other cultural influences. These problems notwithstanding, the therapist does well to try to help antisocial youngsters
appreciate the futility and absurdity of the macho stance.

Sports Sports can provide a healthy outlet for the antisocial
adolescent's pent-up hostility. And this value of sports can be
enjoyed at both the participant and observer levels. Like profanity,
I view sports to be one of the world's greatest inventions. Both allow
for the expression of hostility in a way that does not necessarily
cause physical harm. Although some sports expose the youngster to
the risk of such harm, the therapist should recognize that this
drawback is small compared to the formidable benefits that the
antisocial youngster may derive from involvement in competitive
sports. In Chapter One I quoted a section from D. J. Holmes (1964)
in which he describes the salutary effects of competitive basketball
on a group of boys in a residential treatment center. The reader does
well to refer back to that extensive quotation in that it is an excellent
statement of the salubrious effects of competitive sports. I believe,
however, that there are certain competitive sports in which the
hostility element is so strong that I would not recommend them.
There is no doubt that boxing, for example, causes brain damage,
subdural hematomas, and other forms of head injury. Every year
many young men die in the ring.

I recall many years ago, while serving as a military psychiatrist,
seeing a young man of 19 who sought psychiatric consultation
because he feared he might murder someone. He was brought up in
an inner-city ghetto and spent most of his early and mid-adolescent
period in gyms, especially in training to be a boxer. When he
entered the service he did so with the understanding that he would

be allowed to involve himself primarily in boxing. This promise was kept (unusual for the service) and all was going well with him. However, about one month prior to the consultation he was informed that he was being reassigned and could no longer serve to represent his unit in boxing competitions with other units. His appeal to his superiors that they honor the original commitment made by the recruiting officer was to no avail. In subsequent weeks he found himself becoming increasingly enraged, was filled with homicidal ideation, and feared that he might kill someone. When I saw him in consultation he stated openly that he recognized that boxing protected him from murdering people and that in the ring he could let out the pent-up rage that engulfed him. Fortunately, as a physician and officer, I had more clout with his superiors than he, and I was successful in getting them to reassign this man to another unit where he could function as a boxer. I went so far to state that if this assignment was not made the man should be discharged from the military because there was a real danger that he would indeed murder someone.

I am also hesitant about football. I recognize this is an unpopular thing to say but I believe that pathological factors are operative in many (but certainly not all) of those who are committed deeply to this sport. Many antisocial patients do not readily enter into sports. Some feel like "fish out of water" when they join a team because the other youngsters speak a different language and are turned on by different things. If the therapist is successful in getting the antisocial youngster so involved he or she will be performing a valuable service.

Worthy Causes   Another vehicle for anger release that can be useful for antisocial adolescents is active participation in worthy social causes. Military service is an example of this principle, yet I am not recommending it as the first "line of defense." One of my reasons for hesitating is my belief that it is rare for military combat to be "worthy." Furthermore, recommending military service is a risky business for a therapist, especially because it may result in the youngster's being killed. Although this is an unlikely outcome of the recommendation, it must not be ignored completely. Accordingly, it is safest to make this recommendation "between wars." Also not to be ignored when making such a recommendation is the fact that military service is, without question, one of the most efficient and effective ways for antisocial individuals to act out their anger, rage, and even fury—and still enjoy social sanction for their behavior. Some are given medals for killing. In my two-year stint as an army psychiatrist I met a number of individuals who were well decorated heroes in World War II and the Korean War. Many (but certainly not all) were miserable in peacetime. The thought of war would make them joyful and I remember clearly their glee, in 1961, when the Berlin Wall was erected and we had the "good fortune" to be in Germany at the time when World War III was on the verge of breaking out. (I, in contrast, was ready to start taking antidepressant medication.)

Demonstrations in support of various worthy causes (or those that the youngster considers worthy) can also serve to release pent-up anger and reduce thereby antisocial behavior. This is especially attractive to adolescents who are rebelling anyway. Unfortunately, many antisocial adolescents are not particularly "socially minded." They are much more against society than for it, and many believe that the best thing to do with their anger is to destroy society rather than to correct it. Although channeling such antisocial youngsters' anger into these healthier directions may be difficult, the therapist should still make attempts to do so.

Dating One factor that may be operative in the antisocial boy's hostility is sexual frustration. For many of these youngsters sexual tenderness and the macho image do not fit well together. Accordingly, they deprive themselves of sexual gratification and the resulting frustration contributes to the build-up of their anger. Therapists do well to attempt to discuss girls and sex with these boys. Often, they are shy about doing so, their rough exterior notwithstanding. Sometimes group therapy can be helpful in that once in the presence of girls—especially in a situation where other boys are expressing tenderness—they may be able to let down their guard and allow themselves such displays of affection as well. If the therapist has the opportunity to speak about a situation which caused him or her some sexual excitation during adolescence, the youngster may become more comfortable expressing the sexual desires that must be present at some level.

The Talking, Feeling, and Doing Game Younger adolescents (ages 13 through 15) who may not be particularly receptive to direct talk may find useful *The Talking, Feeling, and Doing Game* (1973b). There are certain cards that are particularly useful for antisocial youngsters and may serve as excellent catalysts for bringing up pertinent issues for discussion. Some examples:

> What do you think about a boy who lets his dog make a mess in the house? What should his parents do?
>
> What is one of the smartest things a person can do? Why?
>
> What is the worst thing you can do to someone?
>
> A girl was the only one in the class not invited to a birthday party. Why do you think she wasn't invited?
>
> Tell about the worst mistake you ever made in your whole life.
>
> What is the worst thing a child can say to his or her father?
>
> Say three curse words. What do you think of people who use these words?
>
> You accidentally break a window and you are quite sure that no one saw you do it. Tell about what you would then do.
>
> How do you feel when you see a bully picking on someone?
>
> What is the worst thing that ever happened to you in your whole life?
>
> A boy came home from school with a black eye. What had happened?
>
> Name three things that could make a person angry.
>
> What was the worst punishment you ever got in your whole life? What had you done wrong?
>
> How do you feel when a person with whom you are playing a game starts to cheat?
>
> You are standing in line to buy something and a child pushes him- or herself in front of you. Show what you would do.
>
> You are standing in line to buy something and an adult pushes him- or herself in front of you. Show what you would do.
>
> Make believe someone grabbed something of yours. Show what you would do.
>
> What is the most selfish thing you ever did? Make believe you are doing that thing now.

Tell about something that makes you angry. Act out what you would do if that thing were happening right now.

Make believe you are doing a bad thing.

Make believe you are smoking a cigarette. What do you think about people who smoke?

Make believe you are having an argument with someone. With whom are you arguing? What are you arguing about?

Make believe you are doing a sneaky thing.

Make believe you are playing a dirty trick on someone. What do you think about people who do that?

Make believe that you just met a bully. Show what you would do.

Group Therapy

Technical Considerations   In Chapter Eleven I have discussed group therapy in general. Here I comment on the specific value of group therapy in the treatment of antisocial adolescents. As mentioned, it is preferable that the antisocial youngsters be in the minority in the adolescent group. If they are in the majority then the "bad apples" are likely to spoil the good ones. In a setting in which the antisocial types are outnumbered by youngsters with other kinds of problems antisocial youngsters may come to appreciate how narrow are their repertoire of things to talk about. Those on drugs soon bore the others with their incessant repetition of the same discussions regarding the number of "trips" they have taken and the different kinds of drugs they have tried. Although those who engage in antisocial behavior such as theft, reckless driving, drunken driving sprees, etc. may have more "adventurous" material to talk about, they soon also seem repetitious to the more "straight" observers. Whereas I generally have an after-group for patients in my adult group, I do not have an after group for the adolescents. This would be especially dangerous when antisocial adolescents are in the group because they may take the after-group opportunity to exploit the straight patients in the group.

One fascinating phenomenon that I have observed in the group therapy of antisocial adolescents is the tendency of many such youngsters not to practice what they preach. On many occasions I have seen one patient tell another about the risks and drawbacks of what he or she is doing. In the sermon the listener is given traditional straight advice and encouraged to mend his or her ways. It is important for the therapist to appreciate that in order for a person to be antisocial he or she must first know what is social. Accordingly, when the therapist tells antisocial youngsters that they are being "bad" and doing the "wrong" things, he or she is not providing any new information. In fact, the therapist may be even providing cues for new forms of antisocial behavior that the youngster didn't think of previously. What may be happening when antisocial adolescent A preaches propriety to antisocial adolescent B is that A is speaking to his or her projected self and vicariously trying to bring about a change in a part of his or her own personality. The group also has the effect of impressing upon antisocial youngsters the effects of their behavior on others. Those who have greater facility with experiencing guilt and putting themselves in another person's position are likely to confront the antisocial youngsters with the effects they have on others. And this can contribute to the growth of the antisocial patient's internal guilt-evoking mechanisms. Often they do not get this feedback elsewhere because they surround themselves with other psychopathic types. In the group they are captive audience for receiving these kinds of messages.

Clinical Example   At this point I present a vignette that demonstrates well some important points regarding the group therapy of antisocial adolescents. In this particular meeting only four of the six group members were present. All four were boys. Tom, age 17, suffered with a moderately severe problem of antisocial behavior. He frequently stole from stores in which he had taken part-time jobs. He cheated on tests, stole money from his parents, and on three occasions had forged checks. He had little if any guilt or remorse over his behavior and rationalized his activities by claiming that most of his friends engaged in similar behavior. Nick, age 16, had a problem in impulse control in that he would blurt out what was on his mind without thinking about the impact on others of what he was doing or saying. He was extremely bright, but was unmotivated to do his schoolwork and so was getting poorer grades than he would otherwise have obtained. Ted, age 16, was also very bright. He came to treatment because of withdrawal from peers and difficulty making friends. He was a quiet, "uptight" youngster, who had trouble asserting himself and expressing openly his thoughts and feelings. Harry, age 15, came to treatment because of a sexual orientation problem. He found himself with both homosexual and heterosexual inclinations and, although ambivalent, entered treatment in the hope that he would go the heterosexual route. He was a strongly religious Catholic, much more religious than his parents. He was seriously thinking of entering the priesthood someday and it was clear from the outset that this career choice was, in part, made because it would protect him from any kind of sexual activity, either homo- or heterosexual.

Here I will focus on one of the group therapy sessions that was particularly useful for Tom, the boy with antisocial behavior. When the session opened Harry showed the group a copy of his school newspaper in which he was quoted. The school was a Catholic parochial school and the student body had been asked who they would choose to be if they had to be transformed into another individual. The newspaper selected what they considered to be some of the best responses. Harry's response was basically a nonresponse. In it he claimed that he was quite satisfied with himself and that he would not want to be anyone else. He focused on the fact that he was leading a good Christian life and that he was quite satisfied with how things were going for him. In the ensuing group discussion it was pointed out to Harry that his answer was basically a cop-out in that he had not really responded to the question asked of who he would choose to be if he *had* to be transformed into another person. He ignored the element in the question that *required* a transformation into *someone else*. In the service of extracting therapeutic mileage from the question, I asked Harry to try to answer the question and to try to select a specific person. I broadened it and suggested that he could choose anyone from the whole history of the world, living or dead, past or present, real or fictional. After some hesitation Harry answered: "Well, if I really had to be someone else, I would choose to be St. Anthony. He devoted himself to God and the poor. He lived in the 1200s and his parents were very rich. His parents were very resistant to his decision to become a priest. But he decided to become a monk and a priest. He gave his money to the poor and devoted his life to the poor. He went around preaching the gospels and carrying out the wishes of Jesus Christ. He lived in poverty and gave to the poor. He trusted in God in every way. He died when he was about 35. After that they made him a saint."

The other members of the group had little to say about Harry's response. Accordingly, I decided to go around the group and have each other member say which person he would choose if he had to be so transformed. Whereas in working with adults I generally would not be so structured, I will frequently utilize more directive techniques in my work with adolescents, because many of them need structure and drawing out. Accordingly, I turned to Tom and asked him the same question. His response: "I'd be H. Ross Perot. He's one of the richest guys on earth. He's got hundreds of millions of dollars. He may even be a billionaire. There's a book called *Where Eagles Dare* that tells about him. He comes from Texas. He made his money in computers. The man's a genius for making money. He owns so much of the Chevrolet company that they were scared that he would take control of the company so they bought him out."

The group had little to say about Tom's response so I turned to Ted for his answer to the question. This was Ted's response: "I would want to be Henry David Thoreau. He took two years out and lived at Walden Pond. It was very quiet and peaceful there and he got in touch with nature. He was a rugged individualist. He believed in civil disobedience if you were angry at the government and wanted to improve it."

Again there was little response to Ted's answer and so I asked Nick whom he would choose. Nick's response: "I would want to be Peter Gabriel, the rock star. He used to belong to the group *Genesis*, but then quit and has gone solo. His album *So* was a big hit last year. He gave away all of his money for worthy causes. He gave a lot of money to Amnesty International and to the World Music Organization. He gave away so much money that he went broke. So he made more records and gave more concerts and now he has more money."

Again, there was little response to Nick's answer. I then asked the group if any generalizations could be made about the four responses and whether the individuals could learn something about themselves from their answers. It became quickly apparent to all four members of the group (and myself) that all but Tom had chosen individuals who had devoted their lives to worthy causes. Harry's choice, St. Anthony, epitomized self-sacrifice for the betterment of others. Nick's choice, Peter Gabriel, was also an individual who gave unstintingly of his wealth. Ted's choice, Henry David Thoreau, was an individual who devoted himself to the betterment of mankind. When the group attempted to point out to Tom that the person he chose epitomized insatiable greed, Tom rationalized his choice by claiming that everyone wants to be rich and that all the people in the world would want to be H. Ross Perot if they could be. He was at first incredulous that the others were not committed to this value. He was dubious that the others would *really* choose to be individuals who were so self-abnegating. Having associated primarily with peers who were similarly psychopathic, he found it hard to believe that the rest of the world was not like this. Although Tom was clearly upset by the group's confrontations, I did not have the feeling that very much "sunk in," even though we spent about a half-hour on his response.

Near the end of the group meeting Harry asked me whom I would choose to be if I had to be so transformed. Were this an adult group I probably would have hesitated because the patients were not there to analyze me but to analyze themselves. For the adolescent group, however—where the emulation-identification element is quite important in treatment—I decided to answer the question. My response: "If I had to be changed, I would want to be Thomas Alva Edison. He's always been a hero of mine. He was a poor boy who through dint of hard work throughout the course of his life made many valuable contributions to mankind. And these were not only things that gave pleasure, like the phonograph record and the moving picture camera, but things that also helped save lives. For example, prior to the invention of the electric light it was very difficult to perform operations on people. Candlelight was hardly adequate, even many candles. They would often have to do operations out in the open at midday, often on rooftops. Obviously, if clouds came over or if it started to rain then things got fouled up. Also, there was a greater chance of infection." The group did not dwell long on my response, but my suspicion is that some seeds were planted regarding the work ethic and contributions to society.

In Tom's ensuing individual session we went over the points made in the group session more carefully. I repeated what I had said many times over with regard to Tom's rationalization that everyone else in the world shared his values. I granted that there were millions who did indeed view multimillionaires as being extra-special people, worthy of our emulation and admiration. But I also impressed upon him that there were millions of others—including people like Nick, Ted, and Harry—who were not in particular admiration of those who were wealthy and did not see money as an end in itself. I informed him that I considered obsessive materialism and exhibitionistic consumption to be psychiatric disorders, that is, a disease. When a disease becomes widespread, it is still a disease. When polio is epidemic it is still a disease. AIDS is still a disease even though it has become epidemic. This point was particularly difficult for Tom to appreciate because of a lifelong worship of the dollar bill.

Although Tom's defenses against these confrontations were strong, the group session represented a kind of breakthrough for him, which was the first step toward his gaining insight into his pathological attitudes toward money. It was in a setting where he had direct experience with others of different values, others with whom he had come to form meaningful relationships, that this breakthrough was possible. Derivative discussions were divided into two categories: 1) His values, i.e. what he considered good and bad, right and wrong. His particular focus was on materialism and its futility. 2) His morals, with particular emphasis on his lack of guilt over unethical and illegal activities. In discussion on both of these areas we made frequent reference to the other three group members and the values and morals exhibited in their choices.

In Harry's private session, as well, there was a subsequent discussion of his choice, St. Anthony. I communicated to him my respect for his selection, especially with regard to the sympathy for the poor and unfortunate. However, the choice also led to a discussion of his aspirations to be a priest and its relationship to his sexual problems. At the time of the discussion Harry was involved with a girl and starting to enjoy the pleasures of sex. There was no question that these enjoyable experiences were contributing to his ambivalence about his decision to become a priest. Another relevant issue that emerged from the discussion related to St. Anthony's parents. Harry saw the similarity between St. Anthony's parents and his own in that both sets of parents were resistant to their sons' becoming priests. Harry was well aware that his parents, although Catholic, were very upset about his career decision because they recognized that it served, in part, as a vehicle for suppressing his homosexuality. This then opened up the issue of defiance and rebellion against parents as a factor in his career choice.

In Ted's individual sessions we discussed his choice of Thoreau. I complimented him on his choice because Thoreau epitomized many of the best values of humankind. Ted originally wished to emphasize Thoreau's "rugged individualism" and his civil disobedience. He spoke about how much he admired Thoreau's willingness to stand up for his opinions even if it meant going to jail. He spoke about an incident in which Thoreau, when jailed for civil disobedience, was visited by Ralph Waldo Emerson who said to Thoreau, "What are you doing in here?" Thoreau answered, "What are *you* doing *out* there?" It was clear, however, that Ted was very much the opposite of Thoreau with regard to self-assertion and forthrightness. Although he admired these qualities in Thoreau, he certainly had a long way to go in this direction. Ted did, however, recognize that his choice related to his isolation and withdrawal from people, something that Thoreau had made into an asset. In the ensuing discussion, Ted was helped to appreciate that he was trying to make an asset out of his liability, i.e., trying to view as a strength his withdrawal from others. Although Thoreau may have put this to good use, in Ted's case it was clearly a liability. Ted also mentioned in his individual session his hesitation to tell Tom how revolting he felt his choice was and how alienated he was by it. I encouraged him to speak up in the following group session not only for his own benefit (in that it would provide him with another experience in expressing himself) but for Tom's benefit as well (in that it would provide Tom with another confrontation with an individual who was not genuinely in awe of billionaires, conspicuous consumers, and those obsessed with exhibitionistic materialism).

In Nick's individual session we spoke about his choice of Peter Gabriel. I complimented him on the sensitivity to the feelings of others implied in his choice and then discussed Nick's own problems in this area. Although he stated that he would want to be a person who gave to others in a self-sacrificial fashion, out of his appreciation for their plight, Nick had to agree that he sometimes had deficiencies in this area and that the choice provided him some compensation for his own weaknesses. Nick, as might have been expected, was most forthright in his condemnation of Tom—in part because he was not sensitive to any pain or embarrassment he might cause Tom by his confrontation. But for Tom's purposes (from the therapeutic point of view) Nick's insensitivity was useful in that a more inhibited and more sensitive person would not have come forth with the critical confrontation.

The reader may have noted that I complimented Nick, Ted, and Harry on their choices, but did not compliment Tom. I am very conservative with regard to paying patients compliments. There are many therapists who consider praising patients to be an important part of treatment. There is no question that many of these go overboard and their compliments then have little value. This is especially the case when the compliments become effusive, patronizing, or condescending. A rare but well-focused compliment is likely to have significant clout and thereby genuinely contribute to enhancement of the patient's self-esteem. Low self-esteem is one of the central factors contributing to the development of psychogenic psychopathology. Anything the therapist can do to enhance a patient's self-worth is likely to be therapeutic. Even though the compliment may not directly relate to the patient's symptoms it will still be useful, because enhanced self-worth of any kind will contribute to the erosion of the factors at the foundation of the symptomatology.

Behavior Modification

In Chapter Fourteen, in the section on hospitalization of antisocial acting-out patients, I will discuss in detail my views on behavior modification as a treatment modality for psychopathic youngsters. I refer the reader to that section for a full statement of my views on that issue. Here I will focus on a few important points. Although behavior modification techniques may be useful for the treatment of phobias, and various types of anxiety and panic states, I believe that such an approach can intensify antisocial behavior. My main reason for this view is that when utilized in its pure form (without meaningful and ongoing concomitant psychotherapy) it does not direct its attention to the creation of inner controls based on morals and guilt; rather, it focuses on avoidance of external punishment as a way of modifying behavior. Under the controlled situation of a behavior modification program—especially one administered in a hospital—the patient may very well appear to improve because the punishments are predictably going to be given. However, once out of the controlled situation the patient is likely to "bounce back" and exhibit psychopathic behavior because the monitors providing 24-hour vigils of the patient are no longer present. Because the treatment program had not directed itself primarily to the development of inner controls, monitored by inner feelings of guilt and shame, the individual is not likely to maintain the ostensible improvement.

ADVISING PARENTS OF
ANTISOCIAL YOUNGSTERS

The Therapist's Relationship
With the Parents

It behooves the therapist to do everything possible to establish a good relationship with both parents of the antisocial adolescent. And this holds regardless of the marital status of the parents. Although this principle is applicable to all children in therapy, it is even more crucial in work with antisocial adolescents. When treating youngsters with other disorders, a compromise in the relationship with the parents (if not too serious) may still allow for successful individual psychotherapy with the youngster. This is possible because one might still be able to have a reasonably good relationship with the youngster in spite of mild to moderate compromises in the parental relationships with the therapist. Because the antisocial adolescent is likely to be antagonistic to and more seriously compromised in forming a relationship with the therapist, involvement with the parents is more crucial if one is to be successful in the treatment of these youngsters. When one is dealing with a situation in which the youngster's involvement is seriously compromised and that of the parents is also deficient, then therapy is not likely to succeed or even commence.

In the initial and extended diagnostic evaluations (Chapters

Three and Four) it is important for the therapist to learn about those situations in the youngster's family and environment that may have contributed to the development of the antisocial behavior. Some of the more common situational factors have been described in detail in Chapter Two. These must be identified as well as possible and every attempt made to reduce or eliminate them. Sometimes the parents can change their tactics and approaches by simple counseling. The behavior is consciously controllable and the parents have been misguided regarding their approach to the problem. For example, the parents may not have made a proper differentiation between antisocial behavior that is harmless and that which is not. They may be coming down heavily on a youngster who insists upon wearing sloppy clothing, sporting an "offbeat" hairstyle, or keeping a room that resembles a pigsty. If the parents can be brought to the point of appreciating that these are innocuous forms of rebellion— and that they should be grateful that the youngster is not resorting to more dangerous forms—then they might be convinced to pull back.

There are other situations, however, in which the parents' contributions to the patient's symptoms are more deep-seated, and therefore less likely to change by simple advice, confrontation, and counseling. In such cases therapy for one or both of the parents may be warranted. The ideal situation is one in which the same therapist treats the youngster and both parents. Some psychoanalysts, especially those of classical persuasion, would view such an arrangement with horror and be unable to see any possible good coming from it. They would have no problem referring each of the two parents to two separate analysts, producing a situation in which three people are seeing three different analysts who may never speak to one another. Whatever benefits may be derived from each of these individual personal relationships (and I do not deny that there may be some), these advantages are more than outweighed by the disadvantages of such an arrangement. New subsystems are set up in the family and these are not necessarily healthy (even though genuine psychoanalysts may be members). The arrangement produces new "secrets," new rivalries and jealousies—all of which the family does not need. More important, the splitting arrangement deprives each therapist of the opportunity to observe interactions among the significant figures in the family and also deprives the youngster's therapist of first-hand information about what is going on in the parents' lives. Even in situations where the therapists communicate with one another, the information is generally not as direct, accurate, and rich as that which is to be gained from the same therapist working with all three. I recognize that there are situations in which this arrangement is not viable. The most blatant example would be one in which one of the parents is having an affair that is not known to the other. Under these circumstances, it is probably better (if not crucial) that the parents see separate therapists.

Structure and Coercion

Although adolescents usually complain that they are not given enough "freedom" and that they want their independence without noxious parental restrictions, there is another part of them that craves for parental guidelines, structure, and even coercion. As mentioned previously, many adolescents do better when they can rationalize their submissiveness by claiming to all that they have been "forced" into doing something. Many youngsters need this excuse in order to provide for themselves a face-saving excuse for "submitting" to treatment. The realities are that if an adolescent really does not want to come for therapy, there is nothing the parents can do to force it. They cannot drag the youngster bodily to treatment, and even if they were foolish enough to utilize such a maneuver, the competent therapist is not likely to attempt treatment under such circumstances. The parents might, however, use such coercive techniques as threatening to withhold allowances, "ground" the patient, etc. if he or she does not attend therapy. If the youngster is making good use of the sessions, in spite of such coercive techniques, then one might continue with such an arrangement and advise the parents that they should continue to provide such threats because the youngster needs them to justify his or her involvement. However, if the youngster submits to the threats and remains silent, or does not use the therapy in a meaningful way, then the treatment should be discontinued after a reasonable trial.

A number of years ago I had an experience with a patient that demonstrates well the need of the adolescent antisocial patient for parental restriction and threats. First, a little geography lesson will help the reader understand this clinical vignette better. I live and practice in Bergen County, in northern New Jersey. The area is basically a suburban community, northwest of Manhattan Island in New York City. The *Bergen Pines Hospital* is a central receiving hospital that includes a psychiatric ward for acute emergencies and short-term treatment. My patient, a 15-year-old girl with severe antisocial behavior problems lived in Bergen County, in one of the communities near my office. Her mother had a close friend who lived in New York City. This friend had a daughter, approximately the same age as my patient, who was also a close friend of my patient. These friends lived in mid-town Manhattan. Greenwich Village, a section of Manhattan, is located near the southern part of the island, about four miles from mid-town. So much for the geography lesson.

My patient, whom I will call Joan, was quite angry at her parents. Her father, a heavy smoker, suffered with lung cancer and, at the time of the incident to be described here, was in what could best be called the pre-terminal phase of his illness. He was only able to work a couple of hours a day but was still at home. It was clear that Joan was furious at him for "leaving her." The mother was a somewhat disorganized person who raised Joan on empty threats and inconsistent disciplinary policies. One day, after about four months of treatment, I received a telephone call from the mother who was in a state of agitation. She told me that Joan and she had had a fight and that Joan packed her bags and while leaving the house said to her: "I've had it. I'm leaving here forever. I'm never coming home again. I'm going out and I'm doing *my thing*. I'm going to do just what I want, when I want it. Sex, drugs, or anything else. I'm going to be a hippie and do my own thing. Name the drug and I'll take it. I'm going to drink and fuck everyone in sight: homosexual, heterosexual, or bisexual. If it feels good I'll do it. I'm going down to Greenwich Village where the people really know how to live." And, just before she slammed the door, she said to her mother, "And the only thing that'll get me back here is if Dr. Gardner sends out the police to take me to *Bergen Pines Hospital*." The mother then told me that about an hour later she received a telephone call from Joan, who was then at the home of their friends in mid-town Manhattan. She informed me that Joan then said to her, "I'm just calling to tell you that if you think I've changed my mind about going down to Greenwich Village, you're wrong! So get that stupid idea out of your head. And as I said to you before, the only thing that'll get me to change my mind is if Dr. Gardner sends the police out after me to commit me to *Bergen Pines Hospital.*" The mother then, still quite upset, asked me what she should do.

I asked the mother how long it had been since the telephone call. She informed me that Joan had called her only a minute previously and had hung up on her after the completion of the aforementioned message. I told the mother to call Joan back *immediately* and to tell her that if she wasn't home in two hours I, personally, would send the police to pick her up and have her committed to *Bergen Pines Hospital.* I told the mother that we should waste no time talking about my reasons for the suggestion, but to do what I said immediately and then we would talk about it subsequently. Accordingly, the mother called Joan and, not surprisingly, she was still at her friend's home. The mother conveyed to her my message and, again not surprisingly, Joan was home in about an hour. During the next couple of days she ranted on to her friends about what a cruel, sadistic animal I was and how I threatened to have her locked up, put in a straitjacket, in a padded cell, in *Bergen Pines Hospital* if she didn't come home. She told them that a person would have to be crazy to use me as a psychiatrist. (Interestingly, Joan continued to see me.) Her basic portrayal of the situation was such that her friends had to agree that she acted most judiciously under the circumstances, because not to return home would clearly have been a misguided choice. All basically agreed that it's better to suffer the indignities of returning home than to find oneself locked up in a padded cell on the psycho ward at *Bergen Pines Hospital.*

Now to explain my actions. First, I have absolutely no power to commit anyone to *Bergen Pines Hospital* (or any other hospital). I cannot say to men in white coats that they should put a particular individual in a straitjacket, drag her off against her will, and lock her in a padded cell. And I believe that at some level the patient was aware as well that I had no such authority. I speculated that as she crossed the George Washington Bridge into New York City she began to have second thoughts about her course of action. The prospect of going to Greenwich Village and involving herself in a program of drug abuse and sexual promiscuity was basically quite frightening to her. In fact, the prospect of merely roaming the streets of Greenwich Village alone was also, I suspected, a source of great anxiety to her. But a 15-year-old cannot come home crawling, and beseechingly say to her mother, "I'm sorry Mommy for what I said. I really am scared about going down to Greenwich Village and doing all those things I threatened to do. Please forgive me. Please let me come home." Three-year-olds talk that way, not 15-year-olds. Adolescents are too "mature," "grown up," and "independent" to speak that way.

But Joan had to find a face-saving way of getting home and the Dr. Gardner-will-commit-me-to-*Bergen-Pines-Hospital* scenario served this end. Accordingly, I provided her with the excuse she needed and enabled her to return home without shame or loss of self-esteem. One of the worst things I could have said would have been that I have no power to commit her and that Joan should be allowed to go to Greenwich Village and have the living experience that life there is not as joyous as she anticipated. As the reader well knows by this time, I am a strong proponent of the living experience notion as an important element in the psychotherapeutic process. However, one should not go too far with this concept. One doesn't sit by when patients are on the verge of committing suicide. Nor does one sit by and do nothing and allow people to have experiences that may prove to be extremely detrimental and may cause lifelong grief. And acquiring a sexually transmitted disease, becoming addicted to drugs, or placing oneself in a situation where one may become mugged, raped, or otherwise exploited is not the kind of living experience that patients need. In short, Joan needed guidance, structure, and coercion and in this situation both I and the mother provided it.

Related to the issue of parents' providing structure and coercion is the one of parents' clearly differentiating between those aspects of their youngsters' lives that they can control and those that they cannot. In Chapter Twelve I presented a lecture ("spiel") that I recommend parents provide their adolescent youngsters. This speech is especially appropriate to the antisocial adolescent in that many of the factors dealt with therein relate to these patients' problems. In essence, the speech involves the parents' making specific statements of the things that they can control (within the home) and those things that they cannot control (outside the home). They can "lay down the law" regarding what goes on in the home, who enters, what places of privacy will be respected and which ones will not, and what degree of the adolescents' antisocial behavior will be tolerated. The lecture also makes reference to some of the underlying psychodynamic factors that are operative in bringing about antisocial behavior, factors which parents and antisocial children should discuss. Therapists do well to utilize these same principles in their therapeutic work.

Changing Friends

Most (in fact, practically all) parents of my patients want quick cures. In fact, the most common reason for discontinuing treatment is disappointment over the fact that I do not provide this kind of magic. One of the manifestations of this desire for quick transformation of an adolescent's antisocial behavior is to insist that the youngster get different kinds of friends. The parents, with justification, are usually upset over the fact that their antisocial youngster is "hanging around with the wrong kinds of kids, the troublemakers, the fringe elements, etc." There is no question that an adolescent's antisocial behavior will be reinforced and intensified by antisocial peers. However, the hope that by associating with healthier youngsters the patient will thereby enjoy an alleviation of the symptoms is rarely realized. First, the unhealthy behavior originates within the child him- or herself. These internal etiological factors are the primary ones that the therapist must deal with in the treatment. Removing the youngster from the external influences, although it may be somewhat salutary, is at best going to have minimal effects. Even if one were successful in persuading the adolescent to remove him- or herself from such friends, the likelihood is that the youngster will not be able to relate well to the non-antisocial types. The youngster is likely to be "like a fish out of water" with these new peers, especially if the antisocial behavior is a longstanding pattern. Under these circumstances the adolescent is not going to have the repertoire of information to enable him or her to relate successfully to the healthier group. Each group has its own set of topics to discuss, special vocabulary, interests, etc. The adolescent youngster is not likely to be able to relate well to the more traditional youngster because of this important difference. The healthier youngster, similarly, will also be out of place in a setting in which the others are primarily antisocial.

This recognition should not preclude parents taking reasonable steps to prevent the youngster from associating with the antisocial types. I generally advise parents to decide who shall be permitted into their home and who shall not. Antisocial types should be excluded from the home with a specific statement regarding the reasons why, especially regarding the particular forms of antisocial behavior that the rejects have exhibited. This restriction does not prevent the youngster from associating with these types outside the home; however, at least the parent has taken some step to increase the likelihood that the patient will gravitate toward the healthier boys and girls. It is hoped that, over time, he or she will be able to relate more comfortably to these healthier adolescents. Of course, this is more likely to occur if the fundamental internal problems that are bringing about the antisocial behavior are being dealt with as well.

Advising Parents About Schools

Parents who can afford it may look into the issue of sending the youngster off to a special boarding school in the hope that there the patient will be removed from the noxious influences of antisocial friends. They often have the vision that the boarding school is populated by healthy, law abiding citizens who will have a good influence on their antisocial child. They fail to appreciate that this is most often not the case, that the other youngsters at the school have been sent there for similar reasons. Although I cannot deny that there are certain benefits that may be potentially derived from such schools, I also believe that placing the child in such an environment—on a 24-hour basis—runs the risk of a perpetuation of the symptomatology via ongoing contact with more antisocial types. Accordingly, I generally discourage parents from giving serious consideration to finding another school as a solution to antisocial problems. I try to get across the point that the problems lie within the youngster's head, the family, and possibly the environment at large and that changing the woodwork that surrounds the youngster is not likely to do very much good because it does not direct itself to the fundamental problems.

There is no question that one source of antisocial behavior is an educational system based on the assumption that all youngsters should be given the opportunity to go to college. Although some provision is made for switching to a noncollege preparatory track in high school, this is often viewed as a less desirable and less prestigious course. This is unfortunate. It results in many youngsters' "hanging in" on the college-preparatory track who have little inclination or motivation for a university education. And the resentment built up under these circumstances contributes to antisocial behavior. There are many youngsters who, at the junior-high-school level, are also clearly not "college material." Yet there is no option for movement into the noncollege-preparatory track at that level. The frustrations and resentments thereby suffered may contribute to antisocial behavior. In many European countries, and elsewhere in the world, youngsters are divided into three tracks between the ages of 9 and 11. One track does ultimately end in a university education. The lowest track involves training in a trade, training that starts at ages 9 to 11. And the middle track is somewhere in between. There is little stigma in these countries for youngsters moving along tracks two and three. Placement in one of the lower tracks does not automatically preclude switching to a higher one but, of course, the longer an individual has been in the second or third track, the more difficult it may be to switch to a higher one. And this same principle holds true for youngsters who proceed along vocational training at the high-school level. (I have discussed this situation in greater detail in Chapter Two.) Therapists do well to help those adolescents who would do better in a noncollege preparatory program switch into that track at the earliest possible time. They should help reduce the patient's feelings of stigmatization that may be associated with such placement and recognize that the structure of our educational system at this point is playing a role in contributing to their patients' difficulties.

One last comment about schools. Unfortunately, many schools in the United States promote youngsters almost automatically. Administrators argue that they do so in order to protect the youngster from the psychological trauma attendant to being retained. I believe that this is misguided benevolence, more often motivated by economic than humane considerations. After all, it costs more to keep a youngster in school 13 or 14 years than it does to educate the youngster for 12 years. What these administrators fail to appreciate is that the psychological trauma of being retained is an *acute* one; whereas the psychological trauma of being improperly advanced is a *chronic* one. The adolescent who repeats a grade must suffer a period of humiliation during the first few days or weeks of school. Generally, the youngster accommodates to the situation and enjoys the position of being at the same level with one's classmates. In contrast, the youngster who is inappropriately advanced suffers daily humiliation associated with the inability to keep up with peers and may have little hope of ever catching up. This is a source of chronic psychological trauma as the youngster sinks deeper and deeper behind and may ultimately end up a drop-out. This, I believe, is one of the common causes of youngsters' dropping out of school. I use the word "drop-out" here not simply to refer to the adolescent who leaves school entirely; I use it also to refer to those who just sit there year in and year out waiting until they are old enough to quit. And the boredom and ennui engendered in such situations can contribute to antisocial behavior. Such behavior becomes especially attractive because it provides excitement in an otherwise dull atmosphere.

I generally advise parents of antisocial youngsters to inform teachers that they would like very much for them to mark examinations strictly and provide the grade that is truly deserved. There should be no mercy passes. Fifty-five averages should not suddenly become 65 averages at the end of the year in order to allow the youngster to pass. This is misguided benevolence. If the patient has failed, he or she should be required to repeat the course in the summer session, and, if enough courses are failed, then the patient should be required to repeat the grade. To do otherwise is to set up a situation in which there is absolutely no repercussion for antisocial school behavior and this perpetuates the youngster's pathology. In addition, the boy or girl is being deprived of a proper education by being given passing grades for courses that are failed.

There are many schools which provide what they consider to be disciplinary measures, but which basically do not serve that purpose at all. For example, there are schools which respond to a youngster's antisocial behavior by giving some kind of negative feedback such as a "pink slip." One school in my area continually gives out pink slips, but absolutely nothing happens after one gets a pink slip. A child can have trunks filled with pink slips, yet there are absolutely no repercussions. I don't know what these people are thinking of when they provide them, but they can't really believe that they are providing a meaningful deterrent with such "disciplinary measures." Another school gives youngsters detentions. This involves keeping the youngster after school. For some this is indeed a punishment and it may serve as a deterrent. For others it is just the opposite. They enjoy spending the time in detention, horsing around with the the others who are detained. In addition, the detention may be a punishment for their parents who have to inconvenience themselves by coming to school for the youngster rather than having the boy or girl return home on the school bus. A situation is thereby set up to provide the youngster with a tool for gratifying further antisocial needs. The school, then, becomes party to the perpetuation of the pathology.

Use and Misuse of Lawyers

Many parents, especially those who have the financial means, reflexively engage the services of an attorney when their youngster's antisocial behavior comes to the attention of the police. Often they seek someone who has a reputation for "getting the kid off." These are people well known for their cunning and their ability to use every maneuver (legal, paralegal, and sometimes illegal) to protect the youngsters from the legally mandated punishments for their illegal acts. Legal technicalities are invoked, the credibility of witnesses is questioned, and other sleazy maneuvers are utilized in the service of protecting such youngsters from suffering the consequences of their illegal acts. Other parents "pull strings." They know someone who knows someone who knows the judge and thereby will obtain leniency and even enable the youngster to get off entirely without any consequences. I believe that these maneuvers are a disservice to the adolescents and serve to perpetuate their pathology. These maneuvers also entrench the delusions of invulnerability with which adolescents so often suffer. Once again, they have proven themselves immune to the punishments that others may be subjected to. Such a parent would do far better to request of the judge (either through a lawyer or directly) that that penalty be imposed which is reasonable and fair for the crime. It should not be overly lenient, nor should it be excessively punitive. This is the ideal approach to such youngsters' illegal behavior.

Sometimes the parents request that the therapist provide a letter to the court, again asking for leniency. Sometimes the lawyers, the hired guns who have been engaged to protect such youngsters and do everything possible to get them exonerated, request and even demand such letters. The hope here is that the court will view the youngster as a "sick kid" not responsible for his or her behavior. I not only advise parents that they are making a mistake by engaging the services of such attorneys but tell them, as well, that I will not be party to this kind of a program. I advise them that if I am to provide a letter it will basically recommend that the court impose whatever penalties are reasonable and just for that particular crime. I tell them, as well, that the kind of letter their lawyer would like—one which communicates to the court that the youngster's psychiatric difficulty compromised his or her ability to refrain from engaging in the crime—is not the kind of letter that I will write. To do so would only perpetuate and intensify the patient's pathology and thereby would not serve the goals of treatment. Not surprisingly, the parents will then change their minds and decide that I should not provide a letter. And their lawyer may consider my position inexplicable, totally at variance with the aims of the adversary system. The lawyer may never have considered—even for one second—the possibility that the adversary system may not be the best for all kinds of people under all circumstances. Elsewhere (1987c) I have discussed the drawbacks of the adversary system in detail.

Sometimes the claim that the youngster is in treatment will be used in court as a mitigating factor. Under these circumstances it is not uncommon for courts to withhold any punishment as long as the youngster remains in therapy. Although ostensibly benevolent, such a ruling is naive on the judge's part. The ruling contaminates the treatment because the youngster may then remain in therapy in order to be protected from the legal consequences of the crime, at a time when he or she may have seriously considered discontinuing the therapy. The ideal position for the judge to take is this: "You have committed X crime for which I am imposing Y punishment. If you want to go into treatment to help you understand why you have done this and to help you lessen the likelihood that you will do it again, that is fine with me. I wish you luck in your treatment and I hope it helps you not to do this again. Know this, if you come here again I will impose upon you a harsher punishment—under the provisions of the law. I will not consider your being in therapy as a mitigating factor. I will not let you use that manipulation nor will I accept a letter from any psychiatrist who naively believes he can use that excuse to protect you from the consequences of your crimes. If you were retarded, psychotic, or suffering with a bona fide physical disease of the brain I would not be talking to you this way. But since you are not suffering with any of these disorders I consider you completely capable of controlling your actions. Next case." Unfortunately, few judges talk this way—much to the disservice of adolescents with antisocial problems.

Shoplifting

A common crime engaged in by early adolescent girls is that of shoplifting. Most often, these youngsters will steal such things as perfume, scarves, and cheap jewelry. Department store owners know this well. When the parents learn about such behavior they are generally amazed. A common response will be: "I can't understand why she steals these things. Our family is quite well off. We could buy these things for her and have offered to do so. She could easily buy these things from her allowance." I believe that many of these thefts relate to the girl's belief that she is stealing something that enhances her sexual attractiveness. At some level, the girl believes that perfume purchased by her mother (an old, sexless object) is not as likely to have the same sexual allure as the same perfume that is stolen. After all, forbidden fruit is much sweeter than that which is acquired honestly. When department store owners catch such girls they generally come down hard on them and make various threats. The usual first response is to call in the parents, put the youngster's name on the store's record, and inform all concerned that the next time this happens the police will be brought in. Parents do well to respond with horror and indignation over the act. One of the worst things they can do is to react with calmness or to excuse the act as normal. They do well to add to the storekeeper's measures those of their own. Just about the worst thing they can do is to bring in one of those honcho lawyers who is going to "protect" the youngster from the consequences of her act. My experience has been that the storekeeper's warnings plus a parental fit is usually adequate to "cure" this problem. Of course, there are a wide variety of other reasons for shoplifting and it is certainly done by people who are not adolescent girls. I am only referring here to this small segment of the shoplifting population, and to the special motivation that is applicable to this age group.

Dealing With the Youngster
Who Abuses Drugs

Youngsters who abuse drugs often have little in their lives that they can point to with pride. Prior to the teen period most youngsters gain a sense of esteem from one or more areas. Some feel good about themselves because of their academic accomplishments. Others may excel in sports, theater, arts, or music. Some may also gain a sense of ego enhancement from social success. These are the three major areas of potential ego enhancement and each youngster may be accomplished in one or more of them. If, however, a youngster reaches the teen period and does not have a sense of high self-worth in at least one of these areas, then that individual is a prime candidate for abusing drugs. By the teen period it is often too late to gain a sense of high self-worth in one of these areas if one has not been doing anything about it previously. One cannot start to catch up academically if, when in the eighth grade, one is still functioning at the third-grade level. Simlarly, the youngsters who by then are local basketball stars have been practicing since age five or six. It is unreasonable to expect a 13-year-old to excel at a sport when he or she starts eight years later than the others. And the same is true for music, dance, theater, and other activities. It is not impossible to catch up, but it is exceedingly difficult. And the older the youngster the more difficult it may be. I am not simply referring to time devoted to the acquisition of a technical skill; I am referring to the whole mental set that precedes the technical dedication: an attitude of receptively, curiosity, and strong motivation to gain competence in a particular area. Nor am I claiming that youngsters who do not achieve competence in any of these three areas will automatically become addicted to drugs. I am only claiming that they will be at higher risk for such addiction. Other factors are clearly operative, but the failure to acquire competence in any of these three areas is an extremely important contributing factor.

Accordingly, parents of youngsters who abuse drugs have to be helped to appreciate what I have just said if they are to help their children. They have to do everything possible to encourage the boy or girl to pursue some area which may result in a genuine feeling of competence. This does not preclude their taking more immediate measures such as watching carefully what money the youngster is given in order to ensure that they are not providing money to support a drug habit. They should not "respect" the youngster's privacy regarding hiding illegal substances in the home. Youngsters without such hidden substances are certainly entitled to their privacy. These youngers are not. To respect their privacy is to contribute to the perpetuation of a habit. Accordingly, the youngster must be told that at the parents' whim any drawer may be searched and any illegal substances found therein will be flushed down the toilet, burned, or otherwise disposed of so they cannot be used by the youngster. The youngster should also be advised by the parents that they will not permit them to see those "friends" who are also on drugs and who thereby serve as a bad influence for the patient. Such youngsters may believe that their drug abuse is normal because of its ubiquity among young people today. My answer to this is simple: when polio was epidemic it was still a disease.

Runaways

As is true of most phenomena, there are many categories of runaways. There are those who are actively or passively, overtly or covertly, encouraged to run away by family members. These are those whose families basically do not want them and are pleased when they suddenly disappear. These are the youngsters who will often find their ways to large cities where, even though in their early teens, they may become prostitutes. And I am not simply referring to young girls who become prostitutes for heterosexual men, but young boys who become prostitutes for homosexual men. Social workers and others who are involved in salvaging these youngsters know well the experience of calling the family and getting responses such as: "I'm glad she's a prostitute; tell her to send home some money. She'll finally be making herself useful." or "We don't know who you're talking about. We don't know her. (Telephone clicks.)" I have had practically no experience with the treatment of such youngsters.

The kinds of runaways I have had some experience with are those whose famlies do indeed want them and are genuinely grieved when the youngster's whereabouts are unknown. These parents are grief stricken over the prospect of the youngster's being killed, exploited, mutilated, etc. These parents are in constant touch with the police and are obsessed with learning about their child's whereabouts. They do not sleep nights, they can hardly eat, and they think of practically nothing but their runaway child. They are glued to the telephone in the hope that every call will convey to them a message about their child.

A common motive for such running away is anger. After all, putting parents through the aforementioned ordeal is a good way of torturing them.The maneuver, however, rests on the assumption that the parents really care. If they do not, then they will not respond with any particular concern and the youngster will thereby be deprived of sadistic gratification. Generally, youngsters in this category take care of themselves and ensure that nothing will happen to them. They may go to the home of a friend who hides them so that even the friend's parents are not aware that the youngster is in the home. Other such youngsters sleep in a park overnight. On occasion a neighbor will take the runaway into the home and protect the youngster from the indignities they have described themselves to be suffering at the hands of their parents. Although some of these neighbors are indeed protecting the youngers from bona fide abuses, often the abuses exist more in the mind of the child and the neighbor than in the actual home form which the child has fled. The neighbor has been duped into becoming an ally and providing support for alienation from the parents and flight from them. Without checking with the parents about the veracity of the youngster's complaint, the neighbor becomes party to the runaway scheme. On occasion I have had parents, who, when learning of the youngster's whereabouts, have called the neighbor only to be told that they agree with the child that he or she should not return. I generally advise parents to make the following statement to such good Samaritans: "Look, I am giving you 10 minutes to have that child back on my doorstep. If you don't I'm going to call the police and find out whether I can bring you up on charges of kidnapping."I have found this statement the best "cure" for such well-meaning but misguided Samaritans.

Sometimes, when a runaway returns after a long period during which his or her whereabouts have been unknown, the parents are so joyous over the child's return that no disciplinary or punitive measures are invoked. I can understand the great relief that such parents experience when the youngster returns. I can appreciate how joyous they are that their children are in good health and that nothing serious has befallen them. However, they are making a mistake when they do not invoke any punitive measures for the ordeal they have been put through. This does not preclude talking with the youngster about the complaints that resulted in the runaway. This does not preclude making attempts to change those factors that were operative in leading the youngster to the decision to flee the home. One can deal with those matters and still punish runaways in order to help them remember not to utilize this method of acting out when there are complaints. Accordingly, I advise such parents to let the youngster know about the grief they were suffering during their ordeal, their sleeplessness, loss of appetite, and obsessive fears that the child would be dead, kidnapped, mutilated, etc. They should try to communicate to the child what a horrible experience they have been through.Then, they should also tell the youngsters how happy and joyous they are about his or her return. And following that, they should advise the child of the punishment they are going to invoke for the runaway behavior. And there should be a punishment so severe that the youngster will long remember it.

Dealing with Incorrigibles

In the battle that antisocial youngsters have with their parents, the parents often consider themselves to be impotent. The realities are that they may be to a certain degree, but they may not be as weak as they sometimes believe. It is important that they maintain the upper hand and let the youngster know that there will be meaningful repercussions to his or her behavior. They can withdraw money from the youngster's account to pay for damaged property. They can refuse to cook meals, do laundry, give allowances, lend the car, carpool to dates, and thus deprive the youngster of a wide variety of services in response to the humiliation and indignities they suffer at the patient's hands.

There are situations in which these measures just do not work. Under those circumstances I generally advise parents to get information about placement outside the home. Although such placement is not easily accomplished, it still does exist. And although the steps that have to be taken in order to accomplish it may be long and arduous, going through them may still be useful. The very fact that the parents are taking such steps serves as a warning that things have gotten out of hand and that there will indeed be repercussions—if not immediately, then in the future. They do well to inform the youngster that there is not only such a thing as "child abuse" but also "parent abuse." Just as children are being inceasingly protected from being abused by their parents, parents too have every right to be protected from their children. The protection works both ways. However, the parents should not embark upon the program of exploring this option if they do not expect to follow it to its completion. Otherwise, it will merely serve as a false threat, which may be just one more empty threat like those that the parents have provided in the past. And this cannot but contribute to the perpetuation of the antisocial behavior.

In the area where I practice, the *Bergen Pines Hospital* (mentioned above in the case of Joan) has an acute observation ward for youngsters that they refer to as "incorrigible." However, parents cannot simply bring such youngsters over to the hospital and have them admitted to the closed ward. There is a step-by-step procedure and screening process. If successful, it may ultimately result in the police actually taking the youngster off to the hospital for observation. Often a week or two on the psychiatric ward at *Bergen Pines Hospital* is enough to sober the youngster up and may be more therapeutic than months and even years of therapy. The youngster is provided with the "living experience" that one cannot just go on wantonly destroying property, threatening one's parents, and indulging oneself in whims. Accordingly, the therapist does well to find out about local facilities and how they deal with such incorrigibles.

The therapist, as well, must let incorrigible youngsters know that he or she is not going to be sitting by passively and allow destructive behavior to take place in the office. If there is any danger that such youngsters may be physicaly acting out against the therapist's person or property that patient has to be firmly warned that office treatment is for those who are healthy enough to restrain themselves. The patient has to be helped to appreciate that any thought or feeling—no matter how unusual, embarrassing, destructive, sadistic, bizarre, etc.—is permitted in this office. However, the patient must be firmly told that threats of damage to the therapist's personal property will not be tolerated. Specifically, the patient should be told that office therapy is for healthier people who can restrain themselves from such acting out and if the youngster is going to place the therapist in a position of fear for his or her personal property then therapy will not be continued. The therapist cannot operate objectively under such tension. In addition, as mentioned previously, I *may* point out to the more threatening youngster my three-button panel, which is within arm's length of the seat in which I usually sit.The buttons provide me with immediate access to the police, the fire department, and emergency ambulances. I also inform such incorrigibles that I am in full support of the parents' steps to pursue the question of placement in a residential treatment center, such as *Bergen Pines Hospital*. Although this approach may seem stringent and even punitive to some readers, I believe that it is warranted in the treatment of antisocial incorrigibles. The message must be gotten across that they cannot wantonly indulge themselves in their destructive behavior without any repercussions. To have that view perpetuates their delusions of invulnerability and contributes to an intensification of their pathology.

In recent years a c ertain amount of publicity has been given to what is referred to as the "tough love" movement. Parents of antisocial youngsters have, with some justification, become dissatisfied with the seemingly more humane and benevolent approaches of psychiatrists, psychologists, and social workers. They believe that our attempts to give sympathy, empathy, and understanding to these youngsters is not in their best interests, that it is to "soft," and that firmer methods are warranted. I am basically in agreement with this criticism of the mental health professionals' approach to the antisocial youngster. I believe that we are indeed too soft and my hope is that the approaches described in this book present a more reasonable way of dealing with these youngsters, especially with regard to being somewhat more "hardnosed" than the traditional methods used by my colleagues. However, I believe that the "tough love" people go too far in the other direction. Many of these parents utilize methods that I would consider far too punitive and easily serve thereby as an outlet for their own pathological sadistic needs. I do not believe that they make proper differentiation between the harmless forms of antisocial behavior and those that are indeed dangerous. The method often involves the youngster's going to the home of another family that is part of the tough-love network. Although there may be certain merits to this decompression and change of scenery, the method requires the availability of a family willing to deal with the youngster's antics. Often this is a family that has spawned and reared one or more antisocial adolescent youngsters themselves and claims success with tough-love techniques. Accordingly, in the context of a curative program, the new family may be providing the antisocial youngster with another environment that induces the pathological behavior. The movement enjoyed a certain amount of publicity in the early 1980s and I am not aware of where it went by the mid- to late-1980s, the time of this writing.

Reporting Parents for Child Abuse

At the time of this writing we are witnessing a new phenomenon on the American scene. I am referring to the practice of reporting people for abusing children. Mothers are reporting fathers. Fathers are reporting mothers. Friends are reporting children. Children are reporting children. And neighbors are reporting neighbors. Children can use a "hotline" to report their parents, teachers, ministers, doctors, therapists (yes, therapists) and anyone else they may wish to—whether the complaint be bona fide or fabricated. And the reporter has a choice of three kinds of abuse: physical, sexual, and emotional. These complaints are received by a community agency that is authorized to conduct an immediate investigation. The investigating agencies often have easy access to courts that may quickly impose various kinds of restrictions on the accused person. On the one hand, one could argue that the growth of such facilities is a boon and that children are now being given more protection than they ever had before. On the other hand, there is no question that such "hotlines" are being abused by children, especially anti-social children. My experience has been that those community workers who respond to these calls tend to assume that the parents are indeed guilty of the accusations. Such an assumption has caused unnecessary grief to many. Many of these agencies are staffed by people with very little experience, some just fresh out of graduate school, with very naive views about the areas they are allegedly trained to deal with. Some are hardly more than adolescents themselves with residua of their own adolescent rebellious attitude toward the adult generation. They thereby blindly join with these youngsters and assume that the parents indeed have subjected them to the described abuses. In such cases therapists can provide a valuable service. Their knowledge of the family can be useful input and help protect innocent parents from significant grief. However, in situations in which there has been bona fide abuse the therapist's report may serve to alienate the parent and thereby compromise significantly the treatment.

In many (if not most) states therapists themselves are required by law to report cases of abuse to the proper agency. Whatever protection this may provide the child it can have an extremely detrimental effect on the therapy—to the point where it may destroy it entirely. As mentioned so often previously, the therapist should do everything possible to form and maintain a good relationship with both parents. Reporting a parent to the police, courts, or other community agency that might take punitive action is clearly one of the quickest ways to compromise or destroy the youngster's treatment. These laws present the therapist with a dilemma. If the patient is in treatment, disclosing the abuse represents a breach of the confidentiality and is unethical. However, not to report the abuse to the proper authorities is illegal and may result in the therapist's being punished. Therapists have been fined and even jailed for not alerting community authorities about the abuse divulgences revealed in the course of treatment. I believe that these laws are misguided. They should give therapists much greater flexibility to decide whether or not reporting is warranted. This is especially the case in situations in which there is an ongoing therapeutic relationship and the treatment indicated for the abuse is already under way. Reporting the abuse to outside authorities is likely to result in the disruption of the therapy because of the breach of confidentiality and the punitive measures administered to the perpetrators. Accordingly, the process that would represent the final recommendation after the disclosure is being destroyed by the revelation. This problem could be avoided if the statutes allowed qualified therapists to withhold disclosure in situations in which a therapeutic relationship had been established and in which the disclosure would clearly and predictably be detrimental to the ongoing therapeutic process.

The above represents my hope for change in the future. But what about now, when we have no such flexibility? Although we may work toward a change in these laws, they have not been changed yet and we have to deal with them as they are at this time (1988). My recommendation to therapists is that they have to make a choice. Some will be quite comfortable reporting the abuse, the disruption of the treatment notwithstanding. Others will withhold the information and thereby preserve the treatment. Those in the latter category must be clearly aware that they are taking a risk and that they may suffer consequences for their flaunting the law. I am not stating that they should avoid this position. I view such failure to report an example of nonviolent civil disobedience. We have models for individuals with deep commitments to the process, people like Henry Thoreau, Mohandes Gandhi, and Martin Luther King. The therapist who chooses to walk in the footsteps of these earthshakers must recognize that significant risks must be taken—risks of fines and incarceration. I myself am in full sympathy with such a position, but I am also sympathetic with those who choose to take the course of compliance. Therapists in both categories, however, should do what they can to bring about a change in these absurd laws.

DEALING WITH ANTISOCIAL BEHAVIOR
RELATED TO PREJUDICE

There are youngsters, especially members of minority groups, who are subjected to various forms of prejudice—overt and covert. The anger engendered by racial slurs, rejections, and taunting may contribute to antisocial behavior. This is especially the case for youngsters who agree with their persecutors that their heritage is indeed something to be ashamed about. When this second factor is present the youngster may try to hide his or her identity and "pass" as a member of what the youngster considers to be the more desirable group. Youngsters who are ashamed of their heritage often have parents with similar attitudes, and the therapist does well to look into such influences when such shame is present. This shame can also contribute to generalized feelings of low self-worth. When these parental influences are present, it is crucial that the therapist work with the parent as well if the problems that generate from the prejudice are to be solved. I will focus here on youngsters who do agree with their persecutors that their ethnic background is something to be ashamed of and their parents have either overtly or covertly communicated this message to the patient.

First, the therapist must interview the parents and find out exactly what their own feelings are about their ethnic background. Such inquiry will be easier if the therapist is of the same heritage as the parents. However, therapists who have any shame over their own heritage—whether it be the same or different from that of the parents—are ill-equipped to deal properly with this problem. The principle is no different from the one in which therapists who have never been married will find themselves when providing marital counseling. It is the same principle that compromises childless therapists in their psychotherapeutic work with children.

The therapist must attempt to help the parents (and by extension the youngster) appreciate that there is absolutely no good reason to consider one ethnic group superior (or inferior) to another. I often try to get across this message by using a number of vignettes. One involves asking the patients (from here on, when I use the word *patients*, I will be referring to the parents and/or the youngster) to envision a globe of the earth and imagine the various streams of migrations—both within and between continents—that have taken place over the history of the human race. They then do well to view the migrations of their own ancestors and trace these as accurately as they can, pinpointing as well as they can the various times in history when the migrations took place. I then point out to them that these migrations generally occurred because of one or more kinds of persecution: political, religious, racial, etc. The therapist might join in and trace his or her own heritage in a similar manner. It is useful to point out that it was extremely rare for the landed aristocracy to remove themselves voluntarily and unilaterally. It was generally only in response to some threat or some hope of bettering one's life situation that the migrations took place. Few sailed away in their yachts. Emphasizing this point can help the patients feel less atypical about their own heritage.

The therapist might ask the parents why they (or their forebears) came to the United States. Generally they will describe some kind of persecution. The family should then be asked why the United States was chosen from approximately 150 other countries on earth that could have been selected. Most often one will receive an answer related to this country as a land of opportunity, greater freedom, etc. Or the family may say that this country, with all its deficiencies, is still the best place on earth to live. The therapist does well, then, to point out that the United States did not achieve this status by pure chance; rather, there were very specific factors in our history that contributed to its enjoying this reputation. And one of these factors relates to the waves of immigrants who came here from all over the earth. Each generation had its own ethnic makeup. One could get more specific and talk about the early English, Spanish, and French settlers in the 15th through 18th centuries. The people who came here then were looking for various kinds of religious and political freedom—just like the forebears of the patient. One could then proceed into the middle 19th century and talk about Irish and German settlers and then the late 19th and early 20th centuries and describe Jewish, Italian, and Slavic immigrants. One can then move up to the late 20th century and talk about the recent influx of Asian people to the United States. All of these immigrants shared in common not only their persecutions abroad but their desire to work hard and enter into the American mainstream. Pointing out that the patient's family is part of this grand plan can help reduce feelings of inferiority.

The family should be helped to appreciate that just as one's heritage is nothing to be ashamed of, one's heritage is also nothing to be proud of. This may come as a surprising statement to many readers. I think it is important to differentiate between identity and pride. By identity I refer to the identification of our particular ethnic group and the individuals who preceded us. By pride I refer to the quality of feeling proud of something. I believe that one can feel pride over some accomplishment, especially one that was attained after great effort. However, I do not believe that the feelings of pride that one has in one's identity work particularly well. After all, nothing was done to achieve any goals here. Rather, one's ethnic identity relates merely to the way the genetic dice fell and where one's position is in the long trains of global migrations. If one had to take a test in heaven—and only the highest scorers were to be allowed to go down to earth and join a particular group—then there might be something to be proud of. Otherwise, the "assignment" has nothing to do with pride. It has something to do with *luck* in that sometimes the assignment is unlucky and sometimes lucky.

Many people try to enhance their pride in their heritage by pointing out illustrious individuals who are members of their ethnic group. This doesn't work very well in enhancing self-respect. The same group fails to point out an equal if not larger number of individuals who certainly have not distinguished themselves nor even contributed to the betterment of their people. The author is of the Jewish heritage and so I can speak with greater knowledge (and safety) of the manifestations of this problem in this particular group. Many Jewish people point with pride to famous Jews such as Albert Einstein, Sigmund Freud, Felix Mendelssohn, Baruch Spinoza, Benjamin Disraeli, Golda Meir etc. My views are as follows: Einstein should certainly be proud of his accomplishments in that few individuals have made such formidable contributions to our knowledge of the universe. His parents have some right to be proud of their input into their son's growth and development. And some of his teachers as well. However, such pride should not extend to everyone else in his synagogue. I, personally, did absolutely nothing to contribute to Einstein's successes and therefore do not deserve any of the enhanced sense of self-worth that came his way. If I attempt to enhance my self-worth by warming myself in his glory, it will do me little good. In fact, it might do me some harm because I will be trying to bolster my self-esteem with a maneuver that is basically specious and thereby ego-debasing.

In the 1960s blacks realized that they were making a terrible error by joining with their persecutors and agreeing with them that there was something to be ashamed of in being black. Accordingly, they began to proclaim that they were *proud* to be black. Black is not ugly; "black is beautiful" they proclaimed. I see no point to all of this. It just won't work. Black is neither ugly nor beautiful. It is neither something to be proud of nor something to be ashamed of. It is just one of the various skin colors that human beings possess.

The family has to be helped to appreciate that anyone who thinks less of them because of their ethnic background has some derangement in thinking: "has a screw loose in his (her) head." In addition, if those who are persecuted believe that there is something wrong with them, then they too have derangements in their thinking and have "screws loose in their heads." Viewing the persecutor as having a defect can help the persecuted react with greater equanimity. The youngster and parents have to be helped to appreciate that there is something wrong with those who are prejudiced against them. Youngsters who retaliate in kind with ethnic slurs have to be helped to appreciate that they are lowering themselves and that they will not thereby enhance their self-worth. At times they should be helped to ignore the taunters and appreciate that they have defective thinking. If they feel compelled to respond they should be helped to do so in a way that addresses itself to the absurdity of the ethnic slur and to communicate the message that there is something strange and odd about the thinking of the persecutor—so strange and odd that the comments cannot be taken seriously.

I have found other comments and discussions to be helpful in this area. For example, I have on occasion told such families about a visit I made to Toronto in the year 1986. Up until the 1950s Toronto was generally considered to be the most English of all Canadian cities. However, since that time there has been a massive influx of a wide variety of ethnic groups. When I visited the city in 1986 I learned that each school district must provide ethnic and language classes for every minority group whose representation exceeds a specific number of youngsters. I no longer recall the specific number, but it was somewhere in the neighborhood of 25 or so. Once this point has been reached the educational system provides after-school classes in which the children are taught about the history and language of their ethnic group. Once a year there is a large festival in which all the ethnic groups participate, generally in their own clusters. But there is significant intermingling.

Many ethnic groups provide their own cultural programs. If the family has not joined one, they should be encouraged to find one in their area, especially for the youngster. Such experiences help the children feel that, although different, they are in no way inferior. The family has to be helped to appreciate that being different does not mean that one is inferior. Nor does it mean that one is superior. The family might also be helped to appreciate Hamlet's wisdom: "...there is nothing either good or bad, but thinking makes it so." If they view their skin color or facial characteristics as bad or ugly, they have to be helped to appreciate that such an attitude exists in the eye of the beholder and that there is absolutely no intrinsic quality that is either good, bad, right, wrong, beautiful, or ugly. In certain African tribes women's necks are stretched with numerous collars and their bodies are scarred. This is considered beautiful. In some societies obesity is viewed as beautiful and in others anorexia is the turn on. What probably is beautiful is the healthy human body. It is truly a marvelous creation and to be ashamed of it is certainly sad. If the therapist is successful in helping the family members develop healthier views about their heritage, the anger in the youngster should be reduced and this contribution to the antisocial acting out diminished.

CONCLUDING COMMENTS

Francois Villon, the 15th century French poet asked us: "But where are the snows of yesteryear? (*Mais où sont les neiges d'antan?*)" I would ask, "But where are the juvenile delinquents of yesteryear?" We see gangs of 15-year-old delinquents roaming the streets, standing on street corners, and looking for trouble. But we don't see bands of

25-year-olds doing the same thing. Obviously, not all have "gone straight" or have enjoyed the benefits of therapy (individual, group, and family). So what happened? The angry kids grow up. Their adjustment improves; their anger diminishes. They gain knowledge, which enhances their self-esteem. They take jobs in which they channel their energies into constructive directions. They become less dependent on their parents and so have less to rebel against. This is not true of all delinquents. Some do end up in jail; others are homeless on the streets; others in mental hospitals; and others nonfunctioning members of society, parasites to those who may become involved with them. But these represent a minority; most outgrow their antisocial behavior. Accordingly, time is on the side of the therapist. After treating such a youngster two or three years there is a good chance that things will get better — even though the therapist's techniques may not have played any role in the improvement. I would like to believe, however, that the things we do can make a difference, especially the kinds of things I have described in this and previous chapters. The reader who is interested in further information on the etiology and treatment of adolescent antisocial behavior does well to refer to the publications of A. M. Johnson (1949), A. M. Johnson and S. A. Szurek (1952), J. S. Schimel, (1974), and R. J. Marshall (1979, 1983).

Antisocial youngsters reflect in part the behavior of their psychopathic society. As mentioned frequently throughout the course of this book, I believe that modern Western society has become increasingly psychopathic. There have been times and places in humankind's history when psychopathy was rampant. Like all things, trends fluctuate. And it may be that the general direction of the civilized people has been in the direction of diminished psychopathy. I can relate most directly, however, to my own life's experience in which I have observed a general deterioration of values in the last 20–30 years. In the course of treating antisocial youngsters it behooves the therapist to point out the manifestations of such psychopathy in the world at large. The therapist who is blind to these compromises, deteriorations of values, and erosion of morals is not likely to help antisocial youngsters to a significant degree. And the therapist who has taken on these values him- or herself (consciously or unconsciously) is going to be impaired even further in helping these youngsters. A therapeutic approach that relies heavily, if not exclusively, on behavior modification is likely to ignore these factors. Therapists with a commitment to the brief-therapy concept, who operate in therapeutic programs that are time limited, do not have proper appreciation for the importance of the therapist-patient relationship and its evolution. They are depriving their patients of the identification and emulation aspects of treatment and the opportunity to incorporate the therapist's morals and values.

Antisocial youngsters have impaired values and they need a therapeutic program in which there has been the development of a strong therapist-patient relationship. This is extremely unlikely to take place when the number of sessions provided is limited and finite and this is known to both at the outset. Therapists who are employed by HMOs and are ever concerned with the "cost effectiveness" of the services they are providing are also likely to compromise the development of this relationship. D. J. Holmes (1964) states this principle well (p. 250):

> It is appalling to see how far it is possible for theory to stray from the ordinary therapeutic forces which support the general society of healthy people. It is so easy to set aside the accumulated wisdom of centuries of cultural evolution as something which has all come about in some utterly random and purposeless fashion. In speaking of ego strengths, for example, or of reinforcing defenses, we have provided ourselves not only with useful conceptual tools but also with easy escape from examining those forces in our lives which really do the most to strengthen egos and reinforce defenses. The ideas connoted by such terms as *authority, moral standards, discipline* and *ideals* have fallen under a heavy shadow of suspicion in our specialty, as though they are all bad. It is even bad to say "bad." But an active day on the ward has a way of reminding one that there is really no such thing as a good boy, at least not in the natural state. They have to become good, just as we did.

FOURTEEN

DEPRESSION, SUICIDE, MEDICATION, AND HOSPITALIZATION

DEPRESSION

A common way of dividing depressive symptomatology is into the *endogenous* and *exogenous*. Endogenous depression refers to depressive symptomatology that arises from within. Generally, genetic predispositions are considered to be present, but internal psychological factors are also operative. Exogenous depressions are generally considered to be the result of external stresses. Psychiatrists tend to be divided with regard to the relative importance of these two factors. In the 1940s and 1950s, primarily under the influence of psychoanalysis, depression was generally viewed as arising from internal psychological conflicts. The genetic predisposition was considered to be minimal if not entirely absent. External factors were also considered to be important. In recent years, with the increasing popularity of the purely biological explanation, many psychiatrists view depression as resulting from genetic, metabolic, and biochemical abnormalities and do not pay much attention to the internal psychological factors and/or the external stresses. I consider the present shift toward the biological explanation to be unfortunate. I believe that there may be some genetic predisposition to depression, but it is small. I believe that the primary causes of depression in most (but not necessarily all) people relate to external stresses and internal psychological factors. The discussion here is based on this assumption.

I recognize that I am in the minority on this subject among my colleagues in the field of psychiatry. I have given serious consideration to new developments in the field that rely heavily on the theory of primary biological etiology, but I still hold that the weight of the evidence supports the position that adolescent depressions of the kind I discuss in this chapter are best understood as manifestations of internal psychological and environmental processes. I am not referring here to manic-depressive psychosis, in which the evidence for a biological-genetic predisposition is strong. I am referring to the much more common types of depression seen in adolescence.

Environmental Factors

With regard to the exogenous factors, it behooves the examiner to look carefully into the family and other environmental factors that may be contributing to the youngster's depression. The extensive evaluation that I described in Chapter Four can serve this purpose well. Not to conduct such an exhaustive evaluation is likely to compromise the treatment because the examiner will be deprived of learning about the environmental factors that are likely to have contributed to the depression. And this is one of my strongest criticisms of biologically oriented psychiatrists. They generally do not delve deeply enough into the details of their patients' backgrounds. Committed to the notion that depression is primarily, if not entirely, biologically derived they can justify their failure to conduct such an investigation. Subscribing to the biological theory also enables them to provide what appears to be a relatively quick and easily administered form of treatment, namely, medication. As I will discuss later in this chapter, I believe that antidepressants may be of symptomatic value in the treatment of the vast majority of depressions. But this is not inconsistent with my belief that environmental and psychological factors are the paramount etiological factors. Palliation is not the same as cure.

Accordingly, the examiner must try to ascertain what the environmental factors have been that have contributed to the depression. Perhaps the youngster has been exposed to ongoing marital conflicts, especially those that culminate in separation and/or divorce. Exposure to and/or embroilment in custody litigation is an even greater environmental trauma because the youngster cannot but feel like a rope in a tug of war. The loyalty conflicts engendered by such litigation are enormous and the likelihood that the youngster will become depressed when so embroiled is extremely high. Elsewhere (1986b), I have discussed in detail the ways in which custody litigation can contribute to a wide variety of psychopathological reactions including depression. Perhaps the youngster suffers with a learning disability and thereby experiences inordinate academic stresses which can lead to depression (Gardner, 1987b). Some youngsters are likely to become depressed in their dealings with members of the opposite sex. The dating period can be extremely anxiety provoking, its gratifications notwithstanding. Rejections in this realm are a common source of depression (and even suicide) among adolescents.

Many youngsters become depressed over the socioeconomic conditions in which they have grown up. Patients used as subjects in studies of depression in childhood and adolescence often come from inner city ghettos. This is an easy population in which to find depressed children. Many adolescents growing up in such areas use drugs as their antidepressant. It is rare for such studies to derive their patients from affluent suburbs. The youngster who does poorly in sports (possibly related to genetic and/or biological weaknesses) may become depressed in an environment which is highly sports oriented. A youngster of average intelligence who grows up in a home with a sibling who is an academic "superstar" may also become depressed. The youngster who cannot live up to his or her parents' inordinately high academic standards is also likely to become depressed. I could provide many other examples. My primary point here is that the examiner should investigate every possible environmental factor that may produce depression and do whatever can be done to alter these. And such changes are most predictably accomplished when the therapist works with both the youngster and the parents.

Internal Psychological Factors

Anger Inhibition   In addition to the exogenous factors, complex internal psychological mechanisms are also often operative in bringing about depression. One factor that may contribute to depression is inhibition in the expression of anger. The person's anger becomes turned inward and directed toward oneself. The inhibition of such rage is likely to produce depressed feelings. Furthermore, individuals who are inhibited in the expression of anger may develop self-flagellatory symptomatology. They constantly castigate themselves with comments such as "I'm stupid to have done that," "What a wretch I am," and "What a fool I've been." The person may justify such self-recrimination by dwelling on past indiscretions that may have long since been forgotten. These are trivial and do not warrant the degree of self-denigration that the individual exhibits. Errors and minor indiscretions become exaggerated into heinous crimes. When self-flagellatory symptoms are present, one can generally assume that such patients are fearful of and/or guilty over directly expressing anger to others, upon whom they may be quite dependent. They therefore direct their anger toward themselves, a safer target. In working with such patients it is important to help them become less inhibited in the expression of their anger. They may have grown up in families where the parents were similarly inhibited. The parents may have boasted that they have been married many years and never had a fight. In such a marriage it is likely that one or both of the parents have anger inhibition problems. Many such inhibited youngsters may have been exposed to harsh disciplinary and punitive measures in the context of which they may have been told, "Nice boys and girls never say such things to their parents. They never even *think* such things."

Guilt   A further contributing factor to depression is guilt. By guilt I refer to the feeling of low self-worth experienced following thoughts, feelings, and acts which the individual has learned are unacceptable to significant figures in his or her environment. In essence, the guilty person is saying: "How terrible a person I am for what I have thought, felt, or done." Feelings of low self-worth attendant to guilt are likely to contribute to the depressive symptomatology. Accordingly, the examiner does well to investigate into factors that may be guilt-evoking. As mentioned, many children are often taught to feel guilty about the expression of hostility toward a parent: "How can you do this to your mother?" and "What a terrible thing to say to your father." The examiner does well to look into things that the youngster him- or herself might be doing that may engender guilty feelings. If the youngster has a healthy superego, then performing such acts as cheating, lying, and stealing may be associated with guilt. In such cases the guilt is appropriate. However, there are youngsters who suffer with inappropriate or exaggerated guilt, such as guilt over sexual feelings, masturbation, or sexual activities at an age-appropriate level (in the examiner's opinion). In such situations, it behooves the examiner to try to reduce such guilt in the service of alleviating the depressive feelings.

When working with patients who have excessive guilt, it is important for the examiner to appreciate that most patients have too little guilt, rather than too much guilt. We are living very much in a psychopathic society. There are some who work on the principle that the therapist should try always to reduce guilt and that increasing guilt cannot but be antitherapeutic. This is absurd. Most people need *more* guilt than less guilt. Accordingly, there are many situations in which the therapist must do everything possible to *increase* guilt in order to help turn the youngster from a psychopathic personality into a civilized human being, sensitive to the feelings of others. But this is an aside. My main point here is that youngsters with an inordinate degree of guilt are prone to become depressed and anything that the examiner can do to reduce guilt will thereby contribute to the alleviation of depression.

Failure to Achieve Certain Aspirations   People who are prone to become depressed are often those with three sets of aspirations that must be maintained if they are to feel worthy. When these goals are not maintained, they tend to react with depressed feelings. The three goals are: 1) the wish to be loved and respected, 2) the wish to be strong, superior, and secure, and 3) the wish to be good and loving rather than hateful and destructive. Some youngsters who are depressed have inordinate needs to be loved and respected. In response to some privations in this area they may have exaggerated needs for compensatory respect and affection. These inordinate needs and demands may result in chronic feelings of dissatisfaction. It it is the job of the therapist to help such youngsters develop more realistic goals with regard to the degree of love and respect they can reasonably hope to obtain from other human beings. Unfortunately, if they are swept up in the romantic love myth—which often promises enormous love and infinite respect—then their frustrations and disillusionment in this area are likely to be formidable.

With regard to the second set of aspirations—to be strong, superior, and secure—boys especially may experience frustration. In the macho world in which they grow up, any signs of weakness or even normal degrees of insecurity may not be tolerable. Inordinate aspirations in this realm are likely to result in the kinds of frustrations and disappointments that contribute to depression. The examiner must help such youngsters gain a more realistic view of what their potentials are and recognize that many who are seemingly stable in this respect are often presenting a facade. Such a youngster has to be helped to appreciate that even those who have exhibited genuine accomplishments still have feelings of insecurity.

With regard to the third realm—the wish to be good and loving rather than hateful and destructive—such youngsters may have the idea that there are all-loving people who do not harbor any hateful feelings at all toward anyone. They have to be helped to appreciate that all human relationships are ambivalent and that even the most loving person harbors within him- or herself deep-seated, hostile, and even hateful feelings. If the therapist is successful in convincing the youngster of the validity of this view, then aspirations may be lowered and this contributing element in depression may be reduced.

Dependency Problems Individuals who easily become depressed are often quite dependent. Not being able to function adequately at age-appropriate levels, they easily slide back into more infantile levels where they gratify their dependent needs. Of course, such individuals require the presence of caretakers who will indulge their dependency demands. Such youngsters are likely to regress to infantile states of helplessness in stressful situations when they do not feel they have the capacity to cope. At such times, depressed patients become clinging and demand support and protection from those around them. It behooves the examiner to help such youngsters deal more adequately with the stresses of life, to learn more about how to cope with reality, and thereby to deal better with stresses. Also, they have to work with the caretaking individuals who might be indulging the dependency gratifications and thereby perpetuating the depression. Sometimes, this is more easily said than done in that the caretakers may rationalize their indulgence to significant degrees. They may view the examiner who requests that they pull back and not provide such indulgences as being cruel and insensitive.

Reactions to Loss Individuals who are depression prone are more likely to react in an exaggerated fashion to significant loss than those who do not become depressed. Sometimes the loss is realistic, such as the loss of a parent, sibling, or loved one. Sometimes the loss is symbolic in that the individual considers the loss to be greater than it really is. A good example of this would be the loss of a boyfriend or girlfriend— someone who, in reality, could be replaced much more easily than the youngster can possibly imagine. Youngsters who are in the latter category should be helped to appreciate that an important factor in the romantic love phenomenon is the projection onto the loved person of one's own aspirations about what an individual should be. In situations where the loss is more real, such as death and divorce, the youngster has to be helped to cope more adequately with these losses. Elsewhere (1983), I have provided advice to such youngsters.

Depression and the Fight/Flight Reaction The fight/flight reactions are of survival value. When confronted with a danger, organisms at all levels either fight or flee. This is an essential mechanism for survival. Some individuals are more likely to fight when confronted with a danger and others more likely to flee. It is probable that both genetic and environmental factors contribute to the pattern that will be selected. The healthy individual is capable of making a judicious decision regarding which mechanism to bring into operation when confronted with a threat. I view many depression-prone individuals as people who are fearful of invoking either of these survival mechanisms, i.e., they are too frightened to fight because they do not view themselves as having effective weapons and they fear flight because they do not consider themselves capable of surviving independently. They need protectors at their side—not only to protect them from the threats of others but to provide for them because they do not feel themselves capable of providing for themselves. They become immobile and paralyzed in a neutral position. They neither fight nor flee. In their immobility they protect themselves from the untoward consequences they anticipate if they were to surge forward and fight the threat. In addition, their immobilization and failure to flee ensures their being protected and taken care of by their protectors.

The "success" of the depressive maneuver requires the attendance of caretaking individuals who will provide the indulgence and protection the depressive person requests, demands, or elicits. Without such individuals the reaction may not be utilized. Well-meaning figures in the depressed person's environment are often drawn into the game, not realizing that their indulgence is a disservice. They may consider themselves loving, sacrificial, giving, and devoted. Although some of those qualities are without doubt present, the caretakers often fail to appreciate that the same maneuvers are perpetuating the depressive symptomatology. Examiners who work with depressed adolescents do well to consider this important possible contribution to the youngster's depression. These young people have to be helped to assert themselves and fight more ardently when the situation warrants it and to develop greater independence so they will not become immobilized and have to rely on caretakers when exposed to external stresses and threats. And the caretaking individuals have to be helped similarly to reduce their indulgence.

Nuclear War We frequently read in newspaper and magazine articles the theory that growing up in a nuclear age can cause young people to become unmotivated and depressed. The prospect of being annihilated in nuclear warfare is said to contribute to poor motivation, boredom, and the lack of commitment to life. And this theory has been invoked to explain teen suicide as well. Although there are certainly youngsters who concern themselves with the prospect of a nuclear holocaust, I have not seen such concern contribute to the formation of clinical symptoms—depression, suicidal attempts, or any other symptoms. Most (but certainly not all) of the youngsters I have seen in my office are not concerned significantly with such issues as politics, wars, and the possibility of a nuclear holocaust. They are much more concerned with their schools, friends, and family. When symptoms develop, they are usually derived from problems in these three areas. When one considers the adolescent's delusions of invulnerability, concerns with nuclear wars become even more remote. In fact, I would go further and say that most adolescents would believe that if there were a nuclear war, they would be among the survivors. And this is not only true regarding exposure to the initial blast, but on the remote level of suffering future consequences of radioactive fallout, burns, etc.

SUICIDE

Adolescent suicide is the second leading cause of death in the United States for individuals between the ages of 15 and 24. (Accidents are the most common cause of death in the teen period.) And the suicidal rate in this age bracket has been increasing. In 1950 the rate was 4.5 per 100,000. This increased to the point where in 1980 it was 12.3 per 100,000. During the 1980s the rate has leveled off, but is still at approximately the 12 per 100,000 range (K. Simmons, 1987a).

Some depressed patients become suicidal. It is important for examiners to appreciate that just about all human beings have suicidal thoughts at times. Life predictably produces frustrations, disappointments, and feelings of impotence. Everyone, at times, gets depressed. People will have the feeling, at times, that "it's just not worth it." Obviously, it would be impossible to obtain normative data regarding just how frequent such thoughts are. It is reasonable to speculate, however, that there is a gradation from the normal level of such thoughts to the pathological frequency. If the examiner worked under the assumption that normal healthy people *never* have such thoughts, then a much higher percentage of patients would be considered suicidal. One wants to learn about the frequency of such thoughts and, of course, the content. Content, especially, will be useful in helping the examiner differentiate between bona fide and fabricated suicidal attempts and preoccupations.

Therapists who work with adolescents may be asked to make a decision regarding whether or not a youngster who threatens suicide should be hospitalized. This is an extremely important question and the ability of the therapist to differentiate between bona fide and fabricated suicidal threats may determine whether a youngster lives or dies. Accordingly, I will present here what I consider to be important differentiating criteria between the two groups. I believe that these criteria will most often enable the therapist to make a decision regarding which category the patient is in. However, there may be occasions when the examiner is not certain. Under these circumstances it is best to err on the side of caution and to hospitalize. I will have more to say about these ambiguous situations below.

I wish to emphasize at this point the importance of the examiner's not conducting a suicide evaluation under conditions of time constraints. That the evaluation may be considered urgent does not mean that the patient need be rushed through it. It is extremely unlikely that the patient is going to try to commit suicide in the therapist's presence. Accordingly, a few hours devoted to the evaluation is reasonable to expect of both the therapist, the patient, and the family. A physician working in an emergency room is in no position to do a proper suicide evaluation. Nor is a therapist working in a clinic setting where the examiner is required to devote only a specific amount of time to each patient. Evaluators working for HMOs that are ever concerned with the "cost effectiveness" of the services provided may also be compromised in their ability to conduct an adequate evaluation for suicide. People do not tell surgeons that they must operate within a particular time frame. All appreciate the fact that the surgeon may not know exactly what to do until the patient is opened. The same principle holds for the psychiatric evaluation and is especially valid when one is considering the possibility of suicide. Evaluators do well, therefore, to refuse to conduct such examinations unless they are given the freedom to spend as much time as they consider warranted.

Bona Fide Suicidal Attempts

First, I will describe those manifestations that generally indicate serious depression. When these factors are present they increase significantly the likelihood that the suicidal threat is genuine. One wants to ascertain whether the threat is made by a youngster who is exhibiting a broader picture of moderately severe to severe depression. Some of the more common manifestations of such depression are psychomotor retardation, severe self-flagellatory and self-deprecatory statements ("I'm no good." "I deserve to die." "I'm loathesome, wretched, etc."). Statements of hopelessness about the future are common as well as profound feelings of helplessness. Patients who spontaneously and frequently speak about their belief that no one will miss them if they die may be a serious suicidal risk. This is an extremely important area to investigate. The realities may be that many close friends and relatives would suffer great grief if the youngster were to commit suicide. If, however, the patient *believes* that none of these individuals care, then the suicidal risk is enhanced formidably.

The presence of psychotic symptoms, such as hallucinations and delusions, increases the suicidal risk. Particularly dangerous are delusions in which the patient views the suicide as a method for joining dead relatives in the afterlife. Of course, if the therapist believes that one does indeed have the opportunity to join dead relatives in the afterlife, then this might not be considered a delusion. It is hoped, however, that the therapist will be of the persuasion that at the age of 16 it is somewhat early for such reconciliation and that it would be better to allow natural forces to determine when this great day of rapprochement takes place. Patients with such a delusion may also hear voices that encourage or order suicide to hasten the journey into the afterlife. Or, the psychotic youngster may respond to delusions of persecution from which the only escape is to kill oneself.

Loss of appetite, loss of sexual desire, sleeplessness, profound feelings of low self-worth, and feelings of painful boredom also enhance the suicidal risk. Other manifestations of severe depression include withdrawal from socialization, loss of interest in friends, lack of pleasure in any activity, weeping episodes, flat depressive affect, and inhibition in expressing anger. In fact, the inhibition in expressing anger may contribute to the aforementioned self-flagellatory statements.

If the patient has a learning disability, then the risk is increased because these youngsters typically exhibit very poor judgment. Even if the gesture or threat is in the manipulative category (see below), the youngster's poor judgment may result in the gesture's becoming an actuality. Youngsters with extremely high academic standards may become suicidal when they do not live up to their and their parents' aspirations. Disappointingly low scores on important examinations (such as the SATs) or failure to gain admission to one's first-choice college may result in suicidal attempts by such youngsters. Generally, the inordinately high standards are not simply self-imposed; most often inordinate pressures are being placed upon the youngster by parents who are obsessed with high grades and prestigious academic institutions. Impaired functioning in school, over a long period, as well as impairments in socialization increase the suicidal risk. The manipulators are more likely to be functioning adequately in these areas.

It is important for the therapist to get a good idea about the degree of stability versus instability that exists (and existed) in the adolescent's home. This cannot be done adequately without interviewing the parents, individually and jointly. Furthermore, family interviews can also be helpful in this regard. The more unhealthy and/or chaotic the youngster's home life, the greater the likelihood the suicidal gesture is genuine. Children who have been exposed to ongoing physical, psychological, and sexual abuse are much more likely to kill themselves than those who come from homes that are reasonably stable. Children from unstable homes are more likely to be runaways and suicide is more likely to occur among runaways. Obviously, a suicidal attempt made by a runaway, when away from home, is not as likely to be detected by potential rescuers and interveners. Even though the youngster may be living at home at the time of the attempt, a history of running away increases the suicidal risk. And if the parents supported the youngster's leaving the home, then the suicidal risk is also enhanced because of the parental rejection signified by such support. These are cases in which the youngsters claim that no one will care if they evaporate from the face of the earth and this may be right.

It is important to get details about the setting in which the suicidal gesture took place and the exact nature of the gesture. Youngsters who make suicidal gestures when alone are more likely to go through with it than those who do so in situations when a parent, sibling, or friend is either in the next room or expected quite soon. In the latter situation, people are being set up to "discover" the gesture before anything serious occurs. The seriousness of the gesture can also provide useful information about the youngster's true intent. If the youngster takes only a few from a large number of pills in a single bottle, then it is most unlikely that the suicidal gesture was genuine. Taking pills, even in large quantities, generally speaks for a lower level of seriousness because of the youngster's recognition of the possibility that he or she may be saved. Wrist slashing, especially when superficial, is rarely a manifestation of a bona fide suicidal attempt. If the attempt involved the use of a gun, then the risk of bona fide suicide is enhanced significantly. In fact, shooting is the most common method of committing suicide among teenagers (K. Simmons, 1987b). But even if the youngster has not threatened to use a gun, if a gun is in the home it should be removed immediately as should any pills that might be used for suicidal purposes. Hanging is also a common method used by those who are successful. Neck slashing is a very serious sign and is not only indicative of a bona fide attempt but is also strongly suggestive of the presence of psychosis. However, psychotics represent only a very small fraction of all those adolescents who successfully kill themselves. Similarly, jumping out of a window, jumping off a roof, or leaping from a high place is obviously genuine and even those who put themselves in a position where they are ready to do so are likely to be serious. However, merely threatening hysterically to take such an action—without any evidence that the youngster is inclined to do so—generally speaks for manipulation.

It is also important to investigate into the history of substance abuse. The abuse of alcohol adds to the suicidal risk. Under its influence the youngster is more likely to exhibit poor judgment and this may turn a fabricated, manipulative suicidal gesture into an actual suicide. A similar situation holds for those who abuse drugs. I am not referring here to death by overdose; I am referring here to the effect of drugs on judgment and cognition. Youngsters involved in criminal behavior are at higher risk. They may be living in dread of being prosecuted and even jailed for their criminal actions. Or, they may live in dread of retaliation for the failure to have fulfilled obligations with their criminal cohorts. I once saw in counseling the parents of a youngster who had committed suicide. The boy, himself, had never been a patient of mine. He had involved himself in both drugs and gambling and had accumulated significant debts. His criminal creditors were constantly harrassing him. In order to mollify them he would borrow more money, gamble more, and thus sunk even deeper into debt. He finally killed himself. It was clear that an important contributing factor to his suicide was the desire to bring about a cessation of his torment. Youngsters who have had difficulties with the law are often impulsive. They think primarily of the moment and do not consider enough the future consequences of their behavior. The same inpulsivity that may result in their involving themselves in criminal acts may result in their making suicidal attempts. Accordingly, the examiner does well to investigate this area, not only with regard to criminal behavior but impulsivity in other areas as well.

One should also investigate the past history of suicidal attempts. Again, one wants to get details about these—especially regarding the situations in which they occurred and the exact nature of the gestures. The greater the number of such gestures, and the more serious each of them was, the greater the likelihood that the one under consideration is serious. A past history of self-destructive behavior and accident proneness also increases the suicidal risk. It is also important to investigate into the family history of suicide. If the youngster's mother or father has indeed committed suicide, then the risk that the youngster will do so as well is significantly increased. This not only relates to the modeling element but to the privation that the youngster must have suffered following the death of the parent. This too is an extremely important differentiating criterion between the bona fide and the fabricated suicidal attempt.

Often the suicidal gesture occurs following a loss or a rejection. Accordingly, one wants to find out about previous reactions to loss or rejection, whether they were tolerated well or whether the youngster reacted severely to them. The more pathological and/or exaggerated the past reactions to loss or rejection, the greater the suicidal risk with regard to the present episode. For example, a youngster might make a suicidal gesture following rejection by a girl friend. If there has been a longstanding history of depression and exaggerated reactions to such rejections, then the likelihood that this rejection will be accompanied by a bona fide suicidal gesture is increased.

Another factor that must be considered is that of the suicide of other adolescents in the community. If the youngster's suicidal attempt was made at a time when other adolescents had committed suicide, especially others in the same area, the likelihood is increased that the youngster's attempt was genuine. This is sometimes referred to as the *cohort effect* or *copycat suicide*. Suicidal attempts, especially adolescent suicidal attempts, sometimes become epidemic. Adolescents are ever concerned with what their peers are doing and reflexively tend to go along with the "in" patterns of behavior—their professions of independence notwithstanding. One good example of this is the anorexia/bulimia phenomenon. When I was in residency training in the late 1950s, this was a relatively rare condition. At the present time anorexia/bulimia is epidemic. Articles on the subject appear consistently in teen magazines. Every classroom has at least a few such girls. And every college dorm also has its share of girls who suffer with the disorder. Suicidal attempts are no exception to the phenomenon of acquiring the psychiatric disorder in vogue at the time.

One factor that has contributed to the spread of the teen suicide phenomenon is the sensationalistic reporting of these deaths in the newspapers. This presents society with a dilemma. On the one hand, we live in a country where we pride ourselves upon our freedom of the press; to suppress, in any way, the freedom of newspapers to report such suicides would be unconstitutional. On the other hand, there is no question that the attention that such suicides provide these youngsters plays a role in encouraging others to perform similar acts. The freedom to describe them in the media, then, contributes to the death of many youngsters every year. I believe that one solution to this dilemma is for newspapers to *voluntarily* restrict such reporting to inconspicuous sections of the newspaper rather than the headlines. In this way their freedom of the press is in no way compromised and the sensationalistic contributing factor to adolescent suicide will be obviated. I recognize, however, that many newspapers will not voluntarily subscribe to this principle because it will involve a loss of income. This is just one example of the prevailing immorality and psychopathy that I see in our society.

One could ask the question here: "Okay, so the youngster is encouraged to commit suicide by the notoriety that peers have 'enjoyed' by their suicides. But don't these kids realize that suicide is final and that they won't be around to read the newspapers?" It may come as a surprise to the reader, but my answer is that they do not appreciate that they won't be around. As mentioned early in this book, one does best to view adolescents as having the bodies of adults but the brains of children. I believe that if one had the opportunity to question adolescents who kill themselves in situations in which suicide is epidemic in their communities, the vast majority would speak of some fantasy relating to their ability to appreciate and even enjoy notoriety after they have died. The fantasy involves people reading about their deaths in the newspapers, crying bitterly at their funerals, and otherwise flagellating themselves for the terrible ways in which they treated the youngster. The fantasy might include the youngster's then getting the love that is not provided in life. The fantasy might involve the youngster's being in heaven and living without the pain and the privations suffered on earth. Or the fantasy might include a degree of attention far beyond what the youngster ever enjoyed in life. And this is especially attractive to withdrawn, alienated youngsters who were ignored and/or rejected to a significant degree. Suddenly, they will be famous. The hitch, of course, is that they will not be there to enjoy their notoriety. But they somehow lose sight of this obvious fact or delude themselves into believing that it will not be that way. Some even have the fantasy that Hollywood will make a film of their lives and this, of course, will result in their becoming famous. The fantasy that they will be there to enjoy their popularity is an extension of the adolescent's delusions of invulnerability. It is also a manifestation of their cognitive simplicity.

Accordingly, therapists do well when evaluating adolescents with suicide potential to focus on this particular area. Attention to this factor has important therapeutic implications. If the youngster does indeed harbor such delusions, then the therapist should do everything to get the youngster to consider other options, options that do not include the existence of some kind of an observing spirit following death. Of course, no examiner can say with 100 percent certainty whether or not such an afterlife exists. The therapist should, however, be reasonable enough on the subject to consider the possibility that there is no such existence and to get the youngster to consider that possibility as well. But, as mentioned, even if the therapist and patient both have deep convictions for the existence of an afterlife, it is hoped that the therapist will at least take the position that the decision regarding *when* an individual should enter into that realm should not be left to an adolescent but to whatever higher forces may be involved in making it.

Another factor that should be taken into consideration when assessing the severity of the suicidal risk is the location in which the youngster lives. Most studies indicate that the rate of suicide is greater in rural areas than in the more populated urban areas. Somehow, areas with very low population density produce more suicides than those in more crowded areas. States like Nevada, Alaska, and Wyoming have suicidal rates among the highest in the country. Perhaps this relates to the isolation of such regions and the boredom that individuals living there may suffer—the beauty of their area notwithstanding. Perhaps the high rate is related to the high American Indian population in these states. This is a group that has a high suicidal rate. And this brings us to the therapist's considering the cultural factors that may be operative. In the American Indian population there is a high rate of alcoholism, unemployment, inadequate education, and a prevailing sense of hopelessness. All of these factors contribute to the higher suicidal rate in this group. But this is just one example. The therapist does well to consider the patient's socioeconomic and/or ethnic group and to investigate the suicidal rate of that group. Obviously, if it is high, then the likelihood of the patient's being suicidal is increased.

If the youngster has left a suicide note, it may be an important source of information about whether or not the attempt has been genuine. One should examine it carefully, read every word, and try to determine which of the criteria provided here are present. I am referring not only to those criteria that support bona fide attempts but fabricated attempts as well. If the note describes in detail the individuals to whom the youngster's possessions should be given, this increases the likelihood that the attempt is genuine. A suicide note in the form of a "last will and testament" also suggests serious intent. The circumstances around which the note was left and read may also provide useful information. A note mailed just before the attempt—a note that could not possibly reach the parents until *after* the death of the youngster—is more likely to be related to a serious gesture. This is also the case for unmailed notes that are not likely to be found until after death. In contrast, notes that provide advance clues to a forthcoming suicidal attempt bespeak for manipulation because they give the finders warning as well as time to interrupt the act.

Fabricated Suicidal Attempts

Now to fabricated suicidal threats and gestures. Often there is an obvious manipulative factor operating. As mentioned, such threats or gestures commonly occur in a situation in which others are present or there is every good reason to believe that others will arrive on the scene quite soon after the gesture. The motive here is to evoke guilt and to manipulate individuals into complying with certain demands. The nature of the gesture is also a telltale sign as to how serious it is. The most common fabricated gestures are wrist slashing and the ingestion of a small fraction of a bottle of pills— often pills that the youngster knows or suspects are nontoxic. In these situations one investigates into the events that led up to the suicidal gesture. Most often one will learn that the youngster has been thwarted with regard to some demand, and the gesture is an obvious attempt to get the parents to change their minds or to feel guilty over the way they have deprived the patient.

Sometimes these gestures serve to get the parents to bring the child to a therapist. Generally, this occurs in situations where the parents have refused to recognize that the youngster has problems and the suicidal attempt can thereby be viewed as a "ticket of admission into treatment." According to J.M. Toolan (1974), manipulative suicidal gestures are much more common in adolescent girls than they are in boys. My own experience bears this out. However, the sex ratio of successful attempts is just the reverse with boys successfully killing themselves much more frequently than girls. In the literature the general figures in both of these categories are four to one, i.e., four girls make attempts to every one boy who makes an attempt, but four boys are successful to every girl who is successful. Accordingly, the examiner should keep these figures in mind when making an evaluation. In short: if the patient is a girl, it is more likely that the gesture is fabricated; if the patient is a boy, it adds to the risk that the attempt is genuine (S. Wensley, 1987).

Dealing with the
Suicidal Patient's Family

I believe that if the therapist carefully considers all of the factors presented above, he or she will be in a good position to make a decision regarding whether or not the suicidal threat is genuine. However, as mentioned, in cases in which the therapist is uncertain it is best to err on the side of caution and to recommend hospitalization. If the therapist does indeed believe that the suicidal risk is present, then he or she does well to pursue one of the following courses. If the therapist believes that the risk is present, but might be reduced by intensive psychotherapy (for example three to five times a week, with the youngster and family)—and if the family is willing to become involved in such intensive treatment—then the therapist might well embark upon such a program and try to do everything possible to avoid hospitalization. But what about situations in which the family refuses both the intensive treatment program and hospitalization. In such cases I will generally remove myself from the case and send a certified letter to the family indicating that I believe that the choice is either intensive outpatient treatment or inpatient therapy. I will then state to the family that because they have refused intensive outpatient treatment and have refused hospitalization, I am discharging myself from the case and am no longer assuming any responsibility for what happens thereafter. I will be sure to include in the letter the name(s) of the hospital(s) that I would recommend they take the patient to and offer to provide recommendations for other therapists if they wish to choose the intensive outpatient treatment option with someone else.

Let us take the situation in which the therapist believes that the suicidal threat is so strong that immediate hospitalization is warranted and that the aforementioned "crash program" would be very risky. And let us consider the situation in which the patient and family refuse to go along with the recommendation for immediate hospitalization. Under these circumstances I would again write a letter in which I remove myself from the case and explain the reasons why. Again, I would strongly urge them to reconsider their decision. It is important for the reader to appreciate that such letters are written not simply because they are good psychiatry but also, considering the risks of malpractice suits at the present time, they are judicious.

Let us now consider the situation in which the family refuses hospitalization but offers the alternative of 24-hour vigils by the parents and other family members. Therapists who agree to this program should hand in their certificates. There is no justification for going along with such a reckless course. Even paid hospital attendants in an institutional setting are not consistently alert enough during their vigils to prevent hospitalized patients from suiciding on occasion. How then can one expect family members to do so? To believe that family members are going to conduct all-night vigils in rotation with one another is foolhardy and absurd. It just won't happen. Perhaps they may last a day or two, or even three, but not much longer. They are bound to slip up and they are bound to be duped by the patient who is determined to commit suicide. Accordingly, if there is indeed a bona fide suicidal risk the patient is likely to commit suicide under these circumstances. I rarely use the words *always* and *never*. However, this is one situation in which I say that the therapist should *never* be party to such an arrangement. Under these circumstances the most judicious thing for the therapist to do is to remove him- or herself from the case with an associated letter of explanation. In it, of course, the therapist must advise the parents to seek hospitalization.

MEDICATION

Introduction

I am in full agreement with those who claim that "for every crooked thought there must be a crooked molecule." There must be a neurological basis for all symptoms. There are some, however, who claim that this dictum makes the differentiation between the psychogenic and organic an anachronism, a residuum of medieval thinking. They would consider such differentiations to be in the category of questions like how many angels can dance on the head of a pin. Although I believe that it is true that there must be a neurological basis for all thoughts and feelings — because one must have a nerve cell to have a thought or a feeling — I do not believe that it necessarily follows that the differentiation between psychogenic and organic symptoms is irrelevant in these modern times. Such differentiation concerns itself with the crucial question of *how* the molecule got "crooked." This is important because the more we know about the pathogenesis of a disorder, the better the likelihood we will be able to do something about it.

In addition, the differentiation has important therapeutic implications. If one believes that the molecule got crooked because of environmental (especially family) influences, then one is more likely to recommend psychotherapy, milieu therapy, family therapy, and other therapeutic approaches that involve personality changes in the patient and his or her associates. In contrast, if one believes that the etiology is metabolic, genetic, biological, etc. then one is more likely to have little faith in the therapeutic efficacy of environmental changes and more conviction that some drug (presently or in the future) will straighten out the molecule. This may very well be the case. This does not, however, negate the aforementioned arguments. Knowledge is power and the more we know about the etiology of a disorder the better we will be able to prevent and treat it. In addition, most of those who use medication in psychiatry will agree that they do not provide complete cures, that whatever straightening of the molecules such drugs can achieve, they still remain somewhat twisted. Accordingly, at this present state of our knowledge (or more accurately ignorance) we do well to utilize all therapeutic modalities, both biological and environmental.

Antidepressants

Compared to other psychiatrists, I consider myself to have a somewhat conservative position on prescribing medication. With regard to medication for depression, I recognize that my position is a rare one in psychiatry today, because I consider the vast majority of depressions to be psychogenic in etiology. With the exception of people with manic-depressive psychosis (still rare in my opinion), the overwhelming majority of people I see who are depressed are so because of psychogenic factors. This does not preclude the presence of a genetic predisposition. Nor does my position preclude the belief that depressed patients can be helped by antidepressant medication. It is probably the case that the antidepressant does not differentiate between depressions that are biological in etiology and those that are environmentally or psychologically induced. However, I believe that the psychiatrist who confines him- or herself to antidepressant medication only, is not dealing with many if not most of the fundamental problems that have contributed to the development of the patient's depression. Although one may achieve with medication some symptomatic alleviation of the depression, one should still be dealing with the life situations that have contributed to its formation and perpetuation.

Viewing depression as primarily, if not exclusively, biological in etiology is attractive because it enables the therapist to prescribe medication only and not involve him- or herself in the more arduous and expensive task of ongoing psychotherapy for the patient and possibly family members. Viewing depression to be primarily if not exclusively biological in etiology is "cost effective," enables therapists to "treat" large numbers of people, and is attractive to hospital administrators, agencies, and those who fund treatment. Rather than view the vast majority of depressed people as being the unfortunate victims of a metabolic disease, I generally approach the problem with the question: "What is the person depressed about?" I believe that depression is being overly diagnosed because making the diagnosis provides the therapist with justification for prescribing antidepressant medication—a quick and easy cure. In recent years, we are told by newspapers, magazines, and psychiatrists that depression is much more common than people previously realized, but there is no reason to lose heart because we have recently enjoyed "good news about depression" and the good news is that doctors have now discovered "miracle" cures. Magazine articles abound describing people who were treated unsuccessfully by psychotherapy for many years and then quickly cured in one or two sessions by a biological psychiatrist. Individual testimonies generally are considered proof that the antidepressant produced the "cure." My own view is that in the last 15 or 20 years, there has been "bad news about depression" in that the emphasis on the biological etiology has diverted people from focusing on its psychodynamics. And this, I believe, is really bad news for people who are depressed. It is also bad news for psychiatry.

Thus far, I have not seen fit to prescribe antidepressant medication for children. Nor have I prescribed it for younger adolescents. On those rare occasions when I have prescribed it for youngsters in the mid-to-late adolescent period, I have found the MAO inhibitors to be more efficacious than the tricyclics. But, even when I do prescribe medication, I combine it with intensive psychotherapy. And I make it known to the patient and family that I view antidepressant medication to be an *adjunct* to the primary treatment, which is psychotherapy and the working out of the complex personal and family problems that have contributed to the development and perpetuation of the patient's symptoms.

Lithium

When I attended medical school in the mid-1950s we were taught that the manic-depressive psychosis is an extremely rare disorder and we considered ourselves fortunate in being able to see such a patient demonstrated to one of our classes. In the late 1950s lithium was introduced as one of the most predictable and effective treatments for the manic phase of manic-depressive psychosis. As the years rolled on, more and more people became diagnosed as having manic-depressive psychosis and various other kinds of manic disorders. I do not believe that there has been any increase in the actual incidence or prevalence of this disorder. What has increased is the frequency with which psychiatrists have diagnosed it, in order to justify giving such patients lithium. So enthusiastic have psychiatrists been about prescribing lithium that it is often even given for people who are depressed, under the theory that it will "flatten" the bipolar fluctuations. And an ever-expanding list of people have been diagnosed as having manic episodes: people who are agitated, hyperactive adolescents (and even preadolescents), anxious people, those who speak under tension, people who go on spending splurges (even though not psychotic), individuals who talk too quickly, and anyone else for whom the psychiatrist wishes to justify prescribing lithium.

I do believe that lithium does help reduce mania in patients suffering with bona fide manic states. I do *not* believe that it alleviates depression and I do *not* believe that it helps people who are *not* genuinely manic. Again, we see a situation in which a good drug is overutilized by psychiatrists who diagnose everyone and anyone who might have symptoms that might justify the drug's utilization. Such overdiagnosing lessens our sense of therapeutic impotence and creates in us the delusion that we can cure more people than we actually can. In the service of this goal bipolar disorders are then suddenly discovered to be more prevalent than previously realized. Armies of new experts now crop up in the service of the same needs. Expert diagnosticians then claim that they have seen incipient manic behavior, early phases of manic behavior, etc., all in the service of justifying prescribing lithium. Here too, investigation into the psychodynamics of the excited states need not be done, all one needs do is prescribe lithium— which is far more efficient, quick, and "cost effective."

Neuroleptics
and Anxiolytics

Although I recognize the value of phenothiazines and other neuroleptics in the treatment of psychotic states, I have had little opportunity to use them in recent years because of my limited experience with psychotic children. I have had more experience with anxiolytic agents, especially diazepam (Valium). I have used diazepam in the treatment of children with separation anxiety disorder and consider it to be of some symptomatic value. However, the primary focus of my treatment of such children is on the symbiotic relationship they most often have with their mothers and on the other psychogenic problems that these children have. R. Gittelman-Klein, and D.F. Klein (1973) and R. Gittelman-Klein (1975) consider imipramine (Tofranil), a tricyclic antidepressant, to be useful in the treatment of separation anxiety disorder. They believe that it blocks the peripheral manifestations of the panic state. Although my experience with imipramine for this purpose has been limited, I have not found it significantly useful in the treatment of these children. One difficulty in assessing its efficacy in the treatment of panic states is that it generally takes a week or two before its effect can be assessed. Diazepam, in contrast, generally works within a half hour and I believe is much more likely to reduce anxiety and panic. I have also prescribed diazepam for children who are severely anxious. One of the problems with diazepam is that youngsters taking it can easily become lethargic in school and so one must become quite careful in monitoring the dosage level.

Psychostimulants

I consider myself to have had extensive experience with psychostimulants, especially methylphenidate (Ritalin), dextroamphetamine (Dexadrine), and pemoline (Cylert). I consider these drugs to be useful for children with hyperactivity, but I do not consider them to be of any value in helping youngsters sustain attention. I consider it important to differentiate between hyperactivity and the impairment in sustaining attention (the so-called attention-deficit disorder). Elsewhere (1987b) I have discussed studies of mine that, I believe, clearly support my view that true attention deficit disorder (ADD) is very rare. Hyperactivity, however, certainly is to be found, but is best considered to be a manifestation of temperamental, genetically determined, high activity level. I believe that psychostimulant medications do three things: 1) reduce hyperactivity, 2) enhance compliance with parents and teachers, and 3) reduce impulsivity. When parents are asked whether psychostimulant medication has helped their youngster, a common reply is: "Doctor, he listens better when he's taking the medicine." When such parents use the words "listens better" in these situations, they are not referring to attention-sustaining capacity; rather, they are referring to the child's *compliance*. If one investigates further into whether or not hyperactive children also have ADD, one will often learn from parents that they will sit for hours watching television and generally have no problem concentrating on their favorite TV programs. I generally prefer methylphenidate and dextroamphetamine over pemoline because of the latter's time lag before becoming effective. Dextroamphetamine and methylphenidate generally work within 30 to 45 minutes, whereas pemoline does not build up to effective dosage levels until seven to ten days. Furthermore, it is much easier for me to monitor the former drugs with my Steadiness Tester (1979b, 1979c) with which I can objectively ascertain whether or not the drug is being effective in reducing hyperactivity. I can also use it to monitor the dosage levels in order to ascertain the level of optimum efficacy.

HOSPITALIZATION

Introduction

I consider myself to have a very conservative position with regard to hospitalizing adolescent patients. I do believe that there certainly are indications for hospitalizing a youngster in this age bracket, but I also believe that the majority of adolescent patients who are presently hospitalized would not have been so had I been the one to make the decision. I generally view hospitalization to be warranted primarily for people who are homicidal, suicidal, or who are in very special situations (to be described below) where it is only by separation from their families that there is any hope for alleviation of their difficulties. Most patients' problems have both intrapsychic and interpersonal contributory elements. The therapist must work in both areas. This usually involves individual work and close work with family members. Plucking the person out of the family context, putting the individual in the hospital, and then treating that person in isolation from the family in the hope that such treatment will help the individual reintegrate him- or herself into the family is often misguided. Doing everything possible to keep the patient in the family, the environment wherein the problems arose and the environment wherein the problems are best worked through is, in my opinion, the preferable approach.

The Medical Model

I believe that one factor that contributes to the ease with which many therapists hospitalize relates to the influence of the medical model on psychiatric practice. Although it is true that the hospital may very well be the optimum place for the treatment of many physical disorders, it does not necessarily follow that the hospital is also the best place for the treatment of many psychiatric disorders. The reflex hospitalization of the patient often reflects doctors' blindly following the medical model.

The Hospital Business

It is important for the reader to appreciate (if he or she doesn't already) that many hospitals are basically businesses, often run and owned by nonmedical people. This is not only the case for private hospitals but, more recently, even for nonprofit and voluntary hospitals as well. Under these circumstances an empty bed means loss of income. The criteria for hospitalization then become expanded—often to include any situation that might justify hospitalization, no matter how weak the justifications. Many fancy and well-appointed hospitals charge enormous amounts of money (hundreds of dollars a day) and are nothing more than hotels. They look good on paper with regard to the kind of staff that is providing treatment, but little meaningful therapy is provided. In such facilities one of the most important (if not the most important) determinants of how long a patient will stay will be how much money the individual has. All other criteria are of secondary importance in determining the length of hospitalization. When the person runs out of insurance coverage (inevitable with such prices), the staff is suddenly talking about discharge from the hospital. At that point the patient is referred back to the referring physician, just as a specialist in a hospital might refer back a patient to a referring general practitioner. The notion of the importance of continuity of treatment and the all-important ongoing therapist-patient relationship are of little concern to those in the hospital business. When they say that the average patient stays 21 days in their hospital, they would like to imply that that was all the patients needed and that they were significantly improved and even "cured" following their sojourn in the facility. What the 21-day average really means is that that was just about all most of their patients could possibly afford before being forcibly discharged.

It is also important for the reader to appreciate that psychiatry is also a business and that a psychiatrist referring a patient for hospitalization may do so more for financial gain than therapeutic indications. Most psychiatrists follow traditional practice in their private offices and charge a specific fee for a traditional 45 to 50 minute session. At this time (1988), the going rate for most psychiatrists is somewhere between $75 and $125 per session. In a hospital, however, one "makes rounds" (again, following the medical model). A patient may be seen for only five or ten minutes and the psychiatrist may easily get away with charging not only standard fees but even more because insurance companies tend to pay more money for people who are in hospitals. Under these circumstances earning $1000 in an hour is not uncommon. And when patients complain about this, they are told that their disgruntlement is just another manifestation of their psychopathology and that if they were healthier they wouldn't be complaining so much. (No wonder so many people hate the psychiatrists they see in such hospitals.)

The Teaching Hospital

Another factor that contaminates the decision regarding hospitalization relates to the situation in teaching hospitals, those closely affiliated with medical schools. These hospitals have an obligation to provide patients for medical students, interns, and residents. In addition, most teaching hospitals train psychologists, psychiatric social workers, and sometimes nurse practitioners, pastoral counselors, and others who want to become therapists. It would seriously compromise the reputation of such an institution if it did not have a good supply of patients for all these students and their teachers. Once again, the criteria for hospitalization become loosened in order to provide such "teaching material."

Situations in Which Hospitalization is Warranted

The Chaotic, Disorganized Home   The aforementioned contaminations regarding admission criteria notwithstanding, there are still patients who do need to be removed from their families. Occasionally, the patient's home life may be so chaotic and the family so incapable of working through their problems that the only way to prevent further deterioration of the youngster is to remove him or her from the home. Under these circumstances, the hospital may be viewed as a way station to placement elsewhere. These are situations in which the family has proven itself to be unworkable regarding any kind of therapeutic intervention. Such "crisis intervention" is certainly indicated. However, even then, day hospitals will sometimes serve (J.C. Westman, 1979). Under these circumstances the hospitals may provide a structure that does not exist in the home. The environment is far more predictable than the chaotic one of the home. And these factors are generally salutary.

It is important for therapists to appreciate that even under these circumstances, there are certain elements in the hospital program that are antitherapeutic. I have already mentioned the lack of continuity of treatment and the lack of appreciation of an ongoing therapist-relationship as the cornerstone of effective psychotherapy. Another drawback is that the youngster is being placed in an environment with other disturbed adolescents, adolescents who may be suffering with moderately severe to severe psychiatric disorders. Whatever benefit may be derived from the healthy therapeutic milieu of the administration and caretaking personnel, there is no question that exposure to other sick adolescents has many antitherapeutic elements. Certainly, one of the aims of treatment is to help the adolescent relate better to peers. But with peers who are severely disturbed, more unhealthy than healthy behavior may be learned. It is common for parents, when visiting such facilities, to comment that their youngster will be placed with a lot of "crazy kids." Traditionally, such parents are reassured that there is nothing antitherapeutic or dangerous about such placement and that their concerns are unwarranted. At best, this is naive; at worst, the reassurance is duplicitous. It is often not believed by the reassurer but he or she doesn't want to lose a "good customer."

J. Christ (1974) puts it well:

> Whenever possible the treatment of an adolescent problem situation should first be attempted on an outpatient basis and with active participation of the family. Even in cases where

psychotic syndromes are present, much understanding can often be gained from an exploration on an individual and family basis. Institutionalization for acute situations should be reserved for life-threatening circumstances. For chronic situations, it will be important first and foremost to assess the strength of the youngster and the family's resources to deal with a given problem. Repetitive crises, which often occur in the matrix of a chronic unsatisfactory situation, can sometimes be dealt with by crisis intervention methods. However, where it has become clear that neither the teenager nor the family has means at their disposal to extricate themselves from a destructive situation, a change in milieu may be necessary. It is in those circumstances that school away from home or institutionalization may be necessary. A structured milieu often has beneficial effects in those cases where clearly no structure had been provided by the parents and where either physical or emotional deprivation had been a problem. It needs to be understood that institutionalization for chronic problems will usually require some considerable time, and the adolescent hospitalized or institutionalized will often fight hard battles with the caring personnel.

Christ mentions that the patients "will often fight hard battles with caring personnel." These battles are often viewed as manifestations of the patient's psychopathology. Unfortunately, this is often not the case. Some of the sickest people gravitate toward jobs in psychiatric hospitals. Many are borderline and some even psychotic. Many are sadistic, psychopathic, or just plain lazy and uninterested. Accordingly, I would rephrase Christ's statement: "will often fight hard battles with *uncaring* personnel." This is another reason for therapists' thinking twice before recommending hospitalization, even for those from chaotic, unstructured homes.

Antisocial Acting Out   Elsewhere in this book (especially in Chapter Thirteen) I discussed the treatment of antisocial disorders in some detail. Here I focus on certain aspects of the treatment of such youngsters related to the issue of hospitalization. Office and clinic treatment is for patients who do not pose a threat to the therapist's person or property. If the therapist has to work under circumstances in which he or she fears harm to him- or herself or destruction of his or her property, then effective psychotherapy is not likely to be possible. The enhanced attention and vigilance associated with such concerns of being harmed by the patient cannot but compromise the therapist's objectivity. Patients who threaten such damage should be told that outpatient treatment is for those who *talk* about their problems rather than those who *act out* on them, especially against their therapists. Although not all patients who threaten harm to their therapists and/or act out against them should necessarily be sent to a hospital, most of them are not reasonably considered candidates for psychotherapy. The alternatives for such patients, then, are either no treatment at all or treatment in a hospital setting where the therapist can be comforted by the protection (not always perfect, to say the least) of the hospital staff. With less tension and vigilance on the therapist's part, there is a greater likelihood that he or she can attend to the patient's problems.

Hospitalization must seriously be considered for antisocial youngsters whose behavior is so dangerous that there is a real risk of homicide. On occasion this relates to reckless driving when inebriated or under the influence of drugs. On other occasions the patient is engaging in such violent antisocial acts that there is a real danger that someone will be killed.

Behavior Modification as a Treatment for Antisocial Adolescents Most hospitals for adolescents provide behavior modification programs. These have been very much in vogue during the last 15 to 20 years and are certainly considered far more "cost effective" than something as inefficient as long-term psychotherapy. I believe that behavior modification programs—as the primary, if not exclusive, modality for antisocial acting out—do more harm than good. I wish to emphasize that I am confining myself here to the use of behavior modification in the treatment of *antisocial disorders*, and I am *not* commenting on the use of behavior modification for the treatment of other disorders such as phobias, for example.

To elaborate. Although behavior therapists differ with regard to their conviction for the role in which underlying psychodynamics contribute to symptom formation, when they use behavior modification therapeutically, they are focusing primarily, if not exclusively, on symptomatic alleviation or removal. For many the symptoms *are* essentially the disease. But even those who have some conviction for the importance of psychodynamic factors in bringing about symptoms, the focus is on symptom removal when behavior modification is utilized. Generally, this is done by providing *positive reinforcement* for desirable behavior. An example of this would be praise or, more formally, rewarding the child with tokens, candy, merit points, or some other desirable item. In addition, attempts to discourage the child from undesirable behavior are made by utilizing *negative reinforcement*. Here, an aversive stimulus that has been applied to discourage the perpetuation and repetition of the behavior is removed. An example of this would be the cessation of scolding a child after he or she has exhibited undesirable behavior or lifting a restriction that has been imposed after exhibiting undesirable behavior. Another technique utilized in behavior modification is *punishment*. Here, an aversive stimulus is applied following undesirable behavior in an attempt to suppress that behavior in the future. An example of this would be placing the child in a locked room, often given a euphemistic name such as "quiet room." Last, *extinction* is also used. Here, an attempt is made to discourage undesirable behavior by suppressing factors that reinforce it. An example of this would be ignoring a youngster who has a tantrum or rage outburst rather than paying attention to him or her. Further details on these approaches are described by I.G. Sarason and B.R. Sarason (1980).

I view these approaches to be, at best, superficial. But when applied as the primary, if not exclusive, mode of treatment for antisocial behavior, they are not only destructive but perpetuate the very symptoms that they are designed to discourage or "extinguish." The latter term is extremely misleading because the approach is just the opposite. They actually entrench the very behavior that they are designed to obliterate. The entrenchment does not take place at the time of the application of the aversive stimuli and negative reinforcement. Rather, it takes place after the youngster is out of the hospital, after the therapists have written their articles describing the wonderful results they have obtained with behavior modification.

To elaborate on this point. Youngsters with antisocial behavior disorders, as described in detail in Chapter One, have defects in the development of the internal guilt-evoking mechanisms (conscience). The therapeutic approach *must* attempt to strengthen these youngsters' sense of guilt. I use the word guilt here, as I have previously, to refer to the feeling of lowered self-worth that the individual experiences after having thoughts, experienced feelings, or committed acts that the person has learned in childhood are wrong or bad. These youngsters need *more* guilt and the therapist should do everything possible to make them feel more guilty. Behavior modification misses this important point. The alleged guilt that a graduate of these behavior modification programs feels, if anything, is more like the guilt that the judge is referring to when he asks an accused whether or not he pleads guilty or innocent. Here, the judge is basically asking whether the individual admits to having committed the crime or not. Nothing is said about intrapsychic processes that may or may not be operative. Actually, we should have two different words to refer to these phenomena – so apart are they. Behavior modification teaches youngsters to deter themselves from performing unacceptable acts by the awareness that if they do so, they will suffer some kind of pain or some pleasure will be removed. Nothing is likely to be said about the victim and no attempt is generally made to internalize the inhibitory mechanisms. Behavior modification deals with externals. Psychotherapy focuses on internals, yet it need not ignore externals (as I have demonstrated so often throughout this book).

Behavior modification is less likely to devote itself to the more formidable task of investigation into intrapsychic processes because it is not "cost effective" and is a far more demanding and time-consuming task. In a behavior modification program, when a youngster is anticipating an antisocial act, he calculates the risk of being caught and what the consequences will be. In a "good" behavior modification program he is able to predict with a fair degree of accuracy exactly what is going to happen to him if caught. He may or may not decide to take his chances. But, even if he does commit the transgression and is caught, he can often "work off" the demerits, punishments, etc. by good works. Accordingly, the system teaches various kinds of manipulations.

Once these youngsters have been "cured" and discharged from the hospital they find themselves in a world completely unlike that of the hospital. No one is walking around with clipboards and check lists. No one is giving them merits and demerits, rewards and punishments, and putting these into a computer. Without such monitoring, and without their having developed any internalized inhibitory mechanisms, they bounce back and become even worse than they were before. It is then that I see them in my office. When I have made these criticisms to people who work in such programs, I am sometimes told that individual psychotherapy is also provided and that attempts are made to instill guilt as well. Although I cannot say that this never takes place, I am somewhat dubious that it is the prevailing approach. First, in most of these facilities, there is not the time to provide intensive individual therapy to all of the patients. Next, the staff personnel are generally not schooled in intensive psychotherapy, rather they are committed more to the seemingly easier and ostensibly more efficient behavior modification.

Other Situations for Which Hospitalization May Be Warranted I have already mentioned bona fide suicidal gestures as a justifiable and even compelling reason for hospitalization. Some adolescent youngsters may need hospitalization for the treatment of drug abuse, because they cannot be trusted to wean themselves from the habit in a noncontrolled situation. Girls suffering with bulimia/anorexia may require hospitalization. These patients generally require a hospital setting in which the personnel are particularly familiar with the treatment of such youngsters. Otherwise, they tend to manipulate hospital personnel into the same kinds of pathological transactions and "games" that they have involved themselves in with their parents. Starving themselves is not unknown among such patients and the likelihood that this can take place may be reduced by removing the youngster from the family milieu in which the symptom is thriving. Because some of these patients literally starve themselves to death, hospitalization in such cases may be lifesaving.

CONCLUDING COMMENTS

I recognize that some readers may consider me to have a somewhat jaundiced view of the value of hospitalization for adolescent patients. It is a view derived primarily from the "outside." What I have seen of the "inside" comes from my residency days as well as my experiences over 25 years as an attending psychiatrist at the New York State Psychiatric Institute at the Columbia-Presbyterian Medical Center. There I have supervised residents who have patients admitted to the inpatient service. My experience has been that the younger the patient the less the likelihood I would have recommended hospitalization. This is certainly the case for many, if not most, on the children's inpatient service. With regard to adolescents, the same principle holds. My experience has been that the younger adolescents, generally, are less likely to require hospitalization than some of the older ones. And the older ones have generally been youngsters with flagrant psychotic episodes which, I will agree, probably do require hospitalization because of the danger to themselves and others if they are not placed in a protected setting. The reader who is interested in further discussion of the subject of hospitalization of adolescent patients does well to refer to articles by D.B. Rinsley (1974), L.A. Stone (1979), and D. Zinn (1979).

CHAPTER FIFTEEN

CONCLUDING COMMENTS AND A LOOK AT THE FUTURE

Although the primary purpose of this book has been to focus on specific psychotherapeutic techniques of use in the treatment of adolescents, I have throughout commented on family and environmental changes that might be therapeutically beneficial for them. I have not, however, discussed in detail how the therapist might bring about changes in the environment. Rather, I have focused my attention primarily on the psychotherapeutic techniques that the therapist might utilize in his or her office when working directly with the patient. Therapists who choose to involve themselves in bringing about these broader changes in society are contributing to the advancement of preventive psychiatry. Obviously, a single individual is only capable of making a small contribution in this realm. However, the greater the number of therapists who involve themselves beyond their offices in bringing about these changes, the greater the likelihood they will come about.

Therapists like myself who devote themselves primarily to individual psychotherapy generally have little time left over for extensive involvement in such causes. However, this does not preclude some involvement. And if these small degrees of involvement are multiplied by large numbers of therapists, then an impact may be made. Therapists do well to think intermittently about these issues and, in the course of their daily living, take those opportunities that may come their way to promulgate their particular causes. Public speaking and writing provide excellent vehicles for spreading one's ideas and therapists do well to avail themselves of such opportunities when they arise. Volumes could be written on the various kinds of social changes that might be psychologically useful for adolescents, both at the preventive and therapeutic levels. Here I will focus on a few areas that are of particular concern to me. Some of these points have already been made in the course of the book, but I repeat them here because I believe they are worthy of emphasis and reiteration.

CHILD CARE

First, I would like to emphasize that I am in sympathy with and support of the feminist movement. There is no question that women have been subjected to terrible persecution and other indignities throughout the course of history and there is no question that we have a long way to go until we reach the point of full egalitarianism. Also, I wish to emphasize at the outset that I am in full support of women being given the opportunity to pursue and work within any career, occupation, or skill. However, just about every social advance is associated with untoward reactions, drawbacks, and undesirable effects—many of which are unforeseen. And women's entrance into the extradomestic realm is no exception to this phenomenon. I focus here on the effects of such liberation on children. Whatever benefits may be derived by women as a result of their changing roles from child rearer to bread winner, there is no question that many children have suffered. The simple facts are that to the degree that the mother invests herself in professional fulfillment she is neglecting her children. But this is true of fathers as well. And I am not referring here simply to the effects of the time parents spend out of the home, but their psychological investment in the extra-domestic activities. When one comes home at the end of the day drained and exhausted, there is little *quality* involvement left over for the children.

As more mothers have entered the workplace, an increasing number of children have been left to the care of others. Many are put in day-care centers and many are left with friends, relatives, and neighbors. The more remote the caretaking individuals are from the mother (biologically and psychologically) the less the likelihood these children will receive optimum care. And the younger the children, the greater the likelihood they will develop psychological problems. The simple facts are these: the biological parent is much more likely to provide optimum care than anyone else on earth. I don't care how many Ph.D.s the people at the day-care center have and I don't care how committed they are to the child-rearing process, they are still not likely to have as strong a psychological bond with the children under their care as the biological mother. And then there is the turnover. They can't possibly maintain ongoing strong ties with children who are being replaced every year or two. And even if ties are formed, they are broken by the structure of the system. This too is detrimental. In line with my theory of the development of the internalized guilt-evoking mechanisms described in Chapter One, I believe that this phenomenon is *one* of the factors operative in producing psychopathic personality types. It is *one* of the factors involved in the erosion of values and morals that I see in our society.

As mentioned earlier in this book, I believe there is a relatively simple solution to this problem. It is rare that I can make such a statement. Most problems are exceedingly complex and it is extremely unusual to be able to say that there is a simple solution. But there is one for this problem. Specifically, we can reasonably restructure our society so that both fathers and mothers alternate work outside the home two to three days a week and spend two to three days within the home during each work week. Both could be home on weekends. And this program is feasible. All of us have had the experience of calling an office and asking to speak with Mr. Jones. We are told that Jones is not available on that day but will be available on the next day; we are asked if we would like to speak with Smith. Under the system I propose here, Jones would be home with his baby rather than merely out of the office working for the company elsewhere. As children get older and attend school, parents could then expand their involvements outside the home. I am not claiming that this program could be easily implemented; I am only claiming that it is feasible and realizable. The vast majority of offices, businesses, and industries can accomodate such a work program for their employees.

Implementation of this plan would not preclude entirely the function of child-care centers. Rather, a smaller percentage of child-care could still be provided by them. I am not claiming that the child-care center experience is 100 percent detrimental to children. They do learn socialization and are provided with opportunities to expand their emotional and intellectual horizons. My main criticism is the quantity of time that many children are spending there and, in many cases, the poor quality of care provided. I believe that society would benefit immensely if the aforementioned parental work plan were implemented because healthier children would develop from it. And healthier children become healthier adults, and strengthen thereby society at large.

I believe also that elderly people are not being properly used in the child-rearing process. Many older people are still quite capable of providing meaningful child care, their infirmities notwithstanding. They often have the time and the patience to take care of children, and such involvement may provide meaning to lives that may otherwise appear meaningless. On occasion I have read or heard about child-care centers that have linked up with old-age homes, much to the benefit of both institutions. Elderly people could also be involved significantly in the operation of child-care centers. I understand that in China this is routinely done. Specifically, while both parents are working out in the fields or in the factories, elderly people take care of the children. They assist in the care of pre-schoolers in day-care centers and involve themselves, as well, in after-school care for older children.

THE PSYCHOLOGICAL PROBLEMS OF BLACK CHILDREN

It is now almost 125 years since the end of the Civil War. Everyone agrees that things have not changed significantly for black children.

Since that time waves of immigrants from practically every country in the world have come to these shores, and each group has somehow found its path into the mainstream of middle America. Except the blacks. Recently, I heard a series of speakers commenting on the fact that now, twenty years after the death of Martin Luther King, very little has changed for the vast majority of black people. All agreed the problems are complex and just about all claimed that one of the things that was needed was more money. Some mentioned that some of the more recent immigrants—especially Chinese, Japanese, Koreans, Indians, and Vietnamese—are moving rapidly into the mainstream of American life and their children are receiving a wide variety of prestigious academic awards. The explanation given for this disparity is the inferior education black children receive in inner cities. I do not question that this is a factor. However, not one speaker spoke about what I consider to be a primary element in explaining the failure of blacks to move ahead into the mainstream of American society.

The basic problem of black children is the absence of a father figure in the home from birth through the formative years. The primary adult model for millions of black children is the mother figure only. And for millions this mother may be a teenager who is still a child being taken care of by her own mother, the infant's maternal grandmother. The child's father is often unknown, or if known is often only intermittently involved, or not involved at all in the child-rearing process. There are few, if any, male models for educational aspiration and/or the extra-domestic work ethic. But there may be models for psychopathic behavior provided by males in the streets who are often involved significantly in crime and drugs. As cited previously in this book, a number of years ago one of the black comedians—I think it was Dick Gregory—made comments along these lines to a group of blacks: "You want to be successful in life? I'll tell you how to be successful in life. Get up in the morning, take a pencil and paper, follow an Oriental around all day, and write down exactly what he does. Then, starting the next day, you do exactly the same things." I don't care how much money is spent in helping blacks. It is not likely to work if some of the money is not spent in the realm of educating people to this important fact. All the other groups who have entered into America's mainstream have had strong family ties in which parents were

involved with children throughout the full course of their upbringing. When I say parents I mean both mothers and fathers, each
playing his or her own role in the child-rearing process. It would be
an error for the reader to conclude that I am proposing this as the
entire solution to the problem of blacks in America. Rather, I am
stating that it is a special problem which, if not solved, will make all
other efforts futile. It may be difficult to bring about changes in this
pattern in a short time. It will probably take many generations.
However, without drawing attention to the problem, the first steps
toward its alleviation are not likely to be taken.

DIVORCE AND CUSTODY LITIGATION

Another common source of psychopathology in children that could
be avoided is that which is associated with divorce and custody
litigation. I am not referring here to the psychopathology that may
arise directly as a result of the divorce; rather, I am referring to the
unnecessary and additional psychopathology that results from the
exposure of children to and their embroilment in their parents'
divorce and custody litigation. People who are divorcing have
enough grief; they don't need the additional stress associated with
having to litigate. In most countries of the world people do not have
to litigate in order to get a divorce. In the United States, probably
more than anywhere else in the world, people who are divorcing
become subjected to the additional psychological traumas of adversary litigation. However, for most people in the U.S. there is an
option that is not being utilized widely enough. I am referring to
mediation. There is no reason why the vast majority of people who
divorce should not go first to a mediator who will help them resolve
their differences. In order to ensure that the final agreement is truly
impartial, each of the parents could have the document reviewed by
his or her own attorney who would assess the instrument for
inequities. These independent attorneys should be individuals who
serve themselves as mediators in other cases. They should not be
lawyers who are the barracuda types who relish adversary litigation
with little heed to the psychological toll on their clients and with

primary concern for the amount of money they can extract from them. If either party or either adversary attorney considered inequities to be present in the agreement derived from the mediation process, then the three attorneys (the mediator and the two independent counselors) could meet together to attempt to iron out any differences that may still be present. Then, the two attorneys could obtain for their clients a noncontested divorce. If the mediator felt the need for consultation with a child psychiatrist (if there were a custody conflict) or an accountant (if complex financial problems arose) then he or she could do so. If, however, the mediation breaks down and the parties are not able to resolve their differences, then they might still have the opportunity to resort to adversary litigation. Of course, there are other mediation programs, but the aforementioned is the one that I prefer.

People divorcing today are easy prey to an army of attorneys who are exploiting them. At the present time there is approximately one attorney for every 800 people in the population. Clearly, all these attorneys cannot possibly make a living as lawyers. Accordingly, there are many "hungry" attorneys, but there is a sea of gullible people who are allowing themselves to be exploited by them. About ten years ago mediation began to move forward and I had hopes that by the end of this century it would be the routine method for obtaining a divorce. Unfortunately, it appears to me that the initial momentum is dying down. From the outset lawyers resisted the movement because of the obvious fact that two lawyers engaging their clients in protracted adversary litigation will bring in far more money to the profession than one lawyer serving as a mediator. Furthermore, ours is very much an adversarial society— the most litigious country on earth (J. K. Lieberman, 1981)—and mediation goes very much against this philosophy. About eight years ago, I wrote that by the end of this century people would look back on the mid- to late-20th century as a time of national craziness with regard to the quickness with which individuals involved themselves in adversary litigation for divorce and custody disputes. I suspect that this prophecy will not be realized and the exploitation of divorcing people will continue into the 21st century as will the sadistic destruction of parents and children that is fomented by embroilment in adversary litigation. Elsewhere (1986b) I have discussed in detail the wide variety of psychological disorders, both in parents and in children, that can result from protracted divorce and custody litigation.

THE AMERICAN EDUCATIONAL SYSTEM

I have mentioned in this book the drawbacks of a seemingly egalitarian educational system which assumes that "all children are created equal" and that all children should receive the same educational exposures. I consider this to be misguided egalitarianism that must blind itself to the obvious intellectual differences that children exhibit from the time of birth. On the one hand, educators appreciate that every intelligence test has its bell-shaped curve. On the other hand, the educational system does not properly accommmodate these differences. I do not claim that there is no appreciation at all of these differences; I only claim that not enough appreciation to these differences is given. Although there are special classes for learning-disabled children, and although there are technical high schools for those who are not academically inclined, the main thrust and orientation of our educational system is toward preparing youngsters to enter colleges and universities. The ideal presented to all youngsters is that they should ultimately be able to attend one of these so-called institutions of higher learning.

Most of the other countries on earth have no problem accepting the fact that not all children should be on a strong academic track. Accordingly, somewhere between the ages of 9 and 11 they are divided into three tracks. The highest track ultimately leads to the university. The lowest track ends formal heavy academic training at about age 11 or 12 and emphasizes various trades and skills. And the middle track is somewhere between the two. Of course, if the child has been placed in the wrong track, there is still a possibility of switching. We would do well in the United States to institute such a system. It would save a lot of children a lot of grief. To say that all people should be *treated* equally before the *law* is certainly reasonable. But to say that all are *created* equal is absurd. What is more reasonable to say (and I don't know who first said it) is that "some are more equal than others." Because public statements of such inegalitarianism are considered undemocratic in our society at this time, it is extremely unlikely that such changes will be introduced into our system in the foreseeable future, certainly not before the end of this century.

I have also mentioned at various points in this book the "college disease" wherein parents suffer terrible humiliation if their children do not go to college. This too is an extension of the all-men-are-created-equal principle. I believe that about 10 to 15 percent of all colleges in the United States are genuinely institutions of higher learning. The rest are merely businesses catering to a gullible population that needs to believe that it is important that children go to college. And the children comply by spending four years in these "educational" centers. They learn something about drinking, drugs, and sex; but they learn little else. Yes, they go through the formal courses, they take examinations, and they get grades. Yet the whole thing does not add up to an education. It adds up to four years of recreation and more dependency. It does not prepare most of these youngsters to function in real life. In most of these institutions it is very difficult to "flunk out." After all, a good businessman does not throw a paying customer out of the store. And grade inflation will ensure that even the feeble-minded obtain high grades, fostering thereby the delusion that something is being learned. I doubt whether this situation will change very much by the end of the century either.

THE FUTURE OF THE FIELD OF PSYCHODYNAMIC PSYCHOTHERAPY

Unfortunately, at the present time, I have a pessimistic view about the future of psychodynamic psychotherapy as a discipline. Many changes are taking place in the world at large, and in medicine in particular, that do not bode well for the future of psychotherapy. I will first discuss the situation in the society at large, then in medicine, then in psychiatry, and finally the implications of these changes for child and adolescent psychotherapists in other disciplines.

The Ever-Burgeoning Psychopathy
in American Society

I believe that American society (in common with many other societies) has become increasingly psychopathic in the last 15 to 20 years. This is not only reflected by increasing rates of homicide, rape, arson, and theft, but by more subtle manifestations of self-serving behavior on the part of people in general. Its manifestations are ubiquitous. Children are being sexually abused with increasing frequency, not only by their parents but by their teachers, scout masters, clergymen, and others who have access to them. Anyone willing to pay $25,000 can get a forged medical degree with associated counterfeit credentials. There was a time when London policeman did not carry guns because even the lowest criminals could be relied upon to refrain from shooting an unarmed person. This is no longer the case. With increasing frequency scientists in academic life are submitting falsified data in order to enhance their reputations and chances for promotion. The U.S. government is facing increasing difficulties getting repayment for student loans. In New York City, census collectors in 1980 were filmed sitting in or standing around their cars filling out batches of census forms while listening to rock music. In the same city construction inspectors have refused to accept promotions because they will then be removed from the more lucrative payoffs to be gained on the street. I could continue and I am sure the reader can supply his or her own examples of the increasing psychopathy of our society.

Payment of Fees

When I was in medical school, a physician who required patients to pay their fees at the time services were rendered would have been considered materialistic, "money hungry," and "grubby." Bills were sent and it was expected that the vast majority of patients in treatment would have a sense of responsibility with regard to their payments. Any physician now who trusts most patients to pay for services in the future is not going to remain in practice very long. Most physicians now unabashedly and unashamedly request that their patients pay at the time services are rendered. In fact, there are many physicians who will not admit a patient to the hospital unless payment is made in advance. And many hospitals (especially private hospitals) utilize the same procedure. This change may not affect significantly practice in other branches of medicine, but it can compromise psychiatric treatment. Implicit in the demand that payment be made at the time services are rendered is the notion of distrust. There is no way to separate the two. The patient is basically being told: "I want you to pay *now*, because I don't trust you to pay me in *the future*." Increasingly, psychiatrists are coming to appreciate that the traditional monthly bill is becoming an anachronism, applicable in simpler times, but no longer consistent with survival in the more cutthroat world of the late 20th century.

At this point I still allow my adult patients to pay me at the end of each month. I take the position that it is better to lose a certain percentage of my billings than to say uniformly to all adult patients that I distrust them. If, however, a patient begins to renege, I am quick to bring this up in treatment and to provide therapeutic justification for more frequent payments or even payment every session. In this situation, distrust cannot be viewed as an inappropriate generalization in which an innocent party is being distrusted because others act in a distrustful way. Rather, my distrust of the patient stems from untrustworthy behavior exhibited by him or her. With my child and adolescent patients, however, I ask the parents to pay at the time of each session. I am not completely happy with this practice, but it is better than the traditional method because of the high parental default rate I was experiencing in recent years. The default rate of childrens' parents was higher than that of adult patients because there was less direct monitoring and surveillance of the parents. Unfortunate as it is, that is the reality of the situation. This practice has not affected my relationship with my child and adolescent patients because it is not *they* I am distrusting, but their parents. One could argue here that I am compromising my relationship with parents and, therefore, as one who has spoken so much about the importance of the therapist's relationship with parents, I am compromising indirectly my child and adolescent patients' treatment. I admit to this compromise. My only answer is that I too have to earn a living.

Malpractice Suits

The everburgeoning rate of malpractice suits has also had its effect on medicine. At the time of this writing there are neurosurgeons in the greater New York City area who pay a malpractice insurance premium of $105,000 per year. And there are neurosurgeons in Florida who pay over $225,000 per year. Although these figures are almost unimaginable, they are true. Young people cannot enter a field in which they have to pay such astronomical premiums starting on the first day they open their offices. Judicious physicians practice what has come to be called "defensive medicine." Here, they must always be thinking about the potential malpractice suit that may be brought in the course of conducting day-to-day medical practice. Tests are ordered which would not previously have been requested because of the remote possibility that the physicians might be accused of being sloppy or negligent. The chances of the test's being positive may be one in 100,000, but the spectre of being cross-examined on a witness stand because of the failure to have ordered a particular test results in this extra expense to the patient. It appears that there are no longer any such things as naturally occurring birth defects. If a child is born with a congenital anomaly, the parents see nothing inappropriate about suing the obstetrician. The situation has gotten so bad that many OB-GYN practitioners have stopped delivering babies entirely and confine themselves soley to gynecological practice. There are thousands of parents of children with neurologically based learning disabilities who are suing obstetricians. The child may have nothing more wrong with him or her than the fact that the IQ is at the 20th percentile level. Accordingly, a normal variation is given a diagnostic label—a disease—and an innocent obstetrician is then sued for malpractice. And schools are being sued for not having brought such children up to normal levels of intellectual functioning. Psychiatrists practice with the fear that their reports will be used as evidence in malpractice litigation. Accordingly, they are becoming increasingly cautious about what they say in their reports, and the result is that these are becoming progressively less useful.

I believe that we in medicine should certainly be accountable for our errors and that we should not be immune from malpractice suits. However, we have a malpractice situation here in the United

States that is unconscionable. At the present time, the ratio of one lawyer for 800 people in the population is actually increasing. There are many hungry lawyers and many doctors who are viewed as being "rich." (Remember the bumper sticker: "Become a doctor and support a lawyer.") Furthermore, we have the despicable practice of the contingency arrangement. Under this program a patient need not put down a cent to institute malpractice litigation. The attorney works for nothing in the hope that he or she will win and thereby receive anywhere from 33 to 50 percent of the award. Most countries in the world consider this an unsavory practice and it is outlawed. But it cannot be so easily outlawed in the United States because the state legislatures are largely populated by attorneys, the friends and relatives of the malpractice lawyers. The malpractice situation is another example of the general psychopathy of our society—the psychopathy that is compromising the clinical practice of psychiatry.

The Craze for Quick Cures

Another manifestation of the psychopathy in our society that is affecting psychiatric practice is the desire for quick solutions and rapid cures. I believe that the vast majority of patients who interrupt treatment prematurely do so because they are dissatisfied with a therapeutic program that involves effort over a long period. Psychodynamic therapies of the kinds described in this book generally take time, and sometimes a long time. The factors that have contributed to the development of the youngster's symptoms may have been generations in the making. The patient may have been exposed to the detrimental environmental influences from the day of birth. It is unreasonable to expect the therapist to undo all these contributing factors in a short period. Yet, most patients and parents want just that. And, as the old law of supply and demand dictates, when people are willing to pay for the things they are demanding, there will be people who will supply what is being demanded and accept payment for their services. It matters little whether the product being supplied is of any value. What matters primarily is whether people are willing to pay money for it.

Accordingly, there is an ever-burgeoning supply of practitioners who promise quick solutions. The most influential of these in the field of psychiatry are the so-called "biological psychiatrists." Although there is a wide range of opinions regarding the role of nature vs. nurture among people who espouse this position, their general view is that nature (genes, constitution, metabolic processes, etc.) is the primary determinant of psychiatric disorder. Theirs is certainly an attractive position. Rather than spend long periods going into background history, rather than undergo the tedious process of trying to understand underlying psychodynamics, all one has to do is provide a medicine that presumably will correct the biological abnormality that is theorized to be the cause of the disorder. When it comes to asking for grants, these people are obviously at an advantage over those of us who want to investigate the longer and presumably less predictably successful kinds of treatment. Those who fund such research (whether it be the government or other institutions) are more likely to be attracted to these presumably more "cost-effective" forms of treatment.

A parallel situation exists in psychology. Psychodynamically oriented psychologists, who believe that prolonged and intensive psychotherapies are likely to be the most efficacious, are not being viewed benevolently by those who provide money for research, training, and teaching. Rather, behavior therapists who believe that inquiry into the unconscious is a waste of time and money are more likely to obtain grants. They are more attractive, as well, to schools and institutions, where large numbers of patients are provided services. There was a time when we spoke of doctors providing treatment to patients. Now the lingo calls us "providers" and our treatment "delivery of services." The word *delivery* connotes to me someone in a truck delivering a product. We have not reached that point yet, but I would not be surprised if very soon we start referring to our patients as "the customers."

Training in Child and Adolescent Psychiatry

As a result of this situation there has been a dramatic shift in the type of training young psychiatrists now receive. Most of the medical school training programs in the United States began in the

1940s and 1950s when psychoanalytic theory reigned supreme. During that period there was hardly a department that was not chaired by a classically oriented psychoanalyst. In the late 1960s and early 1970s the pendulum began to shift in favor of the biological psychiatrists. This occurred at a time when hospitals became increasingly pressured to support ever more complex and sophisticated forms of medical treatment. Furthermore, hospitals could no longer rely on the relatively inexpensive services provided by professionals such as nurses, attendants, laboratory technicians, etc. People could no longer be relied upon to dedicate themselves to the treatment of the ill with little financial remuneration. On the one hand, one could say that the shrinkage of such dedicated individuals was related to a psychopathic society in which fewer individuals were willing to make sacrifices in compliance with noble principles such as self-sacrifice, sympathy for the underprivileged, and dedication to the needs of the poor. On the other hand, one could argue that people decided that they no longer wanted to be exploited by hospital administrators. I believe that both factors operated here with the net result that there are now fewer people who are working in hospitals because of high and noble principles, and there are also fewer people who are being exploited. Unions became stronger, wage demands more stringent, and hospitals had to cut back in every possible way to survive. They became increasingly dependent on their outside funding.

Up to the 1970s a departmental chairperson (there were mainly chair*men* in those days) was chosen primarily on the basis of medical expertise and dedication, and only secondarily on administrative capabilities and funding sources. Hospitals now find themselves in the position of having to use the latter criteria for selection much more than the former. We are living at a time when a person who is a candidate for a departmental chair is judged primarily on his or her "track record" in acquiring funding; medical expertise is of only secondary consideration. The effect of this on psychiatry has been to place psychodynamically oriented people at a tremendous disadvantage with regard to chairing departments. This has reached a point where there is hardly a psychiatry department in the United States today that is chaired by a dynamically oriented psychiatrist. As is to be expected, the chairpersons themselves not only hire people who think the way they do but also favor individuals who themselves have good "track records" regarding funding for their work.

As a result of this situation, the young psychiatrist in training may have little if any psychodynamically oriented therapeutic experience. In many of these departments the primary therapeutic modalities are determined by what is short, seemingly quick, and "cost effective." Drug therapy, obviously, satisfies this proviso. To a lesser extent, behavior modification is attractive for the same reasons. Cognitive therapies, whose primary aim is to change distorted thinking relatively quickly, are also very much in vogue. Many people in these programs see no need to get background history about the patient's family or to investigate into underlying psychodynamics. The symptom is viewed as the disease and symptom alleviation or removal is considered the only goal of treatment. Even the manual of psychiatric diagnoses (DSM-III-R) reflects this philosophy. It is basically antipsychodynamic. The selection of a disorder's name is based primarily, if not exclusively, on the manifest symptoms.

One of the most unfortunate outcomes of all this is the diagnostic category known as *attention deficit disorder* (ADD). If one looks at the charts of child patients in hospitals, clinics, and the offices of child psychiatrists, child neurologists, pediatricians, child psychologists, and school guidance counselors, the "disease" is indeed epidemic. It has become the rubber-stamp diagnosis of the 1980s. Any child who does not listen to his or her parents or teachers is quickly labeled "ADD." If one is to believe these reports, we are experiencing an epidemic greater than we ever had with any other disorder known to medicine.

The implication is that these children are suffering with a neurophysiological derangement which may or may not be associated with hyperactivity (also presumed to be neurophysiologic in etiology). With this assumption, the next step is to provide a convenient drug: enter psychostimulant medication. At this time it is reasonable to say that psychostimulant medication is being prescribed by the ton—literally by the ton. All this is quick and slick, but a terrible disservice to patients. I believe that the vast majority of children who are diagnosed as having ADD have problems that have nothing to do with their attentional capacity, but more to do with psychogenic rather than neurophysiological factors (Gardner,

1989b). Their difficulties, I believe, are more readily explained by family and other environmental influences. Most children who are considered to have ADD are diagnosed on an observational or even hearsay basis. When objective criteria for attentional capacity are utilized (such as the Digit Span, Arithmetic, and Coding subtests of the *WISC-R*) the diagnosis cannot be justified.

Elsewhere (1987b) I discuss in detail my own studies that support my position that the ADD label (not the hyperactivity label) is a myth that exists in the brains of those who make the diagnosis and not in the brains of those who are being so diagnosed. I do believe, however, that *some* hyperactive children are indeed so on a neurophysiological basis and *will* be helped by psychostimulant medication. My main point here is that the popularity of the ADD and hyperactivity labels and the ubiquitous use of psychostimulant medication is another manifestation of the search for quick and simple cures for complicated problems, the worship of cost-effectiveness, the anxieties engendered by introspective psychother-apeutic approaches, the prevailing psychopathy of our society, and the resulting dehumanization of psychiatry.

Prepaid Treatment Plans

Another phenomenon that has compromised significantly the quality of psychiatric care, and threatens to do so even more in the immediate future, is the increasing popularity of prepaid treatment plans. Their main purpose has been to provide patients with lower cost treatment. One can argue that the present medical system leaves much to be desired. Rich patients clearly receive far better care than the poor. They have the opportunity to select their doctors freely and have the wherewithal to pay their fees, no matter how high. On the other end of the scale, the indigent generally attend hospital clinics, have no choice of physicians, and are often treated by those in training. As is usually the case, those in the middle class get something in between. Prepaid insurance plans provide such care, especially for the middle class. There is no question that many physicians have exploited the public with their unconscionable fees. If a person has a brain tumor and all the neurosurgeons in private practice are charging $15,000 for its removal, the patient has little choice but to pay. There is no question that this is a form of exploitation. There is no question that some kind of backlash was predictable. There is no question also that people in clinics have been getting inadequate treatment and that some kind of retaliatory reaction was also foreseeable. However, indigents are less likely to involve themselves effectively in movements for their rights than those who are better educated and in a better financial position. Some of the prepaid plans are manifestations of this backlash. I discuss here some of the most well known, those that do not provide free choice of physician within the plan.

In recent years we have witnessed the establishment of *health maintenance organizations* (HMOs). Many large companies have traditionally provided their workers with the opportunity to select their physicians. Under a typical program the worker would be reimbursed a significant percentage of the cost of medical care. The basic philosophy was that an individual should be free to choose any physician he or she wished to, without any external restrictions. In recent years companies have found that it is more "cost-effective" to engage the services of, and even to build their own, clinics and hospitals and to give their workers a choice. If one chooses the company's medical facilities, one may pay nothing or very little. One is still free to obtain treatment from an outside physician, but one will get little if any reimbursement for doing so. Obviously, under such a program, very few people are going to select the latter course. Large companies have not only set up their own clinics but even their own hospitals. Those who have not set up their own have contracted with private hospitals that were established for this purpose. Insurance companies, as well, have found it an attractive program. The physicians in these organizations are often employees. They are paid specific salaries and their work is monitored, again with regard to whether or not it is "cost-effective." One result of this trend has been a progressive shrinkage of private practice. Young physicians today cannot generally look forward to the autonomy of individual practice because an increasing percentage of their potential patient population is now receiving care from HMOs. They too must become salaried employees if they are to make a living in the field of medicine.

There are four specialities in medicine that have been particularly hurt by HMOs, specifically dermatology, allergy, plastic surgery, and psychiatry. The consensus among administrators of HMOs is that these specialities often provide frivolous treatment and the therapy is frequently prolonged unnecessarily for the financial benefit of the physician. Accordingly, the funds allotted for treatment in these four categories is generally a much smaller fraction of the traditional than in other medical specialties. Although one might argue that much of the "bread and butter" of plastic surgery is unnecessary cosmetic surgery, one cannot as easily give a convincing argument that much of psychiatric therapy is equally frivolous. The result, however, is that physicians and patients under HMO plans are told that they must accomplish their treatment in a fixed number of sessions. Therapists who claim that therapy takes much longer are not likely to remain employed very long. Those who subscribe to a theory that short-term therapy is as good as the long-term variation will be viewed with favor. This is a ripoff on the public. As mentioned so frequently throughout this book, psycho-therapy can only be meaningful in the context of an ongoing relationship, and one cannot put a fixed number of hours on the development, evolution, and therapeutic benefit of this relation-ship. And the next step has already taken place. Therapists in private practice, suffering from the emigration of their patient population to HMOs, are now taking jobs in HMOs. And they are going along with the philosophy that treatment can indeed be accomplished in a predetermined number of sessions.

A related development is the establishment of *preferred-provider organizations* (PPOs). Here, private practitioners, in an attempt to compete with HMOs for patients, group together and bid for service contracts with insurance companies, industries, etc. These organi-zations do comparative shopping in the medical marketplace and contract with a group of providers who agree on a predetermined list of charges. These practitioners, then, are charging higher rates to patients who are not members of these plans than they are to subscribers. Again, it is unreasonable to assume that patients who are receiving care at the lower fee are going to get the same quality of care and attention as those who are paying more. And this is especially the case in psychiatric treatment where the fixed charges are likely to limit the number of sessions available to the patient.

Another arrangement is the *independent practice association* (IPA). IPAs were also established to compete with HMOs for patients. Here, a group of physicians gets together and forms its own service plan. Whereas in HMOs and PPOs an outside organization, such as an industry or an insurance company, sets up the plan, in the IPA the doctors themselves organize and administer the program. They therefore save the costs of paying outside administrators. As is true for PPOs, doctors seeing patients under the IPA plan generally charge two fees, a higher fee for their genuinely private patients and a lower fee for those who come under the service contract. Again, I have the same reservations about IPAs as I do about HMOs and PPOs, namely, that psychiatric care has got to be compromised by the limited amount of time available under these fixed service plans.

Another development that is compromising significantly the quality of care in the field of psychiatry is the growth of the *diagnostic related groups* (DRGs). Again, in order to improve the cost-effectiveness of medical care and to increase the efficiency of such treatment (especially with regard to paperwork), many of the payers of medical care (insurance companies, Blue Cross/Blue Shield, Medicare, Medicaid, etc) have made up a list of hundreds of disorders for which hospitals provide treatment. The hospital is given a fixed amount of money for the treatment of patients suffering with one or more of these disorders—regardless of the number of days in the hospital and regardless of the kinds of medicines, procedures, operations, etc. that are required. The amount of payment is based on the average cost for the treatment of the particular condition in the recent past. Although this approach certainly saves much paperwork and perhaps even reduces the number of days a patient will remain in the hospital, it cannot but compromise psychiatric treatment. It behooves hospitals to discharge patients at the earliest possible time, and this is likely to result in patients' not being allowed to stay the optimum amount of time. Doctors who keep their patients in longer than the average may find that their treatment is becoming "cost ineffective." They will be advised by hospital administrators to shorten the duration of their patients' stays or risk the displeasure of those who pay their salaries and/or determine their suitability for enjoying the benefits of hospital privileges.

I consider all of these prepayment plans to pose the risk of curtailed treatment for patients. To me plans like these, when applied to psychiatry, can be compared to restricting marriages to 7.3 years, because that is the average duration of the marriages in the community in which the couple is marrying. The analogy is applicable because the therapeutic relationship, if a good one, has similarities to the good marriage with regard to the intimacy and closeness that emerges. The other drawback of these prepaid plans is that physicians on salary are not as likely to work as enthusiastically and with as high motivation as those who enjoy the promise of higher earnings for enhanced competence and the establishment for themselves of a reputation for excellence. Most human beings (including doctors) are not so saint-like that they will work as assiduously for a fixed income as they will in a situation where there is the promise of greater rewards. In some ideal world of perfect people, such differentiations may not be made. In our real world, however, real doctors are not going to give as much attention and commitment to their prepaid patients as they will to those who provide promise of greater remuneration. And this difference is especially true in psychiatry when one compares the remuneration for a few sessions under a fixed-fee program and that which is possible from a private patient in an ongoing therapeutic program.

The Dehumanization of Psychiatric Care

If the reader detects a note of pessimism in the above, he or she is correct. I have little reason to feel confident about the future of the field of child and adolescent psychiatry, whether practiced in the hospital, clinic, or private setting. Hospitals and clinics are training automatons who provide a dehumanized kind of treatment. In recent years I am seeing with increasing frequency reports that are completely devoid of information about family background, developmental history, and underlying psychodynamics. The patients are "processed" and the care "delivered." The clinic administrators pride themselves on the total number of people they can "process" in a given period and gloat over comparisons between their own turnover rates and those of previous administrators, who worked when traditional psychotherapeutic techniques were being utilized. Patients come to the clinic and, while waiting to see their doctors, fill out symptom checklists. These are then fed into a computer and compared with previous symptom checklists. By the time the patient is seen, the therapist has the up-to-date data in hand and is allegedly in a position to assess the patient's "progress." The whole session may take five to ten minutes, during which time the primary purpose is to adjust medication and write prescriptions. There is little if any time for any discussion of the human problems that may be contributing significantly to the patient's problems. But even if there were, the doctor has not been trained adequately in psychodynamic therapy and may have little if any conviction for it.

The young physician who is thinking of entering the field of psychiatry and who recognizes how unconscionable the system is, has great difficulty finding training in a more humane setting. If the physician were to find more humanistic therapy being provided in a nonmedical training program, such as psychology for example, he or she would still be faced with formidable problems. Certainly, such training would not be recognized toward certification in a medical specialty and psychologists might not even recognize the physician's training as being adequate for admission to the program. If the individual decided to go through one of the dehumanized medical programs and tolerate its deficiencies in the hope of rectifying them later, he or she will have had little training to serve as a basis for the subsequent more humane type of psychiatric treatment.

Those who recognize how unconscionably inadequate are our present training programs in psychiatry have little place to turn. When young people ask my advice about where in psychiatry they can train, I tell them I know of no center within the field of medicine. I suspect that there may be a few programs in which psychodynamically oriented therapy is still the prevailing approach. However, I have no optimism that such programs will remain long in effect. In every program that I am familiar with, the process has been the same: a psychodynamically oriented chairperson has been replaced by someone with a deep commitment to the biological approach. Dynamically oriented chairpersons have been fired, prematurely retired, eased out, forced out, or thrown out! In short, what we are witnessing is the corruption of a field by lust for money. The aforementioned influences that are eroding the field at a frighteningly rapid rate are formidable, and I see little evidence that things will change in the near future.

CHILD AND ADOLESCENT
PSYCHOTHERAPY IN NONMEDICAL
DISCIPLINES

Now to other disciplines that are providing psychotherapy. There was a time, less than ten years ago, when psychologists were warring with psychiatrists with regard to who has the right to do psychotherapy. That war is over. There was no truce; there was no armistice. Rather, psychiatry just walked away from the battlefield. Psychiatry views itself as having "returned to medicine." The recent attitude of psychiatry has been: "Leave psychotherapy to the psychologist and the social workers, they can hold the hands of people who need that sort of thing." The general public has similarly come to view psychiatrists almost exclusively as the purveyors of drugs and as therapists for psychotics, severe depressives, and others who have physical disorders that require shock therapy and/or medication. Psychologists are now viewed by the general public as the providers of psychotherapy. This may be a good thing considering the deplorable state of present-day medical residency programs. But it is now the psychologists who are fighting with the social workers over who should have the right to do psychotherapy. And others have quickly entered the arena: pastoral counselors, nurse practitioners, family counselors, marital counselors, and a large assortment of others with varying degrees of training and expertise. There is likely to be a Pyrrhic victory in the end because if these people are fighting over patients for private practice, as the HMOs, PPOs, and IPAs continue to grow there will be very few patients left, if any. They will end up finding that what they have "won" will be jobs that will confine them to "cost-effective" therapeutic programs with a specific number of hours allotted to each patient.

FINAL COMMENTS

It would be an error for the reader to concude that I am whitewashing completely psychodynamic psychotherapy in this section of my book. Biological psychiatry, in part, enjoyed popularity as a justifiable backlash against the widespread enthusiasm for classical psychoanalysis and its derivative techniques. There was a grandiosity to some of these practitioners that bordered on the delusional. They considered themselves to have had in the palm of their hands the definitive and the most effective form of psychotherapeutic treatment ever devised in the history of humankind. Those who disagreed with them were viewed as having psychological problems that had not been properly analyzed. Furthermore, the length of the treatment programs they were utilizing was inordinately long, even if there was the funding available for such prolonged treatment. The idea that most patients be treated four or five times a week was patently absurd.

And there are those who were (and still are) providing worthless treatment that is referred to as "play therapy." I have come across numerous child therapists who actually believe that play therapy is nothing more than playing with a child. They have little if any insight into the fact that the play, if it is to justifiably warrant the name *play therapy*, must be more therapy than play and that the play should only be a vehicle for the transmission of therapeutic messages and experiences. These practitioners also may have contributed to the backlash as it has been applied to child therapy. Hundreds of thousands of hours have been wasted while therapists have been taking children to soda fountains, baseball games, circuses, etc. under the aegis of child therapy. And many of these concepts are held by those who work with adolescents—especially younger ones.

So there was much housecleaning that had to be done (and still has to be done) among those who do child and adolescent therapy. I recognize that this is an extremely pessimistic note on which to end a book. However, it is the reality of the world in which we are living and to deny it would be foolish and self-destructive. If all that I predict here regarding psychodynamic psychotherapy comes to pass (and much of it has already happened), then a book like this might not prove very useful—because very few people will be in a position to provide the kind of therapy described herein. I have recognized this while writing this book, but I still felt that it had to be written. I felt that I had to write a compendium of my contributions and pull together my ideas. There are still enough people at this point who have the autonomy and flexibility to practice the kind of psychodynamic therapy described in it. Perhaps one day there will be some kind of backlash against the recent depravities, and more people will come to appreciate how unconscionable many present therapeutic programs are. My hope is that they will work toward bringing us once again into an atmosphere in which more humane therapeutic approaches will prevail. Perhaps this book may serve (admittedly in a small way) to inspire others like myself who are still striving to maintain what was good in the past and to contribute to its reflowering in the future.

RICHARD A. GARDNER, M.D.
P.O. BOX R
155 COUNTY ROAD
CRESSKILL, N.J. 07626-0317

Dear

Attached please find the questionnaire I would like you to fill out about your child. Please bring it with you at the time of your first appointment. In addition, I would appreciate your bringing copies of any other material that you suspect might be useful to me, e.g. reports from psychologists, psychiatrists, child study teams, learning disability consultants, teachers, etc. I am also interested in recent report cards and scores on standardized tests of academic achievement such as the Iowa, CAT, and SAT. Please make copies of these reports so that I can have them for my files.

Unless there are special reasons to do otherwise, my usual procedure is to see the child and both parents in the initial two-hour consultation. The three parties are seen individually and in various combinations, as warranted.

My fee for consultations is $150/60-minute session. Unlike reports from other medical specialists, child psychiatric reports are generally quite lengthy and time consuming to prepare. Accordingly, if a written report is desired, there is an additional charge for its preparation, dictation, and review--which is prorated at the aforementioned rate.

My fee for 45-minute treatment sessions ranges from $110 down to $80. My fee for full-hour sessions ranges from $140 down to $100. The exact fee is determined at the time treatment is instituted. When deciding on the fee it is most helpful to know exactly what insurance coverage (if any) you have. Accordingly, please try to have this information available at the time of the initial consultation. I will discuss with you my policy for payment for missed sessions at the time of the initial consultation. Payment is due at the time services are rendered.

    hours have been reserved for the initial consultation with your child. I would appreciate your paying my secretary the $ fee at the time of the consultation. My secretary will be pleased to provide receipts and assist you in the preparation of forms for subsequent reimbursement to you by insurance companies and other third-party payers.

Please know that I will do everything possible to be helpful to your child. If you have any questions regarding the above, please do not hesitate to call my office.

                                   Sincerely,

RICHARD A. GARDNER, M. D.
155 COUNTY ROAD
CRESSKILL, N. J. 07626
—
TELEPHONE 201 - 567-8989

PLEASE BRING THIS COMPLETED FORM WITH YOU AT THE TIME OF YOUR FIRST APPOINT-

MENT ON_____AT _____

IT IS PREFERABLE THAT BOTH PARENTS ACCOMPANY THE CHILD TO THE CONSULTATION.

Child's name_____Birth date_____Age___Sex_____
             last   **first**   **middle**
Home address_____
             street   city   state   zip
Home telephone number_____
                 area code   number
Child's school_____
           name   address   **grade**
Present placement of child (place check in appropriate bracket):

	Column A Adults with whom child is living	Column B Non-residential adults involved with child
Natural mother	( )___	( )___
Natural father	( )___	( )___
Stepmother	( )___	( )___
Stepfather	( )___	( )___
Adoptive mother	( )___	( )___
Adoptive father	( )___	( )___
Foster mother	( )___	( )___
Foster father	( )___	( )___
Other (specify)	_____ ___	_____ ___

Place the number 1 or 2 next to each check in Column A and provide the
following information about each person:

1. Name_____Occupation_____
         last   first
  Business name_____Business address_____

_____Business tel. No. ( )_____

2. Name_____Occupation_____
         last   first
  Business name_____Business address_____

_____Business tel. No. ( )_____

Place the number 3 next to the person checked in Column B who is most involved
witn the child and provide the following information:

3. Name_____Home address_____
                                           street
_____Home tel. No. ( )_____
   city   state   zip
  Occupation_____Business name_____

Business address_____Bus. Tel. No. (   )_____

Source of referral: Name_____Address_____

_____Tel. No. (   )_____

Purpose of consultation (brief summary of the main problems):_____

_____

_____

_____

_____

PREGNANCY
  Complications:
  Excessive vomiting_____hospitalization required_____

  Excessive staining or blood loss_____

  Threatened miscarriage_____

  Infection(s) (specify)_____

  Toxemia_____

  Operation(s) (specify)_____

  Other illness(es) (specify)_____

  Smoking during pregnancy_____average number of cigarettes per day_____

  Alcoholic consumption during pregnancy_____describe, if beyond an occa-

    sional drink_____

  Medications taken during pregnancy_____

  X-ray studies during pregnancy_____

  Duration_____weeks

DELIVERY
  Type of labor: Spontaneous_____Induced_____
  Forceps: high_____mid_____low_____
  Duration of labor_____hours

  Type of delivery: Vertex (normal)_____breech_____Caesarean_____

  Complications:
    cord around neck_____

    cord presented first_____

    hemorrhage_____

infant injured during delivery_____

other (specify)_____

Birth Weight_____
Appropriate for gestational age (AGA)_____
Small for gestational age (SGA)_____

POST-DELIVERY PERIOD (while in the hospital)
Respiration: immediate_____delayed (if so, how long)_____

Cry: immediate_____delayed (if so, how long)_____

Mucus accumulation_____

Apgar score (if known)_____

Jaundice_____

Rh factor_____transfusion_____

Cyanosis (turned blue)_____

Incubator care_____number of days_____

Suck: strong_____weak_____

Infection (specify)_____

Vomiting_____diarrhea_____

Birth defects (specify)_____

Total number of days baby was in the hospital after the delivery_____

INFANCY-TODDLER PERIOD
Were any of the following present--to a significant degree--during the
first few years of life? If so, describe.

Did not enjoy cuddling _____

Was not calmed by being held and/or stroked _____

Colic_____

Excessive restlessness_____

Diminished sleep because of restlessness and easy arousal _____

Frequent headbanging_____

Constantly into everything_____

Excessive number of accidents compared to other children_____

-4-

DEVELOPMENTAL MILESTONES
If you can recall, record the age at which your child reached the following
developmental milestones. If you cannot recall, check item at right.

	age	I cannot recall exactly, but to the best of my recollection it occurred		
		early	at the normal time	late
Smiled				
Sat without support				
Crawled				
Stood without support				
Walked without assistance				
Spoke first words besides "ma-ma" and "da-da"				
Said phrases				
Said sentences				
Bowel trained, day				
Bowel trained, night				
Bladder trained, day				
Bladder trained, night				
Rode tricycle				
Rode bicycle (without training wheels)				
Buttoned clothing				
Tied shoelaces				
Named colors				
Named coins				
Said alphabet in order				
Began to read				

COORDINATION
Rate your child on the following skills:

	Good	Average	Poor
Walking			
Running			
Throwing			
Catching			
Shoelace tying			
Buttoning			
Writing			
Athletic abilities			

COMPREHENSION AND UNDERSTANDING
  Do you consider your child to understand directions and situations as well
  as other children his or her age?_____If not, why not?_____

_____

  How would you rate your child's overall level of intelligence compared to
  other children? Below average_____Average_____Above average_____

SCHOOL
  Rate your child's school experiences related to <u>academic learning</u>:

	<u>Good</u>	<u>Average</u>	<u>Poor</u>
Nursery school			
Kindergarten			
Current grade			

To the best of your knowledge, at what grade level is your child function-

    ing: reading_____spelling_____arithmetic_____

Has your child ever had to repeat a grade? If so, when_____

Present class placement: regular class_____special class (if so, specify)

_____

Kinds of special therapy or remedial work your child is currently receiving

_____

Describe briefly any academic school problems_____

_____

_____

Rate your child's school experience related to <u>behavior</u>:

	<u>Good</u>	<u>Average</u>	<u>Poor</u>
Nursery school			
Kindergarten			
Current grade			

Does your child's teacher describe any of the following as significant
classroom problems?
  Doesn't sit still in his or her seat_____
  Frequently gets up and walks around the classroom_____
  Shouts out. Doesn't wait to be called upon _____
  Won't wait his or her turn_____

Does not cooperate well in group activities_____

Typically does better in a one-to-one relationship_____

Doesn't respect the rights of others_____

Doesn't pay attention during storytelling_____

Describe briefly any <u>other</u> classroom behavioral problems_____

_____

_____

PEER RELATIONSHIPS

Does your child seek friendships with peers?_____

Is your child sought by peers for friendship?_____

Does your child play primarily with children his or her own age?_____

    younger_____older_____

Describe briefly any problems your child may have with peers_____

_____

_____

HOME BEHAVIOR

All children exhibit, to some degree, the kinds of behavior listed below. Check those that you believe your child exhibits to an excessive or exaggerated degree when compared to other children his or her age.

Hyperactivity (high activity level)_____

Poor attention span_____

Impulsivity (poor self control)_____

Low frustration threshold_____

Temper outbursts_____

Sloppy table manners_____

Interrupts frequently_____

Doesn't listen when being spoken to_____

Sudden outbursts of physical abuse of other children_____

Acts like he or she is driven by a motor_____

Wears out shoes more frequently than siblings_____

Heedless to danger_____

Excessive number of accidents_____

Doesn't learn from experience_____

Poor memory_____

More active than siblings_____

INTERESTS AND ACCOMPLISHMENTS
What are your child's main hobbies and interests?_____ _____

_____

What are your child's areas of greatest accomplishment?_____

_____

What does your child enjoy doing most?_____

_____

What does your child dislike doing most?_____

_____

MEDICAL HISTORY
If your child's medical history includes any of the following, please note
the age when the incident or illness occurred and any other pertinent information.

Childhood diseases (describe any complications)_____

_____

Operations_____

_____

Hospitalizations for illness(es) other than operations_____

_____

Head injuries_____

_____with unconsciousness_____without unconsciousness_____

Convulsions_____

_____with fever_____without fever_____

Coma_____

Meningitis or encephalitis_____

Immunization reactions_____

Persistent high fevers_____highest temperature ever recorded_____

eye problems_____

ear problems_____

poisoning_____

PRESENT MEDICAL STATUS

Present height_____Present weight_____

Present illness(es) for which child is being treated_____

_____

Medications child is taking on an ongoing basis_____

_____

FAMILY HISTORY - MOTHER

Age_____ Age at time of pregnancy with patient_____

Number of previous pregnancies_____Number of spontaneous abortions

(miscarriages)_____Number of induced abortions_____

Sterility problems (specify)_____

School: Highest grade completed_____

  Learning problems (specify)_____grade repeat_____

  Behavior problems (specify)_____

Medical problems (specify)_____

Have any of your blood relatives (not including patient and siblings) ever

had problems similar to those your child has? If so, describe_____

_____

_____

FAMILY HISTORY - FATHER

Age_____Age at the time of the patient's conception _____

Sterility problems (specify)_____

School: Highest grade completed_____

  Learning problems (specify)_____grade repeat_____

  Behavior problems (specify)_____

Medical problems (specify)_____

Have any of your blood relatives (not including patient and siblings) ever

had problems similar to those your child has? If so, describe_____

_____

Most children exhibit, at one time or another, one or more of the symptoms listed below. Place a P next to those that your child has exhibited in the PAST and an N next to those that your child exhibits NOW. Only mark those symptoms that have been or are present to a significant degree over a period of time. Only check as problems behavior that you suspect is unusual or atypical when compared to what you consider to be the normal for your child's age. Then, on page 12, list the symptoms checked off on pages 9-12 and write a brief description including age of onset, duration, and any other pertinent information.

Thumb-sucking ____	Preoccupied with food--what to eat and what not to eat ____	Frequently likes to wear clothing of the opposite sex ____
Baby talk ____		
Overly dependent for age ____	Preoccupation with bowel movements ____	Exhibits gestures and intonations of the opposite sex ____
Frequent temper tantrums ____	Constipation ____	
Excessive silliness and clowning ____	Encopresis (soiling) ____	Frequent headaches ____
Excessive demands for attention ____	Insomnia (difficulty sleeping) ____	Frequent stomach cramps ____
Cries easily and frequently ____	Enuresis (bed wetting) ____	Frequent nausea and vomiting ____
Generally immature ____	Frequent nightmares ____	Often complains of bodily aches and pains ____
Eats non-edible substances ____	Night terrors (terrifying night-time outbursts) ____	Worries over bodily illness ____
Overeating with overweight ____	Sleepwalking ____	Poor motivation ____
Eating binges with overweight ____	Excessive sexual interest and preoccupation ____	Apathy ____
Undereating with underweight ____	Frequent sex play with other children ____	Takes path of least resistance ____
Long periods of dieting and food abstinence with underweight ____	Excessive masturbation ____	Ever trying to avoid responsibility ____

Poor follow-
through ___

Low Curiosity ___

Open defiance of
authority ___

Blatently un-
cooperative ___

Persistant
lying ___

Frequent use of
profanity to
parents, teachers,
and other author-
ities ___

Truancy from
school ___

Runs away from
home ___

Violent outbursts
of rage ___

Stealing ___

Cruelty to animals,
children, and
others ___

Destruction of
property ___

Criminal and/or
dangerous acts ___

Trouble with the
police ___

Violent assault ___

Fire setting ___

Little, if any,
guilt over behavior
that causes others
pain and dis-
comfort ___

Little, if any,
response to pun-
ishment for anti-
social behavior ___

Few, if any,
friends ___

Doesn't seek
friendships ___

Rarely sought by
peers ___

Not accepted by
peer group ___

Selfish ___

Doesn't respect
the rights of
others ___

Wants things own
way with exag-
gerated reaction
if thwarted ___

Trouble putting
self in other
person's position ___

Egocentric
(self-centered) ___

Frequently hits
other children ___

Argumentative ___

Excessively cri-
tical of others ___

Excessively
taunts other
children ___

Ever complaining ___

Is often picked
on and easily
bullied by
other children ___

Suspicious,
distrustful ___

Aloof ___

"Wise-guy" or
smart aleck
attitude ___

Brags or boasts ___

Bribes other
children ___

Excessively
competitive ___

Often cheats when
playing games ___

"Sore loser" ___

"Doesn't know
when to stop" ___

Poor common
sense in social
situations ___

Often feels
cheated or
gypped ___

Feels others
are persecuting
him when there
is no evidence
for such ___

Typically wants
his or her
own way ___

Very stubborn ___

Obstruction-
istic ___

Negativistic
(does just the
opposite of what
is requested) ___

Quietly, or often
silently, de-
fiant of au-
thority ___

Feigns or verbalizes
compliance or
cooperation but
doesn't comply
with requests ___

Drug abuse ___

Alcohol abuse ___

Very tense ___

Nail biting ___

Chews on clothes,
blankets, etc. ___

Head banging ___

Hair pulling ___

Picks on skin ___

Speaks rapidly
and under
pressure ___

Irritability,
easily "flies off
the handle" ___

Fears
dark ___
new situations ___
strangers ___
being alone ___
death ___
separation from
parent ___
school ___
visiting other
children's homes ___
going away to
camp ___
animals ___
other fears
(name)

_____ ___
_____ ___

Anxiety attacks
with palpatations
(heart pounding),
shortness of breath,
sweating, etc. ___

Disorganized ___

Tics such as eye-
blinking, grimacing,
or other spasmodic
repetitious move-
ments ___

Involuntary grunts,
vocalizations
(understandable
or not) ___

Stuttering ___

Depression ___

Frequent crying
spells ___

Excessive worrying
over minor things ___

Suicidal preoccu-
pation, gestures,
or attempts ___

Excessive desire to
please authority ___

"Too good" ___

Often appears in-
sincere and/or
artificial ___

Too mature, fre-
quently acts older
than actual age ___

Excessive guilt over
minor indiscre-
tions ___

Asks to be
punished ___

Low self-esteem ___

Excessive self-
criticism ___

Very poor toleration
of criticism ___

Feelings easily
hurt ___

Dissatisfaction
with appearance
or body part(s) ___

Excessive modesty
over bodily
exposure ___

Perfectionistic,
rarely satisfied
with performance___

Frequently blames
others as a cover-
up for own short-
comings ___

Little concern for
personal appear-
ance or hygiene ___

Little concern for
or pride in per-
sonal property ___

"Gets hooked" on
certain ideas
and remains pre-
occupied ___

Compulsive repe-
tition of seem-
ingly meaningless
physical acts ___

Shy ___

Inhibited self-
expression in
dancing, singing,
laughing, etc. ___

Recoils from affec-
tionate physical
contact ___

| Withdrawn ___ | Mute (refuses to speak) but can ___ | Flat emotional tone ___ |

Fears asserting self ___

Inhibits open expression of anger ___

Allows self to be easily taken advantage of ___

Frequently pouts and/or sulks ___

Mute (refuses to speak) but can ___

Gullible and/or naive ___

Passive and easily led ___

Excessive fantasizing, "lives in his (her) own world" ___

Flat emotional tone ___

Speech non-communicative or poorly communicative ___

Hears voices ___

Sees visions ___

As requested above, please first list below symptoms marked with the letter P and next to each symptom give descriptive information such as age of onset, age of termination, and other important data. Then list symptoms marked with an N and provide similar information.

P or N	Symptom	Brief Description
_____	_____	_____
_____	_____	_____
_____	_____	_____
_____	_____	_____
_____	_____	_____
_____	_____	_____
_____	_____	_____
_____	_____	_____
_____	_____	_____
_____	_____	_____
_____	_____	_____
_____	_____	_____
_____	_____	_____
_____	_____	_____
_____	_____	_____
_____	_____	_____

SIBLINGS

	Name	Age	Medical, social, or academic problems
1.			
2.			
3.			
4.			
5.			

LIST NAMES AND ADDRESSES OF ANY OTHER PROFESSIONALS CONSULTED

1. _____

2. _____

3. _____

4. _____

ADDITIONAL REMARKS

Please use the remainder of this page to write any additional comments you wish to make regarding your child's difficulties.

RICHARD A. GARDNER, M.D.
P.O. BOX R
155 COUNTY RD.
CRESSKILL, N.J. 07626-0317
201-567-8989

Policy for Missed Sessions

Unlike physicians in other medical specialties, I do not have other patients in my waiting room when an appointment is missed. Accordingly, please inform me or my office as soon as you know about anticipated missed appointments. The more advance notice I have, the greater the likelihood I will be able to fill the appointment with another patient. In contrast, the shorter the advance notice, the less the likelihood of my filling the appointment. If I am able to fill the appointment, there will be no charge; if not, then I charge for the time set aside for the appointment. I do not have a cut-off point for determining whether or not there will be a charge; rather, the earlier the advance notice of cancellation, the greater the chance the appointment will be filled.

This policy holds regardless of the reason for the cancellation--whether it be car breakdown, conflicting obligatios, weather conditions, illness, or any other reason for missing the appointment. Of course, if I am not in the office, for any reason whatsoever (including weather conditions), you will be informed in advance and there will be no charge. In situations in which the primary patient is a child who cannot attend, I can usually use the session with a parent. In marital counseling the time can often be used productively by the available spouse. In order to increase the chances of my filling missed sessions calls will be accepted during evenings, weekends, and holidays.

I recognize that some may consider this policy stringent. I hope that those who do so will try to place themselves in my position regarding cancellations. I think the best way for patients to view my policy is to consider themselves to have made a commitment for a time slot in my schedule and that on rare occasions a session will be paid for that was not attended.

I recognize that patients who come to me for treatment have committed themselves to pay me for my services and to comply with my payment policy. I in return promise to commit myself to do whatever I reasonably can to be of help to them and their families.

References

Aichorn, A. (1925), *Wayward Youth*. New York: The World Publishing Co., 1954.

American Handbook of Psychiatry, (1974). New York: Basic Books Inc.

Alexander, F. (1950), Analysis of the therapeutic factors in psychoanalytic treatment. *Psychoanalytic Quarterly*, 19:482–500.

_____ and French, T. (1946), The principle of corrective emotional experience. In *Psychoanalytic Therapy: Principles and Application*, pp. 66–70. New York: The Ronald Press.

The American Psychiatric Association (1987), *Diagnostic and Statistical Manual, Third Edition-Revised (DSM-III-R)*. Washington, D.C.: American Psychiatric Association.

American Psychiatric Association Task Force Report (1973), *Behavior Therapy in Psychiatry*, Report No. 5. Washington, D.C.: American Psychiatric Association.

Axline, V.M. (1947), *Play Therapy*. Boston: Houghton Mifflin Co.

_____ (1964), *Dibs in Search of Self*. Boston: Houghton Mifflin Co.

Bandura, A., and Walters, R.H. (1958), Dependency conflicts in aggressive delinquents. *Journal of Social Sciences*, 14:52–65.

_____ Ross, D. and Ross, S.A. (1963), Imitation of film-mediated aggressive models. *Journal of Abnormal Social Psychology* 66:3–8.

Basic Handbook of Child Psychiatry (1979). New York: Basic Books, Inc.

Becker, E. (1973), *The Denial of Death*. New York: The Free Press (A division of Macmillan Publishing Co., Inc.).

_____ (1975), *Escape from Evil*. New York: The Free Press (A division of Macmillan Publishing Co., Inc.).

Berkovitz, I.H. (1972), *Adolescents Grow in Groups*. New York: Brunner-Mazel.

_____ and Sugar, M. (1975), Indications and contraindications for adolescent group psychotherapy. In *The Adolescent in Group and Family Therapy*, ed. M. Sugar, pp. 3–26. New York: Brunner-Mazel.

Berkowitz, L. and Rawlings, E. (1963), Effects of film violence on inhibitions against subsequent aggression. *Journal of Abnormal Social Psychology*, 66:405–415.

Bieber, I. et al. (1962), *Homosexuality: A Psychoanalytic Study of Male Homosexuals*. New York: Basic Books, Inc.

Bowlby, J. (1944), Forty-four juvenile thieves: Their characters and homelife. *International Journal of Psychoanalysis* 25: 19–53.

_____ (1952) *Maternal Care and Mental Health*. Geneva: World Health Organization.

Christ, J. (1974), Outpatient treatment of adolescents and their families. In *American Handbook of Psychiatry*, ed. G. Caplan, vol. II, pp. 339–352. New York: Basic Books, Inc.

Comstock, G., Chaffee, S., and Katzman, N. (1978), *Television and Human Behavior*. New York: Columbia University Press.

_____ (1983), Media influences on aggression. In *Prevention and Control of Aggression*, ed. A. Goldstein. New York: Pergamon Press.

_____ (1986), Sexual effects of movie and TV violence. *Medical Aspects of Human Sexuality*, 20(7): 50ff.

Coolidge, J.C., Tessman, E., Waldfogel, S., and Miller, M.L. (1962), Patterns of aggression in school phobia. In *The Psychoanalytic Study of the Child*, vol. XVII, pp. 319–333. New York: International Universities Press.

Eisenberg, L. (1958), School Phobia: A study of communication and anxiety. *American Journal of Psychiatry*, 114:712–718.

Ellis, A. (1963), *Reason and Emotion in Psychotherapy*. New York: Lyle

Stuart.

Erikson, E.H. (1950), *Childhood and Society*. New York: W. W. Norton and Co., Inc.

_____ (1968), *Identity: Youth and Crisis*. New York: W.W. Norton and Co., Inc.

Freud, A. (1965), *Normality and Pathology in Childhood*. New York: International Universities Press.

Freud, S. (1900), The Interpretation of Dreams. In *The Basic Writings of Sigmund Freud*, ed. A.A. Brill, pp.. 183–549. New York: Random House, Inc. (The Modern Library), 1938.

_____ (1909), A phobia in a five-year-old boy. In *Collected Papers*, vol. 3, pp 149–209. New York: Basic Books, Inc., 1959.

_____ (1924), The passing of the Oedipus complex. In *Collected Papers*, vol. 2, pp. 269–276. New York: Basic Books, Inc., 1959.

Freud, S. and Breuer, J. (1895), *Studies in Hysteria*. New York: Basic Books, Inc., 1957.

Gardner, R.A. (1968a), The mutual storytelling technique: Use in alleviating childhood oedipal problems. *Contemporary Psychoanalysis*, 4:161–177

_____ (1968b), Book Review, Ginott, H.G. (1965), *Between Parent and Child*. New York: The Macmillan Co. Reviewed in *Psychology Today*, 1(12):15–17.

_____ (1969), The guilt reaction of parents of children with severe physical disease. *The American Journal of Psychiatry*, 126:636–644.

_____ (1970), The use of guilt as a defense against anxiety. *The Psychoanalytic Review*, 57:124–136.

_____ (1971), *Therapeutic Communication with Children: The Mutual Storytelling Technique*. Northvale, New Jersey: Jason Aronson, Inc.

_____ (1972a) Little Hans—the most famous boy in the child psychotherapy literature. *International Journal of Child Psychotherapy*, 1(4): 24–50.

_____ (1972b), *Dr. Gardner's Stories About the Real World*, vol. I. Cresskill, New Jersey: Creative Therapeutics.

_____ (1973a), *Understanding Children: A Parents Guide to Child Rearing*. Cresskill, New Jersey: Creative Therapeutics.

_____ (1973b), *The Talking, Feeling, and Doing Game*. Cresskill, New Jersey: Creative Therapeutics.

_____ (1973c), Treatment of the projected self. *International Journal of Child Psychotherapy*. 2(1):7–12.

_____ (1975), *Psychotherapeutic Approaches to the Resistant Child*. Northvale, New Jersey: Jason Aronson, Inc.

_____ (1976), *Psychotherapy with Children of Divorce*. Northvale, New Jersey: Jason Aronson, Inc.

_____ (1977), *The Parents Book About Divorce*. New York: Doubleday and Co., Inc.

_____ (1979a), *The Parents Book About Divorce*. New York: Bantam Books, Inc.

_____ (1979b), *The Objective Diagnosis of Minimal Brain Dysfunction*. Cresskill, New Jersey: Creative Therapeutics.

_____ Gardner, A.K., Caemmerer, A., and Broman, M. (1979c), An instrument for measuring hyperactivity and other signs of minimal brain dysfunction. *Journal of Clinical Child Psychology*, 8(3):173–179.

_____ (1982), *Family Evaluation in Child Custody Litigation*. Cresskill, New Jersey: Creative Therapeutics.

_____ (1983) *The Boys and Girls Book About One-Parent Families*. Cresskill, New Jersey: Creative Therapeutics.

_____ (1984), *Separation Anxiety Disorder: Psychodynamics and Psychotherapy*. Cresskill, New Jersey: Creative Therapeutics.

_____ (1986a), *The Psychotherapeutic Techniques of Richard A. Gardner*. Cresskill, New Jersey: Creative Therapeutics.

_____ (1986b), *Child Custody Litigation: A Guide for Parents and Mental Health Professionals*. Cresskill, New Jersey: Creative Therapeutics.

_____ (1987a), *Differentiating Between Fabricated and Bona Fide Sex-Abuse Allegations of Children*. Audio cassette tape and video cassette tape. Cresskill, New Jersey: Creative Therapeutics.

_____ (1987b), *Hyperactivity, The So-Called Attention* Deficit Disorder, and The Group of MBD Syndromes. Cresskill, New Jersey: Creative Therapeutics.

_____ (1987c), *The Parental Alienation Syndrome and the Differentiation Between Fabricated and Genuine Child Sex Abuse*. Cresskill, New Jersey: Creative Therapeutics.

_____ (1987d), *Sex Abuse Legitimacy Scale (SAL Scale)*. Cresskill, New Jersey: Creative Therapeutics.

_____ (1989a), The use of the home video cassette recorder in psychotherapy. (in press)

_____ (1989b), *Psychotherapy of Psychogenic Learning Disabilities*. Cresskill, New Jersey: Creative Therapeutics. (in press)

Gittelman-Klein, R. and Klein, D.F. (1973), School phobia:Diagnostic considerations in the light of imipramine effects. *Journal of Nervous and Mental Diseases*, 156:199–215.

Gittelman-Klein, R. (1975), Pharmacotherapy and management of pathological separation anxiety. *International Journal of Mental Health*, 4:255–270.

Haley, J. (1973), *Uncommon Therapy: The Psychiatric Techniques of Milton H. Erikson, M.D.* New York: W.W. Norton and Co.

Hatterer, L.J. (1970), *Changing Homosexuality in the Male*. New York: McGraw-Hill Book Co.

Hess, E.H. (1966), Imprinting. In *Readings for an Introduction to Psychology*, ed. R.A. King, pp. 39–46. New York: McGraw-Hill Book Co.

Holmes, D.J. (1964), *The Adolescent in Psychotherapy*. Boston: Little, Brown and Company.

Johnson, A.M. (1949), Sanctions for superego lacunae of adolescents. In *Searchlights on Delinquency*, ed. K.R. Eissler, pp. 225–245. New York: International Universities Press.

_____ (1959), Juvenile delinquency. In *American Handbook of Psychiatry*, Vol. I, ed. S. Arieti, pp. 844–849. New York: Basic Books, Inc.

_____ and Szurek, S.A. (1952), The genesis of antisocial acting out in children and adults. *Psychoanalytic Quarterly*, 21:323–343,

Kardiner, A. and Ovesey, L. (1951), *The Mark of Oppression*. Cleveland, Ohio: World Publishing Co.

Kessler, J.W. (1966), *Psychopathology of Childhood*. Englewood Cliffs, New Jersey: Prentice-Hall, Inc.

Klein, M. (1932), *The Psychoanalysis of Children*. London: Hogarth Press.

Kolb, L.C. and Brodie, H.K.H. (1982), *Modern Clinical Psychiatry*. Philadelphia: W.B. Saunders Co.

Kraft, I.A. (1979), Group Therapy. In *Basic Handbook of Child Psychiatry*, ed. S.I. Harrison, vol. III, pp. 159–180. New York: Basic Books, Inc.

Kritzberg, N.I. (1966), A new verbal projective test for the expansion of the projective aspects of the clinical interview. *Acta Paedopsychiatrica*, 33(2):48–62.

Kubie, L. (1956), Psychoanalysis and marriage: Practical and theoretical issues. In *Neurotic Interaction in Marriage*, ed. V.W. Eisenstein, pp. 10–43. New York: Basic books, Inc.

Leventhal, T. and Sills, M. (1964), Self-image in school phobia. *American Journal of Orthopsychiatry*, 34:685–695.

Levy, D.M. (1937). Primary affect hunger. *American Journal of Psychiatry*, 94: 644–652.

Lieberman, L.K. (1981), *The Litigious Society*. New York: Basic Books, Inc.

Lippman H.S. (1962), *Treatment of the Child in Emotional Conflict*. New York: McGraw-Hill, Book Co.

Lorenz, K. (1937), The nature of instinct. In *Instinctive Behavior: The Development of a Modern Concept*, ed. C.H. Schiller. London: Methuen.

_____ (1950), The comparative method in studying innate behavior patterns. *Symposium of the Society of Experimental Biology*, 4:221–268.

Machover, K. (1949), *Personality Projection in the Drawing of the Human Figure*. Springfield, Ill: Charles C. Thomas.

_____ (1951), Drawing of the human figure: a method of personality investigation. In *An Introduction of Projective Techniques*, ed. H.H. Anderson and G.L. Anderson, pp. 341–370. Englewood Cliffs, N.J.: Prentice-Hall, Inc.

_____ (1960), Sex differences in the developmental pattern of children as seen in human figure drawings. In *Projective Techniques in Children*, ed. A.I. Rabin and M.R. Haworth, pp. 230–257. New York: Grune & Stratton.

Malamuth, N.M. and Donnerstein, E. (1982), The effects of aggressive-pornographic mass media stimuli. In *Advances in Experimental Social Psychology*, ed. L. Berkowitz, vol. 15, pp. 103–136. New York: Academic Press.

Marshall, R.J. (1979), Antisocial Youth. In *Basic Handbook of Child Psychiatry*, ed. S.I. Harrison, vol. III, pp. 536–554. New York: Basic Books, Inc.

_____ (1983), A psychoanalytic perspective on the diagnosis and development of juvenile delinquents. In *Personality Theory, Moral Development and Criminal Behavior*, ed. W.S. Laufer and J.M. Day, pp. 119–144. Lexington, Mass.: Lexington Books (D.C. Heath and Co.).

Mullahy, P. (1970), *Psychoanalysis and Interpersonal Psychiatry*. Northvale, New Jersey: Jason Aronson, Inc.

Piers, G. and Singer, M.B. (1953), *Shame and Guilt*. Springfield,

Illinois: Charles C. Thomas, Inc.

Psychiatry (1986) New York: Basic Books, Inc.

Ravitch, D. and Finn, C.E. (l987), *What Do Our 17-Year-Olds Know?* New York: Harper & Row.

Riddle, M.A. and Vitulano, L.A. (1986), Group psychotherapy for children and adolescents. In *Psychiatry*, ed. A.J. Solnit, D.J. Cohen, and J.E. Schowalter, vol. VI, *Child Psychiatry*, pp. 469–475. New York: Basic Books, Inc.

Rinsley, D.B. (1974), Residential treatment of adolescents. In *American Handbook of Psychiatry*, ed. G. Caplan, vol. II, pp. 353–366. New York: Basic Books, Inc.

Sarason, I.G. and Sarason, B.R. (1980), *Abnormal Psychology*, Third edition. Englewood Cliffs: Prentice-Hall, Inc.

Schimel, J.S. (1974), Problems of delinquency and their treatment. In *American Handbook of Psychiatry*, ed. G. Kaplan, vol. II, pp. 264–274. New York: Basic Books, Inc.

Simmons, K. (1987a), Adolescent suicide: Second leading death cause. *Journal of the American Medical Association*, 257(24): 3329–3330.

Simmons, K. (1987b), Task force to make recommendations for adolescents in terms of suicidal risk. *Journal of the American Medical Association*, 257(24):3330–3332.

Stone, L.A. (1979), Residential treatment. In *Basic Handbook of Child Psychiatry*, ed. S.I. Harrison, vol. III, pp. 231–262. New York: Basic Books, Inc.

Strupp, H.H. (1975), Psychoanalysis, "focal psychotherapy," and the nature of the therapeutic influence. *Archives of General Psychiatry*, 32:127–135.

Stubblefield, R. L. (1967), Sociopathic personality disorders I: Antisocial and dyssocial reactions. In *Comprehensive Textbook of Psychiatry*, ed. A.M. Freedman and H.I. Kaplan, pp. 1420–1424. Baltimore: Williams and Wilkins.

Sullivan, H.S. (1953), *The Interpersonal Theory of Psychiatry*. New York: W.W. Norton and Co.

Thomas, A., Chess, S. et al. (1963), *Behavioral Individuality in Early Childhood*. New York: New York University Press.

Toolan, J.M. (1974), Depression and suicide. In *American Handbook of Psychiatry*, ed. G. Caplan, vol. II, pp. 294–306. New York: Basic Books, Inc.

Wensley, S. (1987), Portrait of adolescent suicide. In P&S (Columbia University, College of Physicians & Surgeons), 7(2):14–17.

Westman, J.C. (1979), Psychiatric day treatment. In *Basic Handbook of Child Psychiatry*, ed. S.I. Harrison, Vol. III, pp. 288–299. New York: Basic Books, Inc.

Yalom, I.D. (1975), *The Theory and Practice of Group Psychotherapy*. New York: Basic Books, Inc.

Zinn, D. (1979), Hospital treatment of the adolescent. In *Basic Handbook of Child Psychiatry*, ed. S.I. Harrison, vol. III, pp. 263–288. New York: Basic Books, Inc.

Author Index

Subject Index